MINERALOGY AND GEOLOGY
OF RADIOACTIVE RAW MATERIALS

MINERALOGY AND GEOLOGY
OF RADIOACTIVE RAW MATERIALS

E. Wm. Heinrich

Professor of Mineralogy
University of Michigan

1958
McGRAW-HILL BOOK COMPANY, INC.
NEW YORK
TORONTO
LONDON

MINERALOGY AND GEOLOGY OF RADIOACTIVE RAW MATERIALS

For
E. D. H.
and
S. v. T

PREFACE

In 1948 uranium ore production in the United States was about 70,000 tons; by 1956 production had vaulted to approximately 3 million tons; and in the first half of 1957 slightly more than 1,700,000 tons was produced domestically. Measured, indicated, and inferred uranium ore reserves aggregated 67 million tons of 0.27% U_3O_8 by mid-1957, of which 70% is in New Mexico, 16% in Colorado, Utah, and Arizona, and 8% in Wyoming. These figures are a measure of the intensity and success of the uranium exploration and development program that has been mustered in the United States since the early 1950s and in which geologists, mineralogists, and mining engineers, including those of Federal and state agencies, mining and petroleum companies, consulting firms, and universities have cooperated to an extent unprecedented in the history of minerals exploration, not only among themselves but with spectacular success also with "weekend" and professional prospectors and promoters. It has been estimated that since 1952 more man-hours have been spent in searching for uranium alone than had been spent in seeking all other metals in history. Although the most spectacular mass efforts were organized in the United States, where in 1955 some 10,000 laymen and prospectors, replete with Geiger counters, scoured the countryside, similar searches were launched in other countries, chiefly by trained personnel, in many cases with marvelously successful results. Canadian reserves in 1957 probably totaled several hundred million tons, and at the same time reserves in the Union of South Africa were estimated at over 1 billion tons. Other countries, such as Australia and France and doubtless the U.S.S.R., likewise established uranium mining industries.

These efforts in the field and in the laboratory spawned an extraordinary fry of publications on the mineralogy and geology of uranium and, to a lesser extent, thorium, climaxed in 1955 by the papers of the Geneva meetings on the peaceful uses of atomic energy (Geology of uranium and thorium, *Proceedings of the International Conference on the Peaceful Uses of Atomic Energy*, vol. 6, 1956). Nevertheless, there has still remained the necessity for coordinating and summarizing the scientific and technical results of the uranium search; this the writer has attempted in this book.

In 1948 the University of Michigan inaugurated its Michigan Memorial Phoenix Project devoted to research in the peacetime applications of atomic energy. In cooperation with this program the writer offered for the first time in 1953 a course on the mineralogy and geology of radioactive deposits, which has since been taught both on the advanced, graduate student level and on the elementary level (through the University of Michigan Extension Service) to several hundred students. In addition the Phoenix Project has supported the writer's researches on radioactive mineral deposits with several generous grants which have enabled him to study examples of nearly all types of radioactive deposits in the United States and other countries. Without this assistance this book could not have been prepared. The writer acknowledges with gratitude laboratory and field assistance, discussions, information, both oral and written, specimens, photographs, and permission and facilities to examine deposits, from the following individuals: E. M. Abraham, R. A. Anderson, M. S. Archbold, T. Barth, J. E. Bever, H. Björlykke, V. L. Bosazza, R. M. Brander, G. A. Brown, J. B. Cathcart, A. F. Corey, M. S. Corey, R. W. Deane, A. P. De Carvalho, L. F. Dellwig, M. Deul, S. B. Dickinson, J. S. Dudar, A. J. Eardley, D. L. Everhart, M. Fleischer, C. Frondel, R. M. Garrels, A. A. Giardini, M. Gidel, J. L. Gillson, E. N. Goddard, W. R. Griffitts, E. B. Gross, J. W. Gruner, D. Guimarães, K. D. Hester, C. H. Hewitt, D. F. Hewitt, D. E. Jensen, H. E. Kremers, K. K. Landes, E. S. Larsen, S. J. LeFond, D. W. Levandowski, A. A. Levinson, J. T. Lonsdale, J. H. Mackin, D. P. Marcott, C. M. McDaniel, N. McNiece, V. B. Meen, I. Million, A. Montgomery, L. Moyd, K. J. Murata, R. D. Nininger, E. W. Nuffield, A. Pabst, L. R. Page, W. H. Parsons, W. T. Pecora, A. Poldervaart, P. Quensel, H. S. Robinson, R. B. Rowe, J. Satterly, C. Schindler, J. Shappirio, K. G. Smity, H. S. Spence, E. Tavora, A. C. Tester, F. S. Turneaure, H. von Eckermann, S. R. Wallace, R. W. Webb, A. D. Weeks, J. H. Zumberge.

Considerable assistance also was provided by the Department of Mineralogy, University of Michigan, and the writer is especially grateful to its chairman, Professor L. S. Ramsdell, for continuous encouragement and aid. Mr. Fred Anderegg, supervisor of photographic services at the University of Michigan, prepared most of the photomicrographs. Mrs. Margaret Everett not only typed and retyped the manuscript but also made numerous corrections. To Edith D. Heinrich fell much of the drudgery of proofreading.

Although some of the older literature on radioactive minerals has been cited where it is especially pertinent, most of that dealing simply with descriptions of properties or with listings of occurrences has not been included because of the availability of previous reference works in this area, e.g., George, 1949; Palache et al., 1944, 1951; Frondel and Fleischer, 1955.

Throughout Part 2 the writer has attempted to present the descriptions of deposits arranged according to a genetic classification. Some deviations, however, appear; for example, the French epithermal deposits are best described as a unit, rather than split between the siliceous and fluoritic types, and the oxidized Colorado Plateau deposits are described with those that are unoxidized.

Some investigators will disagree, perhaps even violently, with the genetic disposition of various deposits. This is expected in view of the many controversies that have enlivened discussions of their origin, e.g., Blind River, Witwatersrand, and Colorado Plateau. The writer has attempted to present equitably opposing viewpoints.

The eventual future for uranium may prove to be even more fabulous than its recent boom decade. Although at present there is reportedly no uranium shortage for the United States government's military and power development program as projected for the next 10 years, it has been estimated that the cumulative uranium oxide requirements by 1975 for the United States alone can reach 75,000 to 100,000 tons, that the requirement for that year may be of the order of 20,000 to 30,000 tons of concentrate, and that needs of the "free world" by 1975 may approach 40,000 to 100,000 tons of concentrate annually. Certainly the present known reserves, even at contemporary projected rates of production, will have been largely exhausted when the time arrives at which large-scale industrial requirements have been developed. Geologists and prospectors must find more uranium ore. Toward this goal it may be hoped that this summary will provide some assistance.

E. Wm. Heinrich

CONTENTS

Contents   xiii

part 1

MINERALOGY

• chapter one

RADIOACTIVE MINERALS

COMPOSITION

General

The chief naturally occurring radioactive elements are uranium and thorium, both of which are widely distributed in rocks and mineral deposits, thorium being considerably more abundant than uranium in igneous rocks (Table 1.1). However, uranium is at least three times as abundant in sea water as thorium. Natural terrestrial radioactivity stems from (1) Th and the three U isotopes, (2) the short-lived decay products of these elements, including radium (Ra) and radon (Rn) (Tables 1.2, 1.3, and 1.4), and the light radioactive elements (Table 1.5).

Both uranium and thorium, which are strongly concentrated in the upper lithosphere, are markedly oxyphile elements occurring as oxides, hydroxides, oxygen salts, and silicates. They do not occur naturally as native elements, sulfides, arsenides, sulfosalts, or tellurides.

In the crust of the earth uranium averages between 1 to 2 ppm. Its abundance in terrestrial materials is shown in Table 1.6. Since the concentration of uranium in its deposits begins at a lower limit of about 1,000 ppm (McKelvey et al., 1955), deposits are markedly enriched over ordinary rocks.

Radium behaves chemically like barium, but its compounds are even less soluble in water ($RaSO_4$ is 10 times less soluble than $BaSO_4$). In acid solutions uranium is dissolved more readily than radium; thus outcrops of radioactive ores rich in pyrite that are weathered may be leached selectively of uranium, leaving radium. Since the gamma activity of radium is relatively high, radiometric assays of such outcrops will be too high as compared to chemical assays for uranium.

3

TABLE 1.1. *Properties of uranium and thorium*

	Atomic number	Atomic weight	Naturally occurring isotopes	Abundance	Physical properties	Valence in nature	Atomic and ionic radii (A)	Chemical behavior in nature
U	92	238.07	^{234}U—0.0058% ^{235}U—0.71 ^{238}U—99.28	4 g/ton (igneous rocks)	G = 19.05, MP = 1133°C, BP = about 3927°C. At ordinary temperatures the α-orthorhombic phase is present. Two high-temperature phases (β, γ) exist	U^{4+} U^{6+} chiefly as $(UO_2)^{2+}$	U = 1.57 (metallic bonding) U^4 = 1.05[6] U^4 = 0.87[8] U^6 = 0.90	Forms two series of compounds, uranous and uranyl, in numerous minerals
Th	90	232.12	^{232}Th	11.5 g/ton (igneous rocks)	G = 11.7, MP = about 1842°C, BP = about 4500°C. Face-centered cubic, a_0 = 5.09 A	Th^{4+}	Th = 1.80 Th^4 = 1.10[6]	Forms a single series of compounds, in very few minerals

TABLE 1.2. *The uranium family* (*Rankama, 1954*)

Radioelement	Nuclide	Radiation	Half-life *
Uranium I	^{238}U	α	4.50×10^9 y
Uranium X1	^{234}Th	β^-	24.10 d
Uranium X2 †	^{234}Pa	β^-	1.14 m
Uranium II	^{234}U	α	2.52×10^5 y
Ionium	^{230}Th	α	8.0×10^4 y
Radium	^{226}Ra	α	1622 y
Ra emanation, Radon, Niton	^{222}Rn	α	3.825 d
Radium A	^{218}Po	α, β^-	3.05 m

99.96% | 0.04%

| Radium B ($\alpha \downarrow$) (β^-) | ^{214}Pb | β^- | 26.8 m |
| Astatine | ^{218}At | α, β^- | 1.5 s − 2 s |

99.99% | ∼0.01%

| α Radon ($\downarrow \beta^-$) | ^{218}Rn | α | 0.019 s |
| Radium C | ^{214}Bi | β^-, α | 19.7 m |

0.04% | 99.96%

α Radium C′ ($\downarrow \beta^-$)	^{214}Po	α	1.637×10^{-4} s
Radium C″	^{210}Tl	β^-	1.32 m
Radium D	^{210}Pb	β^-	25 y
Radium E	^{210}Bi	β^-, α	5.02 d

∼100% | ∼5 × 10⁻⁵%

Radium F ($\beta^- \downarrow$) (α)	^{210}Po	α	138.3 d
Thallium	^{206}Tl	β^-	4.23 m
Radium G	^{206}Pb	Stable	—

* Abbreviations in Tables 1.2 to 1.5: y = year; d = day; m = minute; s = second.
† Uranium X2(^{234}Pa) forms, by isomeric transition, also uranium Z(^{234}Pa). It is a β^--emitter and decays into uranium II(^{234}U) with a half-life of 6.7 hr.

5

TABLE 1.3. *The thorium family* (*Rankama*, 1954)

Radioelement	Nuclide	Radiation	Half-life
Thorium ↓	^{232}Th	α	1.389×10^{10} y
Mesothorium I ↓	^{228}Ra	β^-	6.7 y
Mesothorium II ↓	^{228}Ac	β^-	6.13 h
Radiothorium ↓	^{228}Th	α	1.90 y
Thorium X ↓	^{224}Ra	α	3.64 d
Th emanation, Thoron ↓	^{220}Rn	α	54.5 s
Thorium A	^{216}Po	α, β^-	0.158 s
$\sim$100% $\mid$ 0.013%			
$\alpha\downarrow$ Thorium B	^{212}Pb	β^-	10.6 h
β^- ↓			
Astatine	^{216}At	α	$\sim 3 \times 10^{-4}$ s
Thorium C	^{212}Bi	β^-, α	1.01 h
66.3% $\mid$ 33.7%			
β^- ↓ Thorium C′	^{212}Po	α	3.04×10^{-7} s
α			
Thorium C″	^{208}Tl	β^-	3.1 m
Thorium D	^{208}Pb	Stable	—

TABLE 1.4. *The actinium family* (*Rankama*, 1954)

Radioelement	Nuclide	Radiation	Half-life
Actinouranium	^{235}U	α	7.07×10^8 y
↓			
Uranium Y	^{231}Th	β^-	25.6 h
↓			
Protactinium	^{231}Pa	α	34.3×10^3 y
↓			
Actinium	^{227}Ac	$\beta^-,\ \alpha$	27.7 y

98.8% │ 1.2%

β^- ↓

| Radioactinium | ^{227}Th | α | 18.6 d |

α

Actinium K	^{223}Fr	β^-	21 m
↓			
Actinium X	^{223}Ra	α	11.2 d
↓			
Ac emanation, Actinon	^{219}Rn	α	3.92 s
↓			
Actinium A	^{215}Po	$\alpha,\ \beta^-$	1.83×10^{-3} s

~100% │ ~5×10^{-4}%

α ↓

| Actinium B | ^{211}Pb | β^- | 36.1 m |

β^-

Astatine	^{215}At	α	10^{-4} s
↓			
Actinium C	^{211}Bi	$\alpha,\ \beta^-$	2.16 m

0.32% │ 99.68%

β^- ↓

| Actinium C′ | ^{211}Po | α | 0.52 s |

α

Actinium C″	^{207}Tl	β^-	4.76 m
↓			
Actinium D	^{207}Pb	Stable	—

TABLE 1.5. *Single naturally radioactive nuclides* (*Rankama*, 1954)

Nuclide	Manner of decay	Decay product	Half-life, years	Conventional abundance, %
^1n	β^-	^{1}H	12.8 m	
^{3}T	β^-	^{3}He	12.46	
^{14}C	β^-	^{14}N	5,568	
^{40}K	88.8% β^- 11.2% K-capture	^{40}Ca ^{40}A	$\left.\begin{array}{c} \\ \\ \end{array}\right\}$ 1.33 × 10^9	0.0119
^{50}V(?)	β^-, or K-capture, or both	^{50}Cr, or ^{50}Ti, or both	>10^{12}(?)	0.24
^{87}Rb	β^-	^{87}Sr	6.15 × 10^{10}	27.85
^{115}In	β^-	^{115}Sn	6 × 10^{14}	95.77
^{123}Sb(?)	β^-	^{123}Te	Probably very long	42.75
^{130}Te	Double β^-	^{130}Xe	~10^{21}	34.49
^{129}I(?)	β^-	^{129}Xe	1.72 × 10^7	
^{138}La	β^- K-capture	^{138}Ce ^{138}Ba	$\left.\begin{array}{c} \\ \\ \end{array}\right\}$ 7 × 10^{10}	0.089
^{150}Nd(?)	β^-	^{150}Pm	2 × 10^{15}(?)	5.60
^{147}Sm	α	^{143}Nd	6.7 × 10^{11}	15.07
^{176}Lu	33% β^- 67% K-capture	^{176}Hf ^{176}Yb	$\left.\begin{array}{c} \\ \\ \end{array}\right\}$ 2.4 × 10^{10}	2.60
^{187}Re	β^-	^{187}Os	4 × 10^{12}	62.93
^{209}Bi	α	^{205}Tl	2.7 × 10^{17}	100.0

TABLE 1.6. *Average concentrations of uranium in various geological units* (*McKelvey et al.*, 1955)

Unit	U concentration, ppm
Low silica igneous rocks........	1
Intermediate igneous rocks.....	2
High silica igneous rocks.......	4
Sedimentary rocks............	2
Ground and stream water......	0.0002
Ocean water.................	0.002
Oil.........................	0.1

Isomorphism

Natural

As U[4], uranium is isomorphous chiefly with Th, Zr, rare-earth elements, Ca, and Fe[2] (Table 1.7) and occurs mainly in oxides, numerous complex (multiple) oxides, anhydrous phosphates, anhydrous silicates, and possibly as organic complexes. Although many complex oxide minerals contain Nb, Ta, and Ti, U[4] is not isomorphous with these elements.

TABLE 1.7. *Isomorphism in* U *and* Th *minerals*

Elements	Examples
1. Uranium (U^4)	
Th...............	Uraninite
Ca...............	Pyrochlore-microlite, apatite, zirkelite, crandallite
Na...............	Pyrochlore-microlite
Zr...............	Uraninite, zircon
Mo...............	Uraninite
Y...............	Uraninite, fergusonite, samarskite, xenotime
Ce^4............	Uraninite
Pb...............	Uraninite, betafite
Fe^2............	Davidite
2. Thorium	
U...............	Thorianite, thorite
Y...............	Priorite, thorite, xenotime, thalenite
Ce^4............	Thorianite, cerianite, eschynite, thorite
Ce^3P^5-Th^4Si^4.....	Monazite, cheralite
Zr...............	Thorianite, zircon
Ca...............	Zirkelite, clarkeite, allanite, chevkinite
Fe^3............	Thorite
Pb...............	Thorite
3. Radium	
Ba...............	Radiobarite
Ca...............	Radiocalcite(?), radiofluorite(?), apatite(?)
4. Other cations	
Nb-Ta...........	Pyrochlore-microlite, samarskite-yttrotantalite
(Nb-Ta)-Ti......	Euxenite-polycrase, betafite, perovskite, sphene
Ce-Y...........	Pyrochlore-microlite, euxenite-polycrase, monazite, xenotime, gadolinite, thalenite
Ti-Si...........	Brannerite, chevkinite
Ti-Sn...........	Sphene
Pb-Ba-Ca.......	Vandendriesscheite
Pb-Na-Ca.......	Clarkeite
Pb-Ca..........	Phosphuranylite-renardite, beta-uranophane
Pb-Ba..........	Renardite
P-Si (PO_4-SiO_4)...	Monazite, cheralite, thorite, uranophane, apatite, xenotime
P-S (PO_4-SO_4)....	Thorogummite, apatite, xenotime
P-V (PO_4-VO_4)....	Apatite
P-As (PO_4-AsO_4)..	Metatorbernite-metazeunerite, saléeite-novacekite, sabugalite, uranospathite, walpurgite, apatite
Ca-Ba..........	Autunite, meta-uranocircite
Ca-Cu..........	Uranophane, autunite
Ca-Mg..........	Autunite, uranophane
Ca-Na_2.........	Perovskite, pyrochlore-microlite, sphene
Ca-K_2..........	Tyuyamunite-carnotite
Ca-Ce..........	Pyrochlore-microlite, perovskite, apatite, allanite, sphene
Ca-Fe^2.........	Chevkinite
Cu-Pb..........	Metatorbernite
Zr-Hf..........	Zircon, baddeleyite
Zr-Fe^3..........	Zircon
5. Anions	
O-$(OH)_2$-F_2......	Microlite, apatite, sphene
SiO_4-$(OH)_4$ *.....	Zircon, thorogummite, huttonite, coffinite
PO_4-$CO_3(OH)$....	Carbonate apatite

* The mechanism of hydroxyl substitution is analogous to that in the hydrogarnets (Frondel, 1953, 1956A).

The U^4 ion (Fig. 1.1) is oxidized readily to U^6, which forms the uranyl ion $(U^6O_2)^2$, a unit of sufficient stability to preserve its identity in solution. It forms a wide variety of mineral compounds of the types

1. $A^{1+}(UO_2)^{2+}(RO_4)^{3-} \cdot xH_2O$
2. $B^{2+}(UO_2)_2^{2+}(RO_4)_2^{3-} \cdot xH_2O$
3. $B^{2+}(UO_2)^{2+}(CO_3)_2^{2-} \cdot xH_2O$

in which A = K, Na, H

B = Ca, Ba, Mg, Cu, Fe^2, Pb

R = P, As, V

None of the uranyl minerals contains Th, Zr, or Ce for uranium, because of the large size and unusual shape of the uranyl ion.

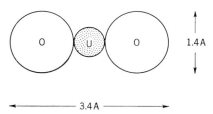

FIG. 1.1. The uranyl ion, UO_2^{2+}.

Thorium (Th^4), like U^4, is isomorphous chiefly with Zr and rare-earth elements, especially Ce^4, but since it cannot be oxidized, the two elements, uranium and thorium, although they may begin their geochemical life together, soon part company. Thorium remains mainly in its few original minerals that are largely insoluble (resistates), whereas uranium in the form of the $(UO_2)^2$ ion combines with many other cations and anions to form numerous new hosts. Thus thorium forms only six minerals of its own (Frondel, 1956A) but appears vicariously in small to moderate amounts in many other species.

Base Exchange

Many uranyl minerals containing alkali and alkaline earth elements undergo reversible base exchange when subjected to concentrated solutions of acids, brines, and various elements, the synthetic phases being isostructural with the original minerals. Some examples are listed in Table 1.8.

STRUCTURAL CHARACTERISTICS

The Metamict State

Certain radioactive minerals are demonstrably amorphous if examined by means of optical, x-ray, or differential thermal analytical techniques, even though they may have crystal faces. Such minerals are referred to as metamict (Pabst, 1952). Only a few of the many radioactive minerals are metamict, and

TABLE 1.8. *Examples of base exchange in uranyl compounds*

Mineral	Exchangeable ion	Replacing ions
Autunite..............	Ca	Na_2, H_2
Synthetic Na-autunite...	Na_2	Ca, K_2, Ba, Mn, Cu, Ni, Pb, Mg
Uranospinite..........	Ca	Na_2, H_2, $(NH_4)_2$
Carnotite............	K_2	Ca
Tyuyamunite..........	Ca	K_2

some species not invariably so, but all metamict minerals are radioactive to some degree. Bombardment by alpha particles from the disintegration of uranium, thorium, and their decay products eventually produces structural disarrangements in those hosts that have weak bonding, rather open structures, or a low degree of chemical stability. Radioactive minerals that are distinguished by numerous different and extensive isomorphous replacements in two or more structural positions (e.g., the multiple oxides) are characterized by inherent structural weaknesses and thus are metamictized commonly (Table 1.9). Alpha-particle irradiation produces little or no structural damage in minerals that are strongly bonded, or have closely packed structures or a high chemical stability.

In a particular mineral structure the amount of damage is a function of the total number of alpha particles impinging on the structure. In a minute a gram of uranium and daughter elements in equilibrium with it produces about 6×10^6 alpha particles; in the same time a gram of thorium and its daughter elements yields about 1.5×10^6 alpha particles. In a single grain or crystal of a particular mineral species the amount of structural damage is a function of the percentage of radioactive elements and the time elapsed since the mineral crystallized, provided that all the alpha-particle energy is employed in breaking bonds. However, only part of the alpha-particle energy is so employed. Thus if the alpha activity and structural stability of a mineral are known, its minimum age may be calculated. Zircon has been used for age determination by measuring the amounts of its irradiation damage (Kulp et al., 1952; Holland, 1954).

Metamictization commonly is accompanied by an increase in nonessential water and by oxidation of Fe^2 and U^4. At least some metamict minerals (zircon, samarskite, and polycrase) give sharp electron-diffraction patterns (Christ et al., 1954), owing to retention of a relict crystallinity sufficient to permit the relatively short-wave electrons ($\lambda = 0.055$ A at 50 kv) to yield resolved patterns.

Recrystallization of metamict minerals by heating does not always return them to their original structure; in fact exact structural restoration appears to be the exception (Berman, 1953). Furthermore, the temperature and type of

TABLE 1.9. *Characteristics of metamict minerals*

1. Weakly to strongly radioactive
2. Originally weakly bonded structures
3. Amorphous to x-rays or yield a faint, fuzzy pattern
4. Isotropic
5. Conchoidal fracture; cleavage absent
6. Abnormally low specific gravity
7. May be focus of fractures radiating into surrounding mineral grains
8. Abnormal amounts of nonessential water
9. Decreased resistance to chemical attack
10. May be pyrognomic, recrystallizing upon heating, usually at a definite temperature, with a considerable to minor evolution of heat (and light), to an aggregate crystalline pseudomorph

recrystallized structure of some metamict minerals depend upon the state of metamictization, upon whether the composition of the mineral is the same as its original composition, and upon the method of treatment (Berman, 1953, 1955).

A sequence of changes in some metamict thorites has been determined by Pabst (1952). All specimens were eventually converted to monoclinic $ThSiO_4$; but first isometric ThO_2 appeared followed by tetragonal $ThSiO_4$ (Fig. 1.2). Berman (1955) obtained generally similar results with thorite heated in air. In samples heated in an inert atmosphere to about 1250°C, monoclinic $ThSiO_4$ was formed in some, tetragonal $ThSiO_4$ in others. Above 1250°C in an inert atmosphere, tetragonal $ThSiO_4$ and some ThO_2 crystallize. Thorogummite and cyrtolite, in which SiO_4 groups are replaced by $(OH)_4$ (Frondel, 1953, 1956A), may be found recrystallized naturally from the metamict state to very fine grained aggregates.

Thorianite, although very strongly radioactive, is always well crystallized. Metamict pitchblende (uraninite) has been reported (Conybeare and Ferguson, 1950), but apparently the diffuse x-ray patterns that may be obtained from some specimens are the result of very fine grain size and marked auto-oxidation of U^4 to U^6 (Brooker and Nuffield, 1952). The fluorite-type structure of these two minerals has a high degree of stability.

Metaforms

Many uranium minerals of the types $A^{1+}(UO_2)^{2+}(RO_4)^{3-} \cdot xH_2O$ and $B^{2+}(UO_2)_2^{2+}(RO_4)_2^{3-} \cdot xH_2O$ contain water that is partly zeolitic, i.e., a certain number of water molecules can be lost more or less continuously with no change in the basic structure and only minor changes in properties (e.g., slightly increasing indices of refraction). If then additional molecules are lost, a distinct structural transition occurs accompanied by marked changes in properties. The transition temperature varies with the nature of the A, B, and R elements and also with the vapor pressure. At low humidities it is generally near room temperature, and from water solutions it is below 100°C. The fully hydrated phase, whether or not it is the dominant phase in nature, is con-

TABLE 1.10. *Principal metamict minerals*

Mineral	State
Multiple oxides:	
Pyrochlore-microlite....	Metamict; or non-metamict in U- and/or Th-low types
Fergusonite-formanite...	Almost in all cases metamict; two non-metamict occurrences of fergusonite are documented
Samarskite-yttrotantalite Euxenite-polycrase Betafite Polymignite Eschynite-priorite Zirkelite Davidite	Apparently almost invariably metamict; non-metamict examples rarely reported, and these show considerable structural damage, e.g., euxenite
Brannerite.............	Either completely metamict or yields very weak and diffuse x-ray patterns
Silicates:	
Thorite................	Crystalline to completely metamict
Huttonite.............	Type material is non-metamict. Some completely metamict "thorites" may have had the huttonite structure originally
Zircon.................	Crystalline to completely metamict. Zones of the two may alternate
Allanite...............	Crystalline to completely metamict in more strongly radioactive types
Gadolinite.............	Commonly metamict; crystalline examples are known
Chevkinite.............	In part metamict
Thalenite..............	Strongly radioactive types are metamict
Ce-earth silicates:	
Chinglusuite	
Rinkolite..............	The variety vudyavrite is metamict
Steenstrupine.........	Some types are metamict

ventionally granted the specific mineral name (e.g., autunite); the lesser hydrate has the name prefixed by meta (e.g., metatorbernite); if two lower hydrates exist, they may be designated meta-I and meta-II (e.g., meta-autunite I, meta-autunite II).

Minerals showing these characteristics form two structurally related groups, the torbernite and metatorbernite groups (Table 1.11). Beintema (1938) has pictured autunite to consist of PO_4 tetrahedra and deformed UO_6 octahedra linked in sheets parallel to (001) (Fig. 1.3). The UO_6 octahedra deviate upward and downward alternately from the plane of the P ions, and because adjacent sheets are mirror images, large spaces exist between sheets, which are filled by H_2O molecules and ions of H, alkalies, alkaline earth metals, or Cu. With transformation to the metahydrate, the unchanged sheets are moved

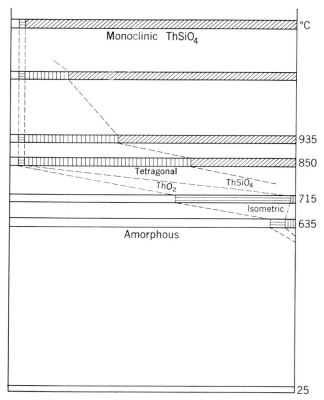

FIG. 1.2. Phase changes produced by heating, in air, metamict thorite from Brevig, Norway (Pabst, 1952; *Am. Mineralogist*).

laterally a distance of $a/2$, permitting a more closely packed structure vertically, and reducing the distance between adjacent sheets from 10.35 to 8.47 A.

Nuffield and Milne (1953) point out that the members of the metatorbernite group are not strictly isostructural, because the water in meta-uranocircite is largely zeolitic, less so in meta-autunite, and largely coordinated in metatorbernite. Thus the metatorbernite structure is the least stable of the three:

	Heating
Metatorbernite	110°C for 24 hr
	collapses structure
Meta-autunite	130°C for 24 hr
	unit cell shrinkage
Meta-uranocircite	105°C for 40 hr
	structure not destroyed

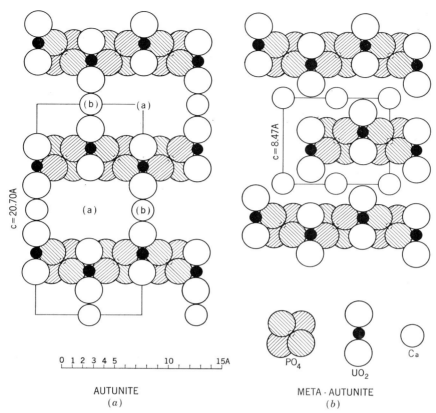

FIG. 1.3. Structure of autunite (*a*) and meta-autunite (*b*), projected on (110) (Nuffield and Milne, 1953; *Am. Mineralogist*).

TABLE 1.11. *Minerals of the torbernite and metatorbernite groups*

Torbernite group	H₂O	Metatorbernite group	H₂O
Autunite....................	12–10	Meta-autunite (I)............	6½–2½
Uranospinite................	10–8	Metatorbernite..............	8
Torbernite..................	12–8	Metazeunerite..............	8
Sabugalite.................	16	Meta-uranocircite..........	8
Saléeite....................	10–8	Abernathyite...............	4
Novacekite.................	10–8	Troegerite.................	8(?)

Anomalous optical effects in these minerals, such as twinning or extinction angle variations, are believed to be due to water molecules that are relatively free to move, i.e., zeolitic rather than coordinated. These effects are most pronounced in meta-uranocircite and are absent in metatorbernite.

As the radius of the cation that binds the sheets in the fully hydrated phase increases, the instability of the structure increases. Thus, in nature some species of the two groups occur only as full hydrates, others as both hydrates, and still others only as metaphases (Table 1.12).

TABLE 1.12. *Relation of cation size to natural occurrence (stability) in hydrated uranyl minerals (modified from Nuffield and Milne, 1953)*

Mineral	A or B		R	Occurrence in nature
Sabugalite.............	HAl		P	⎫
Saléeite................	Mg	increasing ionic radius	P	⎬ Full hydrate only
Novacekite.............	Mg		As	⎭
Uranospinite...........	Ca		As	?
Autunite...............	Ca		P	⎫
Torbernite.............	Cu		P	⎬ More commonly as the metaphase
Metazeunerite..........	Cu		As	⎭
Abernathyite...........	K		As	⎫
Meta-uranocircite........	Ba		P	⎬ Only as the metaphase
Troegerite..............	H		As	⎭

The sulfates zippeite and possibly also uranopilite (meta-uranopilite) exist in differently hydrated phases.

Hydrated U⁶ Oxides

The structures of the hydrated U^6 oxides, becquerelite, schoepite, billietite, masuyite, fourmarierite, and vandendriesscheite, some of which contain essential Pb, Ba, and possibly Ca, are described by Christ and Clark (1955) as based on a pseudohexagonal arrangement of vertical linear $(UO_2)^{2+}$ ions linked into (001) sheets of $(OH)^{1-}$ ions. The small basic pseudohexagonal unit corresponds to the hexagonal unit cell of αUO_3. The sheets are tied together by H_2O molecules or by Ba or Pb ions. The general formula for such minerals is $xA(OH)_2 \cdot yUO_2(OH)_2 \cdot (z\text{-}x\text{-}y)H_2O$, with A = Ba or Pb. Water in excess of that needed for $(OH)^{1-}$ groups is zeolitic.

PROPERTIES [1]

Fluorescence

Uranium as U^{6+} produces fluorescence in many but not all oxidized uranium minerals. No U^{4+} minerals fluoresce. The general types of fluorescence that have been distinguished are (Meixner, 1940B,C; Horne, 1951; Bültemann, 1954):

1. The "uranyl" type in oxygen salts of the alkaline earth metals—phosphates, arsenates, some carbonates, some sulfates
2. The "uranate" type

The uranyl type is strongly to moderately fluorescent. Meixner (1940B,C) recognizes two variations: a yellow green (autunite) and a whitish green (schroeckingerite).

Autunite type	*Schroeckingerite type*
Autunite	Schroeckingerite
Meta-uranocircite	Andersonite
Saléeite	Liebigite
Sabugalite	Swartzite
Uraniferous opal	

In general Ca, Ba, and Na-Ca phosphates, arsenates, and carbonates are strongly fluorescent; Ca-Mg and Mg equivalents are less strongly to weakly fluorescent; and Cu, Fe, Pb, and Bi equivalents are very weakly to nonfluorescent. The fluorescence of glasses tinted green by uranium salts is of the autunite type. However, some exceptions are noteworthy:

1. Some $Pb-UO_2$ phosphates are reported to fluoresce:

Dewindtite	Orange brown
Renardite	Brownish green
Dumontite	Yellow green

2. Metazeunerite, $Cu-UO_2$ arsenate, is weakly fluorescent in yellow green, but the synthetic fully hydrated phase does not fluoresce (Frondel, J., 1951).

[1] A sobering thought on the special properties of radioactive elements and minerals is contained in an Associated Press dispatch from Glasgow, Scotland, in 1955, stating, "Thorium, zinnwaldite, glaucophane and biotite, plus amphibole, pyroxene, uranium, a dash of sphene—and you're off to a running start on a batch of Scotch whisky.

"Trouble is, a spokesman for the Scotch Whisky Association said yesterday, these minerals are found in just the right amounts only in brooks which run through the red granite formations of the Scottish Highlands.

"And a drouth has dried up the brooks, forcing the distilleries into idleness.

"The special quality of this water, a spokesman for the association said, is the whole secret of Scotch whisky. Analyze it and reproduce it chemically? Lawks, ymon! That's been tried."

3. Phosphuranylite, a Ca-UO$_2$ phosphate, is reported to fluoresce orange brown.

The fluorescent properties [1] depend not only on the nature of the cation but also on the degree of hydration. Silicates and vanadates of Ca and K are nonfluorescent to very weakly so.

The rare "uranate" type of fluorescence is orange or red and may be exhibited by epiianthinite, becquerelite, and soddyite.

Thorium minerals also may fluoresce, but weakly: thorite a faint deep blue under short wave (Hutton, 1952) and huttonite a pale dull pinkish white under short wave (Hutton, 1950). Minto (1956) reports thorite(?) with bright green fluorescence under short-wave ultraviolet.

Some weakly radioactive species fluoresce weakly to strongly owing to the presence of certain rare-earth elements, e.g., apatite; xenotime (weak orange yellow—Tb); zircon (yellow, green—Dy; red—Sm and Tb).

Color

The oxides, complex oxides, and silicates of U^4 and Th are usually dark-colored, commonly black or brown, largely owing to the Fe or Ti also present. Many uranyl minerals are brilliantly colored, particularly in shades of orange, yellow, and green (Table 1.13).

The predominance of yellow minerals is extreme and is one of the major difficulties in the easy identification of uranyl minerals. Most of the deeper green minerals owe their color to Cu. Most of the orange to orange-red species are hydrous uranyl oxides.

Other Optical Properties

Optically, most uranium and thorium minerals fall into two very general groups: (1) the dark-colored (black to brown), semitranslucent to opaque, commonly isotropic (metamict) group of radioactive minerals which contain U^4, Th, or both—chiefly oxides, complex (multiple) oxides, and some silicates (the so-called "primary" radioactive minerals); and (2) the bright-colored, translucent to transparent, anisotropic group of uranium minerals that contain uranium as the uranyl ion and do not contain thorium—principally the hydrated or hydrous oxides, carbonates, sulfates, phosphates, arsenates, vanadates, and silicates (the "secondary" uranium minerals).

In the metamict group increasing amount of structural damage is commonly accompanied by an increase in the amount of nonessential water, which also brings about a marked decrease in the refractive index. This decrease is to

[1] Radioactive minerals should be tested under both short- and long-wave ultraviolet. The short-wave range is 2,300 to 3,100 A, with concentrations from commercial equipment at 2,537 or 2,652 A. The long-wave range is from 3,100 to 4,000 A, with 3,650 A predominating. The longer wavelengths are obtained from incandescent filament bulbs and various mercury units operating at moderate to high pressures and relatively high temperatures. Common glass screens out wavelengths below 3,200 A. Short wavelengths are produced by cold quartz tubes utilizing mercury vapor ionization at low temperatures and pressures.

TABLE 1.13. *Colors of uranyl minerals*

Orange, orange red, amber	Yellow, greenish yellow	Yellow green	Green
Masuyite	Schoepite	Andersonite	Vandenbrandeite
Becquerelite	Rutherfordine	Liebigite	Johannite
Billietite	Rabbittite	Swartzite	Torbernite
Curite	Bayleyite	Uranospathite	Metazeunerite
Fourmarierite	Schroeckingerite		Sengierite
Vandendriesscheite	Uranopilite		Cuprosklodowskite
Clarkeite	Autunite		Kasolite
Uranosphaerite	Meta-uranocircite		
Zippeite	Saléeite		
Renardite	Sabugalite		
	Bassetite		
	Phosphuranylite		
	Parsonite		
	Dumontite		
	Dewindtite		
	Uranospinite		
	Novacekite		
	Kahlerite		
	Abernathyite		
	Troegerite		
	Walpurgite		
	Carnotite		
	Tyuyamunite		
	Soddyite		
	Uranophane		
	Beta-uranophane		
	Sklodowskite		
	Kasolite		

some extent offset by the increase resulting from the concomitant oxidation of Fe^2 to Fe^3.

Of the crystalline uranyl minerals most are biaxial (about 85%), crystallizing mainly in the orthorhombic system, less commonly in the monoclinic, rarely in the triclinic. About two-thirds of all uranyl minerals are biaxial ($-$). A number of sulfates (johannite, uranopilite) and carbonates (liebigite, rabbittite, rutherfordine) are biaxial ($+$), as are the oxides vandenbrandeite and uranosphaerite, the phosphate dumontite, and the silicate kasolite. In the uniaxial group (nearly all tetragonal), optically ($-$) species are more common than optically ($+$) ones.

Metatorbernite and andersonite are uniaxial ($+$). The arsenates uranospinite, kahlerite, abernathyite, troegerite, and metazeunerite, and the phosphates torbernite, saléeite, and phosphuranylite are uniaxial ($-$). All other uranyl minerals, including most of the phosphates, silicates, and oxides are biaxial ($-$). Several tetragonal species may be anomalously biaxial, as for example novacekite, uranospinite, metatorbernite, meta-uranocircite, kahlerite, troegerite, saléeite, autunite, and meta-autunite. Similarly a few biaxial species may be anomalously uniaxial—schroeckingerite and phosphuranylite. These variations are closely related to variations in partly zeolitic water.

Among the chemical groups the vanadates and hydrous oxides have the highest refractive indices; silicates, arsenates, phosphates, and sulfates have indices in the intermediate range; and carbonates generally fall in the lowest index range. Within such groups as the phosphates and hydrous oxides, Pb-bearing species usually have the highest refractive indices. The bismuth arsenate walpurgite also has high refractive indices for its group. Increases in values of the refractive indices that result from some of the more widespread isomorphous replacements in the uranyl minerals include: Ba for K, carnotite; Ba for Ca, tyuyamunite; Cu for Ca, autunite; Pb for Cu, torbernite; Pb for Ca, phosphuranylite-renardite; and AsO_4 for PO_4, metatorbernite-metazeunerite.

Physical Properties

Most uranyl minerals have a hardness between 2 and 3; several have H = 3 to 4; and a few have H = 4 to 5. The ranges in specific gravities are shown in Table 1.14. Usually metaphases have higher specific gravities than their fully hydrated equivalents.

The hydrous uranyl oxides and the uranyl phosphates, arsenates ("uranium micas"), and vanadates have perfect basal (001) cleavages. The properties of the metamict minerals have been described previously.

TABLE 1.14. *Specific gravities of uranyl minerals*

Group	Usual range	With Bi	With Pb
Hydrous oxides.......	4.5–5.4	6.2	6.4–7.3
Carbonates..........	2.1–2.8		
Sulfates............	3.3–3.7		
Phosphates.........	3.1–4.1		4.4–5.4
Arsenates...........	3.2–3.7	5.9	
Silicates............	3.5–4.7		5.8–5.9

EXOGENIC EFFECTS

Radioactive minerals, particularly those containing U^4 and/or Th, produce chemical and structural changes in grains of various other minerals in which they are enclosed. These changes are represented by conspicuous discolorations and radial fractures, and less obviously by thermoluminescence and the production of gases.

Discoloration

Pale red feldspar, either sodic plagioclase or microcline or orthoclase, where in contact with Th or U^4 minerals, is usually colored dark red, the darker color surrounding the radioactive species as a zone or shell. However, a red shell in such hosts is not invariably present, as Hutton (1950) has pointed out. The dark red feldspar loses much of its color by heating to about 500°C.

Such color shells may also appear in calcite and scapolite. In some cases the discoloration clearly has resulted from the development of hematite along cleavage planes and fractures. Hutton (1950) suggests that metamictization with its accompanying expansion and fracturing of the host permits ready circulation of solutions that have secured ferric iron from the oxidized metamict mineral.

Fluorite may become colored deep blue, purple, or dark violet, and the color change may be accompanied by sufficient deterioration of the crystal structure so that fluorine gas is liberated on grinding or fracturing. This fluorine reacts with air moisture to produce HF and ozone. The dark color is reportedly due to F-centers, i.e., fluoride-ion gaps (Berman, 1957A). The color may be removed by heating to above 175°C. The liberation of gaseous fluorine can be observed by crushing a fluorite fragment in a liquid in a field of low magnification.

Much dark smoky quartz owes its coloration to alpha-particle bombardment from neighboring radioactive species. The darkening centers are related to the presence of concentrations of Al as a trace element "impurity." Apparently small local internal concentrations of radioactive elements can also darken quartz, as well as adjacent radioactive grains, although the effects of irradiation may have to accumulate for geologically long periods of time (Marshall, 1955). Not all gray to black quartz is discolored by radiation; in some the dark color is due to disseminated carbon or graphite (Boyle, 1953).

Diamonds, where in contact with radioactive minerals, may become colored green surficially. A few such stones have been found in the Witwatersrand gold-pitchblende deposits in the Union of South Africa. The production of a golden tint in some beryl has been ascribed to emanations from neighboring radioactive minerals.

Alpha and beta particles from ^{40}K also can produce discoloration, and do so particularly in halite in which deep blue colors appear (ascribed to chlorine vacancies in the structure).

Pleochroic Halos

Pleochroic halos that consist of concentric shells of discoloration in shades of brown are formed chiefly by alpha radiation and possibly by beta radiation in many minerals that contain some ferrous iron oxidizable to the ferric state by this mechanism (Fig. 1.4). Such species include muscovite, lepidolite, biotite, chlorite, amphiboles (especially hornblende), pyroxenes (especially augite), tourmaline, cordierite, and andalusite. Halos also have been reported in barite.

Halos are especially common in biotite, chlorite, and fluorite. The nuclei minerals are chiefly zircon, monazite, xenotime, apatite, allanite, and sphene; but perovskite, melanite, rutile, and cassiterite, all of exceedingly weak radioactivity, may also serve. Very little radioactivity is necessary for the formation of a recognizable halo.

Halos are particularly common in silicic intrusive rocks or their metamorphic equivalents. They are rare to absent in volcanic rocks. The use of halos for age determination and to yield other information has been effectively summarized by Rankama (1954).

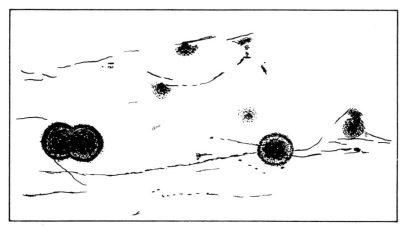

Fig. 1.4. Pleochroic halos in muscovite (about 200×) (adapted from Joly, 1915).

Thermoluminescence

Many minerals that have been exposed to emanations from radioactive neighbors have the property of glowing strongly in the dark if they are heated.[1] Such natural thermoluminescence, which may last for several minutes, cannot be reactivated by cooling and reheating. Common minerals that can display this property include feldspar, quartz, mica, calcite, dolomite, and fluorite. Rocks such as granite and limestone also have been observed to exhibit it. By recording thermoluminescent light intensity as a function of temperature, a characteristic glow curve for the mineral can be obtained, from which the amount of structural damage resulting from radiation may be estimated. For fluorite the thermoluminescent intensity is a function of the age of its mineralization and its radioactivity (Parks and Saunders, 1951; Zeller, 1954; Daniels, 1954).

Radial Fractures

Radioactive minerals, mainly of the metamict type, are commonly the foci of a series of fractures that radiate in all directions, passing through surrounding mineral grains for distances ranging from a faction of an inch to as much as several feet (Fig. 1.5). These radial fracture groups are especially conspicuous in pegmatites around such species as uraninite, euxenite, samarskite, fergusonite, betafite, eschynite, thorite, allanite, gadolinite, and some zircon (var. cyrtolite). In the Baringer Hill, Texas, pegmatite, Landes (1932) noted fissures radiating out 4 to 5 ft from the radioactive mineral core. In granites and gneisses, allanite may be the center of similar microfractures. Fractures show up well in enveloping feldspar and quartz, but also in micas. The nucleus grain

[1] Ellsworth (1932, p. 56) states, "This discovery was made accidentally and independently by two parties of prospectors searching for radioactive minerals in different parts of Ontario and came about as a result of placing mineral specimens on a hot camp stove at night."

is usually also fractured to varying degrees. Detrital grains of various radio-active minerals from sands and sandstones not uncommonly may show sets of radially to irregularly arranged internal fractures (Fig. 1.6). Detrital zircon and uranothorite display them well developed.

Both the internal and external fracturing are regarded by Ellsworth (1932) as resulting from stresses induced by an increase in volume (decrease in specific gravity) accompanying metamictization, a view to which Hutton (1950) subscribes. The fractures associated with uraninite apparently result chiefly from increases in volume due to auto-oxidation of U^4 to U^6. Since the fractures are not found around nonradioactive species nor normally around non-metamict radioactive species, the ideas of Walker and Parsons (1923), Hess and Wells (1930), and Landes (1932), that they result from (*a*) primary growth (expansion) of the focus mineral or (*b*) from expansion of the inclusion or contraction of the host owing to chemical changes or to cooling, do not appear applicable.

CLASSIFICATION

Early extensive tabulations of radioactive minerals were made by Szilard (1909) and by Holmes (1931). An attempt to group systematically the radio-

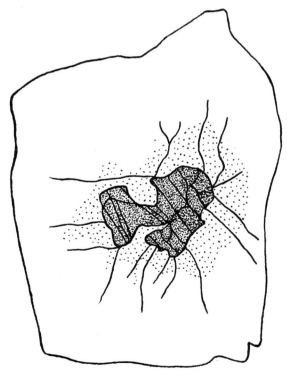

Fɪɢ. 1.5. Radial fractures and hematitic alteration halo around internally fractured allanite in plagioclase. Deep Creek No. 1 pegmatite, Bryson City, N.C. ($\times$1).

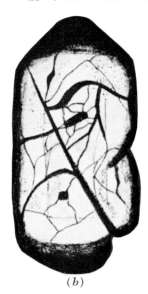

(a)   (b)

FIG. 1.6. Detrital zircon showing internal microfractures (Hutton, 1950; *Geol. Soc. Am.*) (*a*) with zonal structure and opaque core, Slab Hut Dredge, New Zealand (×200), (*b*) Ngahere, New Zealand (×150).

active minerals was that of Ellsworth (1932), who compiled a listing of "Minerals containing uranium, thorium, and the rare earths" under the headings: Fluorides; Oxides, hydroxides; Carbon compounds; Silicates; Titanates, tantalates, columbates; Phosphates; Arsenates; Uranates, vanadates; and Sulfates.

Yagoda (1946A, 1949) classified uranium and thorium minerals into seven groups (A to G) based on decreasing number of alpha particles that escape per second from 1 sq cm of polished mineral surface (Pα). The photographic density of the image of the polished section of a species is proportional to Pα. Recognition of the relative intensity of the autoradiographic image is a useful preliminary step in the identification of the species in polished section.

The classification of George (1949), who has added much new information in his systematic description of uranium and thorium minerals, is partly genetic, partly crystallochemical:

Hypogene minerals	*Supergene uranium minerals*
Uranium minerals	Hydrated oxides
Simple oxides	Hydrated phosphates
Multiple oxides	Hydrated arsenates
Thorium minerals	Hydrated vanadates
Simple oxides	Hydrated sulfates
Complex oxides	Hydrated carbonates
Simple silicates	Hydrated silicates
Complex silicates	
Simple phosphates	

The difficulties of this classification are largely twofold. Among the complex oxides it is difficult and in some cases arbitrary to distinguish between uranium and thorium types; many have both elements in varying amounts. Secondly, and more important, not all hydrated uranyl minerals are necessarily supergene; secondary and supergene are not synonymous. Nor do all investigators believe that pitchblende in all its occurrences is invariably hypogene.

The groupings of Lang (1952) are on a genetic basis: (1) pegmatitic minerals, (2) hydrothermal minerals, and (3) secondary minerals. A highly useful and usable arrangement has been developed by J. Frondel and Fleischer (1950, 1952, 1955), who recognize three major categories: (*a*) uranium and thorium minerals, (*b*) minerals with minor amounts of uranium and thorium, and (*c*) minerals reported to contain uranium and thorium minerals as impurities or intergrowths. This threefold initial subdivision has been followed here with the major subdivisions under the first group, *Uranium and thorium minerals*, being:

Oxides
Complex (multiple) oxides
Hydrated oxides and hydroxides
Carbonates
Sulfates
Phosphates
    Nonhydrated
    Hydrated

Arsenates
Vanadates
Molybdate
Silicates
    Nonhydrated
    Hydrated

Similar groupings are used for the second group, *Minerals with minor U, Th, or Ta,* and for the third, *Minerals with radioactive impurities.* Gummite is retained in a separate category and is used in a generic sense for bright-colored, fine-grained mixtures formed by alteration of uraninite and pitchblende and consisting of a variety of hydrated uranyl minerals. Thucolite also is retained in a special category, although much of it has been demonstrated to consist of hydrocarbons and intermixed uraninite. Minerals of doubtful status, usually because of incomplete data, are grouped at the end of each chemical group, under *Doubtful or poorly defined species.* Varietal names are used as sparingly as possible.

The description of uranium and thorium minerals is by no means complete. Not only are new species still being discovered (witness cerianite, rabbittite, cheralite, sabugalite, novacekite, abernathyite, umohoite, huttonite, and coffinite, all described since 1950), but older minerals have been carefully redefined (clarkeite, vandendriesscheite, bassetite, uranospinite, and thorogummite). Much work also remains to be done on the description of many species (e.g., davidite, brannerite, ianthinite, zippeite, and troegerite), and data on the formation of many species are sparse.

If one excludes doubtful species, varieties, and intermediate members of series, counting only the "end members" and including gummite and thucolite as species, there are 85 uranium and thorium minerals. If the list includes poorly defined or doubtful species that probably will become valid, the total is raised to over 100.

• chapter two

DESCRIPTIONS OF RADIOACTIVE

MINERALS

Uranium and Thorium Minerals

OXIDES

Uraninite and Pitchblende

Composition. Ideally UO_2. U = 46.5 to 88.2%. Normally U^4 is oxidized to U^6 to a varying extent. As the U^4 ion is replaced by the smaller U^6 ion, extra O ions enter to occupy interstitial positions. The limit of oxidation extends to at least $(U^4,U^6)O_{2.6}$ (Brooker and Nuffield, 1952) $(UO_{2.67} = U_3O_8)$. Heating uraninite in air for five minutes will convert it to U_3O_8. The U^6 is regarded as resulting in some cases from auto-oxidation owing to the strong radioactivity, but oxidation is not uniform throughout (Brooker and Nuffield, 1952) in granular material. Analyses of different zones of single crystals (Ellsworth, 1930, 1932; Bakken, Gleditsch, and Pappas, 1948) show that U^6 increases outward. In many pegmatitic uraninites the ratio of UO_2/UO_3 appears to be high; this also appears characteristic of contact metasomatic uraninite, whereas in nonpegmatitic uraninite it is low or variable. No natural material that is exactly UO_2 has been found, although some approaches $UO_{2.2}$. It is possible that some of the U^6 is primary and that the amount of initial U^6 is controlled by the temperature of formation of the uraninite, that forming at lower temperatures having larger amounts of U^6.

Wasserstein (1954) has suggested a threefold classification of uraninites:

γ-uraninite—U_4O_7 (oxygen deficient)

α-uraninite—UO_2, uraninite in the strict sense

β-uraninite—U_3O_7 (oxygen in excess), pitchblende in the strict sense

26

Geffroy and Sarcia (1954, pp. 31–34) have called secondary pitchblende, formed later than "normal" pitchblende and in some cases replacing it, para-pitchblende, distinguished on the basis of inferior hardness and lower re-flectivity; it is high in UO_3. Hydronasturan, a hydrated oxide of U^4 and U^6 (Melkov, 1956), reported as a new uranium mineral from some uranium deposits of the U.S.S.R. as a product of the partial oxidation of pitchblende under alkaline conditions, is probably partly oxidized uraninite.

An important substitute for U is Th, and a complete series exists between uraninite and thorianite,[1] the division between the two species being at $U:Th = 1:1$. The Th content of uraninite ranges up to 45.3%. Hydrothermal vein uraninites usually contain $<0.25\%$ ThO_2, whereas pegmatitic uraninites commonly have $ThO_2 = 2\%$ or more. Bröggerite is a thorian uraninite, with $ThO_2 =$ up to about 14%. Rare-earth elements, particularly of the yttrium group, also may be significant constituents (cleveite, nivenite), at least up to about 10% $(Y,Ce, etc.)_2O_3$. Cerium-group elements rarely predominate over those of the yttrium group. Uraninites rich in rare-earth elements are usually of pegmatitic origin.

Other elements, such as the gases He, A, and N, are present, He being formed as a radioactive decay product. Pb is similarly formed; amounts up to about 16% PbO have been determined. Other elements that may be reported in variable amounts, such as Ta, Fe^{3+}, Mn, Si, alkalies, alkaline earths, and H_2O, are due either to admixture or alteration. Unusual amounts of Zr and Mo are reported from pitchblende from the Central City district, Colo. (Sims, 1955). Noted in Belgian Congo pitchblende are Pb, Fe, Co, Ni, Mo, and Se.

Uraninite alters readily to numerous secondary hydrated oxides, carbonates, sulfates, phosphates, arsenates, vanadates, and silicates of U and other elements. It may also be replaced by thucolite, in some cases pseudomorphously, and by various sulfides, especially chalcopyrite. Uraninite crystals may show well-defined alteration zones, due to selective leaching of some elements. Th is leached most readily; Pb is removed more easily than U^{4+}, but after the conversion U^4 to U^6, U^6 is lost much faster than Pb (Ellsworth, 1932). Uraninite crystals from hypothermal veins in British Columbia show zoning upon etching with concentrated HNO_3 (Stevenson, 1951). Because of the ease of alteration by weathering, hydrothermal solutions, meteoric solutions, and by auto-oxidation, uraninite is exceedingly rare as a detrital mineral.

Pitchblende is a variety of uraninite, and the distinction between the two has been made on a number of characteristics: form (Rogers, 1947); composition (Ellsworth, 1932); origin (Brooker and Nuffield, 1952); alpha activity (Yagoda, 1946A); and grain size (Cohen, 1953; Croft, 1954). A consistent chemical distinction between uraninite and pitchblende is not present, for both may have Th and both may be oxidized.

Structure and form. Crystals common, some of unusual size: Wilberforce, Ont., $11.0 \times 7.1 \times 4.9$ cm, 1,834 g (Meen, 1948) (Fig. 2.1); Rock Landing Quarry, Haddam Neck, Conn., $6 \times 7 \times 10$ cm, 1,200 g (Ingerson, 1938).

---

[1] In nature, some of the intermediate members are poorly represented. Uraninite uncommonly has more than 14% ThO_2.

FIG. 2.1. Uraninite crystals, largest measures $11 \times 7.1 \times 4.9$ cm, from syenitic vein-dikes, Wilberforce, Cardiff Township, Ont. (V. B. Meen).

Commonly, but not invariably, pegmatitic uraninite forms single euhedra or crystal clusters. Uraninite in three-dimensional dendrites of small crystals in perthite is known from the Grafton Center pegmatite, N.H. (Shaub, 1938) (Fig. 2.2). Pyrite-uraninite polycrystals consist of thin alternate crystal zones about a pyrite nucleus (King, 1957).

Pitchblende usually refers to botryoidal, colloform, or massive uraninite, much of which is relatively fine grained, in polycrystalline aggregates and nonpegmatitic in origin. Much vein pitchblende occurs in reniform to botryoidal masses (Fig. 2.3) or spherulites (Figs. 2.4, 2.5), which show concentrically layered and fibrous to columnar structures. The parallel fibers of some botryoidal masses have axes of elongation that consist of the poles of (111) crystal faces (Croft, 1954, p. 53). The botryoidal masses are commonly markedly jointed, with gangue or ore minerals filling the fractures or syneresis cracks (Fig. 2.6). Quartz may replace the spherulites; in some examples it replaces zones selectively. Calcite may be interlayered with pitchblende in spherulites. Inclusions are generally concentrated in the outer parts of the spherulites. Not all vein pitchblende is botryoidal; some is in thin, roughly parallel, sinuous seams, 0.3 to 2.5 cm thick; some is in massive, structureless nodules; some is in irregular masses intricately intergrown with hematite, pyrite, other sulfides, and gangue minerals; some occurs as elongated wisps in gangue minerals or as submicroscopic specks in gangue. In some vein deposits botryoidal pitchblende has been thoroughly broken and the texture is brecciated (Eldorado deposit, Great Bear Lake, Canada; Goldfields district, Canada) (Fig. 2.7). Brecciated pitchblende may be cemented by a second

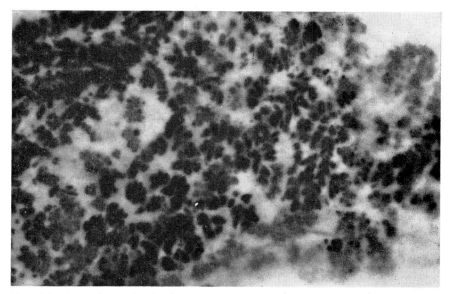

FIG. 2.2. Autoradiograph, dendritic uraninite and alteration products in feldspar. Grafton Center pegmatite, N.H.

FIG. 2.3. Botryoidal pitchblende, St. Priest vein, Forez, France ($\times 1$) (Geffroy and Sarcia, 1954).

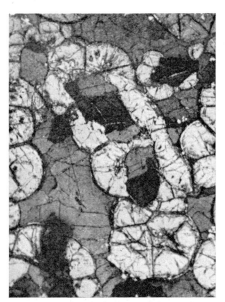

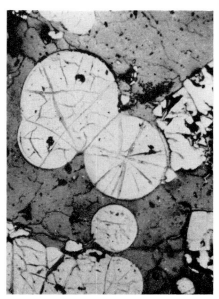

Fig. 2.4. Botryoidal pitchblende, Port Radium, Great Bear Lake, N.W.T., Canada. Cracks and borders of spherulites contain covellite; gangue is quartz (×80) (Kidd, 1932A; *Econ. Geol.*).

Fig. 2.5. Botryoidal pitchblende, St.-Rémy-sur-Durolle, Forez Mts., France. Pyrite crystals (white) on right; in quartz (×100) (Geffroy and Sarcia, 1954).

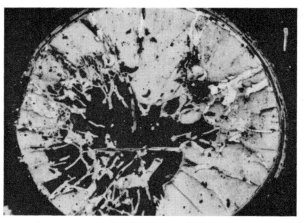

Fig. 2.6. Syneresis fractures in spherulite of pitchblende, filled by galena (white) and quartz (black) which also replaces core. Bigay mine, Lachaux, Auvergne, France (×100) (Geffroy and Sarcia, 1954).

F-IG. 2.7. Brecciated pitchblende spherulites cemented by quartz, Port Radium, Great Bear Lake, N.W.T., Canada (×13) (Kidd, 1932A; *Econ. Geol.*).

generation of massive pitchblende. Masses of pitchblende 10 ft across and weighing 20 tons have been found in the Katanga, Belgian Congo, deposits.

Single euhedral to subhedral crystals of uraninite also are known in vein deposits; cubes in vugs at Shinkolobwe, Belgian Congo, and partial cubes in veins of some deposits in northern Canada and Schneeberg, Saxony. In the Blind River district of Ontario fine-grained euhedral uraninite occurs in the matrix of a quartz-pebble conglomerate; commonly the central portions of crystals are replaced by quartz. In some deposits massive pitchblende cements fragments of earlier minerals or replaces older minerals along cleavages or pseudomorphously.

A few examples of polycrystalline uraninite aggregates in pegmatites also are known. In the Varuträsk, Sweden, pegmatite (Quensel, 1940) uraninite cubes are transected by veinlets of fine-grained botryoidal pitchblende. Microgranular uraninite, 0.01 to 0.2 mm in diameter, occurs at Iisaka, Japan, in green and red feldspar associated with fergusonite (Iimori, 1941). Nodules of pitchblende as heavy as 243 g occur in a pegmatite near Mérida, Mérida State, Venezuela.

In the disseminated deposits of the Colorado Plateau, two general types of pitchblende commonly are recognized: a massive type with a submetallic luster and a sooty type of powdery aspect with a dull luster. Both types are very fine grained to cryptocrystalline (1 to 10 μ). Textural variations are numerous: replacements of woody tissue (both carbonized and silicified), especially cell walls with chalcopyrite occupying cell centers; cement between quartz grains replacing original carbonaceous clay or calcitic cement; peripheral replacements of quartz grains, of quartz or limestone pebbles, and of authigenic quartz overgrowths; replacements of asphaltite, in some cases of metallic sulfides; and ribbons and ellipsoidal aggregates in asphaltite. Sooty pitchblende also occurs in some hydrothermal veins, particularly those of simple mineralogy.

X-ray studies reveal that the cell edge of uraninite (a_0) varies from about 5.38 to about 5.49 A. The cell edge increases with increasing Th content (for thorianite $a_0 = 5.575$ A) and decreases with increasing oxidation of U^4 to U^6, being near 5.38 A for material of composition $UO_{2.6}$ (Brooker and Nuffield, 1952) (Fig. 2.8). Thus although there are no consistent differences in size of cell edge between pegmatitic uraninite and vein or lode pitchblende, much of the latter, containing much U^6 and but little Th, has $a_0 = 5.38$ to 5.44 A, averaging perhaps 5.40 A, whereas pegmatitic uraninites have a_0 averaging near 5.47 A (Rosenzweig, Gruner, and Gardiner, 1954) and range from 5.44 to 5.49 A (Berman, 1955).

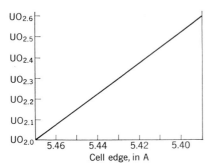

FIG. 2.8. Relation of cell edge in angstroms to oxidation of U^4 to U^6 in uraninite (Brooker and Nuffield, 1952; *Am. Mineralogist*).

Although metamict pitchblende has been reported (Conybeare and Ferguson, 1950), its existence has been effectively disputed by Brooker and Nuffield (1952), who demonstrate that the diffuse x-ray powder patterns also are functions of a reduction in grain size and increasing oxidation of U^4 to U^6.

Robinson and Sabina (1955) have been able to classify 20 uraninites and thorianites from Ontario and Quebec, analyzed for U_3O_8, ThO_2, and PbO, into three groups:

1. Uraninites with 10% or less ThO_2; $a_0 < 5.47$ A; from pegmatite, granite, and syenite dikes; associated minerals are potash and soda feldspars, some quartz, consistent sphene, and zircon, apatite, and fluorite in most deposits.

2. Uraninites containing $ThO_2 = 10$ to 18%; $a_0 = 5.47$ to 5.50 A; from calcite-fluorite-apatite veins and mica pyroxenites also containing these minerals.

3. Uraninites with $ThO_2 > 20\%$ and all thorianites; $a_0 = 5.51$ to 5.65 A; in metasomatic zones in marbles containing calcite, diopside, phlogopite and accessory sphene, thorite, chondrodite, and pyrite.

Occurrence. Uraninite has the following general modes of occurrence:

1. In granitic pegmatites common associates are zircon, monazite, smoky quartz, reddish feldspar, beryl, tourmaline, muscovite, biotite, garnet, apatite, and in some cases thucolite; less usually complex radioactive oxides containing Ta and Nb, such as columbite, betafite, and fergusonite (pages 194–200). Some noteworthy examples are Mt. Lukwengule, Morogoro, East Africa (400 kg reportedly mined); Gordonia district, Union of South Africa (octahedra up to 7 in. on edge); Rock Landing Quarry, Haddam Neck, Conn.; Ruggles mine,

Grafton, and Palermo mine, Groton, N.H.; Bob Ingersoll pegmatite, Black Hills, S.Dak.; Hyatt Beryl pegmatite, Crystal Mountain district, Colo.; Lac la Ronge, northern Sask.; Villeneuve, Ont.; southern Norway; northern Karelia, U.S.S.R.; Brazil, in Minas Gerais at Brejauba and Engenho Central, in Paraiba at Picui and Parelhas, and in Rio Grande do Norte at Acari and Currais.

2. In syenitic pegmatites with cores of calcite-fluorite-apatite rock ("vein-dikes," pages 217–220): Wilberforce, Ont.

3. In rare pyrometasomatic deposits: Goodsprings, Nev.; in contact altered marbles and metapyroxenites of the Bancroft, Ont., district (pages 245–246); in serpentinite near Easton, Pa.

4. In hydrothermal high-temperature veins: with hematite, N.W.T., Canada; with Co-Ni arsenides and molybdenite; Bridge River, B.C.; Carrizal Alto, Chile (pages 265–267).

5. In several types of lower temperature hydrothermal veins, lodes, and disseminated deposits: (*a*) Veins with Co-Ni-Bi-Ag-As minerals (pages 273–298): Great Bear Lake, Canada; Joachimsthal, Bohemia; Shinkolobwe, Belgian Congo. Somewhat similarly in the Sn deposits of Cornwall, England. (*b*) Veins with pyrite, galena (± sphalerite) (pages 298–319): Lake Athabasca, Canada; Urgeirica, Portugal; Coeur d'Alene, Idaho. (*c*) Veins rich in fluorite (pages 343–353): Marysvale, Utah; Wölsendorf, Germany. (*d*) Disseminations in metamorphic rocks: with thucolite and gold—Witwatersrand, Union of South Africa (pages 319–324); with pyrite, monazite, and brannerite—Blind River, Ont. (pages 258–265). (*e*) In unoxidized epigenetic dissemination—replacement lodes in sandstones and conglomerates ("Colorado Plateau types") (Chap. 10) with (*a*) a vanadiferous association including coffinite and low-valence vanadium oxides and locally much asphaltic material—Mi Vida mine, Monticello district; Temple Mountain, San Rafael district; La Sal Creek, Paradox district; or (*b*) a nonvanadiferous association of sulfides of Pb, Cu, Zn, Fe, Co, and Ni—Happy Jack mine, White Canyon district; several deposits in the San Rafael, Green River, and Henry Mountains districts (Weeks and Thompson, 1954).

Detrital uraninite has been identified from a stream placer in British Columbia (Steacy, 1953) and in a few other Canadian placers, but otherwise is very rare (Davidson and Cosgrove, 1955). Most alleged detrital uraninite is uranothorianite.

Uraninite has been synthesized (Gruner, 1952) between 50 and 212°C by reduction of uranyl ions by H_2S or Fe^2, and by organic liquids at room temperature under ultraviolet radiation.

Identification. The modes of occurrence, general physical properties, high radioactivity, and form serve to identify most uraninite. For very fine grained varieties, an x-ray powder pattern may be necessary, especially if coffinite also is present or suspected. Uraninite is soluble in H_2SO_4 and HNO_3. In polished section the reactions to the following standard reagents are rather variable (other reagents negative):

HNO_3—strong to slight effervescence; black to brown differential stain; little reaction

HCl—strong to slight effervescence; black to light brown stain
FeCl$_3$—strong black to slight light brown stain; little reaction.

Thorianite

Composition. (Th,U^4)O$_2$. Forms a complete series, chemically and structurally, with uraninite; the division between the two species is at Th:U =1:1. U up to 46.5%, Th = 45.3 to 87.9%. The U^4 is usually oxidized partly or wholly to U^6. Ce-group elements also substitute for Th (see cerianite). Small

TABLE 2.1. *Properties of uraninite and thorianite*

Mineral	Form	Color, Streak	n	Cleavage and fracture	H	G
Uraninite	Isometric, cubes, octahedra. Octahedral faces common in low-Th types. Not metamict	Black to dark gray. Submetallic to sooty luster. Streak black to dark olive	2.2	Irregular to conchoidal fracture	5–6.5 decreasing with increasing U^6 Sooty types have much lower aggregate H and G	8– 10.5
Thorianite	Isometric, cubes, (111) twins common. Not metamict	Gray to black. Green gray streak. Submetallic to greasy luster	2.12– 2.35. Translucent dark green in very thin pieces	(001) poor	5–7	9.2– 9.7

amounts of Fe^3 and Zr also may be isomorphous with Th. Pb present probably is radiogenic. Other elements reported in minor to trace amounts are Ca, Mn, Mg, and He. Alters rather readily by oxidation of U^4 to U^6 and addition of H$_2$O and other elements to thorogummite. High-Th types are less readily altered than those near uraninite (uranothorianite).

Occurrence. Thorianite (or thorian uraninite) occurs chiefly in impure metasomatized marbles. Notable are occurrences in Ontario and Quebec, where such deposits contain salmon-red calcite, diopside, phlogopite, and accessory sphene, thorite, chondrodite, and pyrite. Examples include Huddersfield, Range V, lots 20, 21, 22, and Range IV, lot 20, in Quebec, and Dungannon, Concession XVI, lot 14, Ont. Reported in sheared biotitic pegmatite at a granite-metasedimentary contact with molybdenite and uraninite on the Row claims, south shore Charlebois Lake, Sask. (Lang, 1952, p. 112). Not nearly so common in granitic pegmatites as uraninite. In granite, Mafufu, Belgian Congo.

In stream placer deposits in Ceylon (first discovery) and in pegmatites in the Galle district of Balangoda; also in placers on Ceylon near Kondrugala, Sabaragamuwa district, and at Getahetta (Mitopola). Associates are thorite, zircon, and ilmenite. On Madagascar in placers with spinel, diopside, and phlogopite (note similarity to Canadian associates) at Andolobe and Betroka, and at Sofia, north of Andranendambe in a phlogopite pyroxenite. In gold placers on the Boshogocha River, Transbaikalia, Siberia. In black sand concentrates from the Missouri River near Helena, Mont., and the Scott River, Siskiyou County, Calif. (George, 1949). In twinned cubes in the placers of the Sweepstakes Creek area, 135 mi east-northeast of Nome, Alaska (Gault et al., 1953); and in black sand with zircon, rutile, platinum, gold, cinnabar, scheelite, sperrylite, and other heavy minerals from Fraser River, near Lytton, B.C. (Thompson, 1954, p. 526).

Identification. Like uraninite but less altered; less easily dissolved in acids. Twinned cubes are characteristic. Detrital and less commonly pegmatitic.

Cerianite

$(Ce,Th)O_2$ with $Ce:Th = 16:1$. Nb, Ta, Zr, and Y-group elements also reported. $ThO_2 = 5.1 \pm 0.5\%$, U not determined. A series to thorianite may exist (Graham, 1955). Isometric; $a_0 = 5.42 \pm 0.01$ A. Minute octahedra. Translucent, dark greenish amber. $G > 3.18$. Occurs in the contact zone of a carbonate rock with silicate-rich inclusions in Lackner Township, Sudbury district, Ont. The inclusions are pods about a foot long of partly resorbed gneissic nepheline syenite containing carbonate, nepheline, feldspar, tremolite, magnetite, ilmenite, apatite, and cerianite.

COMPLEX (MULTIPLE) OXIDES

Pyrochlore-Microlite Series

Composition. The series is between two end members whose idealized compositions may be expressed by:

$NaCaNb_2O_6F$—pyrochlore
$(Na,Ca)_2(Ta,Nb)_2O_6(O,OH,F)$—microlite

The general composition may be expressed as $A_2B_2O_6(O,OH,F)$ with

A = Na, Ca and minor to major amounts of K, Mg, Fe^2, Mn, Ce-group elements, Y-group elements, Zr, U, Th
B = Nb, Ta, variable Ti, Fe^3, minor Sn, W

Small amounts of Pb, Be, Al, Si, Sr, Bi, and Hf also are reported. The main varieties are: uranian (hatchettolite, ellsworthite), cerian, titanian, ferroan, and ferrian. These varieties, and especially those rich in U and Ce-group elements, are more commonly also Nb-rich (pyrochlore). The niobian types, especially those also rich in Ti, usually are considerably hydrated. Uranium occurs in amounts up to about 11.5% UO_2 and up to 15.5% UO_3. Th may be present in amounts up to nearly 8% ThO_2. Zoned crystals of uranian pyrochlore

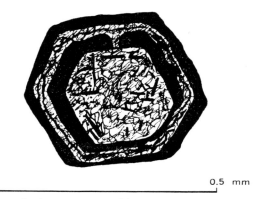

0   0.5 mm

FIG. 2.9. Zoned crystal of uranian pyrochlore, Newman deposit, Lake Nipissing, Ont. (Rowe, 1954; *Geol. Survey Can.*).

are known (Fig. 2.9) in shades of yellow and brown, probably reflecting varying Fe^3 contents. Obruchevite (Melkov, 1956), found in pegmatites in the U.S.S.R., is apparently an yttrian member of the pyrochlore-microlite series (Fleischer, 1958).

Structure and form. Crystals as large as 6 cm have been obtained from the Amelia, Va., pegmatite. Rare spinel-type twins with (111) as the twin plane are known. Marginal replacements and overgrowths of microlite on tapiolite (Kimito, Finland, and Alto do Giz, Rio Grande do Norte, Brazil), on tantalite (Main Tantalite Dike, Strelley, Western Australia), and on stibiotantalite (Varuträsk, Sweden) are known; as are oriented intergrowths of pyrochlore and zircon, (112) of pyrochlore coinciding with (110) of zircon (Ilmen Mts., U.S.S.R.). Intergrowths with apatite, chlorite, and hematite are known.

Occurrence. Pyrochlore occurs chiefly in the following geological environments:

1. In nepheline syenite and syenite pegmatites: Larvik and Langesundfjord, southern Norway, associated with zircon and polymignite (pages 222–223).

2. As disseminated grains in alkali granite, syenite, nepheline syenite, and various other alkalic, silica-deficient dike rocks: Fen, Norway; Manitou Islands, Lake Nipissing, Ont.; Miask, Ilmen Mts., U.S.S.R.; Khibina Tundra, Kola Peninsula, U.S.S.R.; Kaffo Valley, Nigeria (riebeckite granite); Ampasibitika, Madagascar (aegirine-riebeckite granite); in cancrinite syenite, Litchfield, Maine, two varieties, black (4.8% U_3O_8) and orange (14.4% U_3O_8).

3. In pyrometasomatic marbles, skarns, and carbonatites associated with alkalic, silica-poor rocks: Oka district, Two Mountains County, Quebec (Fig. 2.10); Kaiserstuhl, Baden, Germany; Alnö, Sweden; Mbeya, Tanganyika, and others in Africa; Chilwa Island and Tundulu, Nyasaland (Smith, 1953) (Chap. 6); a related type of occurrence is at Barreiro, Araxá, Minas Gerais, Brazil, in a calcite vein cutting an alkalic amphibole-pyroxene metamorphic rock (Ilchenko and Guimarães, 1954), in the contact zone of a mafic alkalic intrusive; also in xenoliths in alkalic rocks (Laacher See, Germany).

4. In eluvial soils with apatite derived from carbonatites (Tororo, Uganda).

5. In placers: Bugaboo placers, Revelstoke district, B.C., with polycrase, allanite, sphene, and zircon, derived from granitic rocks.

Some pyrochlore also occurs in granitic pegmatites: ellsworthite at the Mc-Donald mine and hatchettolite at the Woodcox mine, both near Hybla, Ont., and in the Viking Lake pegmatite, Goldfields area, Sask. In the Bancroft area pyrochlore also occurs rarely in calcite-fluorite-apatite veins.

Microlite occurs principally in zoned granitic pegmatites in which secondary hydrothermal units are strongly developed, especially in those rich in lepidolite, notably in the United States at the Harding mine near Dixon, N.Mex. (two varieties—microlite and hatchettolite), at the Pittlite pegmatite near Rociada,

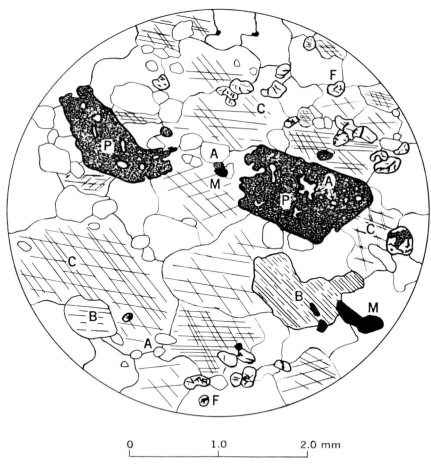

FIG. 2.10. Marble consisting chiefly of calcite (*C*) and containing apatite (*A*), biotite (*B*), magnetite (*M*), forsterite (*F*), and pyrochlore (*P*), Oka district, Two Mts. County, Quebec (Rowe, 1955A; *Geol. Survey Can.*).

N.Mex., and at the Brown Derby pegmatite, Gunnison County, Colo. Other similar occurrences are at Amelia Court House, Va., in octahedra as heavy as 8 lb with cleavelandite, smoky quartz, fluorite, columbite, and monazite; at Topsham, Maine, with albite, lepidolite, tourmaline, and topaz; at Chesterfield, Mass.; in Connecticut at Haddam Neck, Haddam, Portland, and Middleton; in California near Hemet, Riverside County, and at the Tourmaline King and Stewart pegmatites, Pala district. Other noteworthy pegmatitic occurrences include those at Skogböle, Kimito, Finland; Orust, Utö, and Varuträsk, Sweden; Iveland, Moss, and Gjerstad, Norway; Junqueiro mine, Caminho district, Portugal; Donkerhuk, South-West Africa, where occur seven varieties of microlite and tantalite which, from oldest to youngest, increase in Ta and Ca and decrease in H_2O, Nb, Ti, and U (13.5 to 0.5%); Victoria tin district, Ndanga, Rhodesia; west of Mt. Bity, Madagascar—hatchettolite (2.37% BeO, 14.15% U_3O_8); São João del Rei and Brejauba districts (Conceição), Minas Gerais, Brazil; and the Main Tantalite Dike, Strelley, Western Australia.

Microlite also occurs as a detrital mineral with cassiterite in sands in kaolin at Colettes and Echassières, Allier, France, and in stream placers in Western Australia at Greenbushes, Greens Well, and Wodgina.

Identification. Distinctive is the combination of usual light color, isometric form, and relatively low refractive index. For microlite the association with fine-grained lepidolite is helpful.

Fergusonite-Formanite Series

Composition. The type formula for the series is ABO_4, with A mainly Y and Er and minor Ce-group metals, U^4, Th, Zr, Fe^2, and Ca; and with B principally Nb (fergusonite) and Ta (formanite), minor Ti, and very small amounts of Sn and W. Th is usually low, 5.00% ThO_2; U^4 is low to moderate, with a maximum reported of 8.16% UO_2; some U^6 also may be present. U and Th may be zonally concentrated (Pellas, 1954), and a zoned crystal from Satersdalen, Norway, with a more strongly radioactive core is pictured by Frondel et al. (1942). Water, which is nearly always present, is due to alteration. Risörite is a titanian variety; adelpholite and sipylite are synonyms for fergusonite.

Structure and form. Reported as tetragonal, but synthetic $YTaO_4$ is monoclinic and isostructural with fused fergusonite (Ferguson, 1955).

Overgrowths of fergusonite on allanite are known, as are overgrowths of zircon (malacon) and uraninite on fergusonite. Usually metamict, although a few crystalline examples are known: Naegi, Japan (Pellas, 1954), and Hundholmen, Norway (Vogt, 1911). Metamict fergusonite recrystallizes at about 450°C to a dimorph whose powder x-ray pattern can be indexed with orthorhombic axes. At temperatures from 850 to 1050°C it recrystallizes to a dimorph identical with synthetic fergusonite, heretofore indexed with a tetragonal lattice (Berman, 1952). Berman (1952) believes that the structure of the low-temperature dimorph is equivalent to that of the pre-metamict mineral.

Occurrence. Essentially confined to granitic pegmatites, usually in association with combinations of allanite, zircon, samarskite, monazite, euxenite, gadolinite, and other rare-earth minerals. Much fergusonite occurs closely associated and intergrown with large sheets of biotite whose emplacement was fracture-controlled. Less commonly in placers derived from such granitic pegmatites. Also with zircon in granite gneiss, Pattenburg, N.J. (Markewicz et al., 1957). Noteworthy pegmatitic occurrences include:

1. Iveland and Evje districts, Norway, in dikes that also carry thalenite, gadolinite, or zircon (alvite). Other associates are garnet, beryl, allanite, euxenite, monazite, and xenotime. Elsewhere in Norway: at Näskul and other localities near Arendal; at Berg, in Råde; at Hundholmen; at Hampemyr on Tromö Island; near Moss on Dillingö Island; at numerous localities along the coast between Langesund and Grimstad and in Seiland in plumasite pegmatite (oligoclase-muscovite-corundum) with columbite, apatite, zircon, and biotite.

2. At Sardloq, Julianehaab district, Greenland.

3. In the classic pegmatite locality, long abandoned, on the island of Ytterby, near Stockholm, Sweden.

4. At the Blum mine in the Ilmen Mts., Urals, U.S.S.R., with samarskite, zircon, ilmenite, ilmenorutile, and tourmaline.

5. In Africa: at Morogoro, Southern Rhodesia; the Gordonia district, Cape Province, Union of South Africa; and widespread and relatively abundant in pegmatites on Madagascar—west of Ambatovohangy (with betafite and euxenite), in fine crystals with euxenite at Fiadanana; south of Lake Itasy and at several other localities, chiefly in the "potassic" pegmatites, i.e., those in which an albite-rich hydrothermal phase is subordinate.

6. In Japan: at Hakata-mura and Hagata, Iyo Province; at Fukuoka, Mino Province; at Tadati, Nagano; and at Iisaka, Fukushima (with allanite, yttrialite, thorogummite, and zircon).

7. In the United States: at Rockport, Cape Ann, Mass.; in Virginia at Amelia and Little Friar Mt., both with allanite; in North Carolina in the Spruce Pine district; in Texas in the Baringer Hill pegmatite (which is at the bottom of a reservoir) in Llano County, associated with gadolinite, cyrtolite, uraninite, and other radioactive species, in crystals as much as 8 in. long and in crystal aggregates weighing up to 65 lb.

8. In Canada: in Ontario at the Madawaska feldspar pegmatite, Murchison Township (750 lb produced); also in Calvin Township, and in Quebec in Callieres Township and at the Maisonneuve mine.

9. In Brazil in Minas Gerais, Rio Grande do Norte, and Paraiba.

Some of the better-known or well-authenticated placer occurrences of fergusonite are: Rakwana, Ceylon, in gem gravels; Naegi and Takayama, Mino, Japan; Marble Bar district and Cooglegong district (formanite), Western Australia, at the latter with gadolinite, euxenite, and monazite; Burke County, N.C., in gold placers; and at the Tryagain Claim, Lemon Creek, Slocan district, B.C. Also reported from placers in Korea and Malaya.

In a gossan in the Goldfields area, Sask. (Robinson, 1955A).

Identification. A relatively rare radioactive complex oxide mineral of pegmatites. Tapering prismatic form, normally brown color, and weak to negative test for Ti combine to indicate the mineral. Not associated with ilmenite.

Positive identification best by means of x-rays; strongest lines (recrystallized in air): 3.12, 2.96, 2.74.

Samarskite-Yttrotantalite Series

Composition. Samarskite is a complex oxide, mainly of Nb and Ta and Y-group rare-earth elements with significant amounts of U^4 or U^6 or more rarely both, Th, Ca, and Fe^2. Nb_2O_5 normally exceeds Ta_2O_5. The probable formula for samarskite is AB_2O_6 with

A = Y group, some Ce group, U, Th, Fe^2, Ca
B = Nb, Ta, Fe^3, minor Ti, Sn, W

Small amounts of Mg, Mn, Pb, and Al may be present, as are moderate amounts of Zr in some specimens. The mineral is hydrated easily and may contain large amounts of H_2O. Trace amounts of alkalies, Be, Sc, Ba, Sr, Ra, N, and He have been reported. The UO_2 content reaches about 14% (Nuevo, Calif.); that of UO_3 over 17%; ThO_2 has a maximum of about 4%. Zonal variations in the radioactive content have been noted by means of autoradiographs, indicating a possible variation in U content between extremely contrasting zones of 10 to 13% U_3O_8 (Yagoda, 1946B). Zoned samarskite is known from the Wiseman pegmatite, Spruce Pine district, N.C. (Yagoda, 1946A), from Uba, Minas Gerais, Brazil (Frondel et al., 1942), and from Topsham, Maine.

Yttrotantalite is much rarer, and only a few analyses of authenticated material have been made. George (1949), Frondel and Fleischer (1955), and Rosenqvist (1949) believe that samarskite forms the Nb-rich end of a series, and yttrotantalite forms the Ta-rich end, a relation indicated at least as early as 1915 by Levy (1915). This is very likely the case, for the two species are closely related in composition, crystallography (including their axial ratios), and physical and optical properties. Thus the name yttrocolumbite (Lepierre, 1937) probably is a synonym for samarskite.

In Dana (Palache et al., 1944) the type formula for yttrotantalite is presented as ABO_4 with

A = mainly Fe^2, Y, U, minor Ca, Mn, Mg, Ce, Th
B = mainly Nb, Ta, minor Ti, Sn, Zr, W

Minor alkalies, Be, Pb, Al, Si, As, and H_2O also are reported in the three authentic analyses, H_2O being due to secondary hydration and Al and Si probably present in impurities. In the analyzed materials from Berg and Hattevik, Norway, the ratios of $Fe:Y:U = 9:8:1$ and $Nb:Ta = $ about $1:1$. In the supposed yttrocolumbite from Mozambique (Lepierre, 1937) $Nb > Ta$. The UO_2 content ranges from 3.10 to 4.48; ThO_2 from 0.67 to 2.65.

Nohlite resembles samarskite in composition, being a Ca-Fe-Y-U niobate with minor Zr, Mg, Mn, Cu, Ce, and some H_2O. If all iron = Fe^2 the formula is approximately ABO_4 (Palache et al., 1944). From Nohl, near Kongelf, Sweden.

Structure and form. Subparallel growth faces are known. Non-metamict material reported from Kivu, Belgian Congo (van Aubel, 1935). Caps of columbite on samarskite crystals are known from the Blum mine, Ilmen Mts., U.S.S.R., and parallel growths of the two minerals also occur in Norway near Moss at AnnERÖD (annerödite) (Fig. 2.11). Oriented overgrowths of radioactive microlite on samarskite are recorded. Radial aggregates of samarskite with outer parallel oriented columbite occur at Uba, Minas Gerais, Brazil.

Occurrence. Samarskite is essentially confined to zoned granitic pegmatites, typically associated with columbite, zircon, monazite, fergusonite, uraninite, beryl, biotite, and muscovite. Usually not found with euxenite, gadolinite, thalenite, or ilmenite. The better-known localities include the Iveland district, Norway; Moss, AnnERÖD, Norway; Dillingö Island, Vandsjö, east of Moss, Norway, in masses up to 2 kg, commonly intergrown with monazite; Österby, Darlana, Sweden; Miask, southern Ural Mts., and Blum mine, Ilmen Mts., U.S.S.R.; northeastern Ourga, northern Mongolia; Sankara mine, Nellore district, Madras, India; Manendrika (up to 16 cm long), Fefena, and Kiakanjovato, Madagascar (with fergusonite in the absence of beryl and with yttrotantalite in the presence of beryl); Kivu, Belgian Congo; Macotaia, Ribaue-Alto Lingonha district, Mozambique (8 tons produced); Ishikawa, Iwaki, Japan; Machado, Uba, Conceição, Pomba, and Muriahe in Minas Gerais, Brazil.

In the United States at Topsham, Maine; at South Glastonbury and Portland, Conn.; Jones Falls, Md.; McKinney mine in the Spruce Pine district, N.C.; in several pegmatites in Chaffee, Fremont, and El Paso Counties, Colo.; in many pegmatites in the Petaca district, N.Mex.; at Nuevo, Calif.; and at Encampment, Wyo.

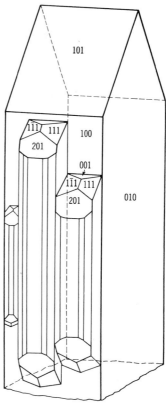

FIG. 2.11. Oriented overgrowth of columbite on samarskite, Moss, AnnERÖD, Norway (Brögger, 1906).

Also in scattered placer deposits: with monazite, Batum area, U.S.S.R.; with other heavy minerals in gold placers near Idaho City, Idaho; and in the Belgian Congo.

Yttrotantalite also is largely restricted to granitic pegmatites: Hattevik and Berg in Råde; Rosas in Iveland; Höydalen, Tördal in Telemark; Bjortjenn, Mykland, all in Norway. In Sweden at Ytterby, Finbo and Brodbo, and Skuleboda. In Mozambique at the Boa Esperance mine near Ribaue. Widespread in tin placers of the Ambabaan district, Swaziland (2 tons obtained in 1955). Detrital yttrotantalite is found at Cooglegong, Split Rock Station, and Hillside Station, Western Australia.

The poorly defined mineral calciosamarskite (which is not a calcian samarskite) may be closely related to yttrotantalite (Palache et al., 1944). It occurs in the Woodcox pegmatite, Monteagle Township, Hastings County, Ont. (mass up to 100 lb), and in Conger Township, Parry Sound district, Ont. (Ellsworth, 1932). It also has been reported from alluvial deposits near Pilbara, Western Australia. It is essentially a high Ca, Y-Nb oxide with subordinate to minor Ce, U^4, Th, Ti, Fe^3, Ta, and H_2O.

Wiikite is a poorly defined mixture of altered minerals containing Nb, Ta, Ti, Si, and Y-earths. In pegmatites in the Impilahti district, Finland, with allanite, monazite, and sphene.

Identification. The combination of form, jet-black color, high luster, and association with columbite are helpful. Positive identification requires x-ray methods. Strongest lines for samarskite heated in air: 2.98, 2.92, 3.13.

Euxenite-Polycrase Series

Composition. A complex oxide of the type formula AB_2O_6 with

A = Y, Ce, U, Th, minor Ca, Mg, Mn, Fe^2
B = Ti, Nb, Ta, minor Fe^3

The series varies mainly between Nb + Ta (euxenite) and Ti (polycrase). If the molecular ratio of $TiO_2:Nb_2O_5 + Ta_2O_5 = 3:1$ or less, the mineral is called euxenite; if this ratio is greater than 3:1 the species is polycrase. Normally euxenite has Nb > Ta, but tantalian types also are known. Y-group elements predominate markedly over those of the Ce group. U may be present as U^4 (maximum UO_2 = about 10%) or U^6 (maximum UO_3 = nearly 14%); ThO_2 up to about 5%. Minor to trace amounts of Na, K, Pb, Sn, Be, He, N, S, Hf, Ge, Sc, and Zr have been detected. H_2O is absent to relatively abundant. Al and Si, reported as important elements in a few analyses, are due to admixture of other minerals. The minerals alter readily by hydration and develop an earthy brownish jacket.

Tanteuxenite (Pilbara, Western Australia) and eschwegite are tantalian euxenites. Khlopinite (or chlopinite and hlopinite) is similar to euxenite, but Ti is lower, $UO_2 = 8.12$, $ThO_2 = 2.22$. Occurs at Khilok, Transbaikalia, Siberia, in pegmatite with monazite. Lyndochite may be a cerian-thorian-uranium–poor variety (Butler, 1957).

Occurrence. Mainly in granitic pegmatites and in placers derived from them. Widespread in the Iveland district, Norway, where euxenite occurs with eschynite, biotite, muscovite, allanite, monazite, xenotime, and zircon, and has been found in masses up to several hundred kilograms. Elsewhere in Norway: Rasvåg on Hitterö Island (polycrase); Kragerö (Kalstad-Lindvikskollen); the Gjerstad district north of Kragerö; Hvaler, near Fredrikstad; Alve on Tromö; Helle, Möresjaer, Röstöl, and Salterö, Festlande; many pegmatites near Arendal (hundreds of kilograms produced); Svenör and Eitland, near Lindesnes; Spangereid, Lister. In Sweden at Ytterby; and at Slättåkra, Lön Jonköping (polycrase). At Karra Akungnak, East Greenland.

Euxenite is the most widely distributed radioactive complex oxide of Madagascar pegmatites, at Vohimasima, Samiresy, Ambatofotsikely, Ankazobe, and in numerous other deposits, usually with monazite, betafite, beryl, muscovite, and locally columbite. At Kivu, Belgian Congo, and at Witkop, Namaqualand. Brazil: in Minas Gerais at Serro, Viçosa, Pomba (polycrase), Vargem Grande, Brejauba, and Carangolo; in São Paulo, at Iguape; also in Paraiba, Rio Grande do Norte, and Esperito Santo.

Euxenite is widespread and locally abundant in Canadian pegmatites, particularly in Ontario in the Grenville geological subprovince, in the townships of Lyndoch, Dill, Monteagle, Henvey, Loughborough, Calvin, Mattawan, Sabine, and South Sherbrooke. In Lyndoch Township, euxenite (lyndochite) occurs with beryl and contains minute remnants of columbite. Next to allanite, euxenite is the most common radioactive mineral in pegmatites in southeastern Canada.

Notable occurrences in the United States are the Pomona Tile Quarry, San Bernardino County, Calif.; Aquarius Range, Ariz.; Baringer Hill, Llano County, Texas (polycrase); Trout Creek Pass, Chaffee County, Colo. (Heinrich, 1948A); Cloud Peak, Big Horn Mts., Wyo.; Zirconia, Henderson County, N.C. (polycrase); Marietta, S.C. (polycrase); Morton, Delaware County, Pa.; and Day, Saratoga County, N.Y.

Placer occurrences of euxenite and polycrase include: Idaho City dredge, Idaho City, Boise County, Idaho (polycrase); Goodluck Creek, Livengood district, Alaska; at Woodstock and Cooglegong, Western Australia (tanteuxenite and polycrase); and in the Belgian Congo.

Identification. Yield a strong reaction for Ti, which is not characteristic of other radioactive oxides they resemble, e.g., samarskite and fergusonite. Distinguished with great difficulty from priorite and eschynite, usually by means of x-rays or analyses. Strongest euxenite lines (heated in air): 2.99, 2.95, 3.66.

Betafite

Composition. $(U,Ca)(Nb,Ta,Ti)_3O_9 \cdot nH_2O(?)$. Formula somewhat uncertain. The species includes several independently described minerals grouped on x-ray and compositional data. Subordinate to minor quantities of Mn, Fe^2, Fe^3, Mg, Pb, Y, Ce, Th, Sn, K, Bi, Al, and Si are reported. A plumbian type is found in Madagascar (samiresite). Normally Nb predominates over Ti and Ta, but titanian varieties also occur (including mendeleyevite). A tantalian variety is known (blomstrandite, but not blomstrandine). U mainly reported as U^6 (up to nearly 27% UO_3); also as UO_2, up to 21%. $ThO_2 = 0.04$ to 1.30%. A greenish-yellow alteration crust of high H_2O content is typical. Some crystals are color-zoned.

Occurrence. In granite pegmatites chiefly; examples include: Tangen and Sjåen on Kragerö, Landsverk in Evje, Ljosland in Iveland, all in Norway; Sludianka, Lake Baikal, Siberia. Abundant in numerous pegmatites on Madagascar, Ambatofotsy (one group of crystals weighed 104 kg), Ambatolampikely (crystals up to 7 cm in diameter), Samiresy (samiresite), Tongafeno, Maharitra, Antanifotsy, Vohimasima, and many other localities. In Minas Gerais, Brazil, at Conceição; and in the Cada Mountains, San Bernardino County,

Inches 1 _____ 0 _____ 1 _____ 2 Inches

FIG. 2.12. Betafite crystals, Basin property, Silver Crater mines, Faraday Township, Hastings County, Ont. (Satterly and Hewitt, 1955; *Ont. Dept. Mines*).

Calif. Placer betafite with uranothorite is reported in the Tambani area, Nyasaland. A mineral related to betafite occurs with monazite in placers of the Pampana River, Sierra Leone. Betafite occurs in volcanic ash at Ndale, near Fort Portal, Uganda.

Occurs as anhedral to euhedral grains, usually less than 0.5 mm in diameter, in metasomatic biotite-rich rocks associated with magnetite, in the Oka district, Two Mountains County, Quebec (Fig. 2.13) (Rowe, 1955A). Also as crystals up to an inch across in a calcite vein in pegmatite and hornblende gneiss with apatite, fluorite, black mica, magnetite, and sphene on the Hogan property, Cardiff Township, Haliburton County, Ont.; as crystals up to 3 in. in a calcite mass with black mica, hornblende, apatite, and zircon (Fig. 2.12), Basin property, Silver Crater mines, Faraday Township, Hastings County, Ont.

Identification. The combination of isometric form and high U content is distinctive. Helpful also are the relatively low specific gravity and low refractive index. Resembles pyrochlore-microlite megascopically.

Polymignite

The type formula is ABO_4 with

A = Ca, Fe_2, Y, Ce, Zr, minor Th
B = Nb, Ti, Ta, Fe^3

Uranium is not reported in available analyses. $ThO_2 = 4\%$. Y-group elements apparently usually exceed Ce, but the reverse may be true (Fredricksvärn, Norway). Minor to trace amounts of Mg, Mn, Sn, Hf, Na, K, Al, Si, and Pb. Loranskite from Impilahti, Pitkäranta, Finland, may be polymignite. A rare species. In nepheline syenite and syenite pegmatite at Fredricksvärn, Norway, with zircon and pyrochlore; also on Svenör Island in augite syenite. With knopite in syenite in Siberia. The high Zr content is characteristic, but *x*-rays are needed for certain identification.

Eschynite-Priorite Series

Composition. The type formula is AB_2O_6 with

A = Ce, Y, Ca, Fe^2, Th, and minor Mg, Mn, Pb, U, Sn, Zr
B = Ti, Nb, minor Ta

In eschynite (or aeschynite) Ce predominates over Y; in priorite the reverse is true. Little U occurs in eschynite; ThO_2 = 11 to 18%. In priorite $ThO_2 < 1$ to 17% and $UO_2 < 1$ to 5%. Minor to trace amounts of Al, Si, He, N, Ra, F, Na, K, Zn, and W may be present; the first two may be due to admixture. Secondary water may be present in moderate amounts. Blomstrandine and blomstrandinite (but not blomstrandite) are synonyms of priorite.

Occurrence. Eschynite characteristically occurs in nepheline syenite and pegmatitic nepheline syenite, less usually in granitic pegmatite; whereas priorite appears principally in granitic pegmatites. Eschynite occurs at Miask, Ilmen Mts., U.S.S.R., and Hitterö, Norway, reported from granite pegmatite at Xiririca, São Paulo, Brazil, and Döbschütz, Silesia. Priorite occurs in Norway in the Frikstad and Kåbuland pegmatites, Iveland, and near Arendal (Möresjaer and Salterö), Hitterö (Urstad), Eitland on Lister, and a few other localities

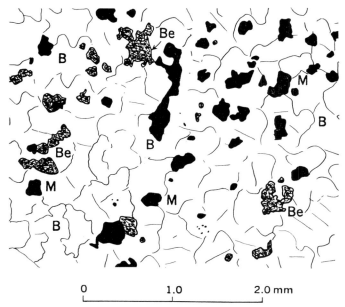

0   1.0   2.0 mm

FIG. 2.13. Betafite (*Be*) and magnetite (*M*) in metasomatic biotite (*B*) rock, Oka district, Two Mts. County, Quebec (Rowe, 1955A; *Geol. Survey Can.*).

TABLE 2.2. *Properties of the radioactive complex oxide minerals, containing Nb and Ta*

Mineral	Form	Optical properties, Streak (S), Luster (L)	Cleavage and fracture	H	G
Pyrochlore and Microlite	Isometric, octahedra or anhedra. Either metamict or crystalline (011), (113), (001) common	Black, brown, yellow brown. S light brown. n = 1.99–2.18. L resinous to vitreous. Pale yellow, brown. S yellow to pale brown. n = 1.99–2.18. Both isotropic	Octahedral	5–6	4.2–6.4 increasing with Ta and decreasing with hydration
Fergusonite and Formanite	Tetragonal(?) to pyramidal. Prismatic with c. Tapered crystals. Radial groups. Anhedral clusters. Usually metamict	Black, brown. Earthy tan coating. S gray to brown. L glossy, surface dull. Translucent in brown shades. Usually isotropic, n = 1.90–2.20, decreasing with hydration. Also rarely uniaxial (+), ω = 2.15, ϵ = 2.19	Remnants (111) cleavage. Subconchoidal fracture	5.5–6.5	5.2–6.2 increasing with Ta and decreasing to 4.2 with alteration
Samarskite and Yttrotantalite	Orthorhombic. Usually metamict. Prismatic with c, rectangular cross sections. Also elongated with b or tabular (100) and (010). Anhedral grains and clusters	Black to dark brown in color and streak. Light brown crusts. Isotropic, n = 2.20–2.31 Black to reddish brown. S pale brown to gray. Both highly lustrous, vitreous to submetallic. Isotropic, n = 2.15	(010) poor. Conchoidal fracture	5–6	5.4–6.2 increasing with Ta, decreasing with hydration to 4.1

Euxenite and Polycrase	Orthorhombic. Metamict or weakly crystalline. Thick prisms, radial and subparallel groups, anhedral. Twinning common on (201). Overgrowths on columbite and priorite (Fig. 2.14)	Jet black altering to yellow. S brown to yellow. L vitreous altering to resinous and earthy. Translucent on thin edges, yellow to brown. Isotropic, $n = 2.05–2.20$, decreasing with hydration to 1.87	Subconchoidal fracture	5.5–6.5	4–5.9 decreasing with hydration, increasing with Ta and Nb over Ti
Betafite	Isometric. Metamict. Octahedra modified by (011). Flattened on (001) or (011). Anhedral grains	Yellow, brown, black. S yellow to dark brown. L vitreous to greasy. Thin edges translucent, yellow to brown. Isotropic. $n = 1.915–2.02$ increasing with Ti, decreasing with H_2O	Conchoidal fracture	4–5.5	3.7–5.25 increasing with Pb, decreasing with hydration
Polymignite	Orthorhombic. Metamict. Prismatic and striated or flattened (100)	Black. S dark brown. L submetallic. Translucent red brown on thin edge. $n = 2.22$	(010), (100)	6.5	4.77–4.85
Aeschynite	Orthorhombic. Metamict. Prismatic with c. Striated parallel with a. Also elongated with a or tabular (010). Anhedral	Black to brown. S black, brown, yellow. L vitreous to submetallic, earthy on alteration. Isotropic. $n = 2.09–2.26$ decreasing with hydration	(010) traces(?). Subconchoidal fracture	5–6	4.5–5.7 lower values with increasing hydration

in southern Norway (usually called blomstrandine). Also at Pomba, Minas Gerais, Brazil; at Miask, U.S.S.R.; in the Ambatofotsy district, at Tongafeno, and at Ambedabao, Madagascar; at Donkerhuk, South-West Africa, and in Swaziland. Both have been reported from placers: eschynite with gold in the

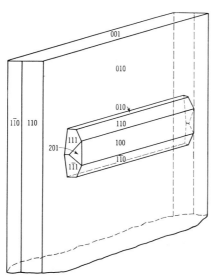

Orenberg district, southern Ural Mts., U.S.S.R.; and priorite with cassiterite from the Ambabaan district, Swaziland.

Identification. Priorite, compositionally, resembles euxenite and polycrase and cannot be differentiated from them by chemical analysis alone. Eschynite is differentiated by its high Ce and Th contents, nil to low U content.

Zirkelite

$(Ca,Ce,Fe,Th,U)_2(Ti,Zr)_2O_5(?)$. U_3O_8 up to 14%, ThO_2 up to 20%. Small amounts of Mn, Mg, Y, and Pb also are reported. The Th/U and Ti/Zr ratios vary considerably. Found at Jacupiranga, São Paulo, Brazil, in magnetite pyroxenite (jacupirangite) with

Fig. 2.14. Oriented overgrowth of polycrase on eschynite. Hitterö, Norway (Brögger, 1906).

baddeleyite and perovskite. Occurs on Ceylon in alluvial deposits associated with spinel, corundum, zircon, monazite, and tourmaline, in the Bambarabotuwa district of Sabaragamuwa Province and at Walaweduwa.

The pseudo-isometric form is distinctive, but probably a partial analysis is necessary. Palache et al. (1944) regard the Ceylon mineral as a species distinct from the Brazilian. George (1949) also notes the variation in the Zr/Ti ratio but points out that the totals of $ZrO_2 + TiO_2$ are essentially the same.

Davidite

Composition. General formula possibly $AB_3(O,OH)_7$ with

A = Fe², rare earths, U, Ca, Na, Zr, Th
B = Ti⁴, Fe³, U, V³, Cr³

The ideal end-member would be $FeTi_3O_7$ (Bannister and Horne, 1950). U_3O_8 as much as 20%; Th as much as 0.12%. The rare earths are apparently chiefly those of the cerium group, although members of the yttrium group are also present (Dixon and Wylie, 1951). Spectrographic analysis also indicates the presence of Nb, Bi, Pb, and Al and the possible presence of Sc (Kerr and Holland, 1951). May replace or be intergrown with ilmenite. Ufertite (Melkov, 1956), found in biotite schist and gneiss in the U.S.S.R., is apparently a variety of davidite (Fleischer, 1958). Ferutite probably also is davidite (Fleischer, 1958).

Occurrence. In the Tete district of Mozambique (Davidson and Bennett, 1950), on the Mavuzi River, 30 mi north-northwest of Tete (some 40- to 50-lb crystals), in norite and anorthosite ("mavudzite," Coelho, 1954) (pages 254–256). Originally found at Radium Hill, near Olary, South Australia, and also discovered at Houghton and in the Crocker's Well area. Reported at Thackeringa, New South Wales. At Radium Hill it occurs in subparallel replacement lodes along fractures in migmatitic gneiss, amphibolite, and quartzite (Parkin and Glasson, 1954) (pages 253–254). Alteration results in the formation of coatings and fracture fillings of carnotite. "Davidite-like" minerals also are reported in Australia, in Queensland in the Mt. Isa–Cloncurry region disseminated in graywacke and 10 mi northwest of Mt. Isa disseminated in hornfels, amphobolite, calc-silicate rock, and pegmatite (Lawrence et al., 1957). Reportedly occurs in some pegmatites in India. Also reported, but not confirmed, from pegmatite in the Baragoi area, Kenya, with samarskite, pitchblende, columbite, monazite, and beryl. A mineral similar to davidite occurs in pegmatite 65 mi east of Swakopmund in South-West Africa. "Uranium-bearing ilmenite, which is questionably related to the mineral davidite occurs in granitic rocks and placer concentrates on the east slope of the Sierra Nevada in the vicinity of Bishop, [Calif.]" (Walker et al., 1956, p. 6).

Identification. Resembles ilmenite, but ilmenite is not normally radioactive. Specimens of pegmatitic or vein "ilmenite" should be checked for radioactivity. Carnotite coatings, if present, and metamict character also differentiate davidite from ilmenite. Probably davidite will be found to be more widespread than heretofore realized. Barely attracted by a powerful hand magnet. Strongest x-ray powder lines (heated in air): 2.87, 3.40, 1.70.

Brannerite

Composition. $(U,Ca,Fe^2,Y,Th)_3(Ti,Si)_5O_{16}(?)$. $U = 27.9$ to 43.6%, $Th = 0.26$ to 4.4%. Most of the uranium is present as U^6, some as U^4. The U/Th ratio varies considerably, and thorian brannerite has been called absite [1] (Whittie, 1954). It contains no UO_2 but about 32% UO_3 and nearly 13% ThO_2. Small amounts to traces of Ba, Sr, Ni, Bi, Pb, Sn, Ta, Nb, Sc, Fe^3, P, He, and Zr also are reported. The rare earths are mainly of the Y group. H_2O is present as a minor constituent. Much brannerite is altered to anatase or rutile.

Occurrence. First found with euxenite in a gold placer, Kelley Gulch, Custer County, Idaho. Occurs in pegmatite near Fuenteovejuna, Córdoba, Spain (George, 1949); material formerly believed to be uraninite pseudomorphous after beryl (López de Azcona and Abbad, 1941). In the canyon of West Walker River, 7 mi south of Coleville, Mono County, Calif., in slender prisms in quartz veins (Pabst, 1954). In the San Bernardino Mountains, San Bernardino County, Calif., as nodules along the foliation of a granite gneiss and as larger nodules along biotitic shear zones across the foliation. Associates are

[1] The name is derived from the discovery of the deposit by means of the *air-borne* scintillometer.

rutile and sodic plagioclase (Hewett et al., 1957). Prismatic crystals of brannerite occur in the molybdenum deposits of Château-Lambert, Vosges, France,
with molybdenite, chalcopyrite, and cubo-octahedral uraninite (Geffroy and
Sarcia, 1954). At the Bou-Azzer mine, at Tichka, Morocco, anhedral grains a
few millimeters across occur in gray quartz, with molybdenite (Jouravski,
1952; Pabst, 1954).

Occurs abundantly in the Blind River district, southern Ontario, in minute
grains in the matrix of metamorphosed quartz-pebble conglomerate in the
Mississagi quartzite, associated with abundant pyrite, sericite, and locally
uraninite and monazite. Other associates are thucolite, chalcopyrite, pyrrhotite,
galena, and hematite. A consolidated placer(?) containing zircon, ilmenite,
and "a refractory mineral of the brannerite type" occurs in a lower Silurian
sandstone in the Spanish provinces of Jaén y Ciudad Real (Alia, 1956B;
Medina, 1956).

Also as small prismatic crystals in the California vein, a quartz-molybdenite-
beryl-tourmaline-muscovite deposit in quartz monzonite southwest of Mt. Antero, Chaffee County, Colo. (Adams, 1953), with rutile, sericite, and molybdite.

As irregular grains and small veinlets cutting quartz monzonite and granodiorite at Crocker's Well, South Australia. Also 5- to 10-cm crystals in rutile-bearing quartz veins here. Disseminated in carbonate beds and lenses 20 mi north
of Mt. Isa, Queensland, Australia. Reported from the Adams-Ross deposit, near
Hessa Lake, Prince of Wales Island, Alaska. Occurs as minute grains (3 mm
or less) in partly open fissures, 0.5 cm wide, in greenschist near Amot, Modum
district, Norway. Pegmatites occur nearby (Van Autenboer and Skjerlie,
1957). Lodochnikite (Melkov, 1956), found in carbonate veins in nepheline
syenite in the U.S.S.R., probably is a variety of brannerite (Fleischer, 1958).

Identification. X-ray powder methods after ignition are necessary for certain identification. Strongest lines: 3.41, 1.90, 2.45.

Doubtful or Poorly Defined Species

Ampangabeite

A complex oxide of Nb, Ta, Y, Ce, Ca, U, Th, Fe[3], and Ti. Usually hydrated. U is reported mainly as UO_2 (7 to 14%); less often as UO_3 (19%) or
as U_3O_8 (12.5%). ThO_2 ranges from about 1 to 2%. Formula uncertain, perhaps $A_2B_7O_{18}$. May represent an inhomogeneous alteration of euxenite. Probably orthorhombic; in stubby prisms of rectangular cross section, usually
rough or rounded and radially arranged. Light to dark brown in color with
brownish streak and greasy to horny luster. Light red-brown transparent in
thin fragments; may be color-zoned. Isotropic, metamict with $n = 2.12$ to 2.13.
Conchoidal to irregular fracture. H = 4. G = 3.36 to 4.64, decreasing with
hydration and increasing with darkening colors. Found in pegmatites on
Madagascar: at Ampangabe, also at Ambatofotsikely and from several other
localities, associated with columbite, monazite, beryl, and euxenite. Also reported from Divino de Ubá, Minas Gerais, Brazil (Florêncio, 1952). Decomposed by HCl.

TABLE 2.3. *Properties of the radioactive complex oxide minerals that do not contain Nb or Ta*

Mineral	Form	Optical Properties, Streak (S), Luster (L)	Cleavage and fracture	H	G
Zirkelite	Hexagonal, pseudoisometric. Metamict. Tabular or prismatic with c. ($10\bar{1}1$) polysynthetic twinning	Black S brown. L resinous to submetallic. Isotropic. $n = 2.19$	(0001) indistinct. Subconchoidal fracture	5.5–6	4.32–5.1
Davidite	Hexagonal. Metamict. Massive, granular. Tabular to pyramidal. Twinning about ($11\bar{2}0$)	Black. S black to dark brown. Reddish brown crust. L submetallic. In reflected light isotropic to weakly anisotropic. Thin splinters translucent red brown to deep red. $n = 2.3$	Subconchoidal fracture. Platy cleavage(?)	5–6	4–5
Brannerite	Monoclinic. Metamict or faintly crystalline. Prismatic, stout to thin. Anhedra 0.3 mm across. Blocky crystals. Detrital grains	Black to reddish brown, thorian type yellow to olive. Alters to brown, green, gray, yellow. S dark greenish brown. L vitreous, resinous with alteration. Translucent brownish yellow to yellow green in thin splinters. Isotropic. $n = 1.96$–2.3, decreasing with H_2O and with Th for U(?)	Conchoidal fracture. Very brittle	4–6	4–5.4

Pisekite, a complex oxide of Nb, Ta, Ti, U, and rare earths, with Th and Sn, occurs with monazite and strueverite in pegmatite at Pisek, Bohemia. Incompletely and poorly defined; may be related to ampangabeite.

Delorenzite

An oxide of Ti, Y, U, Fe, and Sn; perhaps $(Y,U,Fe^2)(Ti,Sn)_3O_8(?)$. Reported $UO_2 = 9.87\%$. Orthorhombic. George (1949) has pointed out the similarity of the crystallographic ratio to that of euxenite. In subparallel aggregates of crystals elongate parallel with c and tabular (010); striations on (100) and (110) parallel with c. Black, translucent brown in thin fragments. Resinous luster. Metamict. Subconchoidal fracture. H = 5.5 to 6. G = 4.7. Found in a pegmatite at Craveggia, Val Vigesso, Piedmont, Italy, with strueverite, ilmenite, and columbite. George (1949) has questioned the validity of the species on the basis that the crystallization of an yttrium titanate with columbite is incompatible.

Fersmite

$(Ca,Ce,Na)(Nb,Ti,Fe,Al)_2(O,OH,F)_6$. Th = 0.42%. Orthorhombic, in imperfect crystals resembling those of columbite and euxenite. H = 4.5. G = 4.69. Black. Biaxial (+?), 2V = large. n = about 2.0, birefringence moderate. Occurs in the Vishnevye Mountains, Urals, U.S.S.R., in syenitic pegmatites.

Hjelmite

Also hielmite. A complex oxide of Ta, subordinate Nb, also containing Y, Fe^2, U^4, Ca, Mn, and Sn. Secondary H_2O present. Formula type may be AB_2O_6 or $A_2B_3O_{10}$. The available analyses (two complete, two partial) on material from Kårarfvet, Sweden, resemble those of microlite and in Dana (Palache et al., 1944, p. 780) a note states that an x-ray powder photograph of supposed hjelmite from Stripåsen, Westmanland, Sweden, is similar to that of microlite. UO_2 = nearly 5%. Orthorhombic(?); rude crystals, which may be tetragonal. Anhedral, rounded, or in prismatic aggregates. Forms are (110), (101), (230), and (201).

Black with gray-black streak. Metallic luster. In very thin splinters translucent dark yellow brown to black. Anisotropic, but isotropic marginally and along cracks. Optically (+), nearly uniaxial; α = 2.30, γ = 2.40 (Li) (Palache et al., 1944). Irregular fracture. H = 5. G = 5.2 to 5.8. Found in pegmatites at the above two localities.

Ishikawaite

$(U^4,Fe^2,Y, etc.)(Nb,Ta)O_4$ (Palache et al., 1944); minor Ca, Mg, Mn, Sn, Ti, Al, Si, and H_2O. $UO_2 = 21.88\%$. Composition close to samarskite but U is higher. Black, opaque, dark brown streak, waxy luster. Crystals tabular (100), supposedly orthorhombic. Conchoidal fracture. H = 5.6. G = 6.2 to 6.4. With samarskite in pegmatite in Ishikawa district, Iwaki Province, Japan.

Yttrocrasite

$(Y,Th,U,Ca)_2Ti_4O_{11}$. Also present are Mn, Pb, Mg, Ce, etc., W, Si, Fe^3, Nb, and Ta. CO_2 and H_2 are secondary. $UO_2 = 1.98$, $UO_3 = 0.64$, $ThO_2 = 8.75\%$.

Orthorhombic(?). In rough crystals, with (100), (010), (001), and other forms. Also anhedral masses. Black altering to brown. Streak brownish(?). Luster resinous altering to dull. Isotropic, metamict, $n = 2.12$ to 2.15. Pale yellow to amber in thin splinters. In a few cases, weakly anisotropic. Uneven fracture. $H = 5.5$ to 6. $G = 4.80$. Known only from a pegmatite in Burnet County, 3 mi east of the Baringer Hill pegmatite, Llano County, Tex.

GUMMITE

Gummite is a fine-grained mixture of various secondary uranium minerals including clarkeite, and several hydrous oxides and silicates. In the low-temperature alteration of uraninite the sequence commonly is (Frondel, 1952B, 1956B) (1) oxidation of U^4 to U^6 with preservation of the uraninite structure; (2) hydration to yield hydrated $Pb(UO_2)^2$ oxides, usually orange red to yellow (traditional gummite), composed mainly of fourmarierite and vandendriesscheite; (3) introduction of Si (and in some cases Ca) to form the silicates uranophane, beta-uranophane, kasolite, and rarely soddyite and sklodowskite. A zone of clarkeite may intervene between the uraninite and the hydrated oxides. Less common species that may be present are becquerelite, curite, schoepite, and rutherfordine. Thus analyses of gummite usually show large amounts of U (chiefly U^6), Pb, and H_2O with variable Ca, Na, Si, Fe^3, Th, rare earths, and minor Mn, Mg, Al, P, and Ba. Outer parts of gummite nodules may be strongly radioactive because of selectively leached and redeposited Ra.

The name can best be used in the same sense as limonite is used for the hydrated iron oxides, in denoting a variable fine-grained mixture of secondary uranium minerals whose identities may, in some cases, be established by means of precise laboratory methods.

Yellow orange and red to reddish brown; streak yellow to brown. Luster waxy, greasy to vitreous, commonly like that of gum. The mean index of refraction varies considerably, but not uncommonly falls in the range $n = 1.80$ to 1.90.

Fracture irregular to conchoidal. Both hardness and specific gravity vary greatly, probably to a considerable extent with the degree of hydration and the grain size of the various minerals in the aggregate; $H = 2.5$ to 5, $G = 3.9$ to 6.4.

Occurs in crusts, alteration rims, irregular masses, and pseudomorphs. Usually replaces uraninite but also has been reported as an alteration of thorian uraninite and uranoan thorianite. Apparently formed either by weathering or by low-temperature hydrothermal processes, more commonly the former.

In the United States pegmatitic gummite occurs in fine specimens at the Fannie Goodge mine and others near Spruce Pine, N.C.; at the Ruggles mine, N.H., and in other pegmatites in Maine and Connecticut. Some foreign pegmatitic occurrences are (1) near Chaomiping, Chungshan district, Eastern Kuangsi Province, China, with phosphuranylite; (2) with uranothorite and autunite and uranophane at La Cañada de Alvarez, Calamuchita, Córdoba, Argentina; (3) at the Villeneuve mine, Papineau County, Quebec; and (4) at the Boquero mine, Parelhas, and at Brejauba, in Minas Gerais, and in Paraiba, Brazil.

Noteworthy occurrences of nonpegmatitic gummite are at Joachimsthal, Johanngeorgenstadt, and Schneeberg in Bohemia and Saxony; Wölsendorf, Bavaria; in France at the Margnac and La Crouzille deposits in Haute-Vienne, and at numerous deposits in Puy-de-Dôme, Vendée, and Haut-Rhin; Shinkolobwe, Luiswishi, and Kambove, Belgian Congo; Great Bear Lake, N.W.T.; the Bolger Group deposits, Ace Lake, Sask.; Hazelton Camp, B.C.; Delta mine, San Rafael Swell, Utah; Monument No. 2 mine, Ariz. The Russian material urgite probably is gummite (Fleischer, 1957).

HYDRATED OXIDES AND HYDROXIDES

Masuyite

$UO_3 \cdot 2H_2O$. Pb reported in the original analysis by Vaes (1947) but not found in supposedly authentic material (Frondel and Fleischer, 1955). The role of Pb needs further definition.

A rare oxidation product of pitchblende in which it occurs in small geodes at Shinkolobwe, Katanga, Belgian Congo. In the Goldfields area, Sask., as an alteration of pitchblende. Strongest x-ray powder lines: 7.10, 3.15, 3.54.

Ianthinite (Branche et al., 1951)
"Ianthinite francaise" (Bignand, 1955)

Presumably $2UO_2 \cdot 7H_2O$ with traces of Fe. Shown by Bignand (1955) to be distinct from an ianthinite of Belgian Congo (see Ianthinite under carbonates). Occurs in France at Bigay, Lachaux, Puy-de-Dôme; on level 15 at La Crouzille, and Margnac II, Haute-Vienne; and at Les Bois Noirs, Loire. Alters readily to a hydrated U^6 oxide, changing in color from purple to maroon, then gray, and finally yellow (epiianthinite) (Branche et al., 1951; Chervet and Branche, 1955).

Epiianthinite

Ianthinite alters to hydrated U^6 oxide, epiianthinite, probably $UO_3 \cdot 2H_2O$, the alteration of U^4 to U^6 being accompanied by a change in color from purple to maroon, then gray and finally yellow (Branche et al., 1951). $UO_3 = 88\%$, some UO_2 may be present. Occurs as alteration rim and replacement of ianthinite (Schoep and Stradiot, 1947) at Shinkolobwe, Belgian Congo (Frondel and Cuttitta, 1954) and in France at Lachaux and La Crouzille (Branche et al., 1951).

The "hydrate violet" produced by Bignand (1955) appears to be similar to epiianthinite. He gives its composition as $UO_{2.84} \cdot xH_2O$, yet its powder pattern is similar to "ianthinite francaise" (Bignand, 1955) which is reportedly $2UO_2 \cdot 7H_2O$ (Branche et al., 1951). Further work is needed to clarify the relations among ianthinite, "ianthinite francaise," and epiianthinite.

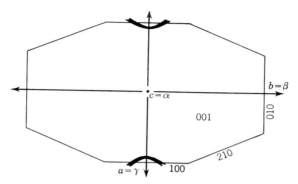

Fig. 2.15. Optical orientation of schoepite.

Schoepite

Probably $UO_3 \cdot 2H_2O$ (Frondel and Fleischer, 1955; Bignand, 1955). Some Pb, Te, and Fe^3 may be present. $UO_3 = 89\%$. Paraschoepite is either identical with schoepite (Frondel and Fleischer, 1955) or may be a different hydrate (Guillemin and Pierrot, 1956C), with $\alpha = 1.705$, $\beta = 1.760$, $\gamma = 1.770$, $(-)$ $2V = 46°$, $r > v$.

Best known occurrence is at Kasolo, Katanga, Belgian Congo, with cobaltian wad, curite, becquerelite, and other secondary uranium minerals, as an alteration of pitchblende or ianthinite. Occurs at Wölsendorf, Bavaria, with becquerelite and ianthinite on fluorite; also at Hagendorf, Bavaria (Bültemann, 1954); and at Margnac II deposit, Haute-Vienne, France (Guillemin and Pierrot, 1956C). Also found as a relatively uncommon constituent of the oxidized zone of gummite. Noted by Frondel (1956B) at the Beryl Mountain pegmatite, N.H., pseudomorphous after uraninite. Occurs at the Happy Jack and Frey No. 4 mines, San Juan County, at the Delta and Consolidated (Gruner and Gardiner, 1952) mines, San Rafael Swell, Utah. Found at Hottah Lake, Canada. Synthesized ($G = 6.54!$) by hydrolysis of a solution of uranium acetate (Bignand, 1955) and by dropping ammonia into a dilute H_2O solution of uranyl chloride (Frondel et al., 1954). Strongest x-ray powder lines are: 7.49, 3.26, 3.64.

Becquerelite

Composition. $U_7^6O_{20}(OH)_2 \cdot 10H_2O$. $UO_3 = 89$ to 90% (Frondel and Cuttitta, 1953). The original becquerelite (Schoep, 1922) contained Pb. Schoep and Stradiot (1948) also described Pb-free becquerelite, but Vaes (1949) considered that the Pb was mistakenly reported for Ba and that the original becquerelite was identical with billietite (Vaes, 1947). No authenticated Pb-becquerelite is described, but it may exist, as it has been synthesized (Frondel et al., 1954) and reported (Derriks and Vaes, 1956). Protas (1957A) reports Ca in Congo material, which is identical with synthetic $CaU_6O_{18}(OH)_2 \cdot 10H_2O$.

Occurrence. A relatively rare mineral (except at Shinkolobwe), formed by oxidation and hydration (by ground water or weathering) of uraninite, which

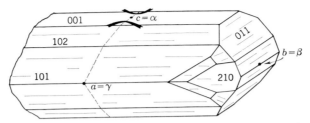

F
IG. 2.16. Optical orientation of becquerelite (adapted from Buttgenbach, 1925B).

it replaces. At Shinkolobwe associated with curite, uranophane, and ianthinite. In veinlets cutting uraninite nodules at Bemasoandro, Malakialina district and at Befarafara, Vohemar district, Madagascar (Chervet and Branche, 1955). At Wölsendorf, Bavaria, on uranophane. In a few Colorado Plateau deposits of the oxidized nonvanadiferous type (Weeks, 1955): the Delta, Consolidated (Gruner and Gardiner, 1952), and Lucky Strike No. 2 mines, San Rafael Swell, Utah; Oyler mine near Fruita, Utah; Posey and Frey No. 4 mines, White Canyon district, Utah; Big Buck claims, San Juan County, Utah; the Cato Sells and Monument No. 2 mines, Monument Valley district, Ariz. (Weeks and Thompson, 1954; Frondel, 1956B); and the Jackpile mine, Grants, N.Mex. Reported as an alteration of pitchblende from Lake Athabaska, Canada, and at the Eldorado mine, N.W.T. (Gruner and Gardiner, 1950), and as an uncommon constituent of gummite (Frondel, 1956B). Found by Branche et al. (1951) at Bigay, France, as rare crystalline crusts 0.2 mm thick in translucent prismatic crystals, but Pb is reported present and the indices are notably above those listed for Pb-free material ($\alpha = 1.75$, $\beta = 1.87$, $\gamma = 1.88$). This material needs further checking, but it may be Pb-becquerelite. Also in France at La Grouzille, in Haute-Vienne, and at Les Bois Noirs in Allier. Synthesized by Gruner (1952) at room temperature.

Identification. X-ray pattern and cell constants like those of billietite, and optical properties of the two species are similar. Their distinction is difficult and requires x-ray powder photograph measurements and tests for Ba. The x-ray pattern of becquerelite (strongest lines are 7.50, 3.22, 3.75) also resembles that of schoepite, which has lower refractive indices.

Billietite

$BaU_6^6O_{16}(OH)_6 \cdot 8H_2O$. $UO_3 = 82$ to 84%. Isostructural with becquerelite. Very rare. Occurs at Shinkolobwe, Belgian Congo, with soddyite coating curite and soddyite. In France at Kruth (Haut-Rhin) in a pitchblende–copper sulfide deposit associated with gummite, uranophane, zeunerite, and barite; at Margnac (Haute-Vienne) with gummite and uranophane; and at Outeloup (Saône-et-Loire) with uranocircite. Synthesized by Frondel et al. (1954) by addition of ammonia to a water solution of uranyl chloride and barium chloride and by Protas (1956) (G = 5.18) from an aqueous solution of uranium acetate and barium nitrate. Resembles becquerelite. Dissolves in HNO_3, yielding upon evaporation a white residue of barium nitrate. Strongest x-ray powder lines are 7.53, 3.77, 3.17 (Frondel et al., 1956).

Curite

$Pb_3U_8O_{27} \cdot 4H_2O$ (?). $UO_3 = 73$ to 74%. Traces of Fe^3.

A rare supergene alteration of pitchblende. Apparently the Pb may be derived from galena or may be radiogenic. Found originally at Kasolo, Katanga, Belgian Congo, associated with soddyite, fourmarierite, sklodowskite, and torbernite (Schoep, 1927A). Also reported from Shinkolobwe, Katanga (Bignand, 1955). Occurs at the Eldorado mine, Great Bear Lake, Canada. Reported from Wölsendorf, Bavaria (Bültemann, 1954). Occurs at Malakialina, Madagascar, and probably at La Crouzille, France (Branche et al., 1951). Synthesized at 180° (Gruner, 1952) and at 160°C (Bignand, 1955).

Identification. By x-ray powder pattern. Strongest lines: 6.28, 3.97, 3.14. Fourmarierite has lower indices.

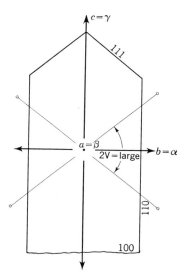

Fig. 2.17. Optical orientation of curite.

Fourmarierite

Composition. $PbU_4O_{13} \cdot 7H_2O$ (Brasseur, 1948). $UO_3 = 77$ to 78%. Exact formula uncertain; original analysis made on material with admixed kasolite and torbernite. The Pb content of natural material varies over a wide range, and fourmarierite has been formed from solutions that vary widely in their U/Pb ratios (Frondel et al., 1954).

Occurrence. A relatively uncommon secondary supergene alteration of uraninite. Found originally at Kasolo, Katanga, Belgian Congo, with curite, torbernite, and kasolite. Occurs at Wölsendorf, Bavaria, with dewindtite, ianthinite, and anglesite. The Pb may be radiogenic or derived from galena. Also a constituent of the hydrated Pb-U oxide zone of gummite with vandendriesscheite, clarkeite, becquerelite, curite, and schoepite (Frondel, 1952B, 1956B). Identified by Frondel (1956B) in gummite at Tvedestrand, Norway; Bisundi, Rajputana, India; Great Bear Lake, Canada; Newry, Maine; Spruce Pine, N.C.; and Mica Lakes area, Hahns Peak, Colo. Identified as an alteration of pitchblende in the Goldfields area, Sask. Occurs rarely on the Colorado Plateau at the Lucky Strike No. 2 mine, San Rafael district, and Monument No. 2 mine, Monument Valley district (Weeks and Thompson, 1954). Synthesized by Gruner (1952), and also by Bignand (1955) at 100°C from an equimolecular solution of uranyl acetate and lead acetate. Also synthesized by Frondel et al. (1954) in solutions of stepped concentrations of U:Pb = 1:.09 to 1:.9 (in mols) at room temperature.

TABLE 2.4. *Properties of the hydrated uranium oxides and hydroxides, Pb-free or Pb-poor*

Mineral	Form	Color, Streak (S), Luster (L), Fluorescence (F)	Pleochroism	Indices and orientation	Cleavage and fracture	H	G
Masuyite	Orthorhombic. Minute pseudohexagonal plates. Twinned (101)	Orange red	α = pale yellow $\beta = \gamma$ = deep gold	$\alpha = b = 1.785$ $\beta = a = 1.906$ $\gamma = c = 1.917$ $(-)$ 2V = 50-large, r > v. Also β and γ between 2.11–2.15 (due to Pb?)	(010)? reported	—	—
Ianthinite	Orthorhombic. Prismatic, acicular, radial fibers	Black violet to amethystine	Intense. Black normal to length. Orange parallel to length	$\beta = 1.88$ $\gamma = 1.91$ $(-)$	—	—	—
Epiianthinite	Orthorhombic. Minute needles	Yellow. F yellow brown (long wave)	α = pale yellow or pink β = yellow, orange γ = deep yellow or dark purple	$\alpha = c = 1.695$–1.70 $\beta = b = 1.730$–1.79 $\gamma = a = 1.790$–1.793 $(-)$ 2V = 50°	—	—	Slightly less than 3.5

Mineral	Crystal habit	Color / luster / fluorescence	Pleochroism	Optical constants	Cleavage	Hardness	Density
Schoepite	Orthorhombic. Tabular (001), short prisms, radial fibers, equant crystals	Deep lemon yellow. S yellow. L adamantine. F strong yellow green	Weak. α = colorless $\beta = \gamma$ = lemon yellow	$\alpha = c = 1.690\text{–}1.705$; 1.683 $\beta = b = 1.714\text{–}1.730$; 1.740 $\gamma = a = 1.730\text{–}1.740$; 1.755 $(-)$ 2V = large to 89°. r > v. Indices increase with Pb?	Perfect (001)	2–3	4.49–4.8
Becquerelite	Orthorhombic. Elongated and striated with b, flattened (001). Twinned on (110) to pseudohexagonal groups	Yellow to amber. S yellow. L brilliant to greasy. F none or weak yellow brown	α = colorless to pale yellow $\beta = \gamma$ = yellow to deep yellow	$\alpha = c = 1.72\text{–}1.75$ $\beta = b = 1.81\text{–}1.82$ $\gamma = a = 1.82\text{–}1.83$ $\gamma - \alpha = 0.08\text{–}0.11$ $(-)$ 2V = 30°, r > v	(001) perfect, also (101)	2–3	5.3
Billietite	Orthorhombic. (001) tablets, twinned on (110) and (111) to pseudohexagonal groups	Amber. F none or weak yellow green(?)	α = colorless to pale yellow β = greenish yellow to deep yellow γ = deep yellow, golden yellow	$\alpha = c = 1.725\text{–}1.735$ $\beta = a = 1.780\text{–}1.822$ $\gamma = b = 1.790\text{–}1.829$ $\gamma - \alpha = 0.065\text{–}0.099$ $(-)$ 2V = 35°, 47°. r > v strong (Frondel and Cuttitta, 1953; Brasseur, 1949; Chervet and Branche, 1955)	(001) perfect (110), (010) reported	2–3?	5.28–5.36

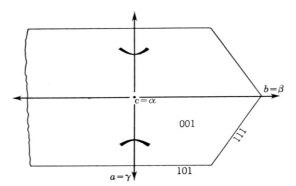

F<small>IG</small>. 2.18. Optical orientation of fourmarierite.

Identification. By optical properties together with x-ray powder pattern (strongest lines: 3.44, 3.08, 1.90), which resembles those of schoepite, masuyite, and vandendriesscheite.

Vandendriesscheite

$PbO \cdot 7UO_3 \cdot 12H_2O$. Some Ba and Ca may substitute for Pb (Frondel, 1956B). $UO_3 = 76\%$.

A supergene alteration product of pitchblende. First found at Shinkolobwe, Katanga, Belgian Congo, it was next noted at Great Bear Lake (Mineral X of Palache and Berman, 1933). Frondel (1956B) also reports it in the oxide zone of the gummitic alteration of uraninite with fourmarierite at the Wiseman, McKinney, and Dake pegmatites, Spruce Pine district, N.C.; Newry, Maine; Palermo and Ruggles pegmatites, N.H.; at Hottah Lake, Canada; and at Joachimsthal, Bohemia. Synthesized by Frondel et al. (1954) by adding ammonia to an aqueous solution of uranyl and lead chloride.

Identification by a combination of x-ray pattern and optics. Powder pattern (strongest lines: 7.31, 3.19, 3.58) similar to those of schoepite, masuyite, and richetite.

Wölsendorfite

(Pb, Ca) $U_2O_7 \cdot 2H_2O$, $Pb:Ca = 5:1$. $UO_3 = 69.8\%$ (Protas, 1957B). Formerly confused with fourmarierite. Occurs in fluorite at Wölsendorf, Bavaria; on pitchblende at Great Bear Lake, and at Kerségalec, Lignol, France; and as small nodules at Shinkolobwe. Strongest x-ray lines: 3.09, 3.47, 6.93.

Clarkeite

Composition. $(Na,Ca,Pb,Th,H_2O)_2U_2(O,H_2O)_7$ (Frondel and Meyrowitz, 1956). $UO_3 = 83\%$. Small amounts of Mg, Ba, Si, Fe^3, and Al are probably contaminants; rare earths are also present in minor amounts (Ross et al., 1931; Gruner, 1954B). Natural materials are solid solutions among $Na_2U_2O_7$, CaU_2O_7, and PbU_2O in which cation vacancies are occupied by neutral H_2O molecules and in which valance compensation is effected by concomitant substitution of (OH) or H_2O for O (Frondel and Meyrowitz, 1956).

In some specimens a core of uraninite has successive shells of clarkeite, gummite, and uranophane; or of clarkeite, fourmarierite, and uranophane. X-ray patterns agree closely with those of synthetic $Na_2U_2O_7$ and $Ca_2U_2O_7$ and with synthetic clarkeite prepared from uranyl nitrate and $CaCO_3$ (Gruner, 1954B).

Occurrence. An alteration product of uraninite from a pegmatite near Spruce Pine, N.C., along with orange-red gummite and yellow uranophane (Ross et al., 1931). With fourmarierite and uranophane in successive shell alterations of uraninite crystals in pegmatite, Ajmer district, Rajputana, India (Frondel and Meyrowitz, 1956). Clarkeite is a less common constituent of gummite (Frondel, 1952B, 1956B). Apparently formed as a late-stage low-temperature hydrothermal mineral or a supergene mineral. Synthesized at 258°C (Gruner, 1954B).

Identification. Requires x-ray study for positive identification; strongest lines: 3.17, 3.34, 5.77. Its presence may be suspected in complex bright-colored to brown alterations of uraninite.

Vandenbrandeite

$CuUO_4 \cdot 2H_2O$. $UO_3 = 70$ to 71%. Attached to vug walls on (110). Partially coated by kasolite. Numerous microscopic inclusions of kasolite and of liquid with gas bubbles (Milne and Nuffield, 1951).

At Kalongwe (Schoep, 1932) and Shinkolobwe (uranolepidite, Thoreau, 1933), Belgian Congo. A supergene oxidation product, at Shinkolobwe, on a curite-uranophane mass associated with a black cobaltian wad. At Kalongwe with kasolite, sklodowskite, uraninite, chalcopyrite, goethite, and malachite. Reported by Nininger (1954, p. 225) to be "present in small amounts in some of the copper-uranium deposits of the Colorado Plateau," but unconfirmed. Synthesized at 140°C (Bignand, 1955) together with curite by heating in a tube for 48 hr an equimolecular solution of copper acetate and uranylacetate, also by heating schoepite in a tube to 140°C in a solution containing an excess of copper acetate.

The optical properties are distinctive. Strongest x-ray powder lines: 4.29, 2.92, 2.56, 1.42.

Uranosphaerite

$(BiO)(UO_2)(OH)_3$(?) (Frondel and Fleischer, 1955; Berman, 1957B). $UO_3 = 51$ to 52%.

A very rare supergene oxidation product of uraninite with uranium arsenates, uranophane(?), gummite, and cobaltian wad in the Walpurgis vein, Weisser Hirsch mine, Schneeberg, Saxony.

Decrepitates with heating, forming masses of small, brown, silky needles. Only known hydrated uranium-bismuth oxide. Strongest x-ray powder lines: 3.16, 1.83, 3.87.

Doubtful or Poorly Defined Species

Richetite

Hydrated(?). Pb-U oxide(?). Monoclinic in pseudohexagonal plates in minute (0.1 mm) needles of uranophane at Shinkolobwe, Belgian Congo. Perfect

TABLE 2.5. *Properties of the hydrated uranium oxides and hydroxides with Pb, Cu, or Bi*

Mineral	Form	Color, Streak (S), Luster (L), Fluorescence (F)	Pleochroism	Indices and orientation	Cleavage and fracture	H	G
Curite	Orthorhombic. Sugary masses. Needles elongated and striated (c)	Orange red. S orange. L adamantine	α = pale yellow β = light red orange γ = dark red orange	$\alpha = b = 2.05\text{-}2.06$ $\beta = a = 2.07\text{-}2.11$ $\gamma = c = 2.11\text{-}2.15$ $(-)$ 2V = large, r > v strong	(100)	4–5	7.12–7.26
Fourmarierite	Orthorhombic. Thin (001) tablets, elongated and striated with *b*	Red, golden red, brown, darkening with increasing Pb. S red brown. L adamantine	Strong. α = colorless β = pale yellow to orange γ = orange	$\alpha = c = 1.85\text{-}1.86$ $\beta = b = 1.90\text{-}1.92$ $\gamma = a = 1.90\text{-}1.94$ $(-)$ 2V = moderate to large, r > v strong	(110) perfect	3–4	6.0
Vanden-driesscheite	Orthorhombic. Barrel-shaped pseudohexagonal crystals. Thin (001) plates in subparallel groups. Tablets elongated with *b*	Orange, amber, orange red. S light orange	α = colorless $\beta = \gamma$ = yellow to yellow gold	$\alpha = c = 1.76\text{-}1.79$ $\beta = b = 1.81\text{-}1.84$ $\gamma = a = 1.82\text{-}1.85$ decreasing with increasing Ca and Ba. $(-)$ 2V = medium to large, r > v strong	(001) perfect	3+	

	Crystal system and habit	Color	Pleochroism	Optical properties	Cleavage flake indices:	Hardness	Sp. gr.
Wölsendorfite	Orthorhombic. Crusts, nodules, spherulites	Orange, red, carmine	—	$n_1 = 2.09$ $n_2 = 2.05$	(001) good	—	6.8
Clarkeite	Orthorhombic. Massive fine-grained	Red brown, dark brown. S yellowish brown. L waxy	Slight in yellow and orange	$\alpha = 2.00$ $\beta = 2.10$ $\gamma = 2.11$ $(-), 2V = 30\text{-}50°$, r < v weak	Conchoidal fracture	4-4.5	6.29-6.39
Vandenbrandeite	Triclinic. Pseudomonoclinic. Small crystals flattened (001), elongated with (001) ∧ (110) edge. Lozenge outline. Anhedral masses	Dark green to nearly black. S green	In yellow- and blue-green	$\alpha = 1.76\text{-}1.77$ $\beta = 1.78\text{-}1.792$ $\gamma = 1.80$ $(+) 2V \cong 90°$, dispersion strong, $\gamma \wedge$ elongation = 40°. An optic axis nearly ⊥ (110). Cleavage pieces nonpleochroic and of very low birefringence	(110) perfect. May be 1 or 2 others in zone parallel with c	3-4	5.03
Uranosphaerite	Orthorhombic(?). Elongated with c, in hemispherical groups	Orange to brick red. S yellow. L greasy	?	$\alpha = a = 1.959$ $\beta = b = 1.981$ $\gamma = c = 2.06$ $(+) 2V = 56°$, r < v strong	(100)	2-3	6.36

(010) cleavage, black color. Biaxial $(-)$, 2V large, β and γ between 2.00 and 2.07. Extinction on (010) = 6° (Vaes, 1947). Powder pattern like those of fourmarierite, schoepite, masuyite, and vandendriesscheite (Frondel, 1956B).

CARBONATES

Rutherfordine

Composition. $(UO_2)CO_3$. Pb, Ca, and Si usually appear, owing to admixed kasolite and uranophane. UO_3 = 86 to 87%. Diderichite is a synonym. Effervesces strongly in dilute HCl. Intergrown and admixed minutely with kasolite and uranophane. Some crystals zoned with a pale yellow envelope on a brown core.

Occurrence. Originally found with kasolite and uranophane as a supergene alteration of uraninite and as pseudomorphs after uraninite in a mica pegmatite in the Morogoro district in the Uruguru Mountains, East Africa (Marckwald, 1906). Also at Shinkolobwe, Belgian Congo (Vaes, 1947). Occurs abundantly at Beryl Mountain, N.H., as dense to earthy pseudomorphs after uraninite in pegmatite, associated with schoepite, vandendriesscheite, and uranophane; and at Newry, Maine, in pegmatite as an alteration of uraninite (Frondel and Meyrowitz, 1956). May also be present as a constituent of some gummite from the Ruggles and Palermo pegmatites, N.H. (Frondel and Meyrowitz, 1956). Found rarely in some oxidized nonvanadiferous uranium ores of the Colorado Plateau (Weeks, 1955); at the Lucky Mc mine, Fremont County, Wyo. Synthesized by heating $UO_3 \cdot nH_2O$ at 300°C at 15,000 lb/sq in. CO_2 (Frondel and Meyrowitz, 1956).

Identification. Differs from other uranium carbonates in higher indices or biaxial $(+)$ character. Strongest x-ray lines: 4.60, 3.21, 4.29.

Andersonite

$Na_2Ca(UO_2)(CO_3)_3 \cdot 6H_2O$. UO_3 = 43%. Soluble in water; effervesces in HCl. An efflorescence on mine wall with schroeckingerite, gypsum, bayleyite, and swartzite on mica schist at the Hillside mine, Yavapai County, Ariz. (Axelrod et al., 1951). Also at the Skinny No. 1 mine, Yellow Cat group, Thompsons district, Utah (Weeks and Thompson, 1954). Distinguished from schroeckingerite by lack of SO_4 and uniaxial character. Strongest x-ray lines: 13.0, 7.97, 5.68.

Liebigite

Composition. $Ca_2(UO_2)(CO_3)_3 \cdot 10-11H_2O$ (Appleman, 1956). UO_2 = 36 to 37%. Uranothallite is identical (Evans and Frondel, 1950). Soluble in H_2O; effervesces in HCl.

Occurrence. First described in 1848 from near Adrianople, Turkey, as an alteration of uraninite. Other localities are Schneeberg and Johanngeorgenstadt, Saxony; Joachimsthal, Bohemia; Eisleben-Mansfield, Harz Mts., Germany; Schmiedeberg, Silesia (uranothallite—Meixner, 1940A); and Wheal Basset, Cornwall, England. In the United States at Pumpkin Buttes, Wyo., as secondary coatings; Lucky Mc mine, Fremont County, Wyo.; Lusk, Wyo., as an alteration of uranophane(?) (George, 1949); and the Black Ape mine, Thompsons district, Grand County, Utah (Weeks and Thompson, 1954). In Canada at the Eldorado mine, Great Bear Lake and in the Goldfields region at the Martin Lake mine and the Rix deposit, as well as about a dozen other deposits in the region.

Identification. Differs from bayleyite in being (+), from rabbittite in different indices and stronger fluorescence. Strongest x-ray lines: 6.81, 5.40, 8.68.

Swartzite

$CaMg(UO_2)(CO_3)_3 \cdot 12H_2O$. $UO_3 = 37\%$. Traces of alkalies, Al and Sr are present, as is minor SO_4. Dehydrates in dry atmosphere. The dehydrated modification shows weak fluorescence of uncertain color (Axelrod et al., 1951).

As a mine-wall efflorescence with schroeckingerite, gypsum, andersonite, and bayleyite, intergrown in small clusters with granular gypsum (Axelrod et al., 1951) at the Hillside mine, Yavapai County, Ariz. Strongest x-ray lines: 5.50, 8.76, 7.31.

Rabbittite

$Ca_3Mg_3(UO_2)_2(CO_3)_6(OH)_4 \cdot 18H_2O$. $UO_3 = 37\%$. Traces of Si, Al, and Y reported (Thompson et al., 1955). Soluble slowly in water. Effervesces in HCl.

An efflorescence on a pillar of partly oxidized high-grade pitchblende ore in the Lucky Strike No. 2 mine, San Rafael Swell, Emery County, Utah, in Shinarump conglomerate, associated with uranium sulfates, gypsum, sphaerocobaltite, and bieberite. Swartzite has much stronger birefringence, is (−), and has stronger fluorescence.

Bayleyite

Composition. $Mg(UO_2)(CO_3)_3 \cdot 18H_2O$. Traces of Ca, Fe, Al, Si, and Sr and small amounts of SO_4 (Axelrod et al., 1951; Branche et al., 1951; Stern and Weeks, 1952). $UO_3 = 30$ to 32%. Soluble in water, almost instantly soluble in hot water. Same material (Arizona and Morocco) in dry atmosphere loses water and disintegrates to a powder. The dehydration product has $\alpha = 1.502$, $\gamma = 1.551$, and fluoresces moderate whitish green.

Occurrence. At the Hillside mine, Yavapai County, Ariz., as a mine-wall efflorescence coating gypsum and intergrown with schroeckingerite, accompanied by andersonite and swartzite. Material altered by dehydration to dull crystals, finally disintegrating to yellow powder. In the copper-uranium deposit at the Hideout (Tiger) mine, White Canyon district, Utah (Stern and Weeks, 1952), with gypsum and schroeckingerite as a coating on the mine wall. This material did not dehydrate in the laboratory. In the Pumpkin Buttes area of Wyoming forming where seepage occurs along banks of dry stream beds (Weeks and Thompson, 1954). At the P.J. mine, Central City district, Colo., and at the Rifle mine, Rifle, Colo. Also occurs at the Azgour mine in Morocco in an upper level as an efflorescence on dolomite, accompanied by epsomite, as an alteration of uraninite.

Identification. Effervesces in HCl; soluble in water. Low refractive indices for a U mineral. Resembles liebigite which has Ca and slightly higher refractive indices. Strongest x-ray lines: 7.66, 13.1, 3.83.

Schroeckingerite

Composition. $NaCa_3(UO_2)(CO_3)(SO_4)F \cdot 10H_2O$ (Jaffe et al., 1948). $UO_3 = 31\%$. Dakeite is a synonym. Soluble in H_2O; effervesces in acid. Minor elements ($<1\%$) are Mg, Al, Fe, K, Si, Al, Sr, Zn, Ti, and Mn (Axelrod et al., 1951; Weeks and Thompson, 1954). Can be readily dehydrated over sulfuric acid to the $4H_2O$ hydrate (Hurlbut, 1954) which is: hexagonal, uniaxial $(-)$, with $\omega = 1.581$; $\epsilon = 1.532$. The change is reversible.

Occurrence. An uncommon secondary mineral. In altered pitchblende deposits at Joachimsthal, Bohemia; Johanngeorgenstadt, Saxony; Radhausberg, Badgastein, Hohe Tauern, Austria (Haberlandt and Schiener, 1951); at Graf Hohenthal and Vitzthum mines, Eisleben, Harz, Germany (Bültemann, 1954); and with zippeite and pitchblende at Ronchamp (Haute-Saône), France. Also occurs at the La Soberania mine, San Isidro, Argentina (Hurlbut, 1954). In the United States as elongated pisolites in clays and sands of Wasatch or younger age on the banks of Lost Creek, Red Desert area, Sweetwater County, north of Wamsutter, Wyo. (Larsen and Gonyer, 1937); as coatings on drift walls at the Hillside mine, Yavapai County, Ariz. (Axelrod et al., 1951) with gypsum, bayleyite, swartzite, and andersonite; with bayleyite in efflorescent crusts on mine walls at the Hideout No. 1 mine, Deer Flats, White Canyon, San Juan County, Utah (Stern and Weeks, 1952); in a near-surface deposit in clay at the McCoy group, Thompsons district, Grand County, Utah; as an alteration of pitchblende at the Crabapple claim, San Juan County, Utah; at the Parco No. 25 mine, Yellow Cat group, Thompsons district, Utah, the Shinarump No. 3 mine, White Canyon district, Utah (Weeks and Thompson, 1954); the Sevastopol claims, Butler Wash, San Juan County, Trader Smith's claims, near Cisco, and Shinarump No. 1 mine, Grand County, Marysvale, Piute County, all in Utah (Gruner and Gardiner, 1952).

Identification. Combination of fluorescence, water solubility, sulfate test, and optical properties. Strongest x-ray lines: 7.26, 4.79, 8.48.

Doubtful or Poorly Defined Species

Ianthinite (*Schoep, 1926A; Bignand, 1955*)

Composition. Described by Schoep (1926A,B) as $2UO_2 \cdot 7H_2O(?)$. Bignand (1955) on Congo material (type material?) has found the mineral to be a hydrated oxycarbonate of Ca, U^6 with minor U^4, probably $Ca_3U^4(UO_2)_6$-$(CO_3)_2O_9 \cdot 10H_2O$ $[2CO_2 \cdot 3CaO \cdot UO_2 \cdot 6UO_3 \cdot 10H_2O$ or $2CO_2 \cdot 3CaO \cdot 7$-$(UO_{2.83}) \cdot 10H_2O]$. $UO_3 = 71.6\%$, $UO_2 = 10.9\%$. Derriks and Vaes (1956) list the ianthinite of the Congo as a uranium oxide; so it is possible that two distinctly different species have been described from the Shinkolobwe deposit under the name of ianthinite.

Traces of Fe[3] were found by both Schoep and Bignand. The study by Bignand (1955) has apparently demonstrated that the original(?) Congo ianthinite is not identical with the "ianthinite" from Lachaux and La Crouzille, France, described by Branche et al. (1951) as $2UO_2 \cdot 7H_2O$(?) with a trace of Fe. This material, which was x-rayed by Bignand (1955) and called "ianthinite francaise," has a powder pattern very similar to material studied by Frondel and Cuttitta (1954), but a $UO_3 \cdot 2H_2O$ composition, and is optically similar to epiianthinite of Schoep and Stradiot (1947). The properties described below are largely those observed by Bignand (1955).

Structure and form. Orthorhombic. Tiny rectangular (001) plates elongated with *b*. Also in thick tabular (001) plates and prismatic parallel with *b*. Also in radial fibrous aggregates and nodules.

Optical properties. Violet to violet black. Partly altered to brownish yellow (epiianthinite). Brown-violet streak. Submetallic luster. Biaxial $(-)$, 2V = 48° (Bignand, 1955).

$\alpha = c = 1.674$, colorless
$\beta = b = 1.88-1.90$, violet
$\gamma = a = 1.91-1.92$, dark violet

Physical properties. Perfect (001) cleavage; (010) and (100) reported (Bignand, 1955). H = 3 to 4. G = 4.94 (Bignand, 1955). H = 2 to 3 (Schoep, 1926A).

Occurrence. A rare supergene oxidation product of uraninite at Shinkolobwe-Kasolo, Katanga, Belgian Congo, associated with schoepite and becquerelite. Also reported at Wölsendorf, Bavaria, with fourmarierite, becquerelite, schoepite, kasolite, parsonite, and dewindtite (Schoep and Scholz, 1931) (oxide or the oxycarbonate?). Needs further study.

Sharpite

$(UO_2)(CO_3) \cdot H_2O$ or $(UO_2)_6(CO_3)_5(OH)_2 \cdot 7H_2O$ (Mélon, 1938). Orthorhombic(?); fibrous crusts. Greenish yellow. $\alpha = 1.633$ (brownish), $\gamma = 1.72$ (greenish yellow). γ = elongation, β normal to flattening. Biaxial $(+)$. $G > 3.33$. H = about 2.5. Effervesces in dilute acid. Occurs at Katanga with uranophane, curite, and becquerelite as a supergene mineral. Type specimens destroyed during World War II (Frondel and Meyrowitz, 1956). Identified provisionally from two deposits in France: Kruth (Haut-Rhin) and at the Brugeaud mine near Bessines (Chervet and Branche, 1955).

Studtite

Hydrated $Pb-UO_2$ carbonate(?) (Vaes, 1947). Crusts of flexible fibers. Orthorbombic(?). Yellow. $\alpha = 1.545$, $\beta = 1.555$, $\gamma = 1.68$. γ = elongation. Biaxial $(-)$, 2V large. Occurs at Shinkolobwe, Katanga, Belgian Congo, as a supergene mineral. Reported by Robinson (1955A) in the Goldfields area, Sask. Fluoresces medium yellow green (Horne, 1951).

TABLE 2.6. *Properties of the uranyl carbonate minerals*

Mineral	Form	Color, Streak (S), Luster (L), Fluorescence (F)	Pleochroism	Indices and orientation	Cleavage and fracture	H	G
Rutherfordine	Orthorhombic. Minute fibers in crusts. Elongated with c	Yellow, orange, yellow green. S yellow. L earthy. F none or weak yellow green	Slight α = colorless β = pale yellow γ = pale greenish yellow	$\alpha = b = 1.715$–1.723 $\beta = c = 1.728$–1.730 $\gamma = a = 1.790$–1.795 $(+)$ 2V = 53° (Clark and Christ, 1956)	(010) perfect, (001) lesser	Soft	4.82
Andersonite	Hexagonal rhombohedral. Minute pseudocubic crystals in thin granular coatings	Bright yellow green. F bright yellow green	ω = colorless ϵ = pale yellow	$\omega = 1.520$ $\epsilon = 1.540$ $(+)$	—	—	2.8
Liebigite	Orthorhombic. Granular, scaly and botryoidal aggregates. Crystals, rounded with convex faces, are equant or stubby prismatic with c	Apple green to weak bright greenish yellow. S pale green. L vitreous, pearly (100). F vivid green, white green, blue green (long and short wave)	α = nearly colorless $\beta = \gamma$ = pale greenish yellow	$\alpha = a = 1.494$–1.501 $\beta = 1.498$–1.506 $\gamma = 1.535$–1.545 $(+)$ 2V = 15–42°, r > v	(100)	2.5–3	2.41

Mineral	Crystal form	Color	Pleochroism	Optics	Cleavage	Hardness	Sp. Gr.
Swartzite	Monoclinic. Minute prismatic crystals	Green, alters to dull whitish yellow. F bright yellowish green	α = colorless, β = γ = yellow	α = 1.465, β = 1.51, γ = 1.540, (−) 2V = 40°		<3	2.3
Rabbittite	Monoclinic. Fibrous with c, bent. Flattened (100)	Pale green or greenish yellow. L silky. F weak	—	α = 1.502, β = b = 1.508, γ = 1.525, (+) 2V large. $\gamma \wedge c$ = 15°	(110) perfect, (001)	2.5	2.57
Bayleyite	Monoclinic. Minute prisms. Groups with striated aggregate faces	Yellow, whitish yellow. S yellowish. L vitreous. F weak yellow green	α = pinkish, β = γ = pale yellow	α = 1.453-1.455, β = 1.490-1.492, γ = b = 1.498-1.500, (−) 2V = 30°, $\gamma \wedge c$ = 8-14°	Conchoidal	2-2.5	2.05
Schroeckingerite	Orthorhombic. Pseudo-hexagonal scales (001), in aggregates, rosettes, and pisolites	Yellow to greenish yellow. S pale yellow to greenish yellow. L pearly to vitreous. F strong greenish yellow to whitish green	Weak, α = very pale yellow, β = γ = pale yellowish green	α = c = 1.489-1.492, β = b = 1.537-1.543, γ = a = 1.538-1.544, (−) 2V = 0-25°	(001) perfect	2.5	2.51-2.55

Voglite

$Ca_2CuU(CO_3)_5 \cdot 6H_2O(?)$. $UO_2 = 37\%$. Effervesces in acids. Triclinic. Rhomboidal scales like gypsum in thin coatings. Lamellar twinning parallel with plates. Emerald green to bright grass green. Pale green streak. Pearly luster.

$\alpha = 1.541$, deep bluish green
$\beta = 1.547$, deep bluish green
$\gamma = 1.564$, pale yellowish

Biaxial $(+)$, $2V = 60°$, $r < v$, very strong. $\alpha =$ nearly normal to the plates, $\gamma \wedge$ elongation $= 33°$ in the acute angle. Fluoresces bluish green. Crystals veined and rimmed by an isotropic, darker green substance with an index about 1.60 (George, 1949). Described only from the Elias mine, Joachimsthal, Bohemia, with liebigite, as an alteration of pitchblende. Reportedly synthesized by Frondel et al. (1954) by reaction at room temperature in a hydrous solution of U, Ca, and Cu nitrates and Na_2CO_3.

SULFATES

Zippeite

Composition. Either $(UO_2)_3(SO_4)_2(OH)_2 \cdot 8H_2O$, i.e., $3UO_3 \cdot 2SO_3 \cdot 9H_2O$, or $(UO_2)_2(SO_4)(OH)_2 \cdot 4H_2O$, i.e., $2UO_3 \cdot SO_3 \cdot 5H_2O$. $UO_3 = 72$ to 75%. The H_2O content is known to vary from about 3 to 8. Material called zippeite includes more than one species; different hydrates are represented and may occur together (Novacek, 1935); different polymorphs may also be represented. Some are probably monoclinic (Weeks and Thompson, 1954; Chervet and Branche, 1955). Traill (1952) found a monoclinic symmetry for synthetic material.

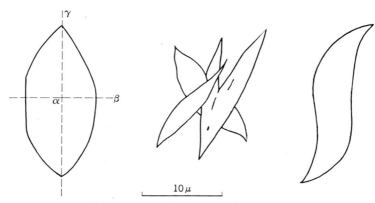

10μ

Fig. 2.19. Lensoid and spindle-shaped crystals of zippeite, Joachimsthal, Bohemia (Novacek, 1935).

Occurrence. A secondary, supergene, sulfatic alteration of pitchblende in veins and in Colorado Plateau deposits; in the former type at Anmerk, Pribram, Schlaggenwald, Dürrmaul, Schönficht, Joachimsthal, and Johanngeorgenstadt of the Erzgebirge region; La Crouzille and Ronchamp (Haute-Saône), France; Cornwall, England (11 localities reported); ABC group at Lake Athabaska and several other deposits; Eldorado mine on Great Bear Lake, both in Canada. At the Telegraph, Diamond Joe, and Kirk mines, Central City district, Colo. Common associates are gypsum, limonite, and uranophane. Colorado Plateau occurrences include: Consolidated and Lucky Strike No. 2 mines, and Dexter Claims, San Rafael Swell; Happy Jack mine, White Canyon, Utah; Frey No. 4 mine and Sodaroll Claim, San Juan County, Utah; Grand Wash, Fruita, Wayne County, Utah; and Oyler mine, Wayne County, Utah. Associates are johannite, uranopilite, and pitchblende. Synthesized by Bignand (1955), Traill (1952), and Gruner (1952) in various ways including the laboratory alteration of pitchblende.

Identification. Tests positive for SO_4, negative for Cu. Distinguished from uranopilite on basis of optical properties.

Uranopilite

Composition. $(UO_2)_6(SO_4)(OH)_{10} \cdot 12H_2O$. $UO_3 =$ 79 to 81%. Meta-uranopilite is reported as the $5H_2O$ hydrate, but its validity as a species is doubtful (Frondel and Fleischer, 1955) (see beta-uranopilite). Insoluble in cold H_2O; soluble in boiling H_2O and dilute acids.

Occurrence. A secondary mineral, occurring as a coating in oxidized ore deposits that contain pitchblende and primary sulfides; as efflorescences on mine walls. Zippeite and gypsum are common associates. Localities include Wölsendorf, Bavaria; Johanngeorgenstadt, Saxony; Joachimsthal and Pribram, Bohemia; St.

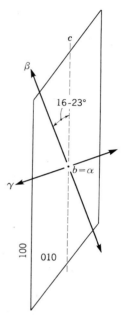

FIG. 2.20. Optical orientation of uranopilite (adapted from Frondel, 1952A; *Am. Mineralogist*).

Just, Cornwall; Urgeirica mine, Viseu district, Portugal; La Crouzille (Haute-Vienne), La Faye, Grury and Bauzot mine (Saône-et-Loire), and in minor amounts in several other deposits in France; Shinkolobwe, Belgian Congo; Great Bear Lake, Hottah Lake, and Goldfields, Canada (Traill, 1952); abundant in the Happy Jack mine, White Canyon district, Utah, with johannite and zippeite; Marysvale district, Utah.

Synthesized from a mixture of pulverized pyrite and U_3O_8 placed in water at ordinary temperatures for 3 to 4 weeks, as a crust, appearing after an insoluble U-Ca sulfate (Bignand, 1955).

Identification. Resembles zippeite from which it is distinguished by optical or x-ray diffraction tests. Distinguished from johannite by Cu test. Strongest x-ray lines: 7.12, 9.18, 4.28.

TABLE 2.7. *Properties of the uranyl sulfate minerals*

Mineral	Form	Color, Streak (S), Luster (L), Fluorescence (F)	Pleochroism	Indices and orientation	Cleavage and fracture	H	G
Zippeite	Orthorhombic. (010) plates usually lensoid, lathlike or rhomboid in crusts, or reniform to spheroidal masses or parallel groups. Synthetics are twinned across (001). Also monoclinic	Golden yellow. S yellow. L vitreous, dull in aggregates. F green, yellowish, or absent	α = colorless $\beta = \gamma$ = yellow to orange	$\alpha = b = 1.655\text{–}1.66$ $\beta = c = 1.717\text{–}1.72$ $\gamma = a = 1.765\text{–}1.77$ (–) 2V = large – $80°$ With 15% H_2O (Novacek, 1935): $\alpha = 1.570$ $\gamma = 1.641$ Also: $\alpha = b = 1.630$ $\beta = 1.689$ $\gamma = 1.739$ Monoclinic types: $\gamma \wedge a = 3°$ (Traill, 1952); $\gamma \wedge c = 40°$ (Weeks and Thompson, 1954)	(010) perfect	About 2	3.5

Uranopilite	Apparently monoclinic (Frondel, 1952A). Suggested triclinic (Branche et al., 1951). Minute needles parallel with c, flattened (010) in botryoidal crust and felted reniform masses	Lemon yellow. S pale yellow. L silky. F bright yellow green. Dehydration destroys fluorescence	α = colorless $\beta = \gamma$ = yellow. Pleochroism intensified with dehydration	$\alpha = b = 1.620\text{–}1.623$ $\beta = 1.622\text{–}1.625$ $\gamma = 1.630\text{–}1.634$ $(+)$ $\beta \wedge c = 16\text{–}23°$. $2V = 50°$ (Na), $0°$ (some λ). $r > v$ strong and $r < v$ extreme. (100) sections show Berlin blue interference colors. Indices increase with dehydration and birefringence decreases. $\beta = \gamma = 1.89$ (152°C, Frondel, 1952A)	(010) perfect	2–3	3.7–4.0
Johannite	Triclinic, pseudomonoclinic (Peacock, 1935; Hurlbut, 1950). Prismatic with c, flattened (100) coatings and small spheroids. Multiple lamellar twinning common. c = twin axis (Appleman, 1957)	Light to emerald green. S pale yellow or green. L vitreous	α = colorless β = pale yellow γ = yellow to greenish yellow	$\alpha = 1.572\text{–}1.577$ $\beta = 1.592\text{–}1.597$ $\gamma = 1.611\text{–}1.616$ (1.625 for synthetic). $2V = 90°$. $(+)$ $r < v$ strong. $(-)$ $r > v$ strong	(100) good	2–2.5	3.32

Johannite

Composition. $Cu(UO_2)_2(SO_4)_2(OH)_2 \cdot 6H_2O$. $UO_3 = 61\%$. Soluble in acids, decomposed by water. Bitter taste.

Occurrence. On the Colorado Plateau at the Happy Jack and Frey No. 4 mines, White Canyon district, San Juan County, Utah, and at the Oyler mine, Henry Mts. district, Utah, as wall and fracture coatings with uranopilite, zippeite, brochantite, chalcanthite; as coatings on covellite, chalcopyrite, and pitchblende (Weeks and Thompson, 1954). As an alteration (gilpinite) of pitchblende from Central City, Gilpin County, Colo. At the Hillside mine, Yavapai County, Ariz. In Canada at the Eldorado mine, Great Bear Lake, and at the ABC group, Beaverlodge Lake (Bültemann, 1954). In Bohemia at Joachimsthal and Johanngeorgenstadt; and at Cornwall, England. In France at Limouzat and at Les Bois Noirs by Saint-Priest-la-Prugne, Allier, as a coating on pitchblende. Synthesized by reaction between altered pitchblende, pyrite, and chalcopyrite (Guillemin and Pierrot, 1956A).

Identification. The only authenticated copper-uranyl sulfate. Uranopilite is yellow and fluoresces; zippeite is yellow to orange. Strongest x-ray lines: 7.73, 6.16, 3.41.

Doubtful or Poorly Defined Species

Beta-uranopilite

$(UO_2)_6(SO_4)(OH)_{10} \cdot 5H_2O(?)$. $UO_3 = 82\%$. Grayish, dirty green, or brownish. $\alpha = 1.72$, $\beta = 1.76$, $\gamma = 1.76$ (Novacek, 1935). Biaxial $(-)$. β parallel with elongation of needles or laths, α normal to flattening of laths. Fluorescent medium to strong yellow green (Horne, 1951). Only a single specimen from Joachimsthal, Bohemia, known. Regarded as a dehydration product of uranopilite, which seems unlikely. If a valid species, it should be referred to as meta-uranopilite (Frondel, 1952A).

Cuprozippeite

Supposedly $Cu(UO_2)_3(SO_4)_3(OH)_2 \cdot 11H_2O$. Validity doubtful.

Uranochalcite

A poorly defined substance, very likely not a valid species but mixtures of various uranium sulfates, carbonates, and silicates.

Voglianite

A hydrous Ca-U sulfate of questionable validity.

PHOSPHATES

NONHYDRATED PHOSPHATES

Monazite

Composition. $(Ce,La)PO_4$. The lanthanons consist principally of lanthanum, and commonly are present in about a 1:1 ratio with Ce. Nd, Pr, and Sm are apparently the most common. Y-earths substitute in minor amounts for (Ce,La) in amounts up to about 4% Y_2O_3, etc. Th usually is present in amounts up to about 12% ThO_2. Monazite with as much as 28.20% ThO_2 has been reported from Ratnapura, Ceylon (Wadia and Fernando, 1945). Varieties essentially Th-free have been reported (Gordon, 1939). U is absent or low. Analyses of 10 monazites from various localities showed $U_3O_8 = 0.10$ to 1.09% (George, 1949). Hutton (1950) reports a New Zealand monazite with $(Ta, Nb)_2O_5 = 5.48\%$. Small to minor amounts of Ca, Mg, Mn, Fe^2, Fe^3, Pb, Zr, Be, Sn, Al, and Si may be present. Some Si may be due to admixed thorite; some is in the coupled isomorphous substitution: $Th^4Si^4 - Ce^3P^5$. Growth zones have been noted. Magnetic, but less so than xenotime.

Structure and form. Monoclinic. Commonly euhedral in minute to large crystals. Habit usually tablets flattened parallel with (100) or elongated parallel with *b*. In some cases wedge-shaped due to ($\bar{1}11$) and (100) markedly developed; or prismatic resulting from the elongation of (111). Radial fan-shaped masses also are known, as are anhedral pods. Detrital grains are (100) tablets with rounded corners; (001) cleavage pieces variously rounded; strongly rounded ovoid grains; or very slightly abraded euhedra of varying complexity (Fig. 2.21). Faces on larger crystals may be rough to irregular. Inclusions of zircon, rutile, and opaque dust appear in some grains. Some detrital grains show etching. Secondary enlargements have been reported (Derby, 1900) as clusters of spindle-shaped prolongations from the two ends of an original ovoid grain.

Occurrence.

1. Widespread as small accessory grains and crystals in granite, granite aplite, quartz monzonite, granodiorite, and syenite.

2. In granitic and, to a lesser extent, in syenitic pegmatites in large masses and crystals; less commonly in diorite pegmatite (Gray Goose No. 1 claim, Deer Creek district, Beaverhead County, Mont., Trites and Tooker, 1953, p. 164). Some of the more important and interesting occurrences in granite pegmatites are, in the United States at Portland, Conn.; with microlite at Amelia, Va.; Spruce Pine district, N.C.; Petaca district, N.Mex., with samarskite; Glorietta, N.Mex.; Brown Derby pegmatite, Gunnison County, Colo.; Trout Creek Pass and Cotopaxi areas, Chaffee County, Colo. (Heinrich, 1948A); Nuevo, Calif.; Aquarius Range, Ariz. In Quebec, West Portland Township, in crystals up to ¾ lb with allanite and euxenite.

Also in India at Pichhli, Gaya district; Bihar and Orissa with uraninite and

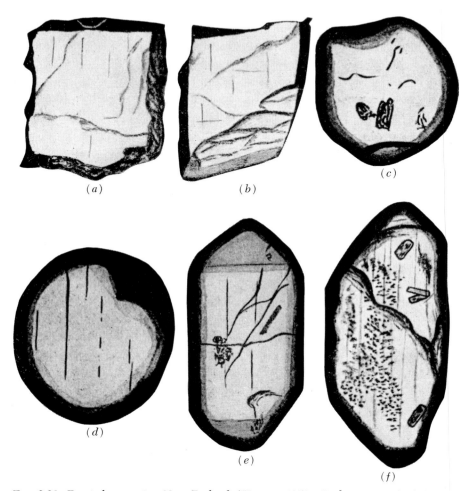

Fig. 2.21. Detrital monazite, New Zealand (Hutton, 1950; *Geol. Soc. Am.*). (*a*), (*b*) (001) cleavage pieces with traces of (100) and (010) cleavages (×480). Blackball Creek dredge. (*c*), (*d*) Rounded (×360). Barrytown. (*e*), (*f*) Euhedral (100) tablet with traces of (010) cleavage. Barrytown (×250); Arau (×150).

its alteration minerals. On Ceylon in weathered pegmatite with zircon, chryso-beryl, and xenotime at Nuwara Eliya, at Nugatenne near Teldeniya, and at Denegama in Balangoda. In the Union of South Africa in the Zoutpansberg district at Houtenbek 392, 70 mi northeast of Pretoria. About ¾ ton has been produced from Muane and Entata in the Libaue-Alto Lingonha district, Mozambique. At Moolyella and Cooglegong (in masses up to 100 lb), Western Australia. In Japan at Ishikawa, Iwaki Province. In Minas Gerais, Brazil, at Conceição, Divino de Uba, Pomba, and Guanhoes Sabinapolis; also in the states of Bahia, Espirito Santo, Paraiba, Rio de Janeiro, São Paulo, and Rio Grande do Norte.

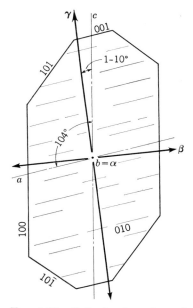

Widespread in Norway, especially in the Iveland district, Arendal, near Moss, Hitterö, and Risör and Tvedestrand. In Sweden at Kårarfvet; at Holma, Bohus; and at Lilla Holma near Stromstad.

3. In Alpine (low-temperature) veins with anatase, especially in those cutting metasedimentary rocks: Binnenthal and Tavetsch, Switzerland. Some Alpine monazites are very low in Th.

4. In various other types of veins. The Steenkampskraal deposit, Van Rhysdorp, Cape Province, Union of South Africa (pages 325–326). Also at Mineral Hill, Lemhi County, Idaho. In Alexander County, N.C., with quartz crystals, rutile crystals, siderite, and abundant muscovite. In a quartz vein with muscovite and rutile at São João da Chapada, Diamantina, Brazil.

FIG. 2.22. Optical orientation of monazite.

In small veins with gold, cutting quartzite at the Kings Bluff mine, Olary, South Australia. In cassiterite veins at Llallagua, Bolivia, very low in thorium (Gordon, 1939). With uraninite, Co-Ni sulfides, molybdenite, and other minerals in hypothermal veins in British Columbia. At Shinkolobwe, Belgian Congo. Doubtless monazite forms over a considerable temperature-pressure range in the hydrothermal environment.

5. In carbonatite and in an associated calcite vein in the Sulphide Queen carbonate body, chiefly in dolomitic parts, Mountain Pass, San Bernardino County, Calif.; likewise at Iron Hill, Powderhorn district, Gunnison County, Colo.

6. As a widespread accessory in various metamorphic rocks including granite gneiss, granulite, charnockite, biotite gneiss, injection gneiss, biotite schist, sericite schist, sillimanite gneiss, kyanite schist, metaconglomerate, and sanidinite. A notable metasomatic(?) type occurs in the Goldfields, Sask., area in migmatite (pages 222–223). A somewhat similar type occurs in associa-

tion with pegmatites in southern India where biotite-rich schists bordering a pegmatite injection zone contain monazite (Davidson, 1949) (pages 222–223).

7. Very common in placers both fluvial and beach, and from these has come the bulk of the world's monazite (pages 494–516). In the United States: Harley area, Blaine County, and Centerville, Boise County, Idaho; the Piedmont of Virginia, North and South Carolina, particularly in Burke, Lincoln, Polk, McDowell, Cleveland, and Rutherford Counties, N.C.; and Laurens, Spartanburg, and Cherokee Counties, S.C. and Ga.; Jacksonville, Fla. In Brazil mainly in Bahia, Rio de Janeiro, and Espirito Santo (beach placers); in Travancore, India; on Ceylon along the west coast; in Indonesia; in Malaya; in Queensland, Australia. Also to a lesser extent in Thailand; Korea; Taiwan; Japan; New Zealand; northwest Spain; Nigeria (with thorite); Belgian Congo; Ural Mts., Pamir Range, Lake Baikal, and Lena and Yenisei Rivers, all in the U.S.S.R.

Also in "fossil" or consolidated placers or in metaconglomerates, notably on Bald Mountain, Big Horn Mts., Wyo., in the base of the Deadwood (Cambrian) formation, and in the Goodrich quartzite, Palmer, Mich.

Identification. Resembles xenotime and bastnaesite. Bastnaesite is uniaxial, with lower minimum and maximum refractive indices. Xenotime also has lower indices but much higher birefringence. Sphene has higher birefringence, much stronger dispersion, and a distinctive habit.

Cheralite

A silico-phosphate of the type ABO_4 with A = Th, rare earths (Ce, La, lesser Pr, Nd, Yt), Ca, and U, minor Fe^3, Al, Pb, and H_2O. B = P, subordinate Si. Essentially an intermediate member of the series: $CePO_4$ (monazite) – $CaTh(PO_4)_2$ (known only as a synthetic compound) (Frondel and Fleischer, 1955). $ThO_2 = 32\%$, $U_3O_8 = 4\%$. Monoclinic. Isostructural with monazite, huttonite, and synthetic $CaTh(PO_4)_2$ (Bowie and Horne, 1953).

Found only in kaolinized pegmatite at Kuttakuzhi, 23 mi east-southeast of Trivandrum, Travancore, India, with schorl, chrysoberyl, zircon, smoky quartz, and monazite; also in the wall rock, a kaolinized granite gneiss (Bowie and Horne, 1953). More strongly radioactive than monazite.

HYDRATED PHOSPHATES

Autunite and Meta-autunite

Composition. $Ca(UO_2)_2(PO_4)_2 \cdot 10–12H_2O$ (autunite). Mg, and Cu in small amounts, may proxy for Ca, and there may be a series to meta-uranocircite with Ba for Ca (Saint-Priest-la-Prugne, Loire, France, and Madagascar). $UO_3 = 58$ to 63%. The amount of hydrogen can be variable, and synthetic hydrogen meta-autunite has been prepared from acid solutions (Ross, 1955). Na also replaces Ca if the mineral (metaform) is subjected to strong brines.

TABLE 2.8. *Properties of the radioactive rare-earth phosphates and zircon*

Mineral	Crystal structure	Color, Streak (S), Luster (L), Fluorescence (F)	Pleochroism	Indices and orientation	Cleavage and fracture	H	G
Monazite	Monoclinic	Yellow, yellow brown, red brown, greenish, yellow, pale brown. L waxy, vitreous	α = light yellow β = dark yellow γ = greenish yellow	$\alpha = b = 1.785$–1.800 $\beta = 1.787$–1.801 $\gamma = 1.837$–1.849 increasing with Th and Si. (+) 2V = 6–19°. $\gamma \wedge c = 1$–$10°$. r < v, r > v weak	(001) perfect. (100) distinct. (010) poor. Conchoidal to uneven fracture	5–5.5	4.6–5.47 incr. with Th
Cheralite	Monoclinic	Green. S white. L resinous to vitreous	$\alpha = \beta$ = green γ = yellow green	$\alpha = b = 1.779$ $\beta = 1.780$ $\gamma = 1.816$ (+) 2V = 18°. $\gamma \wedge c = 7°$	(010) distinct. Uneven fracture	5	5.28
Xenotime (pp. 131–132)	Tetragonal	Yellow brown, red brown, pink, yellow. S colorless, pale yellow, pink, or pale brown. L vitreous to resinous. F absent or orange yellow (Tb)	ω = rose, buff, pale yellow ϵ = yellow, gray brown, pale yellow green	$\omega = 1.720$–1.724 $\epsilon = 1.816$–1.828 (+)	(110) fair. Fracture uneven	4–5	4.45–5.11
Zircon (pp. 134–139)	Tetragonal. May be metamict in whole or part	Colorless, pale yellow, pink, red, purple, blue, green, gray, red brown. Markedly radioactive types usually dark colored. S colorless, yellow, red, brown. L adamantine, resinous, dull upon alteration. F common in yellow, green	None	$\omega = 1.920$–1.960 $\epsilon = 1.967$–2.015 (+). Also biaxial (+), 2V = 10°. Metamict types are isotropic with $n = 1.82$–1.84. $\omega - \epsilon$ 0.01–0.02	(110) and (111) imperfect. Conchoidal fracture	7.5, 6–3 with alteration	4.6–4.7; 4.1–3.6 with alteration

79

Structure and form.

Autunite	Meta-I $(6\frac{1}{2}-2\frac{1}{2}H_2O)$ (natural)	Meta-II $(6-0H_2O)$ (synthetic)
Tetragonal; usually anomalously biaxial	Tetragonal; usually anomalously biaxial. Formed by drying in a warm, dry atmosphere; can be rehydrated to autunite	Orthorhombic; formed by heating meta-I to about 80 °C; reaction not reversible

Occurrence. A widespread secondary mineral formed under weathering and oxidizing conditions chiefly in (1) uraniferous phosphatic pegmatites, (2) pitchblende veins and lodes, and (3) oxidized Colorado Plateau types of deposits where V is absent or minor and PO_4 is available from leached igneous rocks or fossil bone. Among pegmatitic occurrences of note are the Ruggles mine, Grafton Center, N.H.; Bedford, N.Y.; various pegmatites in the Spruce Pine district, N.C.; Bob Ingersoll pegmatite, Black Hills, S.Dak.; Hagendorf, Zwiesel, and Pleystein, Bavaria, Germany. Significant occurrences in oxidized pitchblende veins or lodes include Saint-Symphorien, La Troche and other deposits near Autun, Saône-et-Loire, and in other deposits of the Massif Central, France, including Deux-Sèvres (Vendée), Lauchaux region (Puy-de-Dôme), Saint-Priest-la-Prugne and Les Bois Noirs (Loire), as well as deposits in Creuse, Aveyron, Haute-Loire, Loire-Inferieure, Haut-Rhin, and Vosges; Sabugal and Frogos, Portugal; Annaberg, Zschorlau, Gottesberg, Lauter, Schneeberg, Sosa, Rockelmann, Schwarzeberg, Johanngeorgenstadt, and Falkenstein (Saxony), Henneberg (Thuringia), Ottofelsen (Harz Mts.), Reichenbach, Lengenfeld, Rothenbach, Schreiersgrün, Klingenthal, and Bergen (Vogtland), Wölsendorf (Bavaria), all in Germany; Koralps, Styria; Streltscha and Bukhovo, Bulgaria; several localities (some seven are recorded) in Cornwall, England; Roccaforte di Mondovi, Cuneo-Lurisia district, Italy; Katanga district, Belgian Congo; Mt. Painter and Edith River (meta-I), Australia; Lander County, Nev., with metatorbernite; near Mt. Spokane, Wash., as crystals exceptional in size and quality at an argillite-granite contact (Fig. 15.1); Marysvale, Utah; Boulder area, Mont.; White Signal district, N.Mex., in diabase; Martha E. mine, Front Range, Colo.; W. Wilson mine, Clancy, Mont. (meta-I).

Deposits of disseminated autunite chiefly in sandstones are represented by Lawrence County, S.Dak., in the Deadwood formation (Cambrian); also sparse in rocks of the Inyan Kara group (Lower Cretaceous), Fall River County, S.Dak.; in the Wind River formation (Eocene) of the Gas Hills area of Fremont and Natrona Counties, Wyo. (meta-I), associated with uranospinite; in Tertiary conglomerate, Tallahassee Creek, Fremont County, Colo.; Soledad district, Rosamond, Kern County, the Harvard Hills near Barstow, San Bernardino County, and Buckhorn claims, Lassen County, Calif. (in tuff); and in Karnes County, Tex., in the Jackson formation (Eocene). On the Colorado Plateau: Wild Horse claims, Temple Mt.; Bonnie Bell claims, Jensen, Uintah County, Utah; Thom claim, Grand County, Utah; Poison

Spring Canyon, Garfield County, Utah (meta-I); Jack claim, Navajo County, Ariz. (meta-I); Poison Canyon, Grants, N.Mex.; and Desanti mine, Gallup, N.Mex. With phosphuranylite in sandstone and conglomerate (Athabasca Series) at Middle Lake, Sask.

Autunite also occurs disseminated or along fractures in altered granitic rocks, as for example at the Miracle mine, Kern Canyon, and at the Rafferty property, Los Angeles County, Calif., and at Fairmount, Philadelphia County, Pa.; in fissures in granite at Oberbadenweiler and Wittichen, Baden, Germany; and at Filfila, near Philippeville, Algeria.

Identification. The combination of habit, color, and strong fluorescence is characteristic. Uranocircite yields a test for Ba. Strongest x-ray lines: (autunite) 10.33, 4.96, 3.59, 3.49; (meta-I) 8.51, 3.50, 3.63, 3.24. Not brittle.

Sodium Autunite

$(Na,Ca)(UO_2)_2(PO_4)_2 \cdot 6\frac{1}{2}-8H_2O$. $UO_3 = 62\%$. Soluble in acids. Occurs in granodiorite in the U.S.S.R. (Melkov, 1956; Chernikov et al., 1957; Fleischer, 1958). Well-known synthetically (Fairchild, 1929). Strongest x-ray powder lines are 3.67, 2.675, 1.566, 1.540.

Torbernite and Metatorbernite

Composition. $Cu(UO_2)_2(PO_4)_2 \cdot 8-12H_2O$ (torbernite). $Cu(UO_2)_2(PO_4)_2 \cdot 8H_2O$ (metatorbernite). $UO_3 = 57$ to 61%. As may substitute for P, usually in small amounts; however, varieties intermediate between metatorbernite and metazeunerite have been reported (Killen and Ordway, 1955). Pb substitutes in minor amounts for Cu. Minor to trace amounts of Na, Ba, Ca, Mg, Mn, Mo, Te, Fe, and Si have been detected. Chalcolite and uran-mica are synonyms. Parallel growths are common with autunite; they also occur with zeunerite, bassetite, and uranospinite. Enclosed autunite is commonly octagonal in outline, whereas the enclosing torbernite or metatorbernite is square or rectangular. Anomalous fluorescence is due to parallel intergrown autunite (Meixner, 1940B,C; Lyon, 1956) (Fig. 2.23*a*).

Occurrence. Both are common and widespread secondary oxidation products in uraniferous pegmatites and in a variety of pitchblende veins and lodes, especially in gossans of such veins that also contain copper sulfides. Metatorbernite probably more abundant. Most probably formed by supergene solutions, but in some deposits these minerals may be hypogene. Some pegmatite occurrences are Haddam Neck, Conn.; in some other New England pegmatites; Hallifield mine, Mitchell County, N.C.; with meta-autunite at the Moye pegmatite, Barnesville, Lamar County, Ga.; and in a few Black Hills pegmatites. Other United States deposits of note are: on the Colorado Plateau (Weeks and Thompson, 1954) in sandstones with metazeunerite, chalcanthite, alunite, chalcopyrite, and pyrite at Markey No. 3 and W. N. mines, White Canyon district; Black King No. 5 claim, Placerville area; Grey Dawn mine, Paradox district; Skyline mine, Monument Valley district; Mineral Ten claim, Green River district; Temple Mountain and Flat Top Mesa, San Rafael Swell; Hack Canyon mine, Mohave County, Ariz. Also in Idaho in several sulfide-quartz veins in the North Fork-Shoup district. At the Silver Cliff mine, Lusk,

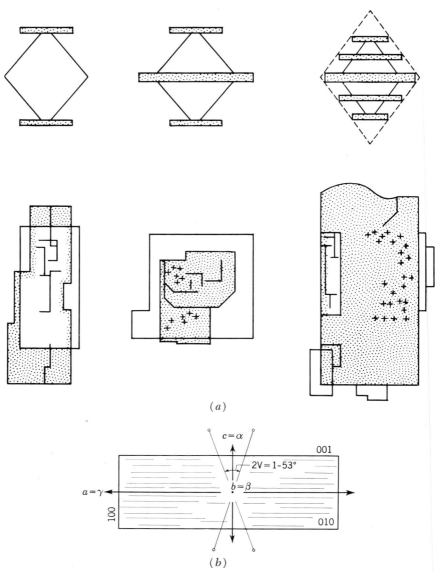

FIG. 2.23. (*a*) *Top*, tablets of torbernite (clear) with overgrown and intergrown plates of autunite (stippled), Lachaux, Puy-de-Dôme, France (Chervet and Branche, 1955). *Bottom*, composite torbernite (clear) and autunite (stippled) cleavage flakes, 0.1 to 0.2 mm across and 0.005 to 0.015 mm thick. Crosses are crystallites of a brown unidentified species (Lyon, 1956; *Am. Mineralogist*). (*b*) Optical orientation of autunite.

Wyo., with uranophane. In New Mexico, in the White Signal district near Silver City, and in the San Lorenzo district, Socorro County. In Colorado: disseminated in granite near Climax, and in granite and schist near St. Kevin, both in Lake County; in veins and impregnations in wall-rock gneiss and amphibolite in the Eureka Gulch area, Central City district, Gilpin County; in fluorite veins in the Jamestown district, Boulder County; and seven mines in the Central City district (metatorbernite at the Two Sisters and RHD mines). At Majuba Hill, Nev., in a rhyolite plug in a Cu-Sn vein, and also in Nevada at the West Willys No. 7 deposit in the East Walker River area in quartz veins in granite (Staatz and Bauer, 1953). At the W. Wilson mine near Clancy, Mont. In California in quartz veins at the Perry Jones claims, Plumas County. Reported from a cassiterite greisen at the Turner Tin prospect, Lake Ramsay, New Ross, Nova Scotia.

Widespread in the Erzgebirge, at Breitenbrunn, Neustädtel, Oberschlema, Schneeberg, Johanngeorgenstadt, Joachimsthal, Zinnwald, Schönficht, Schlaggenwald, Aue, Klingenthal, and Auerbach in Vogtland; Marienbad, St. Viti Zeche; Wölsendorf, Bavaria; Henneberg, Leopoldsdorf, and Rudolfstein in

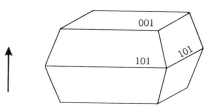

Fig. 2.24. Torbernite crystal of simple habit.

the Fichtelgebirge; and in the Michael vein, Weiler, near Geroldseck and at Bühlhof, Hinterhambachertal, Baden. At many localities in France, for example, Chanteloube; La Faye, Grury, Saône-et-Loire; at Lachaux, Bigay, Rophin mine, and Saint-Rémy-sur-Durolle in Puy-de-Dôme; at Les Bois Noirs, Loire; in Vendée at Deux Sèvres; in Aveyron; in Lozère and elsewhere. In Belgium at Vielsalm. Found in fine specimens at many localities (some 24 are recorded) in the Cornwall area, England: Wheal Basset, Bottalack, Carn Brea mines, Old Gunnislake mine, Wheal Owles, Wheal James, Stennagwyn, and Ting Tang. In Portugal near Sabugal and Viseu; at Frogos; and at Vizea, Beira Alta. In Spain reported in granite at Trasquilón, 9 km south of Cáceres, central Estremadura (Webel, 1955; anomalously fluorescent—probably intergrown with autunite); and at Mina Flor de El Espinas, San Rafael. In Bulgaria an ore mineral at Goten, near Bukhova, 20 km north of Sofia.

Abundant and an ore mineral at Shinkolobwe and elsewhere in the Katanga district, Belgian Congo. In South Australia, at Mt. Painter and in Queensland at the Pine Log mine, Bakerville. In Brazil at Moeda, Minas Gerais.

Identification. Color, crystal form, test for Cu, absence of As and of fluorescence. Torbernite has lower indices and lower specific gravity than metatorbernite, which also is (+). More brittle than autunite.

Meta-uranocircite

Composition. $Ba(UO_2)_2(PO_4)_2 \cdot 8H_2O$. The higher hydrate (uranocircite), with $8-12H_2O$, is stable only in a moist environment and apparently does not normally persist in nature. Meta-uranocircite soaked in H_2O loses moisture rapidly, even in immersion oils (Nuffield and Milne, 1953). $UO_3 = 56$ to 57%.

Ca may substitute for Ba (George, 1949), and a series probably exists to meta-autunite. Parallel growths with torbernite and autunite.

Occurrence. As a secondary mineral in pitchblende veins, in their oxidized zones, the Ba presumably from barite. Such occurrences are in the Erzgebirge at Bergen (Falkenstein) a.d. Trieb, Ölsnitz, Schneeberg, Reichenbach, Kirchberg, Streitberg, Lauter b. Aue, Riesenberg b. Eibenstock; also in Bavaria at Brensdorf, Wölsendorf, Wittichen, and Reinerzau (Bültemann, 1954). In France at Le Batou and Outeloup in Saône-et-Loire; at La Crouzille, Haute-Vienne; at Saint-Priest-la-Prugne, Loire; and in the Entraygues region, Aveyron (Pulou, 1957). Reported at Rosmaneira, Portugal; at Srdnia Gora in the Hungarian Banat; at Strelca, Bulgaria (Meixner, 1940B); and at the W. Wilson mine, Clancy, Mont.

On Madagascar in peat, clay, and sand in a lacustrine deposit at Vinaninkarena. In the United States in a channel sandstone of the Chadron formation of Oligocene age in the White River Badlands of Pennington County, S.Dak., associated with barite and apatite (Moore and Levish, 1955).

Identification. Gives test for Ba and has higher indices than autunite. Brittle.

Saléeite

Composition. $Mg(UO_2)_2(PO_4)_2 \cdot 8-10H_2O$, the phosphatic end member of the saléeite-novacekite series (PO_4-AsO_4). Some As usually is present and the break in the series is at P:As = 1:1. UO_3 = 60 to 64%. Small amounts of Pb and Al substitute for Mg (Frondel, 1951B).

Occurrence. In oxidized pitchblende deposits in the zone of weathering, if arsenides of Co, Ni, and Fe occur in the ore. The original discovery was made at the Shinkolobwe mine, Belgian Congo (Thoreau and Vaes, 1932) in siliceous rock associated with torbernite and dewindtite. At Schneeberg, Saxony, in limonitic vein material with zeunerite and uranophane (Mrose, 1950). At Plessis près de Mortagne (Deux-Sèvres), France, with autunite and limonite. At the Mina da Quarta Seira, Sabugal, Beira Province, Portugal, in weathered granite or fine-grained pegmatite thickly incrusted with meta-autunite, sabugalite, and minor phosphuranylite (Frondel, 1951B). At Dyson's deposit, Rum Jungle, Northern Territory, Australia.

Identification. X-ray pattern like that of novacekite, which has higher refractive indices. Also resembles autunite, and a test for Mg is required. Strongest x-ray lines: 9.85, 3.49, 4.95.

Sabugalite

Composition. $HAl(UO_2)_4(PO_4)_4 \cdot 16H_2O$ (Frondel, 1951A). UO_3 = 65%. Some AsO_4 replaces PO_4. Traces of Fe and Ca may be present. Between 68 and 101°C changes nonreversibly to a form isostructural with the artificial meta-autunite II; the equivalent of the intermediate meta-autunite I does not form.

Occurrence. In Portugal: (1) Mina da Quarta Seira, Sabugal, Beira Province, on brecciated quartz-feldspar pegmatite with meta-autunite, saléeite, and phosphuranylite; (2) at Kariz in Minho Province (arsenatian) on brecciated milky quartz–kaolinized feldspar pegmatite and mixed with and underlain by

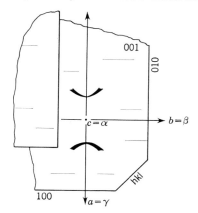

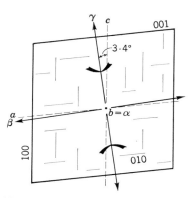

Fig. 2.25. Optical orientation of sabugalite (adapted from Guillemin and Pierrot, 1956B).

Fig. 2.26. Optical orientation of bassetite (adapted from Chervet and Branche, 1955).

meta-autunite; (3) at Bendada, Beira Province, as a thin coating mixed with meta-autunite and perhaps saléeite on limonitic quartz vein material (Frondel, 1951A). A supergene secondary mineral. Reported from the Happy Jack mine, White Canyon, Utah (Gruner and Gardiner, 1952). Found at the La Crouzille and Margnac II deposit, Haute-Vienne, France (Guillemin and Pierrot, 1956B), and also at Le Poitou, Le Plessis, Savenay (Deux-Sèvres) (Chervet and Branche, 1955). In Morocco at Midelt. Also occurs at the Tusas Mt. prospect, Rio Arriba County, N.Mex., with uraninite, metatorbernite, pyrite, quartz, and fluorite in mica schist zenoliths (Precambrian Hopewell series) enclosed in Tusas granite. With metatorbernite and other uranyl minerals at the Huskin mines in the Chinle formation, near Cameron, Ariz.

Identification. Autunite has slightly lower indices and strong dispersion and yields a test for Ca. Slightly flexible.

Bassetite

Composition. $Fe(UO_2)_2(PO_4)_2 \cdot 8H_2O$. The Fe^2 member of the torbernite group (Frondel, 1954). Soluble in acids. In part in oriented intergrowths with torbernite and uranospathite.

Occurrence. In the oxidized sections of pitchblende deposits; rare. Found at Wheal Basset and Huel Basset, Cornwall (Frondel, 1954) with uranospathite. Also at La Crouzille and Les Sagnes (Haute-Vienne), France, with autunite; and at Orb mine, Herault, France. At the Denise No. 1 mine, Green River district, Utah, in sandstone. With pitchblende, metatyuyamunite, meta-autunite, metatorbernite, and sulfides in or near carbonaceous slates associated with soft-iron ores in northern Michigan (Vickers, 1956D) (page 553).

Identification. Resembles autunite but is nonfluorescent. A test for Fe is required. Strongest x-ray lines: 4.89, 3.46, 8.59, 2.20.

TABLE 2.9. *Properties of the uranyl phosphates (except phosphuranylite and Pb-bearing species)*

Mineral	Form	Color, Streak (S), Luster (L), Fluorescence (F)	Pleochroism	Indices and orientation	Cleavage and fracture	H	G
Autunite	Tetragonal. (001) tablets in crusts. Some (110) twinning	Yellow, yellow green to pale green (with Cu). S yellowish. L vitreous, pearly (001). F strong yellow green	α (or ϵ) = colorless to pale yellow; $\beta = \gamma$ (or ω) = yellow to dark yellow	α (or ϵ) = 1.552–1.577; β = 1.575–1.598; γ (or ω) = c = 1.577–1.608. Indices increase with Cu and with decreasing H_2O. Usually biaxial (−), 2V = 53–1° decreasing with decreasing H_2O. r > v strong. Also biaxial (−). May show abnormal interference colors	(001) perfect. (100) indistinct	2–2.5	3.1–3.2
Meta-autunite I	Tetragonal. (001) tablets in crusts. Some (110) twinning	Yellow, yellow green to pale green (with Cu). S yellowish. L vitreous, pearly (001). F weaker yellow green	α (or ϵ) = colorless to pale yellow; $\beta = \gamma$ (or ω) = yellow to dark yellow	α (or ϵ) = 1.585–1.600; β = 1.595–1.610; γ (or ω) = 1.595–1.613. Usually biaxial (−). Plates divided into 4 diagonal sectors with optic plane parallel to bordering prism face. Also uniaxial (−). Indices increase with decreasing H_2O	(001) perfect. (100) indistinct	2–2.5	Slightly higher

Mineral	Habit	Color / Luster	Pleochroism	Optical properties	Cleavage	H	G
Sodium autunite	Tetragonal. Plates in radiating and foliated masses	Lemon yellow L pearly (001), otherwise vitreous. F strong yellow green	Weak ω = light yellow ε = pale yellow	ω = 1.578 ε = 1.559 (−). With dehydration ω = 1.585 ε = 1.564	(001) perfect. (100) less perfect	2–2.5	3.584, 3.89 (calc. for 8H_2O)
Torbernite	Tetragonal. (001) tablets of square, rectangular or octagonal shape. In sheafs or rosettes of curved plates. Rare (110) twins	Pale to dark green. S light green. L vitreous, pearly (001)	ω = sky blue ε = green	ω = 1.592 ε = 1.580–1.582 (−) r > v very strong. Abnormal interference tints. Indices increase with decreasing H_2O	(001) perfect. (100) poor	2.5	3.2
Metatorbernite				ω = 1.624–1.630 ε = 1.626–1.632 (+) r > v extreme. Abnormal interference tints. Indices increase with decreasing H_2O. Rarely biaxial. 2V = small-30°		2.5	3.5–3.7
Meta-uranocircite	Tetragonal. Thin to thick (001) plates, square, rectangular, octagonal shape. Foliated masses. "Microcline type" twinning common, (010), (100)	Yellow to yellow green. S pale greenish yellow. L pearly (001). F vivid yellow green	Weak α = nearly colorless β = γ = pale yellow	α = c = 1.606–1.610 β = 1.618–1.623 γ = 1.620–1.623 Usually biaxial (−). May be uniaxial (−). 2V = 0-27°. Indices decrease with Ca for Ba. Twin extinction = 6–45° from twin planes, increasing with Ca for Ba	(001) perfect. (100) good	2–3	3.56, 4.08

TABLE 2.9. *Properties of the uranyl phosphates (except phosphuranylite and Pb-bearing species (Continued)*

Mineral	Form	Color, Streak (S), Luster (L), Fluorescence (F)	Pleochroism	Indices and orientation	Cleavage and fracture	H	G
Saléeite	Tetragonal. Small thin (001) rectangular plates. In interlocking or subparallel aggregates	Lemon to greenish yellow. S pale yellow. L pearly. F bright yellow (long wave) to pale yellow or yellow green (short wave)	α (or ϵ) = nearly colorless $\beta = \gamma$ (or ω) = pale yellow to pale greenish yellow	α (or ϵ) = 1.554–1.565 β = 1.570–1.582 γ (or ω) = 1.571–1.585 Indices increase with As/P ratio, and with decreasing H_2O. Uniaxial or biaxial (−). $2V = 0$–65°, r > v marked. Plates may be split into 2–4 sections with optic planes normal to each other and parallel with plate edges	(001) perfect. (010), (110) indistinct	2.5	3.27

Sabugalite	Tetragonal. Crusts of thin (001) plates of square or rectangular outline. Warped faces and subparallel growths common	Bright yellow. F bright yellow (air-dried material) (both short and long wave)	α (or ϵ) = colorless β = γ (or ω) = pale yellow	α (or ω) = c = 1.564-1.567 β = b = 1.581-1.583 γ (or ϵ) = a = 1.582-1.584. Indices decrease with H_2O. Usually biaxial (−). Rarely uniaxial (−). 2V = 0-40°. Some plates with uniaxial cores and biaxial margins	(001) perfect. (100) poor	2.5	3.20
Bassetite	Monoclinic. Pseudotetragonal. Thin (010) tablets nearly rectangular in fans or checkerboard groups. Aggregates of laths elongated with c. Commonly twinned with units at 90° having (010) in common	Yellow, bronze. S colorless. L vitreous	α = pale yellow β = γ = deep yellow	α = b = 1.56 β = 1.574 γ = 1.580 (−) 2V = 52-62°. $\gamma \wedge c$ = 3-4°. Upon air drying, α = 1.603, β = 1.610, γ = 1.617. 2V = about 90°, $\gamma \wedge c$ = 16-40°, plates subdivide into 4 sectors with axial planes $\perp$ to each other	(010) perfect. (100), (001) distinct. Conchoidal fracture	2-2.5	3.08-3.4

Phosphuranylite

Composition. $Ca(UO_2)_4(PO_4)_2(OH)_4 \cdot 9H_2O$, or less probably $Ca(UO_2)_6$ $(PO_4)_4(OH)_2 \cdot 10H_2O$ (Hogarth and Nuffield, 1954). UO_3 = 73 to 79%. Material is usually rather impure; commonly argillaceous. The H_2O content may be somewhat variable. The formula proposed by Bignand et al. (1954) is $Ca(UO_2)_4(PO_4)_2(OH)_4 \cdot 2H_2O$. There is a complete series between phosphuranylite and renardite (Ca–Pb).

Occurrence. A rather widely distributed secondary uranium phosphate formed under supergene conditions in uraniferous pegmatites, pitchblende veins, and Colorado Plateau type of deposits. In pegmatites, where apatite contributes PO_4 and Ca, the mineral coats irregular fractures in quartz and feldspar near altered uraninite or fills cubic molds of uraninite crystals. It may replace meta-autunite but usually is formed before that species. In pitchblende veins it may be pseudomorphous after autunite, forming in place of renardite, if the deposits are Pb-poor. In Colorado Plateau deposits the Ca and PO_4 may have been contributed originally by fossil bone. Localities in the United States include:

1. Pegmatitic (Frondel, 1950B): Flat Rock mine, Spruce Pine district, N.C., with meta-autunite; Newry, Oxford County, Maine; Ruggles mine, Grafton Center, N.H., with meta-autunite and parsonite; Palermo mine, North Groton, N.H., with meta-autunite and gummite; Branchville, Conn. (plumbian); Bedford, N.Y.; Malakialina, Madagascar (in gummite).

2. Colorado Plateau deposits (Weeks and Thompson, 1954): North Point–Gonway claim and Posey mine, White Canyon district; Cobalt No. 2 and Cactus Rat mines, Thompsons district; Delta group and Wild Horse claims, San Rafael Swell; Grey Dawn mine, Paradox district; Mineral Ten claim, Green River district; Lucky Mc mine, Fremont County, Wyo. Similarly in sandstone and conglomerate (Athabasca Series) at Middle Lake, Sask., with autunite.

3. Altered vein deposits: J. and L. alunite mine near Marysvale, Utah.

In South America: Pamplonita, Norte de Santander, Colombia (pegmatite); Memoes, near Equador, Rio Grande do Norte, Brazil. At Wölsendorf, Bavaria. In Portugal, Carrasca mine and Rosmaneira at Sabugal (in granite?); Urgeirica at Cannas de Senhorim (plumbian) and Frogos. In France at Ambazac, La Crouzille, Margnac II, and Brugeaud mine in Haute-Vienne; at Broailles in Saône-et-Loire, and at Herbiers and La Gorandière in Vendée. On Madagascar in veinlets in clay at Vatovory, Vinaninkarena (Bignand et al., 1954). In North Africa at Midelt (Morocco) with autunite, uranocircite, and sabugalite and at Adrar des Iforas (Hoggar) with autunite. Synthesized under alkaline conditions (Ross, 1956).

Identification. Requires x-ray. Strongest lines: 7.83, 3.97, 5.83.

Renardite

Composition. $Pb(UO_2)_4(PO_4)_2(OH)_4 \cdot 7H_2O$. UO_3 = 68 to 73%. The water content is probably variable. Bignand et al. (1954) list $2H_2O$ as does Bignand (1955) for synthetic material. There is apparently a complete series with phosphuranylite, and also Ba may replace Pb. Bignand et al. (1954) state that dewindtite is renardite on the basis of a "dewindtite" pattern on Wölsendorf material being identical with that of renardite, but this material may actually be renardite. It remains to be shown that type dewindtite is renardite. Nevertheless the two species need clarification, as both are reportedly isostructural with phosphuranylite.

Occurrence. A rare secondary mineral of supergene origin where Pb (either from galena or radiogenic?) and PO_4 (from apatite or autunite) are available. Occurs at the Kasolo mine, Katanga, Belgian Congo, with torbernite, dewindtite, and autunite. In France at Bauzot with autunite, uranophane, and purple fluorite; at Reliez, Bigay, with torbernite, at Saint-Rémy-sur-Durolles with torbernite, and at several other deposits in Puy-de-Dôme; at La Crouzille, Haute-Vienne, with pitchblende and uranophane; at La Faye, Grury, Saône-et-Loire, with torbernite, autunite, and kasolite usually near altered galena and earthy pitchblende; at Les Bois Noirs and Limouzat, Loire; and at Les Herbiers, Vendée. As an alteration of uraninite in a pegmatite at Grabo, Ivory Coast. In pitchblende nodules at Bemasoandro, Madagascar. May be pseudomorphous after autunite.

Identification. Tests for Pb and PO_4 are desirable. Higher indices than phosphuranylite. Strongest x-ray lines: 7.97, 3.99, 5.83.

Parsonite

Composition. $Pb_2(UO_2)(PO_4)_2 \cdot 2H_2O$. UO_3 = 31 to 34%. Some variation in H_2O. Anhydrous material synthesized by Bignand (1955). Traces of As may be present.

Occurrence. Originally found at Kasolo, Belgian Congo, with torbernite, kasolite, and dewindtite. On uranocircite at Wölsendorf, Bavaria, with purple

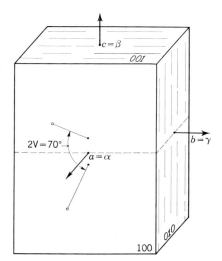

Fɪɢ. 2.27. Optical orientation of renardite (adapted from Chervet and Branche, 1955).

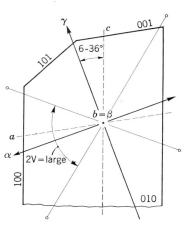

Fɪɢ. 2.28. Optical orientation of parsonite from Belgian Congo.

TABLE 2.10. *Properties of phosphuranylite and the Pb-uranyl phosphate minerals*

Minerals	Form	Color, Streak (S), Luster (L), Fluorescence (F)	Pleochroism	Indices and orientation	Cleavage and fracture	H	G
Phosphuranylite	Orthorhombic. Thin crusts of scales and laths, rectangular to irregular in shape. Some may be tetragonal	Golden yellow. S yellow. L pearly. F none or orange brown	α (or ϵ) = colorless to pale yellow β = yellow γ (or ω) = golden yellow	α (or ϵ) = a = 1.658–1.695 β = b = 1.696–1.77 γ (or ω) = c = 1.698–1.77 Indices increase with Pb. Usually biaxial (−). 2V = 5–51°, usually <20°. Rarely uniaxial (−)	(001) perfect	3	4.05–4.14
Renardite	Orthorhombic. Rectangular (100) plates; acicular with c or a. Fibrous radial aggregates, drusy crusts	Golden yellow to brown. S pale yellow. L vitreous to adamantine. F brownish green	α = colorless β = γ = yellow	α = a = 1.715–1.716 β = c = 1.736 γ = b = 1.739–1.740 (−) 2V = 70°, r > v. Indices decrease with Ca	(100) perfect	3.5	4.35
Parsonite	Monoclinic. Tabular (010) laths elongated with c, terminated by (001), (101) faces curved. Spicular to tufted crusts and fibrous radial groups	Citron yellow, brownish green, also rose or colorless but brown owing to dense inclusions. S pale yellow. L greasy to adamantine. Crystals transparent at terminations to translucent at base	None	α = 1.84–1.87 β = b γ = 1.86–1.89 Indices decrease with hydration(?) to α = 1.795, γ = 1.815. (−), 2V large. Strong dispersion. $\gamma \wedge c$ = 6–36°, also reported $\alpha \wedge c$ = 6–36°. Lower ends of crystals may have lower indices	(010) difficult. Conchoidal fracture	3	5.37–5.75. 6.29 (anhydrous)
Dumontite	Orthorhombic. Prismatic with c, flattened (010)	Yellow. S light yellow. F yellow green	Strong α = pale yellow β = yellow γ = deep yellow	α = a = 1.88 β = c = 1.89 γ = b = 1.90 (est.) (+), 2V = large. r < v			

92

fluorite and limonitic quartz crystals. In the Ruggles pegmatite, Grafton, N.H., along fractures in quartz and feldspar near uraninite and gummite, associated with phosphuranylite and autunite. In France at Lachaux, Puy-de-Dôme, in the Rophin, Reliez, Bancherelle, Gourniaud, Gagnols, Bigay, and Les Peux deposits; as an ore mineral in cavities in siliceous breccia rich in opal accompanied by later pyromorphite and cerrusite and earlier torbernite (Branche et al., 1951). Also at the La Faye deposit, Grury, Saône-et-Loire, France, with earlier renardite and later torbernite; and at Les Bois Noirs and Gadaillère deposits, Loire. At Midelt, Morocco, and at Boko Songho, French Equatorial Africa.

Identification. Distinguished from other Pb-U phosphates: (1) dumontite fluoresces yellow green; (2) dewindtite fluoresces orange brown; (3) renardite fluoresces brownish green. Strongest x-ray lines: 4.25, 3.28, 2.13.

Dumontite

$Pb_2(UO_2)_3(PO_4)_2(OH)_4 \cdot 3H_2O$. $UO_3 = 56\%$. Very rare, supergene. Known from Shinkolobwe, Belgian Congo, filling cavities in torbernite masses. Reported from the White Oak mine, Nogales, Ariz., with kasolite, uranophane, and autunite (Nininger, 1954). Has higher indices than renardite. Strongest x-ray lines: 4.29, 3.02, 3.75.

Doubtful or Poorly Defined Species

Dewindtite

Suggested as either $Pb_3(UO_2)_6(PO_4)_4(OH)_6 \cdot 10H_2O$ or $Pb_2(UO_2)_4(PO_4)_3\text{-}OH_3 \cdot 7H_2O$ (Hogarth and Nuffield, 1954). $UO_3 = 54$ to 56%. Orthorhombic (pseudotetragonal). Microscopic rectangular tablets flattened (100) and terminated by (001). Striated parallel with *c*. Interlayered with metatorbernite. Also powdery masses. Canary yellow. Yellow streak. Weakly pleochroic. Biaxial (+), 2V = large, r > v extreme. $\alpha = b = 1.762$, $\beta = c = 1.763$, $\gamma = a = 1.765$

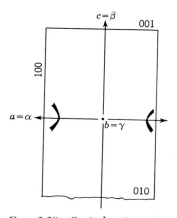
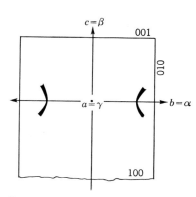

FIG. 2.29. Optical orientation of dumontite.

FIG. 2.30. Optical orientation of dewindtite.

(Fig. 2.30). Fluoresces orange brown (Bültemann, 1954); very weak yellow brown to (?) medium yellow green (Horne, 1951). (100) cleavage. G = 5.03. A rare secondary supergene mineral. Known certainly at Kasolo, Katanga, Belgian Congo; Wölsendorf, Bavaria (some = renardite?). Reported at the Green Monster mine, Clark County, Nev.

Validity questionable. X-ray data show it to be isostructural with renardite but chemical analysis implies a chemically distinct phase. Attempts at synthesis by Ross (1956) yield Pb-autunite and renardite in equilibrium at the composition attributed to dewindtite.

Fritzcheite

$Mn(UO_2)_2[(P,V)O_4]_2 8H_2O(?)$. Supposedly the Mn analog of torbernite. Basal (001) plates, with rectangular outline. Perfect (001) cleavage. Vitreous to pearly luster. Reddish brown. H = 2 to 3. G = 3.50(?). A synthetic Mn-autunite (Fairchild, 1929) consisted of plates of mosaic structure, some parts isotropic, others weakly birefringent. Some plates were biaxial with moderately high birefringence; some showed abnormal blue interference tints. Twinning on (110) common. $\omega = 1.60$, ranging from 1.598 to 1.601.

Reported from a hematite mine at Neuhammer, near Neudeck, Bohemia, with autunite and torbernite; at Johanngeorgenstadt and Steinig, Saxony; and at Autun, France. Needs a complete new study.

Lermontovite

$(U,Ca,RE)_3(PO_4)_4 \cdot 6H_2O(?)$ (Melkov, 1956; Soboleva and Pudovkina, 1957; Getseva and Savel'eva, 1956; Fleischer, 1958). Radial fibers in botryoidal aggregates. Gray green. Luster dull to silky. Pleochroic in green and green brown. Indices variable, even in single sample. $\alpha = 1.562$ to 1.574, $\gamma = 1.702$ to 1.726. Parallel extinction. Very brittle. G = 4.50. Occurs in the U.S.S.R. in hydrothermal deposits in the zone of cementation under reducing conditions.

Przhevalskite

$Pb(UO_2)_2(PO_4)_2 \cdot 2H_2O(?)$ (Melkov, 1956; Soboleva and Pudovkina, 1957; Getseva and Savel'eva, 1956; Fleischer, 1958). Soluble in acid. Orthorhombic. Foliated aggregates of minute tabular crystals. Bright yellow with greenish tint. Luster adamantine, vitreous. $\alpha = 1.739$ (colorless), $\beta = 1.749$ to 1.750 (pale yellow), $\gamma = 1.752$ to 1.753 (deep yellow) $(-)$, 2V = about 30°. A rare supergene species in oxidized zone of pitchblende-sulfide deposit of the U.S.S.R. with Fe and Mn oxides, metahalloysite, autunite, torbernite, dumontite, renardite, uranophane, and wulfenite. Strongest x-ray lines: 3.61, 9.08, 1.62, 1.53.

ARSENATES

Metazeunerite and Zeunerite

Composition. $Cu(UO_2)_2(AsO_4)_2 \cdot 8H_2O$. The name zeunerite, originally given to the species represented by the above composition, has been changed to metazeunerite after x-ray and dehydration studies indicated that the natural mineral corresponded in water content and structure to the meta-I lower hydrate of autunite, in most cases. Synthetic zeunerite exists in two and possibly three hydrates: one with $16-10H_2O$; one with $8-5H_2O$, corresponding to natural metazeunerite (Guillemin, 1956); and possibly a still lower hydrate with $2\frac{1}{2}H_2O(?)$ (Frondel, J., 1951). In these respects the mineral resembles both autunite and torbernite. Fully hydrated natural zeunerite has been found by Berman (1957B) in material from the original Saxony locality. $UO_3 = 56\%$. P substitutes for As, and a variety intermediate between metazeunerite and torbernite has been reported (Killeen and Ordway, 1955). Parallel overgrowths with troegerite, uranospinite, and novacekite are known.

Occurrence. A supergene mineral formed in the oxidized parts of pitchblende deposits that also contain primary Cu and As minerals. Originally found at the Weisser Hirsch mine near Schneeberg, Saxony, with uranospinite, troegerite, walpurgite, and pitchblende. Also at Zinnwald and Joachimsthal, Bohemia; St. Anton mine near Wittichen, Black Forest, Bavaria; in the Sophie and Unverhofft Glück mines, Reinerzau, Württenburg; Wheal Gorland, Cornwall, England; Cap Garonne (Var), Kruth and Le Temple (Haut-Rhin), France; Cala Maestra, Monte Cristo Island, Italy.

In the Centennial Eureka mine, Tintic, Utah, with secondary copper arsenates; at Majuba Hill, Nev., in a rhyolite plug with torbernite; and in a pitchblende vein at the W. Wilson mine, Clancy, Mont. On the Colorado Plateau at the Sunrise claim, Markey No. 3 and Happy Jack mines, White Canyon district, Utah; Pay Day, Green Vein No. 5, and Original Green Vein mines, San Rafael district, Utah; and Monument No. 2 mine, Ariz. (Weeks and Thompson, 1954); and at the Lucky Mc Mine, Fremont County, Wyo. Tentatively identified with torbernite in quartz veins in California at the Perry Jones claims, Plumas County, and the Truckee Canyon group, Nevada County (Walker et al., 1956). Abundant at Brooks Mountain, Seward Peninsula, Alaska, where it occurs in a contact metamorphic deposit in granite with hematite, siderite, pyrrhotite, chalcopyrite, arsenopyrite (note Cu and As minerals), fluorite, and scheelite; also here (primary?) in quartz-tourmaline veins in fractures in granite (West and White, 1952). Also in Alaska in the Lower Yukon–Kuskokwim region, Russian Mts., in veins cutting quartz monzonite, containing hematite, pyrite, quartz, arsenopyrite, and chalcocite (primary?) (Wedow et al., 1953). Phosphatian metazeunerite occurs in the oxidized parts of a replacement-fissure filling lode associated with quartz-tourmaline veins and tourmalinized mafic dikes cutting granite on the slopes of Ears Peak, Seward Peninsula, Alaska. Found in Canada with uranophane, kasolite, and cuprosklodowskite in the oxidized part of the Nicholson No. 1 extension pitchblende deposit (Hogarth, 1951). Occurs in the surficial parts of a pitchblende deposit near Atlin, B.C. Synthesized in several ways (Guillemin, 1956).

Identification. Resembles torbernite, which has lower indices (<1.60), and yields reactions for PO_4. Strongest x-ray lines: 8.93, 3.72, 3.30.

Uranospinite

Composition. $Ca(UO_2)_2(AsO_4)_2 \cdot 8-10H_2O$. $UO_3 = 59\%$. Synthetic compounds of the same formula type have been prepared in which H_2, Na_2, or

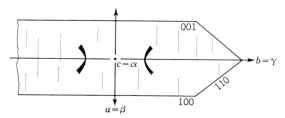

Fɪɢ. 2.31. Optical orientation of uranospathite (adapted from Chervet and Branche, 1955).

$(NH_4)_2$ substitute for Ca (Mrose, 1953). The water is partly zeolitic. Guillemin (1956) reports a higher hydrate (synthetic) with $10-16H_2O$ and also a meta-II form. Parallel overgrowths on metazeunerite are known.

Occurrence. A relatively rare secondary mineral. Found first at the Weisser Hirsch mine, Neustädtel, near Schneeberg, Saxony, with walpurgite, troegerite, zeunerite, and uranocircite. Also reported at the Military mine near Zinnwald, Erzgebirge (Bültemann, 1954). George (1949) believes it is probably present at the Solitaria mine, Argentina. Reported by Butler et al. (1920) from near Pahreah, Kane County, Utah. Locally abundant with autunite in sandstone of the Wasatch formation (Eocene) in the Gas Hills area, Wyo. (Love, 1954A). With pitchblende and torbernite in the Golden Gate Canyon district, Jefferson County, Colo.

Sodium uranospinite with some Ca and PO_4 (Table 2.11) has been described by Kopchenova and Skvortsova (1957) (Fleischer, 1958) from the U.S.S.R. from the oxidized zone of a hydrothermal pitchblende-sulfide deposit. The zone also contains metazeunerite, uranophane, troegerite, orpiment, realgar, scorodite, mansfieldite, and arseniosiderite.

Identification. Troegerite has higher indices. A test for phosphate or x-ray powder data should be obtained to distinguish uranospinite from autunite. Strongest x-ray lines are 8.85, 3.59, 3.34.

Novacekite

Composition. The arsenate member of the novacekite-saléeite series, $Mg(UO_2)_2(AsO_4)_2 \cdot 8-10H_2O$. An intermediate type is known with P:As $= 1:1.01$ (Frondel, 1951B). $UO_3 = 57$ to 60%. Small amounts of Al, Fe, Cu, and Ca have been found, along with traces of Ti, Sr, and Ba (Weeks and Thompson, 1954). Some crystals from Schneeberg, Saxony, have cores of metazeunerite in parallel orientation (Frondel, 1951B).

Occurrence.

1. In a supergene altered quartzose vein at Schneeberg, Saxony, with limonite and metazeunerite, filling cavities (Frondel, 1951B).

2. At the Woodrow deposit, Laguna, N.Mex., coating iron-stained quartz sand grains in the Westwater member of the Morrison formation (Stern and Annell, 1954).

3. In recent sediments and Permian redbeds in $SE\frac{1}{4}SE\frac{1}{4}$ sec. 23, T. 3 N., R. 14 W. and $\frac{1}{2}$ mi northwest of Twin Mountain, Wichita Mts., Okla. (Huang, 1956).

Identification. X-ray powder pattern like that of saléeite, but latter has lower indices. Resembles uranospinite in color, habit, fluorescence, and presence of As, but uranospinite has lower indices. Strongest x-ray lines: 10.15, 3.58, 5.06.

Uranospathite

$Cu(UO_2)_2[(As,P)O_4]_2 \cdot 11H_2O(?)$. Soluble in acid. The As:P ratio = 2:1 (Frondel, 1954). The water is partly zeolitic.

Found at Redruth, Cornwall, England, with bassetite (Frondel, 1954) and at La Crouzille and Sagnes in Haute-Vienne, France (Chervet and Branche, 1955).

Kahlerite

$Fe(UO_2)_2(AsO_4)_2 \cdot nH_2O$, $n = 8(?)$ (Meixner, 1953). The arsenate analog of bassetite. Tetragonal plates (001). Other forms are (111), (021), (012), (011), and (010). Perfect (001) cleavage. Nearly uniaxial to biaxial $(-)$, $2V = 9$ to $33°$. $\beta = 1.632$, $\gamma = 1.634$. Not fluorescent. Yellow in color, like autunite. Occurs at Hüttenberg, Carinthia, on altered löllingite with scorodite, symplesite, and pitticite.

Abernathyite

$K(UO_2)(AsO_4) \cdot 4H_2O$, the potassium analog of uranospinite (Thompson et al., 1956). $UO_3 = 55\%$. A small amount of P substitutes for As.

Found at the Fuemrol No. 2 mine, Temple Mt., Emery County, Utah. In the Shinarump conglomerate near the lower end of the "collapse" zone at Temple Mountain sandstone nodules composed of sand grains cemented by pyrite and asphaltite have an outer layer containing metazeunerite, sphalerite, and native arsenic. Other mine minerals are orpiment, realgar, jarosite, pitticite, metazeunerite, and two uranyl arsenates (Thompson et al., 1956). Abernathyite occurs as a crystalline coating lining a fracture in the sandstone associated with scorodite. Strongest x-ray lines: 9.14, 3.84, 3.34.

Troegerite

Composition. Probably $H_2(UO_2)_2(AsO_4)_2 \cdot 8-10H_2O$ (Mrose, 1953). A new analysis is required. $UO_3 = 64$ to 65%. Isostructural with metatorbernite(?). Probably corresponds structurally and chemically to synthetic hydrogen-uranospinite (Mrose, 1953). Much material called troegerite has been mislabeled and some has been shown to be saléeite and novacekite (Frondel, 1951B). Parallel overgrowths of metazeunerite are common. A higher hydrate may be possible, and a lower hydrate ($5H_2O$), meta-II, has been obtained (Guillemin, 1956).

Occurrence. Rare. A supergene oxidation product in some pitchblende veins. Occurs with walpurgite and metazeunerite in the Weisser Hirsch and Daniel mines (Bültemann, 1954), Schneeberg, Saxony. Probably also at Joachimsthal, Bohemia (Mrose, 1953). "H-uranospinite" is reported from U.S.S.R. uranium ores by Melkov (1956).

Identification. Difficult. Mineral requires additional study. X-rays and qualitative chemical tests required, i.e., presence of As and absence of Ca and Mg. Strongest x-ray lines for synthetic material: 8.59, 3.79, 3.30.

TABLE 2.11. *Properties of the uranyl arsenate minerals*

Mineral	Form	Color, Streak (S), Luster (L), Fluorescence (F)	Pleochroism	Indices and orientation	Cleavage and fracture	H	G
Metazeunerite	Tetragonal. Square to rectangular (001) tablets. Also rare acute pyramidal crystals. Forms except (001) usually rough and horizontally striated. Foliated aggregates and coatings	Green. S pale green. L vitreous, pearly. F weak yellow green (long wave)	Moderate ω = grass green ϵ = pale green	ω = 1.640–1.651 ϵ = 1.623–1.635 (−), weak dispersion. Indices increase continuously with decreasing H_2O within stability limits of phase	(001) perfect. Fracture uneven. Brittle	2–2.5	3.2–3.64. 3.84 (synthetic)
Zeunerite	Tetragonal. Minute orthogonal crystals bounded by (001), (110)	Green. L vitreous. F none	None or weak	ω = 1.610 ϵ = 1.582 (−)	(001) best (110) good	—	3.47
Uranospinite	Tetragonal. Thin, square to rectangular (001) tablets. Micaceous crusts	Yellow to pale green. S pale yellow. L pearly (010). F bright yellow green decreasing with dehydration (long and short wave)	Weak α = nearly colorless $\beta = \gamma$ = pale yellow, pale yellowish green	α (or ϵ) = c = 1.55–1.560 β = 1.567–1.582 γ (or ω) = $a(?)$ = 1.572–1.587 Indices increase with dehydration. Usually biaxial (−). 2V = 0–62°, r > v moderate to strong. Also uniaxial (−). Zoned with uniaxial and biaxial parts	(001) perfect. (100) distinct	2–3	3.45

98

Sodium uranospinite	Tetragonal. Tabular to elongated crystals. Radial fibrous aggregates. Square pseudomorphs after metazeunerite. Faces corroded	Yellow green, lemon yellow, straw yellow. L vitreous, pearly. (001). F strong yellow green	Weak α = colorless $\beta = \gamma$ = yellowish	$\alpha = 1.585$ $\gamma = 1.612$ (−), anomalously biaxial, 2V = very small	(001) perfect	2.5	3.85
Novacekite	Tetragonal (001) tablets, rectangular to square. Rounded (h0l) forms. Scaly aggregates, cavity fillings, grain coatings	Straw yellow. L waxy to pearly. F dull green, pale yellow green, lemon yellow (long and short wave)	α (or ϵ) = nearly colorless $\beta = \gamma$ (or ω) = pale yellow, pale yellow green	α (or ϵ) = 1.604-1.625 β = 1.620-1.641 γ (or ω) = 1.620-1.641 Usually biaxial (−). 2V = 0-20°, r > v. Also uniaxial (−). Indices increase with dehydration and with As for P. Mottled extinction	(001) perfect	2.5	3.3–3.7
Uranospathite	Orthorhombic. Pseudotetragonal. Fans of striated rectangular laths and plates (001). May show cruciform twinning (110)	Yellow to pale green. F strong yellow green	α = pale yellow $\beta = \gamma$ = deep yellow	$\alpha = c = 1.485-1.495$ $\beta = a = 1.510-1.527$ $\gamma = b = 1.521-1.532$ (−) 2V = 55-72°. With dehydration indices increase and becomes uniaxial	(001) perfect. Also (100) or (010)	2.5	2.50
Abernathyite	Tetragonal. Thin to thick tablets, (001) and (110) prominent	Yellow. S pale yellow. L vitreous. F moderately yellow green (long and short wave)	Colorless to pale yellow	$\omega = 1.597$ $\epsilon = 1.570$ Uniaxial (−), 2V < 5°. Also biaxial	(001) perfect but not micaceous	2.5	3.74

TABLE 2.11. *Properties of the uranyl arsenate minerals* (*Continued*)

Mineral	Form	Color, Streak (S), Luster (L), Fluorescence (F)	Pleochroism	Indices and orientation	Cleavage and fracture	H	G
Troegerite	Tetragonal(?). Thin (001) tablets, striated faces. Pseudomonoclinic habit. Subparallel aggregates	Lemon yellow. S pale yellow. L pearly (001)	None or weak. α = colorless $\beta = \gamma$ = pale yellow	α (or ϵ) = c = 1.580–1.600 β = 1.620–1.629 γ (or ω) = 1.623–1.631 Uniaxial or biaxial (−), 2V = 0–40°, r > v moderate. Indices increase with dehydration	(001) perfect. (100) good	2–3	3.55 (synthetic)
Walpurgite	Triclinic. Thin (010) scales, tablets, or laths parallel with c. Twinned on (010) to pseudomonoclinic habit and striated on (100). Radial and subparallel groups	Yellow. S yellowish. L greasy to brilliant. Crystals opaque with clear terminations	α = colorless $\beta = \gamma$ = faint greenish yellow	α = 1.871–1.91 β = 1.975–2.01 γ = 2.005–2.06 (−), 2V = 50–60°, dispersion slight. γ nearly $\perp$ plates, $\alpha \wedge b$ = small. $\beta \wedge c$ = 12° on (010), 8° on (100). Indices increase with As for P	(010) perfect	3.5	5.95

100

Walpurgite

Probably $Bi_4(UO_2)(AsO_4)_2O_4\cdot3H_2O$. UO_3 = 16 to 19%. Considerable PO_4 may substitute for AsO_4. Crystals zoned with variation in As/P ratio. A very rare supergene mineral found in the Walpurgis vein, Weisser Hirsch mine, Neustädtel, Schneeberg, Saxony, with torbernite, troegerite, uranospinite, uranosphaerite, and metazeunerite. Also at Joachimsthal, Bohemia. The optical properties together with a Bi test are distinctive. Strongest x-ray lines: 3.11, 3.25, 3.05.

VANADATES

Carnotite

Composition. $K_2(UO_2)_2(UO_4)_2\cdot1-3H_2O$. UO_3 = 63 to 65%. Small amounts of Ca, Na, Ba, Sr, Mg, Fe^2, Al, and Si (0.01 to 1%) are reported in many analyses. The water is partly zeolitic, varying with humidity at ordinary temperatures. May be converted to tyuyamunite by hydration and base exchange (in calcium bicarbonate solution).

Occurrence. Very widespread and probably the most abundant secondary uranium ore mineral. Formed under oxidizing conditions in fully oxidized U-V ore of Colorado Plateau type deposits in which pitchblende, coffinite, roscoelite, and montroseite were the chief primary U-V minerals; associated in these with tyuyamunite, metatyuyamunite, rauvite, hewettite, and corvusite. On the Colorado Plateau in the states of Colorado, Utah, New Mexico, and Arizona, in most of the U-V mines of the following districts (Weeks and Thompson, 1954): Gateway, Uravan, Thompsons, Paradox, Bull Canyon, Temple Mountain of the San Rafael Swell, Gypsum Valley, Moab, Slick Rock, Monticello, Monument Valley, and Grants in sandstones and conglomerates principally of Triassic and Jurassic age, but especially in the Shinarump, Chinle, and lower parts of the Morrison (Fig. 2.32). Also in the United States: in the Pumpkin Buttes area, Wyo., in the Wasatch (Eocene) formation; in Fall River County, S.Dak., in sandstones of the Inyan Kara group (Early Cretaceous); near Mauch Chunk (now Jim Thorpe), Pa., in the Pottsville conglomerate and Pocono sandstone (Pennsylvanian and Mississippian); in Permian sandstone at Garo, Park County, Colo.; in the Old Leyden coal

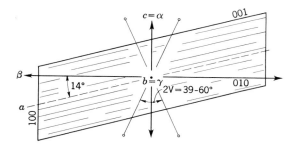

FIG. 2.32. Optical orientation of carnotite.

mine, near Golden, Colo.; at the Red Bluff deposit in Precambrian quartzite, Gila County, Ariz. In Texas at Tordilla Hill, Karnes County, in the upper Jackson formation (Eocene); in the Catahoula formation (Miocene) near Sample, Gonzales County; and in the Gueydan formation (Miocene) near Freer, Duvall County. In Nevada along fractures in rhyolite near Sloan, and in Permian sandstone north of Goodsprings, both in Clark County. In California in Miocene clays and marls with clay, opal, and Fe and Mn oxides in the Vanuray and Kramer Hills deposits, west of Barstow.

Some noteworthy foreign occurrences are: with tyuyamunite and cinnabar in clay, filling limestone caverns and solution channels near San Carlos, Chihuahua, Mexico. At the Santa Lucía quarry, Cerro Santa Lucía, northwest of Timotes, Mérida, Venezuela. In red sandstone, Katanga, Belgian Congo. As an alteration of davidite at Radium Hill, South Australia. In the U.S.S.R. in southwestern Siberia around the towns of Ferghana and Kokand in Miocene sandstone as scattered deposits over an area 1,000 sq mi. In phosphorite of Louis Gentil and El Borouj, Morocco.

Reported from the Pitche (Lang, 1952) and Urvan deposits (Bültemann, 1954), Beaverlodge, Canada, and in volcanic rocks of the Valdes formation, Quadra Island, B.C.

Identification. Has higher indices than tyuyamunite and any other common yellow secondary U mineral. Both carnotite and tyuyamunite turn red brown (V test) when touched with a drop of concentrated HCl. Tyuyamunite fuses with ease; carnotite is infusible. Lack of fluorescence helps rule out many other secondary yellow U minerals. Strongest x-ray lines are 6.56, 3.12, 3.53.

Tyuyamunite and Metatyuyamunite

Composition. $Ca(UO_2)_2(VO_4)_2 \cdot 7-10\frac{1}{2}H_2O$ (tyuyamunite); $Ca(UO_2)_2$ $(VO_4)_2 \cdot 3-5H_2O$ (metatyuyamunite) (Stern et al., 1956). $UO_3 = 57$ to 58%. The water content ordinarily is 9 to 10 but varies markedly at ordinary temperatures with the humidity. K replaces Ca in both (Donnay and Donnay, 1953; Stern et al., 1956). Tyuyamunite may be converted to carnotite by interchange of K for Ca and with dehydration (e.g., in potassium–mercuric iodide solution). In small amounts Ba, Cu, Pb, and Mg are reported, some of which may be isomorphous for Ca.

Occurrence. Tyuyamunite is widely distributed on the Colorado Plateau, particularly in western Colorado and Utah, and especially in the Grants, N.Mex., district at Haystack Butte in the Todilto limestone. Occurs with metatyuyamunite, carnotite, corvusite, rauvite, and hewettite. Also in the Pumpkin Buttes, Wyo., area (metatyuyamunite) in the Wasatch formation (Eocene) (Troyer et al., 1954); in the Mayoworth area, Johnson County, Wyo. (metatyuyamunite) in the Sundance formation (late Jurassic) (Love, 1954B); in the Hueco limestone (Permian) in the Hueco Mountains, northeast corner of El Paso County, Tex.; near Bisbee, Ariz.; at the Red Bluff deposit, Gila County, Ariz., in Precambrian quartzite with carnotite and uranophane; at Garo, Park County, Colo., with carnotite in Permian sandstone.

Metatyuyamunite has been found at more than thirty-five localities on the Colorado Plateau, first at the Jo Dandy mine, Montrose County, Colo. (Stern et al., 1956); in the Shinarump, Chinle, Todilto limestone; and Salt Wash member of the Morrison, commonly mixed with carnotite; also associated with clay and gypsum. Also occurs in Fall River County, S.Dak. In Nevada in caliche in Quaternary alluvium between the railroad stations at Erie and Arden in Clark County.

Originally tyuyamunite was found at Tyuya Muyun, 62 km southeast of Fedchenko in Ferghana, Turkestan, U.S.S.R., in a vertical fracture zone in Carboniferous limestone. Occurs also at the northwest end of the Kara-Tau range in northeastern Turkestan in Cambrian black slate along fractures with torbernite. In France in a clayey sandstone at Le Bourdet in Deux-Sèvres. In Morocco at Assaïkaidji and Sidi Ayad.

Identification. Tyuyamunite and carnotite do not fluoresce; they turn red brown when touched by a drop of concentrated HCl (V test). A test for Ca or the *x*-ray powder pattern may be needed to distinguish between them. Tyuyamunite has higher refractive indices than metatyuyamunite; both fuse more easily than carnotite. Strongest *x*-ray lines: (tyuyamunite) 10.18, 5.02, 3.20; (metatyuyamunite) 8.43, 4.17, 3.28.

Francevillite

$(Ba,Pb)(UO_2)_2(VO_4)_2 \cdot 5H_2O$, with $Ba:Pb = 2:1$ or Pb may be absent entirely (Branche et al., 1957). $UO_3 = 55\%$. The Ba analog of metatyuyamunite (Fleischer, 1958). Occurs as impregnations, cryptocrystalline veinlets, and small plates in sandstones in the Franceville region, French Equatorial Africa. Strongest *x*-ray lines are 8.30, 2.98, 4.17, 2.57.

Sengierite

Composition. $Cu(UO_2)(VO_4)(OH) \cdot 4–5H_2O(?)$. $UO_3 = 52\%$. Some Fe^3 or Al was reported in the only analysis (Vaes and Kerr, 1949). Soluble in dilute HCl. The mineral as found is reported to contain $10H_2O$.

Occurrence. Found as flaky fracture coatings along fissures in a chlorite-talc rock of the Mine series (Precambrian) in the Elisabethville-Jadotville area of Katanga, Belgian Congo. Accompanied by black oxides of Fe, Cu, Co, and Ni, and volborthite, less commonly by malachite, garnierite, chrysocolla, vanden-brandeite, and nearby pitchblende and kasolite. Occurs as thin coatings and mammilary crusts in fissures in a fine-grained sandstone containing carbonaceous plant debris at Amelal in the region of Argana Bigoudine in Morocco

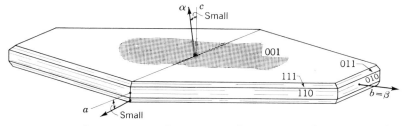

Fig. 2.33. Optical orientation of sengierite showing central opaque inclusions (adapted from Vaes and Kerr, 1949; *Am. Mineralogist*).

TABLE 2.12. *Properties of the uranyl vanadate minerals*

Mineral	Form	Color, Streak (S), Luster (L), Fluorescence (F)	Pleochroism	Indices and orientation	Cleavage and fracture	H	G
Carnotite	Monoclinic (001) plates; (110) rhomboidal; laths parallel with *b*. Rare (001) twins. Very fine grained anhedra in crusts, cement, veinlets, and fossil wood replacements	Lemon yellow, greenish yellow. Rarely orange. S yellow. L earthy in aggregates; in crystals, pearly to silky. F none; rarely weak greenish	Weak α = colorless to gray yellow β = gray yellow, lemon yellow, greenish yellow γ = lemon yellow, greenish yellow	$\alpha = c = 1.750$–1.89 $\beta = 1.895$–2.06 $\gamma = 1.920$–2.08 $(-)$ 2V = 39–60°; r < v weak to moderate. $\beta \wedge a$ = 14°. Indices increase with Ba and dehydration. Cleavage pieces yield centered *Bxa* figure and have birefringence of 0.025	(001) perfect	2–3	4.6
Tyuyamunite	Orthorhombic (001) scales and laths, elongated with *a*, as thin coatings, radial aggregates and crystalline masses. Very fine grained. Faces may be curved. Structure destroyed by vigorous grinding	Yellow, greenish yellow. Turns green with exposure to sunlight. S yellow. L adamantine, pearly (001), earthy to waxy in aggregates	Weak to moderate α = nearly colorless β = pale to greenish yellow γ = canary to green yellow	$\alpha = c = 1.72$–1.75 $\beta = b = 1.868$–1.932 $\gamma = a = 1.953$–1.968 Older indices may be wrong owing to dehydration in immersion melts. $(-)$, 2V = 30–35°; r < v moderate to strong. Indices increase with Ba and dehydration	(001) perfect. (010), (100) distinct	About 2	3.62

Metatyuya-munite	Orthorhombic (001) scales and laths, elongated with a, as thin coatings, radial aggregates and crystalline masses. Very fine grained. Faces may be curved. Structure destroyed by vigorous grinding	Yellow, greenish yellow. Turns green with exposure to sunlight. S yellow. L adamantine, pearly (001), earthy to waxy in aggregates	Weak to moderate α = nearly colorless β = pale to greenish yellow γ = canary to green yellow	$\alpha = c = 1.62\text{-}1.69$ $\beta = a = 1.835\text{-}1.842$ $\gamma = b = 1.865\text{-}1.90$ $(-), 2V = 45\text{-}48°$, $r < v$ weak. Indices increase with dehydration	(001) perfect. (010), (100) distinct	About 2	3.8-3.9
Francevillite	Orthorhombic (001) plates	Yellow. F none	α = colorless $\beta = \gamma$ = yellow	$\alpha = c = 1.750\text{-}1.785$ $\beta = b = 1.910\text{-}1.952$ $\gamma = a = 1.945\text{-}2.002$ increasing with Pb. $(-)$ $2V = 46\text{-}53°$	(001) perfect	3	4.55 (Pb-bearing)
Sengierite	Monoclinic (Donnay and Donnay, 1953). Small, hexagonal (001) tablets. Central dark inclusions. Fracture coatings, pulverulent masses	Green to greenish yellow. S light green. L vitreous to adamantine	Distinct α = bluish green β = olive green γ = colorless to yellowish green	$\alpha = 1.71$ $\beta = b = 1.935$ $\gamma = 1.960$ $(-), 2V = 37\text{-}39°$, $r > v$ strong. Basal sections show anomalous interference colors. $\alpha \wedge c$ = small Older indices higher owing to dehydration in melts	(001) perfect. Brittle	2.5	4.41

(Chervet and Branche, 1955). It is associated with iron oxides, dioptase, and rarely with cuprosklodowskite. Also found (Hutton, 1957) at the Cole shaft, Bisbee, Ariz., in a vein with chalcocite, covellite, cerargyrite, and malachite.

Identification. Can be recognized as a vanadate by touching it with drops of concentrated HCl which forms a brown ring. A test for Cu distinguishes it from carnotite and tyuyamunite whose x-ray powder photographs are similar. Strongest x-ray lines: 9.82, 4.91, 3.73.

Rauvite

Composition. $CaU_2V_{10}O_{32} \cdot 16H_2O$(?). Some V^4 is present as well as V^5.

Structure and form. Crystal system not known. Very fine grained. Forms botryoidal crusts, fracture fillings, interstitial cement, filmy coatings, and structureless, slickensided masses. Commonly shows shrinkage cracks. Fresh samples dehydrate and crack.

Optical properties. Commonly brownish red to purplish black, less usually dirty orange yellow (Weeks and Thompson, 1954). Yellow brown streak. Adamantine to waxy luster. Indices and birefringence variable, from low birefringence, with $n = 1.89$, to high birefringence, with $n = 1.95$. Biaxial $(-)$ (?). No fluorescence.

Physical properties. Sectile to brittle. G = 2.92. No cleavage.

Occurrence. Probably results from the reaction of materials derived from altered pitchblende and low-valence vanadium oxide minerals. Possibly also forms by alteration of tyuyamunite (Weeks and Thompson, 1954). Occurs on the Colorado Plateau at the following localities (Weeks and Thompson, 1954): Hummer mine, Bull Canyon district; Corvusite, Small Spot, and Arrowhead mines, Gateway district; Monument No. 2 mine, Monument Valley district; Temple Mountain, San Rafael district; and Cactus Rat mine, Thompsons district. Also in Fall River County, S.Dak., at the Road Hog 3A claim, Coal Canyon.

Identification. Differs from tyuyamunite in color and x-ray pattern. Highly variable in physical properties. Strongest x-ray lines: 10.70, 2.95, 3.49.

Doubtful or Poorly Defined Species

Ferghanite

Supposedly $U_3(VO_4)_2 \cdot 6H_2O$. Analyses (2) show 1.22 and 3.49% Li_2O. May be a leached tyuyamunite. Occurs as (001) scales with six-sided outlines. Sulfur yellow. Luster waxy. Not pleochroic. Biaxial, 2V large. Indices and birefringence low. $\alpha = c$, $\beta = b$, $\gamma = a$. Perfect (001) cleavage. H = about 2.5. G = 3.31. Occurs at Tyuya Muyun, Ferghana district, Turkestan, U.S.S.R., with other uranium minerals.

Uvanite

$U_2V_6O_{21} \cdot 15H_2O$(?). Orthorhombic(?). Masses and coatings of minute crystals. Brownish-yellow color. Biaxial $(+)$, 2V = 52°.

$\alpha = 1.817$, light brown
$\beta = 1.879$, dark brown
$\gamma = 2.057$, greenish yellow

Found at Temple Mountain, San Rafael Swell, Utah (Hess and Schaller, 1914). Needs further study. May be related to rauvite (Weeks and Thompson, 1954).

MOLYBDATES

Umohoite

Regarded as $(UO_2)(MoO_4) \cdot 4H_2O$ by Brophy and Kerr (1953). Coleman and Appleman (1957) confirm the U:Mo ratio of 1:1 but suggest that the U, or Mo, or both are in an oxidation state lower than hexavalent. $UO_3 = 57\%$. Monoclinic. Small flakes with triangular markings; rosettes of tablets with acute angle points. Black, blue black, dark green. Submetallic luster. Opaque to translucent. α = dark blue, β = light blue, γ = olive green. α (calc.) = 1.66, $\beta = b = 1.831$, $\gamma = 1.915$. $\alpha \wedge a = 9°$. $(-)$ $2V = 65°$ (Na), $r > v$ strong. Alters to a yellow uranyl molybdate. $H = 2$. $G = 4.55$ to 4.66.

In veinlets and disseminated specks in a 4- to 6-ft clay-mineral alteration zone alone, or with fluorite, pyrite, quartz, and uraninite or with ilsemannite or jordisite at the Freedom No. 2 mine, Marysvale, Utah (Walker and Osterwald, 1956A). The vein along which it occurs is just below the oxidized zone in quartz monzonite.

Also at the Lucky Mc mine, Gas Hills area, Wyo., in partly oxidized ore, intergrown with gypsum, occurring with iron sulfides and uraninite. Strongest x-ray lines: 7.31 to 6.96, 3.22, 14.10. Structure disrupted upon grinding.

Doubtful or Poorly Defined Species

Iriginite

$U_2^6(MoO_4)(OH)_4 \cdot 4H_2O$ (Melkov, 1956; Soboleva and Pudovkina, 1957; Getseva and Savel'eva, 1956; Fleischer, 1958). $UO_3 = 42\%$. Fine-grained yellow aggregates, some pseudomorphous after brannerite. Dull luster. Monoclinic. $\alpha = 1.82$, $\gamma = 1.93$. $H = 4$ to 5. $G = 3.84$. Uneven to conchoidal fracture. Strongest x-ray lines: 3.22, 1.13, 2.63, 2.14.

Moluranite

$UO_2 \cdot 2UO_3 \cdot 5MoO_3 \cdot 12H_2O(?)$ or $2UO_2 \cdot 3MoO_3 \cdot 11H_2O(?)$ (Melkov, 1956; Soboleva and Pudovkina, 1957; Getseva and Savel'eva, 1956; Fleischer, 1958). $U_3O_8 = 42.32\%$. Upon heating to 500° is transformed to iriginite. Black, brown in thin fragments. Isotropic. Amorphous(?). $n = 1.97$ to 1.98. Occurs as colloform masses with brannerite and other U-Mo minerals in one deposit in the U.S.S.R., in the central parts of narrow fissures in granulated albitite, associated with molybdenite, chalcopyrite, and galena.

SILICATES

NONHYDRATED SILICATES

Thorite

Composition. ThSiO₄. U usually is present (uranothorite) in amounts up to about 10%. ThO_2 = 49 to 75%. Other elements commonly present in small to minor amounts are Ca, Mg, Fe^2, alkalies, Ce earths, P, Ta, Ti, Zr, Sn, and Al. Y elements also may occur. Pb and Fe^3 (ferrothorite) may be abundant. Secondary water usually present in minor to large amounts (orangite). Other varietal names and synonyms include auerlite (phosphatian thorite), enalite (uranothorite), and eucrasite and freyalite (cerian thorites).

Structure and form. Tetragonal. Metamict or non-metamict. Isostructural with zircon (Pabst, 1951B). Crystals are square prisms (110) with pyramidal terminations (111) like zircon (Fig. 2.34). Also in slightly waterworn grains (Fig. 2.35). Uranothorite is commonly anhedral. Upon ignition metamict thorite and uranothorite do not revert to their original crystal structures but yield a cubic powder pattern which is essentially identical with that of thorianite (Phair and Shimamoto, 1952). In some deposits crystalline thorite, thorite with metamict patches, and completely metamict thorite occur together, as at Mountain Pass, Calif. (Olson et al., 1954).

Inclusions are numerous (Fig. 2.36); zoning in alternating brown-green layers is reported, as are irregularly distributed varying color areas. Thorite from Mountain Pass, Calif., is crowded with minute specks of hematite and goethite which also may be zonally distributed (Olson et al., 1954).

Occurrence.

1. In granite pegmatites: Norway, Iveland district, Birketveit 1 deposit; Evje district, Landsverk deposit; Tangen, 4 km west of Kragerö; Hitterö; Moss. Ben Bhreck, Tongue, Scotland. Blueberry Mountain, near Boston, Mass., with allanite and cyrtolite. Near Forest Home, San Bernardino County, Calif., with allanite. Probable altered equivalents occurred in the Baringer Hill, Tex., pegmatite. In the Bancroft, Ont., district at the McDonald mine with allanite, cyrtolite, and ellsworthite; also either thorite or uranothorite occur in several other nonzoned pegmatites in the district (e.g., Centre Lake and Croft Uranium). Also in Canada in Manitoba, in a zone of pegmatite-biotite schist-biotite gneiss with uraninite and cyrtolite on the East Found group of claims, 10 mi west of Rennic Station; in Saskatchewan in the Viking Lake pegmatite with pyrochlore, Goldfields area; in Ontario in pegmatite with magnetite, uraninite, and molybdenite on the Bybery property, 30 mi east of Kenora, and 2 mi west of Marathon in sheared pegmatite.

In pegmatite float, Willow Creek district, south-central Alaska with uraninite, cyrtolite, and allanite (Moxham and Nelson, 1952A). In the Wodgina area of Western Australia, strongly altered with tantalite. On Madagascar in deposits from the Sahavary basin (orangite), from Befaritra (uranothorite), from south of Lake Itasy (orangite); from Fiadanana, Soarivola, and Sambaina (orangite), in some cases in betafite or zircon aggregates; at Ambodivoandelaka, orangite

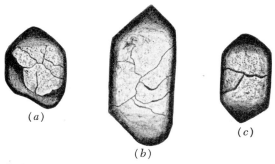

FIG. 2.34. Euhedral detrital uranothorite, New Zealand (Hutton, 1950; *Geol. Soc. Am.*). (*a*) (×60) Harihari; (*b*) (×115) (Harihari; (*c*) (×90) Gillespie's Beach.

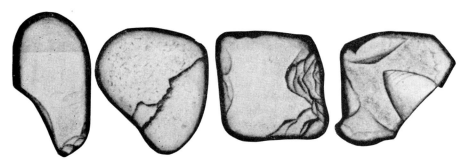

FIG. 2.35. Waterworn grains of uranothorite. California beach sands, mouth of Año Nuevo Creek (×200) (Hutton, 1952; *Calif. Dept. Nat. Resources Div. Mines*).

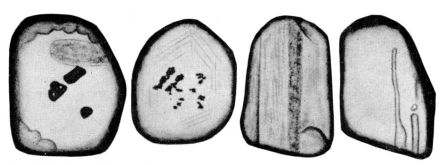

FIG. 2.36. Detrital uranothorite grains with inclusions, California beach sands, mouth of Año Nuevo Creek (×200) (Hutton, 1952; *Calif. Dept. Nat. Resources Div. Mines*). Farthest right contains gas cavities; others have unidentified opaque to semiopaque minerals.

in columbite. Reported in pegmatite-migmatite zones with allanite and euxenite on the Southern Rhodesia–Union of South Africa border.

2. As an accessory mineral in granitic rocks: granitic gneiss in Henderson County, N.C., with zircon, monazite, and xenotime; in granite, Upper Flint Creek, near Long, Ruby-Poorman district, west-central Alaska, with allanite and zircon (White and Stevens, 1953); in greisenized granite at Kuperlisai, North Kirghizia, U.S.S.R. (Starik et al., 1941) (ferrithorite) with xenotime and zeunerite.

3. As an accessory mineral in syenites and alkali syenites: southern Norway at Esmark, and on Lövö Island in augite syenite. Also in nepheline-syenite pegmatites in the Langesundfjord district, Norway.

4. In pyrometasomatically altered marbles and metapyroxenites (uranothorite), Bancroft district, Ont.

5. In carbonatites: in association with the Sulphide Queen bastnaesite carbonatite body of the Mountain Pass district, San Bernardino County, Calif., thorite occurs as lustrous, dark red to yellow-brown grains up to 3 mm in diameter principally in shear zones in Precambrian gneiss with hematite, goethite, sericite, chlorite, quartz, and carbonate; to a lesser extent in carbonate veins also containing bastnaesite, hematite, and magnetite (Olson et al., 1954). Somewhat similar occurrences are in veins in the Powderhorn district, Gunnison County, Colo., associated with the Iron Hill alkalic-subsilicic intrusive and its carbonatite. These veins contain thorite with quartz, calcite, dolomite, cerium-fluorapatite, and bastnaesite.

6. In quartz-hematite-barite veins: Lemhi Pass area, Idaho and Mont., at Trapper No. 1 claim, on North Frying Pan Creek and on other properties (Trites and Tooker, 1953); Wet Mountains, Custer and Fremont Counties, Colo., on the Haputa and Tuttle Ranches and other deposits, also with less common thorogummite, fluorite, siderite, pyrite, chalcopyrite, bornite, and galena (Christman et al., 1953).

7. In low- to medium-temperature fluorite-rich veins: in the Blue Jay mine, Jamestown district, Boulder County, Colo., in breccia ore, surrounded by radioactive halos in purple fluorite, in euhedra 0.02 to 0.10 mm across, associated with carbonates, pyrite, galena, sphalerite, uraninite, quartz, clay minerals, and altered feldspar (Phair and Shimamoto, 1952).

8. In placers, both stream and beach: tin placers of Nigeria with monazite; gold placers in the Belgian Congo with monazite, euxenite, samarskite, and zircon; Pekoerigan River, Central Celebes (wisaksonite, Hutton, 1954), with zircon and cassiterite; Gillespie's Beach, South Westland, New Zealand (Fig. 2.34) (Hutton, 1950); with betafite in the Tambani area, Nyasaland; South Fork of Quartz Creek, a tributary of the Kiwalik River, Buckland-Kiwalik district, Alaska; Gold Bench, South Fork Koyukuk River, Alaska; Cache Creek area, Kentna district, Alaska; numerous beach sands, between Princeton and Monterey Bay, Calif. (Hutton, 1952) (Figs. 2.35, 2.36); green uranothorite is a widespread constituent of black sands in gold placers of central and southern California, particularly along the Tuolumne River near LaGrange (George, 1949, 1951).

Identification. The combination of tetragonal form, general metamict character, high radioactivity, and relatively low refractive indices is characteristic. Much disseminated thorite from granitic rocks is green. Both thorite and uranothorite resist hot concentrated acids strongly even when powdered. Fragments of thorite, if boiled for 2 min in a strong solution of oxalic acid, washed, and dried, will show films of white thorium oxalate (Hutton, 1952).

Huttonite

$ThSiO_4$, a dimorph of thorite. Monoclinic, isostructural with monazite (Pabst, 1951A). Contains minor Fe^3 and Ce elements and traces of Mn and PO_4. Some (OH) for O in SiO_4 groups may be possible (Frondel et al., 1954). In minute grains, less than 0.2 mm in maximum diameter in beach sands from Harihari, Salt Water Creek, Okarito, Five Mile Beach, Bruce Bay, north and south of the mouth of the Waikukupa River and Gillespie's Beach in South Westland, New Zealand (Hutton, 1950, 1951A), associated with scheelite, tantalian cassiterite, uranothorite, gold, zircon, and ilmenite.

Thorite is eventually converted to a monoclinic dimorph when heated in air (Pabst, 1952). In two specimens the change began to appear at 715°C after prolonged heating. The monoclinic phase is the principal phase present after heating to 935 or 950°C in most cases (Pabst, 1952) (Fig. 1.2). According to Frondel et al. (1954), huttonite and thorite form hydrothermally over the same temperature range (300 to 700°C), the formation of huttonite being favored by alkaline conditions, that of thorite by acid conditions. The unit cell dimensions of huttonite appear to vary with temperature of formation (Frondel et al., 1954), probably due to $(OH)_4$ substitution for SiO_4. Huttonite can also be synthesized by dry sintering in the range 1300 to 1400°C. Thorite, synthesized similarly in the range 1000 to 1250°C, was not found to convert to huttonite at 1400°C (Frondel et al., 1954).

Resembles scheelite from which it is distinguished by lower indices, dull white fluorescence, and lack of reaction in boiling HCl; scheelite boiled in HCl for 2 to 3 min forms a canary-yellow coating.

Thorogummite

Composition. $Th(SiO_4)_{1-x}(OH)_{4x}$, with x known to range at least between 0.99 to 1.31 (Frondel, 1953). U = 2.5 to 31.4%, Th = 18.2 to 50.8%. Usually some additional nonessential water also is present. PO_4 and SO_4 may substitute for SiO_4. Minor to trace amounts of Ce, Y, Ca, Mg, Mn, Pb, Fe^3, Fe^2, Be, Al, Ti, Zr, Hf, alkalies, As, Sb, Sn, Nb, and Ta may be present. Synonyms are chlorothorite, hyblite, hydrothorite, mackintoshite, maitlandite, and nicolayite.

Structure. Tetragonal, isostructural with thorite; cell dimensions essentially identical with those of thorite. Pseudomorphs after and alterations of thorite, uranothorite, yttrialite, and thorianite. Also in very fine grained nodules, crypto- to microcrystalline; in minute specks, rods, or fibers. Relicts of thorite are commonly enclosed.

Occurrence. Chiefly in pegmatites and to a lesser extent in hydrothermal deposits as a secondary mineral. Also as an alteration of detrital thorite. Verified and probable localities include (Frondel, 1953): Baringer Hill, Tex.; Jamestown, Colo.; Easton, Pa.; Henderson County, N.C.; in soil derived from a pegmatite in the Wasau area, Marathon County, Wis.; Tuolumne River, Calif.; Hybla, Ont.; Langesundfjord, Norway; Befarita, Madagascar; Mineral Claim 107, Wodgina, Western Australia (maitlandite, nicolayite, and hydrothorite) with pilbarite, albite, spessartite, gahnite, apatite, and lithiophilite. Naegi and Iisaka, Japan; South Manchuria. Also reported from the Sweepstakes Creek area 135 mi east-northeast of Nome, Alaska, as a white fibrous, faintly birefringent aggregate replacing placer thorianite (Gault et al., 1953). With thorite in veins in the Wet Mountain area, Custer and Fremont Counties, Colo. Synthesized hydrothermally between 150 to 700°C, with decreasing substitution of $(OH)_4$ for SiO_4, accompanied by decreasing size of the unit cell (Frondel et al., 1954). Pilbarite, from Western Australia (Simpson, 1928), is a thorogummite-kasolite mixture (Honea, 1957).

Identification. The x-ray pattern is essentially that of thorite. Softer and with a lower specific gravity. Large amounts of water are indicative.

Coffinite

Composition. $U(SiO_4)_{1-x}(OH)_{4x}$ (Stern et al., 1955; Stieff et al., 1955, 1956). Most of the uranium exists as U^4. In concentrated but not pure samples $UO_2 = 46$ to 68%. Analyses of coffinite concentrates also reveal the presence of As, V, and Al, which are not, however, essential constituents.

Structure and form. Tetragonal, isostructural with thorite and zircon. Very fine grained, yielding broadened lines in its x-ray powder diffraction pattern. Intimately associated with carbonaceous material.

Properties. Black. Adamantine luster. Very fine particles (−325 mesh) pale to dark brown in transmitted light, otherwise opaque except on thin edges. $n = 1.83$ to 1.85. Maximum G for concentrates relatively free of organic material is 5.1.

Occurrence. A major uranium mineral in the unoxidized ores of the Colorado Plateau. Also in asphaltic pellets in sedimentary rocks of Texas and Oklahoma; and at "several foreign localities" (Stern et al., 1955; Stieff et al., 1955). Reported at the Lowley deposit, Spokane Indian Reservation, Wash. Probably will be found at numerous other localities. Synthesized by Hoekstra and Fuchs (1956) by crystallizing a slightly alkaline sodium metasilicate gel in which UCl_4 has been dissolved. Nenadkevite (Melkov, 1956) is probably coffinite (Fleischer, 1958).

Identification. Best identified by its x-ray powder pattern. Otherwise very similar to fine-grained disseminated pitchblende. Strongest lines are 4.66, 3.47, 2.64.

HYDRATED SILICATES

Soddyite

Composition. $(UO_2)_5(SiO_4)_2(OH)_2 \cdot 5H_2O$. $UO_3 = 85$ to 86%. In anhedral intergrowths with curite. Larger crystals show zoning with opaque centers and translucent margins.

TABLE 2.13. *Properties of Th silicate minerals*

Mineral	Form	Color, Streak (S), Luster (L), Fluorescence (F)	Pleochroism	Indices and orientation	Cleavage and fracture	H	G
Thorite	Tetragonal. Metamict or non-metamict	Black, brown, orange, yellow, green. S yellow, orange, light brown, greenish. L glassy, dull if altered. F none or faint deep blue	None	Isotropic. $n = 1.66–1.88$, decreasing with hydration. Rarely uniaxial (+). $\epsilon = 1.8–1.850$ $\omega = 1.79–1.825$	(110) distinct, conchoidal fracture	4.5–5, lower if altered	4.4–6.7, lower if strongly altered
Huttonite	Monoclinic	Colorless to pale cream. F pale pinkish white	None	$\alpha = 1.898$ $\beta = 1.900$ $\gamma = 1.922$ (+), $2V = 25°$, $r < v$ moderate	(100) (001) imperfect		7.1
Thorogummite	Tetragonal	White, yellow, buff, red, green. L dull, earthy, waxy	None	n (mean) $= 1.62–1.77$ $\epsilon - \omega =$ about 0.01 Indices increase with dehydration		3.5–4.5	3.3–5.4

TABLE 2.14. *Coffinite localities listed by mine or property name and geologic formation (Stieff et al., 1956)*

Occurrence	Deposit	County	State
Browns Park formation (Miocene)	Poison Basin claims	Carbon	Wyo.
Wind River formation (Eocene)	Vitro Uranium and Lucky Mc mines	Fremont	Wyo.
Fort Union formation (Eocene)	Kell Roy No. 3 mine	Johnson	Wyo.
Vein deposit (Tertiary)	Copper King mine	Larimer	Colo.
Laramie formation (Cretaceous)	Old Leyden mine	Jefferson	Colo.
Mesaverde formation (Cretaceous)	La Ventana	Sandoval	N.Mex.
	Arrowhead mine		
	Black Mama mine		
	La Sal No. 2 mine	Mesa	Colo.
	Matchless mine		
	Small Spot mine		
	Shattuck Denn shaft		
	Virgin No. 2 mine		
	Wild Steer mine		
Morrison formation (Jurassic)	Oversight mine	Montrose	Colo.
	J. J. mine		
	Peanut mine		
	Little Muriel mine	San Miguel	Colo.

Formation	Mine	County	State
Chinle formation (Triassic)	Corvusite mine	Grand	Utah
	Grey Dawn mine	San Juan	Utah
	Jack Pile mine	Valencia	N.Mex.
	Woodrow Pipe mine		
	Wind Whip mine		
	Poison Canyon mine		
	Mesa Top mine	San Juan	Utah
	Mi Vida mine		
	Cal Uranium mine		
	Homestake mine	Navajo	Ariz.
	Ruth group mine		
Shinarump conglomerate (Triassic)	Stinking Spring Mountain	Emery	Utah
Dolores formation (Triassic)	Denise No. 1 mine	San Miguel	Colo.
Cutler formation (Permian)	Robinson property, near Placerville		
	Weatherly property, near Placerville		
Garber formation (Permian)	J. B. Smith farm, sec. unit 1, Saddle Mountain	Kiowa	Okla.
San Andres formation (Permian)	Sec. 63, block 47, H. and T. C. Survey	Potter	Texas
Dripping Spring quartzite (Precambrian)	Workman No. 1 mine	Gila	Ariz.
	Little Mo mine		
Vein (unknown age)	(Arrowhead No. 1)	Fremont	Wyo.

Occurrence. A rare supergene species first found at Kasolo, Belgian Congo, where it occurs in anhedral masses intimately mixed with curite and as cross-fiber fissure fillings in the curite-soddyite aggregate. Euhedral crystals and crystal groups occur with sklodowskite and kasolite needles on curite, the soddyite having formed after curite and before sklodowskite. Also found in the Norrabees pegmatite district, Namaqualand (Gevers et al., 1937) as blades with malachite on quartz. Identified at the Moye pegmatite, near Barnesville, Lamar County, Ga. (Furcron, 1955). In the Honeycomb Hills near Callao, Utah, with fluorite, sklodowskite, and uranocircite.

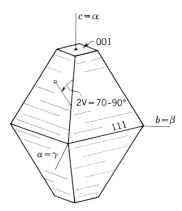

FIG. 2.37. Optical orientation of soddyite (adapted from Gorman, 1952; *Am. Mineralogist*).

Also a relatively uncommon constituent of the outer silicate alteration zone in gummite after uraninite. Noted thus by Frondel (1956B) at the Ruggles, N.H., pegmatite. Synthesized by Gruner (1952) at 180°C and higher.

Identification. Resembles kasolite megascopically but differs in having much lower indices, $(-)$ sign, and larger 2V; also kasolite is monoclinic. Strongest x-ray lines (Frondel et al., 1956): 3.32, 4.48, 6.14.

Uranophane

Composition. $Ca(UO_2)_2(SiO_3)_2(OH)_2 \cdot 5H_2O$. $UO_3 = 67\%$. Some Mg may proxy for Ca, and some analyses show appreciable amounts of Cu, Co, Ni, and Fe. Minor Al, Pb, Ba, and Sr also have been detected, as has PO_4. Uranotile, α-uranotile, and lambertite are synonyms. Dimorphous with beta-uranophane (Gorman and Nuffield, 1955). Smith et al. (1957) suggest that the formula is $Ca(H_3O)_2(UO_2)_2(SiO_4)_2 \cdot 3H_2O$.

Occurrence. Uranophane is the most abundant and most widely distributed of the various uranium silicates; in fact it is one of the most common of the secondary uranium minerals. Commonly associated with such species as autunite, torbernite, and beta-uranophane; also as the chief constituent of the outer silicate zone of the gummite type of alteration of uraninite. Most uranophane appears to be of supergene origin, appearing in the oxidized parts of deposits—pegmatites, veins, lodes, and Colorado Plateau type of deposits. Some uranophane in pegmatites may be hydrothermal in origin. Of the many occurrences the following may be noted: United States, numerous pegmatites in the Spruce Pine district, N.C.; in New Hampshire (Ruggles, Palermo); in Maine; in Connecticut; in Colorado; in the Black Hills; at the Silver Cliff mine near Lusk, Wyo., along fractures and as replacements in sandstone (Larsen et al., 1926; Wilmarth and Johnson, 1954); at Stone Mountain, Ga., along fractures in granite; in the Grants district, N.Mex., coating limestone; in sandstone at Pumpkin Buttes, and at the Cato Sells deposit, Poison

Basin area, Wyo.; Monument Valley district, Ariz.; Freedom No. 2 mine, Marysvale, Utah; several deposits, White Canyon district, San Juan County, Utah; Henry Mountains, Utah; Grey Dawn mine, Paradox district, Utah; in silicified breccia, Atlanta mine, Lincoln County, Nev., and the W. Wilson mine, Clancy, Mont.; in Tertiary welded tuff, Quinn Canyon, Presidio County, Tex.

In Canada: Theano Point, Ont.; Lake Athabasca district, Sask. (e.g., Nicholson and Gunnar Lake mines); Eldorado mine, Great Bear Lake; Wilberforce, Ont.; Dyno mines, Cardiff Township, Ont.; and Kenora district, Ont.

Reported from Mexico (Gorman and Nuffield, 1955) and from Calamuchita, Córdoba, Argentina. In Africa abundant at Luiswishi, Kasolo, and Shinkolobwe, Katanga, Belgian Congo; Namaqualand (pegmatitic?); Morogoro, Tanganyika (pegmatitic).

Widespread in the Bavaria-Saxony-Bohemia uranium districts: at Wölsendorf and Nabburg (Bavaria), Joachimsthal, Schneeberg, Neustädtel, Johanngeorgenstadt, Aue, Henneberg b. Wurzbach (Thuringia), Eisleben in the Harz (Graf Hohenthal and Vitzthum mines); and Schmiedeberg and Kupferberg (Silesia). Also occurs in the pitchblende deposits of Portugal; in many of France: La Faye, Lachaux, La Crouzille, Margnac, Gourmand, Saint-Rémy-sur-Durolles, La Vaufranche, Bauzot, and many others; with kasolite, pitchblende, and copper minerals in pegmatite, Straumsheia, Norway (Neumann, 1954); and in Karelia, U.S.S.R. In Rajputana, India (pegmatitic).

Identification. Lower indices than beta-uranophane. Absence of essential Cu distinguishes it from cuprosklodowskite. Strongest x-ray lines: 7.88, 3.94, 2.99, 2.91.

Beta-uranophane

Composition. $Ca(UO_2)_2(SiO_3)_2(OH)_2 \cdot 5H_2O$. $UO_3 = 67\%$. On the basis of considerable variation of optical properties, Steinocher and Novacek (1939) concluded that variable H_2O content is insufficient to account for the range in optics and suggested it was due to Pb for Ca or variation in the degree of oxidation of U. The latter seems unlikely, since the mineral occurs in the oxidized zone, but Branche et al. (1951) have established the presence of traces of Pb and Fe. Beta-uranotile is a synonym. Randite is a mixture of beta-uranophane, tyuyamunite, and calcite. Dimorphous with uranophane. Can be converted to uranophane by strong pressure during grinding (Weeks and Thompson, 1954).

Occurrence. A secondary supergene constituent of uraniferous pegmatites, veins, and lodes. Some well-studied pegmatite occurrences include Spruce Pine, N.C. (Deer Park and Flat Rock mines); Newry, Maine; Bedford, N.Y. (originally called schroeckingerite by Armstrong, 1935); Ruggles and Palermo pegmatites, N.H.; Moye pegmatite, near Barnesville, Lamar County, Ga.; Faraday Township, Hastings County, Ont.; on samarskite at Sankara, Nellore, India; Rajputana, India; La Chiquita mine, San Javia, Córdoba, Argentina. In pegmatites it may be a constituent of the outer silicate alteration zone in gummite after uraninite. Representative of vein deposits are: Joachimsthal, Bohemia (Novacek, 1935); Wölsendorf, Bavaria, and Graf Hohenthal mine, Eisleben, Harz Mts., Germany; in France especially at Lachaux, Bigay, at Gourmand, at the Bauzot mine at Saint-Rémy-sur-Durolles, and at Margnac, Brugeaud, and La Crouzille; with uranophane and other secondary uranium

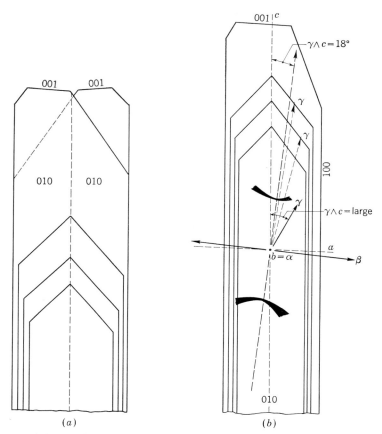

Fig. 2.38. (*a*) Zoned, twinned crystal of beta-uranophane (Steinocher and Nova-cek, 1939). (*b*) Optical orientation of zoned beta-uranophane (adapted from Steinocher and Novacek, 1939).

minerals in a gold-quartz vein at Radhausberg, Badgastein, Austria. In Canada, at Theano Point, Ont., in MacNicol Township, Kenora district, Ont. (Satterly, 1955), in granite pegmatite, lot 23, conc. A, Faraday Township, Hastings County, Ont., and in Huddersfield Township, Pontiac County, Quebec, on marble with uranoan thorianite (Gorman and Nuffield, 1955). In the United States at Easton, Pa.; possibly on the Colorado Plateau (Weeks and Thompson, 1954); at the Freedom No. 2 mine, Marysvale, Utah, with uranophane. In an oxidized pitchblende vein, W. Wilson mine, Clancy, Mont. Inclusions of an earlier phase of the Chalk Mountain rhyolite porphyry intrusive near Climax, Colo., contain beta-uranophane and pitchblende(?) (King et al., 1953).

Identification. Differs from uranophane in having inclined extinction, higher indices, and, in some cases, a larger 2V. Strongest x-ray lines: 7.83, 3.90, 3.51.

Sklodowskite

Composition. $Mg(UO_2)_2(SiO_3)_2(OH)_2 \cdot 6H_2O$. $UO_3 = 68\%$. K, Na, Te, Co, and Ni are reported in traces (in impurities?). Chinkolobwite is a synonym. Gelatinizes with acid.

Occurrence. A very rare secondary mineral. Found principally at Shinkolobwe, Katanga, Belgian Congo, where it is relatively common as disseminations in the oxidized zone. Also fills fractures in a siliceous breccia. Associates are uranophane, curite, soddyite, schoepite, and kasolite. Reported from Wölsendorf, Bavaria, by Bültemann (1954). Said to be an uncommon constituent of the outer, silicate zone of gummite-type alterations of uraninite (Frondel, 1956B). Occurs in the Goldfields area, Sask. Reported at the Oyler Tunnel claim, southeast of Fruita, Utah, in sandstone (Gruner and Gardiner, 1952). Found in the Honeycomb Hills area near Callao, Utah, with fluorite, soddyite, and uranocircite.

Identification. First a definition as a silicate (acid gelatinization), and then a test for Mg (absence of Ca and Cu). Strongest x-ray lines (Gorman, 1957): 8.04, 4.08, 3.23.

Cuprosklodowskite

Composition. $Cu(UO_2)_2(SiO_3)_2(OH)_2 \cdot 5H_2O$. $UO_3 = 65\%$. Isostructural with sklodowskite.

Occurrence. A very rare secondary silicate formed in the weathering zone of pitchblende deposits that also contain some primary copper minerals. Found originally at Kalongwe, Belgian Congo, in fissures in a talcose argillaceous rock. Occurs also at Joachimsthal and Johanngeorgenstadt, Erzgebirge (Novacek, 1935), at the former on limonitic gangue ("uranochalcite"). Reported at the Nicholson No. 1 Extension vein, Goldfields district, Sask. (Hogarth, 1951), associated with uranophane, and also in another deposit in the district. Found as thin green fracture coatings with brochantite in becquerelite at the Posey mine, White Canyon district, Utah (Weeks and Thompson, 1954); with ardennite in the Grants district, N.Mex. (Sun and Weber, 1955); and at the Frey No. 4 mine, San Juan County, Utah (Gruner and Gardiner, 1952). With dioptase in a sandstone at Amelal in the region of Argana Bigoudine, Morocco (Chervet and Branche, 1955).

Identification. Sklodowskite has somewhat lower refractive indices and a large 2V, and β parallel to the elongation. Uranophane is optically somewhat similar but has stronger birefringence and r < v, extreme. Strongest x-ray lines: 8.18, 4.09, 2.97.

Kasolite

Composition. $Pb(UO_2)(SiO_3)(OH)_2$. $UO_3 = 48$ to 49%. Traces of Fe^3, Ca, and Mg are reported by Buttgenbach (1925B), traces of Fe^3, Na, Ba, and Cu by Branche et al. (1951).

Occurrence. A secondary supergene alteration in pitchblende veins. At Kasolo, Belgian Congo, in close association with curite, schoepite, soddyite, and uranophane. Also at Kalongwe, Belgian Congo. In France at La Faye, Grury, Saône-et-Loire, with torbernite, at Bigay (with torbernite), and Reliez (with renardite), Lachaux, Puy-de-Dôme; at Boko Songho (Branche et al.,

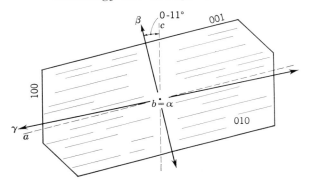

Fig. 2.39. Optical orientation of kasolite.

1951); and at Les Bois Noirs, Loire (Chervet and Branche, 1955). At Urgeirica, Portugal; Wölsendorf, Bavaria; and Tyndrum, Perthshire, England.

At Marysvale, Utah. With torbernite in veins and impregnations in gneiss and amphibolite in the Eureka Gulch area, Central City district, Gilpin County, Colo. (Sims et al., 1955). At Duffields, El Paso County, Colo., in a vein with pitchblende(?) in granite. In a vein with oxidized Pb, Zn, and Cu minerals at the Green Monster mine, Clark County, and the West Willys claim in veins with pitchblende, East Walker River, Lyon County, both in Nevada (Lovering, 1954). At the White Oak mine, Nogales, Ariz. With uranophane in sedimentary rocks 0.4 mi south of Penn Haven Junction, Carbon County, Pa. In magnetite-allanite–rich bands in granite gneiss, with uraninite, uranophane, and metatorbernite, West Milford, N.J.

At the No. 1 zone Extension, Nicholson mine, Lake Athabasca, Sask., with metazeunerite, uranophane, and cuprosklodowskite (Hogarth, 1951), and at the Bolger group, Lake Athabaska. At Wölsendorf, Bavaria. In pegmatite with copper minerals and pitchblende in Straumsheia, Norway (Neumann, 1954). Occurs in the silicate zone of gummite with uranophane after uraninite. Frondel (1956B) has recognized it in this type of occurrence at the Ruggles pegmatite, N.H.; at Kakanas and Gordonia, Africa; and at Bisundi, Rajputana, India. Synthesized at 180°C and higher by Gruner (1952).

Identification. The only uranyl silicate with major Pb. Strongest x-ray lines: 3.26, 2.93, 4.19.

Boltwoodite

$K_2(UO_2)_2(SiO_3)_2(OH)_2 \cdot 5H_2O$ (Frondel and Ito, 1956). Structurally related to sklodowskite. Occurs at the Delta mine, San Rafael Swell, Utah, with brochantite, becquerelite, gypsum, and an unidentified uranyl silicate, coating fractures in sandstone. Also as an alteration of thorian uraninite in serpentinite at Easton, Pa., with thorogummite and uranophane (Montgomery, 1957). Strongest x-ray lines: 6.81, 3.39, 2.94.

Doubtful or Poorly Defined Species

Droogmansite

Composition not known. Not a phosphate. Soluble in HCl (Buttgenbach, 1925A). Acicular and tabular crystals. Orange yellow, nonpleochroic. Weak birefringence, parallel extinction, $(-)$ elongation. *Bxa* normal to plates. Biaxial $(-)$, strong dispersion, $n > 1.74$. Occurs at Shinkolobwe, Belgian Congo, as small globules ($<\frac{1}{2}$ mm) of radial fibrous structure on sklodowskite with curite and cobaltian wad.

Gastunite

Spectrographic analyses show main constituents are U, Ca, Si, and some Pb. X-ray pattern different from uranophane and beta-uranophane (Haberlandt and Schiener, 1951). Yellow green. Pleochroic weakly, α = colorless to pale citron yellow = 1.596, γ = darker citron yellow = 1.597. Parallel extinction. As hemispherical spherulites of radial fibers on desmine with uranophane, beta-uranophane, schroeckingerite, zippeite(?), a Pb-U silicate, and two other unidentified uranium minerals in a gold-quartz vein at Radhausberg, Badgastein, Hohe Tauern, Austria.

Orlite

$3PbO \cdot 3UO_3 \cdot 4SiO_2 \cdot 6H_2O(?)$ (Melkov, 1956; Getseva and Savel'eva, 1956; Soboleva and Pudovkina, 1957; Fleischer, 1958). $UO_3 = 43.57\%$. Gelatinizes in HCl. Radial aggregates of minute acicular crystals. Light creamy yellow. Not fluorescent. Waxy luster. Parallel extinction, negative elongation. $\beta = 1.788$, $\gamma = 1.793$. Occurs in the U.S.S.R. at one locality in the middle zone of an oxidized uranium deposit in rhyolite with uranophane and kasolite. Resembles kasolite. Strongest x-ray lines: 3.23, 1.68, 1.97, 1.85.

THUCOLITE AND RELATED RADIOACTIVE HYDROCARBON COMPLEXES

Composition. Uraniferous mineral hydrocarbon complexes have been known since 1868 (Davidson and Bowie, 1951) and have been described under numerous names—"anthracite," "coal," grahamite, glance pitch, carburan, asphaltite, sogrenite, and anthraxolite. In 1928 Ellsworth (1928A) applied the name thucolite to a radioactive hydrocarbon that occurs in Canadian pegmatites. The name describes the composition in elements: Th, U, C, O + -lite. Since then the term has been generally accepted as a generic name for radioactive mineral hydrocarbon assemblages in which one or more hydrocarbons or oxyhydrocarbons are admixed with a radioactive mineral, commonly uraninite (or pitchblende) (Davidson and Bowie, 1951; Bowie, 1955; Davidson, 1955).

Some 20 analyses of thucolites from various localities show the following ranges in composition:

Fixed C	23–61%, generally 42–52%
Volatiles	26–40%
Ash	7–38%, generally 15–27%

TABLE 2.15. *Properties of the uranyl silicate minerals*

Mineral	Form	Color, Streak (S), Luster (L), Fluorescence (F)	Pleochroism	Indices and orientation	Cleavage and fracture	H	G
Soddyite	Orthorhombic. Euhedra of dipyramidal habit. Also elongate with c; equidimensional; platy. Heavily striated. Some barrel-shaped. Parallel to divergent clusters	Greenish yellow, canary yellow, amber. S pale yellow. L vitreous to adamantine; opaque types dull; massive material earthy. F none or dull orange brown	Weak α = colorless β = pale yellow γ = pale green yellow. Larger crystals largely opaque	$\alpha = c = 1.650$–1.654 $\beta = b = 1.68$–1.685 $\gamma = a = 1.699$–1.715 (–) 2V = 70–90°. No appreciable dispersion (Gorman, 1952)	(001) perfect. (111) good	3–4	4.70
Uranophane	Monoclinic. Prismatic to acicular euhedra, elongate with b, in reticulate and divergent clusters. Scaly crusts and films; anhedra in powdery masses	Pale yellow, yellow, orange yellow. S pale yellow. L pearly to greasy; needle aggregates are silky; massive material is earthy to waxy. F none or faint yellow green	α = colorless β = pale yellow γ = pale to canary yellow	$\alpha = 1.641$–1.645 $\beta = 1.664$–1.667 $\gamma = b = 1.667$–1.672 (–) 2V = 32–45°. r < v marked to strong. Extinction angles small	(100) perfect	2–3	3.68–3.86
Beta-uranophane	Monoclinic. Minute acicular crystals elongated with c, flattened on (010) in radial tufts or reticulate groups. (100) faces vertically striated. Some twinning on (100) into two units	Greenish to orange yellow. S pale yellow. L silky for acicular type, vitreous to greasy for larger crystals, pearly (010), waxy for scaly aggregates. F none or dull yellowish to weak green; also bright green (Satterly, 1955) and zoned (Haberlandt and Schiener, 1951)	Strong α = colorless to yellowish $\beta = \gamma$ = lemon, deep, or greenish yellow	$\alpha = b = 1.661$–1.67 $\beta = 1.682$–1.70 $\gamma = 1.689$–1.710 Zoned crystals have centers with lower indices and birefringence and larger extinction angles than margins. (–) 2V = 35–70°. r > v extreme crossed dispersion. $\gamma \wedge c = 18$–62°. Abnormal interference tints may appear	(010) perfect, also (100)	2–3	3.98

Sklodow-skite	Monoclinic. Minute prisms elongate with *b*. Fine-grained anhedral and felted masses. Radial fibrous aggregates	Citron yellow. S pale yellow. L pearly. F none or pale yellowish to yellowish green	Strong α = colorless β = yellow γ = pale yellow	α = 1.613 β = b = 1.635 γ = 1.657 (−), 2V large, r < v distinct	(100) perfect	2-3	3.54, 3.64
Cuprosklo-dowskite	Orthorhombic. Minute prisms or needles elongated with *c*, somewhat flattened on (100)(?). Radial groups, reniform crusts, thin films	Grass green. Green cores and greenish yellow margins may appear. S pale green. L pearly, silky, dull	α = β = yellowish green to colorless γ = pale greenish yellow	α = a = 1.653-1.655 β = b = 1.662-1.663 γ = c = 1.662-1.665 Interference tints may be abnormal. (−) 2V small, r > v strong	(100) (010)	3-4	3.5
Boltwoodite	Orthorhombic or monoclinic(?). Fibrous aggregates as fracture coatings. If monoclinic, elongated along *b*.	Yellow. F weak dull green	α = colorless β = γ = yellow	α = 1.668 β = 1.696(?) γ = 1.703 (+) parallel extinction in fibers			3.6
Kasolite	Monoclinic. Minute prisms elongate with *b* or (001) tablets in radial groups. Anhedral granular; colloform crusts	Yellow to brownish yellow. Also green (Fe) (Branche et al., 1951). Gray to nearly black. S pale yellow to brown or green to gray. L resinous to greasy	Nil or faint in greenish yellows	α = b = 1.877-1.90 β = 1.880-1.910 γ = 1.935-1.96 (+) 2V = 40-50°, dispersion weak. β ∧ c = 1-11°	(001) perfect. (100) and (010) difficult	4-5	5.83-5.96

123

The ash contains from 1 to 70% U_3O_8, <1 to 48% ThO_2, <1 to 35% rare-earth oxides (both Ce and Y groups), and small to trace amounts of Na, K, Ca, Mg, Mn, Fe^3, Al, Si, Ti, B, Co, Ni, Zn, Pb, Cu, Zr, W, Be, V, As, and P in various assemblages. A titanium-rich (TiO_2 = 4.5%) variety (titanothucolite) also is known (Aminoff, 1943; Grip and Ödman, 1944).

Polished section studies (Davidson and Bowie, 1951) reveal the presence of admixed (1) uraninite, thorianite(?) or thorian uraninite, usually with one or more sulfides from the group: pyrite, pyrrhotite, arsenopyrite, chalcopyrite, bornite, covellite, and galena; (2) quartz or calcite, and (3) rare gold. Thus most, if not all, of the metallic elements of the ash may be referred to the various inclusions. Barthauer et al. (1953) have shown that the volatile material of thucolite from Ontario consists mainly of water, carbon dioxide, and methane, with lesser nitrogen, carbon monoxide, and hydrogen, and that the composition of the "volatile" fractions is a function of the particular technique used to evolve them. Also detected in thucolites are A, S, Cl, and F.

Structure and form. Highly variable: as nodules, reniform to botryoidal masses, seams, veinlets, dendritic aggregates, and partial to nearly complete pseudomorphs after uraninite crystals (cubic ± dodecahedral faces). Ellsworth (1928B) also records thucolite pseudomorphous after tourmaline at the Wallingford mine, Quebec. Outer surfaces of nodules may have embedded or intergrown cyrtolite. Also forms rims on or fills cracks in uraninite (and pitchblende). Included pitchblende appears in subangular grains, in ovoid, spherical, or hemispherical particles and granules, thin fracture fillings, and cavity fillings. The pitchblende particles commonly range in size from several tens of microns to less than one micron. Syneresis cracks in thucolite may also be filled by sulfides and carbonate as well as by pitchblende.

Optical properties. Jet black. Black to brown-black streak. Brilliant to resinous luster. Opaque. In polished sections one to three different hydrocarbons have been detected, of varying grayish hues and optical properties. Some are strongly anisotropic (in grays and browns) others moderately anisotropic; still others are isotropic. Some are weakly pleochroic. Reflectivity is variable, between 4 to 15% (Davidson and Bowie, 1951; Ramdohr, 1955B). Undulatory extinction characterizes some varieties.

Physical properties. Conchoidal fracture. Commonly brittle. Also may be friable. H = 2.5 to 4. G = 1.512 to 2.066. Can be burned.

Occurrence. In pegmatites and hydrothermal veins and lodes. Pegmatitic localities include: Conger and Henvey Townships, Perry Sound district, Ont.; Wallingford feldspar pegmatite, near Buckingham, Quebec; De Kalb junction, Lawrence County, N.Y.; Amaki village, Fukuoka prefecture, Japan; various Swedish pegmatites, e.g., Österby, Dalarna—"asphaltite"—(Mason and Roberts, 1949); and northern Karelia, U.S.S.R. Vein and lode localities include: Front Range, Colo.; Moonta Mines, South Australia; Boliden mine, Sweden (titanothucolite); various skarn iron-ore deposits in Sweden (Dannemora); Nicholson mine, Goldfields, Sask.; Port Arthur area, Ont., in Ag veins (nickeliferous anthraxolite); Blind River, Ont.; Laxey, Isle of Man; very extensive in gold ores of the Witwatersrand, in South Africa and Transvaal. Hydrocarbons similar to thucolite occur in several areas on the Colorado Plateau, especially at and near Temple Mountain, San Rafael Swell, Utah; also in vein deposits at the Black King and White Spar mines near Placerville, Colo. Asphaltic pellets that contain uraninite, smaltite, and an unidentified uranium mineral occur in shale and sandstone (Permian) in southwestern Oklahoma (Hill, 1954). Believed to have been formed by the polymerization of natural gases (or possibly petroleum fractions) by radioactive minerals (Davidson and Bowie, 1951).

Identification. Volatility and lack of structure.

Minerals with Minor U, Th, or Ra

OXIDES

Baddeleyite

According to Nininger (1954, pp. 228–229), baddeleyite "may contain appreciable thorium and small amounts of uranium." The ideal composition is ZrO_2, probably with variable Hf and minor Ti, Fe^3, Mg, Ca, Mn, Al, and alkalies. Monoclinic. Prismatic crystals flattened with (100); (100) and prism faces vertically striated. Also radially fibrous, in concentric bands in botryoidal masses. Usually twinned, commonly on (100) and polysynthetically, also on (110) or combined (110) and (100); rarely on (201). Colorless, yellow, green, red brown, brown, black; streak white to brownish white. Colorless to brown in transmitted light; dark types translucent only on thin edges. May show color bands. Pleochroic in shades of yellow, green, and brown. Biaxial (−). $2V = 30°$, $r > v$, strong. $\alpha = 2.13$, 2.136; $\gamma = 2.20$, 2.243. $\alpha \wedge c = 13°$. Cleavage (001) nearly perfect; also (110) and (010). $H = 6.5$. $G = 5.4$ to 6.02.

Occurs in gem placer gravels on Ceylon. In diamond placers of the Verdinho River, Brazil. Also in Brazil at Jacupiranga in the contact marble zone and as pebbles and radial fibrous masses in the Serra de Caldas, Minas Gerais. Caldasite is a zirconium ore from Caldas, Minas Gerais and São Paulo, Brazil, consisting of a mixture of fibrous baddeleyite, zircon, and altered zircon (Fig. 2.40). Brazilite and zirkite are similar. Such material contains nil to 0.92% U_3O_8; in caldasite from Morro do Bloca, Cascata, Aquas da Prata, São Paulo $eU_3O_8 = 2.9\%$ (Guimarães et al., 1953). It is not known, however, whether the radioactivity is in baddeleyite, or in zircon, or in both. Baddeleyite occurs at Mt. Somma, Italy, in contact-metamorphosed blocks of sanidinite. In gold placers of Nedi, Kilo, Belgian Congo, and in talus with zircon and thorianite at Phalaborwa, eastern Transvaal, derived from carbonatites (Hiemstra, 1955). Reported from the Davis Mountains, Tex.

Perovskite

$(Ca,Na,Ce)(Ti,Nb)O_3$. Other varieties have Fe^2, Fe^3, Na, and Y earths. Cerian, alkaline, niobian perovskite is called loparite, which may be radio-

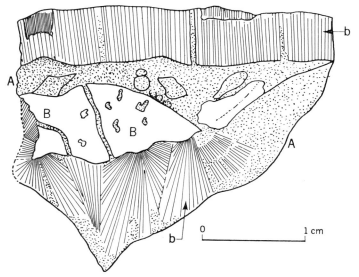

Fig. 2.40. Caldasite, Poços de Caldas, Minas Gerais, Brazil. Veinlets of fine-grained zircon (A) cutting massive baddeleyite (B). Some baddeleyite in cross-fiber veins and radial-fibrous aggregates (b) (Franco and Loewenstein, 1948; *Am. Mineralogist*).

active, with Th = 0.68 to 0.75%, U = 0.032 to 0.054%, Ra = 1.09 to 1.80×10^{-9} (Bohnstedt et al., 1937). Irinite is a thorian variety of loparite, $(\mathrm{Na,Ce,Th})_{1-x}$ $(\mathrm{Ti,Nb})[\mathrm{O}_{3-x}(\mathrm{OH})_x]$, with Th = 11.4% (Frondel and Fleischer, 1955).

Crystals of loparite are isometric in form but anisotropic, having inverted to monoclinic or orthorhombic structure. Crystals are cubic or cubo-octahedral; other forms are common. Penetration twins on (111) are nearly universal. Occurs almost exclusively as crystals or crystal groups, 1 mm to 1½ cm across. Black to gray black. Brown streak. Metallic luster. In transmitted light brownish red. May be zoned with brownish-red core, yellowish-red margin. Divided into anisotropic sections. n = 2.3 to 2.4. H = 5.5 to 6. G = 4.75 to 4.89. Irregular fracture.

Occurs in the nepheline-syenitic plutons of the Khibina tundra, U.S.S.R., in segregations and pegmatites and as an accessory mineral of the rocks themselves, particularly in the contact zone with sphene, nepheline, aegirine, eudialyte, and microcline; less usually with albite, astrophyllite, and ramsayite. Radioactive perovskite also occurs with betafite and pyrochlore in metasomatized marbles associated with alkalic intrusives in the Oka district, Two Mountains County, Quebec.

RARE-EARTH CARBONATES

Specimens of most of the rare-earth carbonate minerals shown in Table 2.16 are known to contain very small amounts of Th or Th and U.

TABLE 2.16. *Composition and radioactivity of rare-earth carbonates*

Name	Composition	% Th ± U reported
Ancylite.........	$(Ce,La)_4(Sr,Ca)_3(CO_3)_7(OH)_4 \cdot 3H_2O$	$ThO_2 = 0.20\%$
Bastnaesite.......	$(Ce,La)FCO_3$	$<1\%$ Th + U; up to 0.39% Th
Cordylite........	$(Ce,La)_2Ba(CO_3)_3F_2$	$ThO_2 = 0.30\%$
Doverite.........	$YCa(CO_3)_2F$	$ThO_2 = 1.62\%$
Lanthanite.......	$(La,Ce)_2(CO_3)_3 \cdot 8H_2O$	
Parisite..........	$(Ce,La)_2Ca(CO_3)_3F_2$	$ThO_2 = $ trace; 0.03% eU; 0.002% U
Roentgenite......	$(Ce,La)_2Ca_2(CO_3)_4F_2$	?
Synchisite.......	$(Ce,La)Ca(CO_3)_2F$	$ThO_2 = 0.30$
Tengerite........	$CaY_3(CO_3)_4(OH)_3 \cdot 3H_2O$	$ThO_2 = 0.3$

All are rare minerals, except bastnaesite which occurs abundantly in carbonatite at Mountain Pass, San Bernardino County, where it is a Ce-earth ore mineral. Burbankite, $(Na,Ca,Sr,Ba,Ce)_6(CO_3)_5$, and calkinsite, $(Ce,La)_2(CO_3)_3 \cdot 4H_2O$, (Pecora and Kerr, 1953) are not radioactive; nor is sahamalite, $(Mg,Fe^2)(Ce,La)_2(CO_3)_4$ (Jaffe et al., 1953).

SULFATE

Radiobarite

A variety of barite containing Ra. Hokutolite, a plumbian variety of barite, probably contains Ra, Th, and U, and occurs as hot springs deposits at Hokuto, Taiwan Island, and at Shibukuro, Japan. The radioactivity of Shibukuro barites ranges from 0.32 to 1.37×10^{-10} curies; that of Hokuto material is 2.06×10^{-10} curies (Ohashi, 1920).

Hoffman (1940) found U values for spring-deposited barites from Teplitz and Karlsbad, Czechoslovakia, as follows:

1. Honey-colored barite, Teplitz
   Surface of crystal .... $4 \times 10^{-4}\%$ U
   In crystals .... $2 \times 10^{-4}\%$ U
2. Blue-green barite, Teplitz, Hügel Spring .... $1.5 \times 10^{-2}\%$ U
3. Green-blue barite, Steinbad Spring .... $1.4 \times 10^{-2}\%$ U
4. Honey-colored barite, Tetschen .... $7 \times 10^{-6}\%$ U

Some of the Ra appears to have been adsorbed surficially.

Radiobarite is reportedly relatively abundant in the upper parts of the Tyuya Muyun deposits of Ferghana Valley, in Soviet central Asia, along with uranyl vanadates and reported radiocarbonate, $(Ca,Ra)CO_3$.

Radiobarite (0.001% U; 0.077% eU) is reported by Hill and Beroni (1953) from a tuffaceous spring deposit overlying basal Permian formations in the Limestone Hills area, Kiowa County, Okla. The uranium may be related to nearby uraniferous asphaltic pellets. The mineral is also known from the Bitter Creek mine, Colorado Plateau, Colo., and at La Baja, Colombia (Bueno, 1955).

PHOSPHATES

Apatite

Fluorapatite is $Ca_5(PO_4)_3F_2$. A wide variation in composition is possible in apatite:

for Ca: Ce earths, Y earths, Sr, Ba, Na, Mn, Mg, Pb, also Th and minor U^4. Ra may be possible (McConnell, 1953)
for F: OH, Cl, S, and extra O
for PO_4: SO_4, AsO_4, VO_4, CrO_4, SiO_4, AlO_4, CO_3OH

Radioactive varieties of apatite fall into two main categories: rare-earth-bearing types and marine carbonate-fluorapatite. In primary igneous apatite, U is typically $0.00x\%$; some late-stage igneous apatite has $0.0x\%$ U.

Th-bearing types include abukumalite ($ThO_2 = 0.90$), $(Ca,Y)(Si,P,Al)O_4$-(O,F), which is very rare, and occurs with euxenite in a pegmatite at Iisaka, Abukuma range, Fukushima prefecture, Japan. Rare-earth fluorapatite with 0.15% ThO_2 and 0.32% U occurs in magnetite ore in the Old Bed and Smith mines, Mineville, N.Y. (McKeown and Klemic, 1953; McKelvey, 1956). Erikite, a hydrous silicophosphate containing Ca, Na, Ce earths, and Al, with $ThO_2 = 3.26\%$ is similar to abukumalite. It occurs in foidal syenite pegmatite with arfvedsonite, aegirine, analcite, and natrolite at Nunarssuatsiaq, Julianehaab district, Greenland. Erikite from Khibina, U.S.S.R., has $ThO_2 = 0.32\%$.

In carbonate-fluorapatite, which may contain up to about 0.02% U, U substitutes for Ca in the apatite structure (Altschuler et al., 1954); the ionic radii are nearly identical: $Ca = 1.06$ A, $U^4 = 1.05$ A. The anisotropic ("crystalline") variety is called francolite; the cryptocrystalline, isotropic variety is called collophane. Francolite and collophane are the main varieties of apatite occurring in sedimentary phosphorites, which are widely distributed over the world in marine strata of many ages.

Carbonate-fluorapatite has the following properties: hexagonal, fibrous to fine-grained, massive, commonly in oolites, which are concentrically layered with some also showing radial fibrous structure, or in ovules, which are structureless, massive (Fig. 2.41). These bodies are generally ellipsoidal or may be flattened and indented, with cores of clastic mineral grains (especially quartz), pyrite cubes, or fossil fragments. Cores of oolites may be massive with zoning marginal. Some show color-banding; others show bleaching. In some types, zones of collophane and francolite alternate, or collophane alternates with calcite. Oolites may be veined or partly replaced by calcite or chalcedony. Carbonate-fluorapatite also forms larger ovoid masses, including pisolites, nodules,

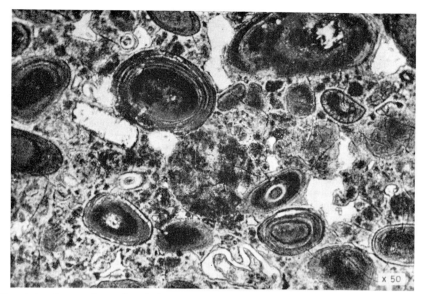

FIG. 2.41. Gray oolitic phosphorite with oolites of collophane and francolite layers; white quartz grains. Phosphoria formation, Deer Creek–Wells Canyon area, Idaho (Lowell, 1952, *U.S. Geol. Survey*).

and concretions and is the chief constituent of fossil bone, teeth, some invertebrate shells, and fecal pellets.

Color gray white, yellow, buff, brown and black. Luster dull, subresinous, weakly vitreous.

$\omega = 1.625$ to 1.630, $\epsilon = 1.614$ to 1.624. Also for very fine grained types with nonessential water, indices are lower, 1.56 to 1.61. Cleavage does not develop, fracture of massive material is irregular, blocky to subconchoidal. H = 3 to 4. G = 2.5 to 3.0.

Uraniferous carbonate-fluorapatite is widely distributed. Waxy, gray-green uraniferous carbonate-fluorapatite occurs as cement and fracture fillings in the Tertiary Wind River sandstone and conglomerates that are the host rocks for uranium mineralization at the Lucky Mc mine, Fremont County, Wyo. (Grutt, 1956). In the United States in the Phosphoria formation (Permian) of Montana, Idaho, Utah, and Wyoming; in Florida in the Bone Valley formation (Tertiary). Also in Mexico, Brazil, North Africa, France, Belgium, England, Ireland, Germany, and U.S.S.R. (pages 453–482).

The textural features are usually distinctive for the identification of carbonate-fluorapatite. Soluble in HCl or HNO_3 and shows slight effervescence.

Aluminum Phosphates

Wavellite, $Al_3(PO_4)_2(OH)_3 \cdot 5H_2O$, and crandallite (pseudowavellite), $CaAl_3(PO_4)_2(OH)_5 \cdot H_2O$, are the main phosphatic minerals in the lateroidal "leached zones" that overlie the marine phosphorites of Florida, Senegal, and Nigeria. The average U contents of these materials are:

Florida	0.012% U_3O_8
Senegal	400 g/ton
Nigeria	0.006–0.011% eU_3O_8

Millisite, $(Na,K)CaAl_6(PO_4)_4(OH)_9 \cdot 3H_2O$, also occurs in the Florida leached zone. Altschuler et al. (1955) report for the Florida phosphates:

Concentrated crandallite and millisite	0.03–0.04% U
Concentrated pure wavellite	0.002–0.004% U

Since only traces of secondary uranium minerals have been found in these deposits, it seems probable that the uranium is in the aluminum phosphate minerals, although doubtless some of the uranium is in residual collophane. In crandallite it may substitute for Ca, but this is not possible for wavellite. Evansite, $Al_3(PO_4)(OH)_6 \cdot 6H_2O$, also is reported to be slightly radioactive, rarely. Since the "leached zones" are formed under oxidizing conditions and uranium in the parent francolite-collophane exists as U^4, it is possible that the element has been oxidized to U^6. It is improbable that U^6 can substitute either for P or for Al, in view of the great differences in ionic radii. This problem has been discussed by Altschuler et al. (1956) and by McKelvey (1956).

Fischerite, which is identical with wavellite (Fleischer, 1956) and is also reported to contain small amounts of uranium, occurs in fractures in shale and ferruginous sandstone at Nizhne Tagilsk in the Ural Mts., U.S.S.R.

The properties of wavellite and crandallite are shown in Table 2.17.

TABLE 2.17. *Properties of the aluminous phosphates*

Wavellite	Crandallite
Orthorhombic	Hexagonal
Radial fibrous	Fibrous, concentric layers
White, yellow, green, brown, black	White, yellow, gray
Streak white	Streak white
Vitreous to resinous luster	Vitreous to chalky luster
Biaxial (+)	Uniaxial (+)
$2V = 71°$, r > v weak	
$\alpha = b = 1.520–1.535$, greenish	$\epsilon = 1.59–1.631$
$\beta = a = 1.526–1.543$	$\omega = 1.60–1.622$
$\gamma = c = 1.545–1.561$, yellowish	
Cleavages (110) perfect, (101) and (010) distinct	Cleavage (0001) perfect
H = 3–4	H = 5
G = 2.36	G = 2.78–2.92

Xenotime

Composition. YPO_4. Other Y-group elements (Nd,Pd,Er,Tb,Ho), especially Er, usually present; also Ce, La, Sc. UO_2 up to about 5% (Yu, Japan); UO_3 up to about 3.5% reported. ThO_2 up to about 3.3%. Some varieties show very low radioactivity. Ca, Be, Al, Zr, Mn, Pb, and Fe^2 may be present in small amounts. SiO_4 in amounts up to several per cent, and SO_4 up to about 1% SO_3, can substitute for PO_4. Magnetic, approaching ilmenite.

Structure and form. Tetragonal. Isostructural with zircon. Habit long or short prismatic, like zircon. Terminated by (011). Common forms are (001), (100), (110), and (101). Usually in small euhedral crystals, simply developed. May be intergrown parallel with zircon; less usually with tourmaline. Rarely in botryoidal nodules (Kawabe, Japan). Zircon and magnetite specks may be included. Detrital grains are usually doubly terminated euhedra, slightly abraded or somewhat rounded prisms; some detrital basal plates also are known (Fig. 2.42). For properties see Table 2.8.

Occurrence.

1. As an accessory mineral of acid and alkali plutonic rocks, chiefly granite, syenite, less usually diorite.

2. As large grains and crystals in granitic pegmatites.

3. In veins of the Alpine type and in some other quartz or metallic veins.

4. As an accessory constituent of such metamorphic rocks as granite gneiss, quartzose gneiss, mica gneiss, mica schist, rarely marble.

5. Relatively common as a detrital mineral.

Some noteworthy pegmatite localities are: Iveland district, Norway, including, among others, the deposits Tveit, Birketveit, Ertveit, Omdal, Mölland, and Ljosland. Also elsewhere in Norway in Hitterö, Moss, Kragerö, Tvedestrand, Hvalo, Aro, and Naersto areas. Very rare in nepheline-syenite pegmatites of Langesundfjord area, Norway. At Ytterby, Sweden. At Kawabe, Ishikawa, Yu, and Iisaka, Japan. In El Paso County, Colo., in Cheyenne Canyon, with bastnaesite and tysonite. In the Bancroft district, Ont. (D. F. Hewitt, pers. com.). In Brazil at Machado, Minas Gerais and Rio de Contas, Bahia.

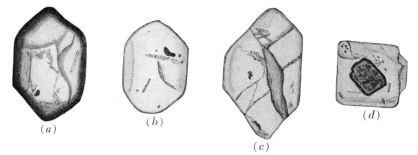

FIG. 2.42. Detrital xenotime, Snowy River dredge, New Zealand (Hutton, 1950; *Geol. Soc. Am.*). (*a*) In Canada balsam ($\times$215). (*b*)–(*d*) In hydrax ($n = 1.70$. (*b*)–(*c*) ($\times$215). (*d*) Worn basal plate ($\times$110).

Alpine vein occurrences are in Switzerland in the Binnenthal, in the Ta-vetschthal, on Mt. Fibia southwest of St. Gotthard, and at Cavradi. Xenotime occurs with monazite in cassiterite veins at Llallagua, Bolivia. With doverite, bastnaesite, hematite, and quartz at the Scrub Oaks iron mine at Dover, Morris County, N.J.

Detrital occurrences of note include: The gold placers of Burke, Henderson, Mitchell, and Alexander Counties, N.C., and those near Cartersville, Ga., and placers near Aiken, S.C. (Fig. 2.43). In river sands in North Westland, New Zealand. In alluvial deposits at Kiravoravo, Madagascar. In Brazil in Minas Gerais at Pomba, Machado, Diamantina; also with diamonds in Bahia. Eluvial xenotime with cassiterite and monazite is abundant on weathered granite in the Muntok district, Northwest Banka, Indonesia.

Identification. Resembles zircon in habit, but has lower indices and much higher birefringence. Sphene has higher indices and very marked dispersion. Monazite is biaxial. Can be withdrawn from a mixed xenotime-monazite ag-gregate by use of an Alnico magnet of suitable power. A field determination of xenotime can be made in reflected sunlight with a hand spectroscope (Mertie, 1953). Two absorption bands appear in the green, centering at 521 and 539 mμ, caused by Er and Ho, respectively,

SILICATES

Opal

$SiO_2 \cdot nH_2O$. Some varieties, particularly hyalite, are uraniferous, but the U content varies greatly, with some as low as U = 0.000048% (Frondel and Fleischer, 1955); some as high as U = 0.12% (Staatz and Bauer, 1951B). Radio-active opal shows very pale green to bright green fluorescence, the intensity of the response increasing with an increasing U content. The U is not in the form of crystalline inclusions, but, having been adsorbed early in process of the accumulation of the siliceous gels, is highly dispersed, probably commonly as colloidal uranyl sulfate, phosphate, or silicate.

Radioactive opals vary greatly in color. Some are glass clear (hyalite), many are milky, others are gray, yellowish, or greenish; even some purple varieties fluoresce greenish.

The index of refraction of opal increases with decreasing H_2O content, n = 1.406 to 1.460. Isotropic (amorphous). Vitreous to waxy luster. H = 5.5 to 6.5. G = 1.9 to 2.3, usually 2.1 to 2.2. Conchoidal fracture.

Uraniferous opal may be either supergene or hypogene. Much uraniferous opal occurs in silicic igneous rocks (both intrusive and extrusive), in pegma-tites, and in hydrothermal veins and lodes. Opal that occurs in basalts is very weakly to nonradioactive. Some notable pegmatitic examples include deposits in Mitchell County, N.C.; Bedford, N.Y.; Sementina, Bellinzona, Switzerland; Zelking, Melk, Austria; the island of Elba; Setesdal, Norway; Spitzkopje, South-West Africa; and Naegi and Tanokami, Japan. In granite of Stone Mountain, Ga., with uranophane. Examples of hydrothermal uraniferous opals occur at Radhausberg at Bockstein, Salzburg, Austria, with calcite and gypsum

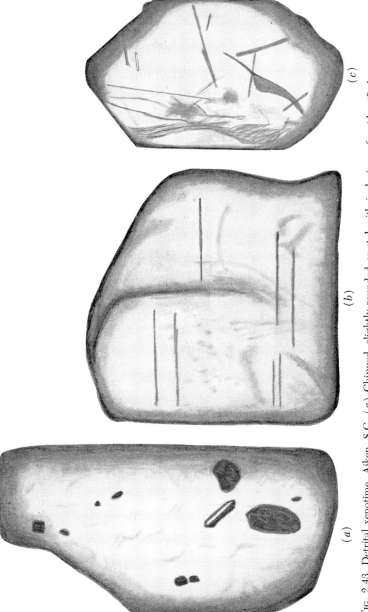

FIG. 2.43. Detrital xenotime, Aiken, S.C. (*a*) Chipped, slightly rounded crystal with inclusions of unidentified opaque minerals and an apatite(?) crystal (×240). (*b*) Basal plate, somewhat rounded (×240). (*c*) Euhedral crystal with red semi-opaque needles and fibrous clusters (×180).

133

in fissures in granite gneiss and in the uraniferous veins of the Boulder batholith, Mont. (e.g., the Free Enterprise prospect). Uraniferous opals also occur in or near some Colorado Plateau deposits, e.g., in the Shinarump conglomerate in the Monument Valley area, Utah (Lewis, 1955); the U content is 50 to 200 ppm. Uraniferous opals are widespread in volcanic ash and tuff, especially those of rhyolitic composition. Of exceptional extent and grade are the Virgin Valley, Nev., deposits where opal is in as many as 15 discontinuous layers as much as 6 ft thick and ½ mi long, parallel with the bedding (Staatz and Bauer, 1951B). Occurs along a zone of fracturing in a silicified Tertiary rhyolite at the Antelope Wells prospect, Hidalgo County, N.Mex.

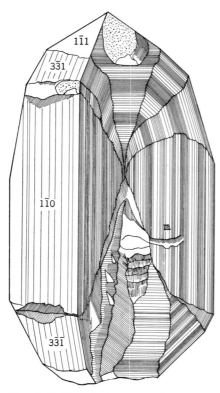

FIG. 2.44. Zoned zircon, syenite pegmatite, southern Norway (Brögger, 1890).

Zircon

Composition. Ideally $ZrSiO_4$. Usually U and Th are low, but as much as nearly 3% U and about 13% Th have been found in some varieties. The $\alpha/mg/hr$ count for about 40 zircons reported in the literature ranges from 10 to 1,500 (Larsen et al., 1952; Hurley, 1952; Jaffe, 1955). Higher activities also have been noted by Gottfried et al. (1956A), who found for 21 Ceylon zircons, $\alpha/mg/hr$ = 103 to 2,210 or U in ppm = 330 to 6,450. There is no close relationship between amount of radioactivity and type of rock or deposit. Zircons from a single rock generally show variable radioactivity. The Th/U ratio is relatively constant for accessory zircons from individual granite plutons (0.2 to 0.6). In large pegmatitic zircons the Th/U ratio is more varied, with a tendency to be higher in more radioactive zircons (0.1 to 2.2) (Hurley and Fairbairn, 1955).

Hf usually is present. The Hf/Zr ratio in zircons from granitic rocks is higher than that of Zr minerals from nepheline syenites (Barth, 1927). Zircon from granitic pegmatites has among the highest Hf/Zr ratios (Fleischer, 1955). In a comagmatic series the youngest rocks (most silicic) have zircon richest in Hf (Gottfried et al., 1956). The HfO_2 content of zircon may reach 16%, in alvite from Kragerö, Norway (Hevesy and Jantzen, 1924). Rare-earth elements also may be present up to a total of $(Y, Ce, etc.)_2O_3$ = about 16%, although usually much lower. The Y group predominates. Dennen and Shields

(1956) for 15 zircons found $Y_2O_3 = 1.6$ to 4.3%, with the mean near 2.5%. Detected have been Yb, Tm, Ho, Dy, Lu (Tilton et al., 1954), in addition to Y, Er, Ce, La.

Some zircons also contain Fe^3 and Fe^2; Ca, Mg in small amounts; and Mn, Mg, alkalies, Al, and Pb in minor amounts. Traces of B, Sr, V, Ga, Ti, Ba, Cr, Ag, Sn, and Cu have been noted (Tilton et al., 1954; Larsen et al., 1953). In a few zircons PO_4 substitutes for SiO_4 (yamagutilite).

Many zircons show alteration, particularly the more radioactive pegmatitic varieties known as cyrtolite or alvite. Such zircons contain considerable H_2O and are SiO_2-deficient (Frondel, 1953), allowing for the substitution $SiO_4—(OH)_4$ and their formulas may be expressed as: $Zr(SiO_4)_{1-x}(OH)_{4x}$. Malacon is a hydrated or altered zircon. Zircon has been synthesized hydrothermally in the range 150 to 700°C (Frondel et al., 1954) and with decreasing temperature of formation the unit cell volume increases, probably owing to increasing substitution of $(OH)_4$ for SiO_4. In some cyrtolites the radioactivity is nonuniform in distribution (Norton, 1957).

Zoning is common, including color-zoning and zoning of alternating crystalline and metamict shells (Fig. 2.44).

Structure and form. Tetragonal. Commonly euhedral or subhedral, in long prismatic (110) crystals with a square cross section, terminated by (111). Also in thick prisms with (100) and (311). In some varieties, especially cyrtolite, terminal faces are commonly curved. Knee-shaped twins, twinned on (101), occur. Also in anhedral masses and aggregates. Detrital zircon shows a variety of shapes from euhedral to rounded (Fig. 2.45); angular pieces are rare. Pink, red, and purple types (hyacinth) usually are more rounded than the colorless type. Since zircon is a very widespread and persistent heavy accessory detrital mineral and since it shows considerable variation in form, shape, size, color, zoning, and inclusions, it is used to a considerable extent in provenance determination of sediments and in reconstructing the parentage and history of metamorphic rocks. One widely measured characteristic is the elongation ratio (length/width or breadth). Zircon from sandstones is generally well rounded; euhedral crystals and angular fragments are minor; elongations usually are <2.0 (Poldervaart, 1955). In siltstones more broken zircon occurs and grains also are smaller. In clastic sediments partly rounded grains have been found which show sharply faced, crystallographically oriented outgrowths, usually localized on a prism face or on a pyramid (Butterfield, 1936; Smithson, 1937; Bond, 1948; Kilpady and Deshpande, 1955) (Fig. 2.46).

Zircons from felsic to intermediate plutonic rocks are euhedral, usually with elongations >2.0. Zircons from some granites regarded as autochthonous show outgrowths, overgrowth zoning, and parallel aggregates (Fig. 2.47) (Poldervaart and Eckelmann, 1955).

Inclusions are widespread, in many cases very minute or "dusty," giving the grains a turbid aspect. Inclusions are of gas, liquid, or other minerals (Fig. 2.48). Larger mineral grains also are included, among them apatite, monazite, xenotime, rutile, hematite, magnetite, ilmenite, cassiterite, biotite, tourmaline, and quartz. Some zircons show conspicuous microfractures. Large zircon crys-

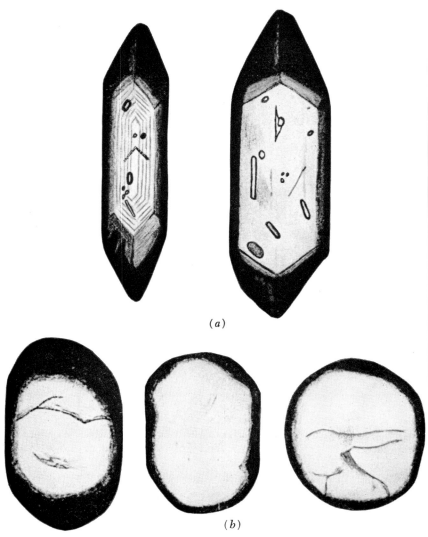

(a)

(b)

FIG. 2.45. (a) Euhedral detrital zircon with inclusions, Snowy River dredge, New Zealand (×100) (Hutton, 1950; *Geol. Soc. Am.*). The steep pyramid is (331) and the left grain also shows fine zoning. (b) Rounded detrital zircon, free of inclusions, Ngahere, New Zealand (×80) (Hutton, 1950; *Geol. Soc. Am.*).

136

tals with hollow cores (due to removal of cyrtolitic cores?) occur with allanite crystals in pegmatite in Pacoima Canyon, Los Angeles County, Calif. (Patchick, 1955).

Where zircons occur in iron-bearing minerals they are usually surrounded by a strong pleochroic halo; host species showing halos include biotite, chlorite, tourmaline, hornblende, andalusite, and cordierite.

Some zircons are metamict; others have metamict zones or parts; many of those relatively rich in U and/or Th show varying degrees of structural damage which reduces their refractive indices, density, and hardness and increases the size of the unit cell (Hurley and Fairbairn, 1953; Holland, 1954). The amount of structural damage is proportional to the total radiation received; thus zircons (except those of abnormal composition and those excessively heated since their formation) may be used as age determination minerals. In a zoned zircon from Quanah Mountain, Okla., with crystalline and metamict shells, Larsen et al. (1953) have demonstrated that the metamict parts are richer in both U and Th.

Frondel (1953) has shown that many altered zircons, especially those called cyrtolite, are pseudomorphous recrystallization products of metamict zircon, with a microgranular to microfibrous structure, in some cases with relicts of metamict material. The recrystallization follows cracks, lineage boundaries, or particular growth zones. The recrystallized material yields the zircon x-ray pattern. Some zircons are so strongly altered that they do not recrystallize upon ignition. With increasing structural damage, indices and birefringence decrease. Microcrystalline recrystallized types also have low indices, owing to structural OH. In zoned crystals, cores have either higher or lower indices than marginal zones. Outgrowths may show higher indices.

Fig. 2.46. Outgrowth on detrital zircon (0.18 mm in length) from clastic sedimentary rock (Poldervaart, 1955; Am. J. Sci.).

Fluorescence. Commonly may be vividly fluorescent in yellow, green, or red. The red has been ascribed to Sm and Tb, the green to Dy. Either short or long radiation or both causes excitation. The fluorescence varies from faint to intense. With a change from short- to long-wave source the intensity may be increased, diminished, or unchanged. Igneous zircon concentrates tend to give a uniform bulk response; sedimentary zircon concentrates tend to be nonuniform (Foster, 1948). The presence of fluorescent zircon in placers nearly always indicates the copresence of monazite (George, 1949).

Occurrence.

1. As a widely distributed accessory in small crystals in felsic to intermediate igneous rocks, especially granite, granodiorite, syenite, and feldspathoidal syenite; less common in tonalite and diorite.

2. As larger euhedra or subhedral groups (including cyrtolite), in granitic, syenitic, and nepheline-syenitic pegmatites.

FIG. 2.47. Zircons with distinct cores, whose axis may be skew with that of the overgrowths. Central grain is 0.1 mm long. From autochthonous granite gneiss, Beartooth Mts., Mont.-Wyo. (Poldervaart and Eckelmann, 1955; *Geol. Soc. Am.*).

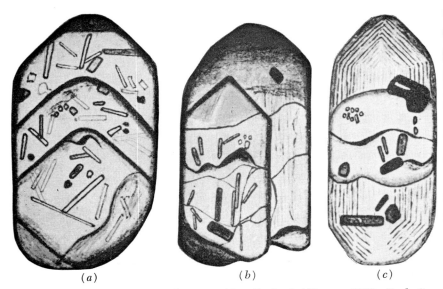

(*a*)   (*b*)   (*c*)

FIG. 2.48. Inclusion-rich detrital zircon, New Zealand (Hutton, 1950; *Geol. Soc. Am.*). (*a*) With zonal structure (mounted in hydrax, $n = 1.70$) ($\times 65$), Ngahere. (*b*) Parallel growth ($\times 105$), Atarau. (*c*) With zonal structure and abraded core (mounted in hydrax, $n = 1.70$) ($\times 75$), Atarau.

3. As a common accessory of such metamorphic rocks as mica schist, biotite gneiss, granite gneiss, chlorite schist, charnockite, less commonly in marble, quartzite, and hematite or magnetite schists.

4. Cyrtolite occurs in the Bancroft, Ont., region in skarn and metapyroxenite associated with calcite, fluorite, and apatite.

5. As an accessory mineral in sands (both river and beach placers), sandstone, siltstone, arkose, less usually in shale.

Some pegmatitic localities of note are the following in the United States: in gabbro(!) pegmatite with calcic plagioclase, hornblende, and biotite in needles $7\frac{1}{4} \times \frac{1}{16}$ to $\frac{1}{8}$ in., near Mellen, Wis. (Wilcox, 1936); Wausau, Wis.; Baringer Hill, Tex. (cyrtolite); Cady Mountains, San Bernardino County, Calif.; Eureka tunnel, St. Peters Dome west of Colorado Springs, Colo., with quartz and microcline (brown-yellow zircon and few deep green crystals occur together); Quanah Mountain, Wichita Mts., Okla.; Hendersonville, N.C.; Bedford, N.Y.; Ruggles mine, N.H.; Branchville, Conn.; Rockport, Mass.

In Canada in Renfrew, Haliburton and Hastings Counties, Ont., in very large crystals, abundant in pegmatites rich in calcite; at the Bessner mine in Conger Township near Parry Sound, at the Lyndoch, McDonald, Woodcox, and Wallingford (Quebec) mines; fine crystals in serpentinized pyroxenite with calcite, apatite, phlogopite, and pyrite in North Burgess Township, Lanark County, Ont. (Palache and Ellsworth, 1928); also the East Found group, Star Lake, Manitoba. In Brazil in Rio Grande do Norte at the Onca and Alto Mamoes mines; also in caldasite (see baddeleyite). In Norway in syenitic and nepheline-syenitic pegmatites of the Langesundfjord region; in granitic pegmatites in the Hitterö, Kragerö, and Iveland districts (alvite), in the latter at the deposits Tveit, Fröysa, Rosås, Ljosland, and others. In Sweden at Ytterby (cyrtolite). On Greenland in the Julianehaab district. Between the Mias and Ilmen Lakes, Ilmen Mts., Urals, U.S.S.R. In pegmatites cutting charnockite in the Musgrave Range, northwestern South Australia; the pegmatitic zircon is nonfluorescent, but that of the charnockite fluoresces (Wilson, 1947). On Madagascar on Mt. Ampanobe and at Itrongahy near Betroka. In Japan at Yamaguti, Nagano prefecture (yamagutilite); Ishikawa, Iwaki Province (intergrown with xenotime in radial groups); Ooro, Kyoto prefecture; Kutinokura, Nara prefecture (both yamagutilite); Masaki, Hukoka prefecture; and Takayama, Mino.

Some productive or relatively rich placers occur at Jacksonville and Trail Ridge, Fla.; with gold in Henderson County, N.C.; in beaches along the east coast of Australia between Ballina, New South Wales, and Stradbroke Island, Queensland; on Ceylon, on the Brazilian coast, and in other monazite placers in many places in the world.

Identification. Distinguished from thorite by lower radioactivity and fluorescence. Has lower birefringence than sphene and a markedly different crystal form. Zircon is harder than xenotime, has higher indices and lower birefringence.

Allanite

Composition. $(Ca,Ce,Th)_2(Al,Fe^3,Mn,Mg)_3(SiO_4)_3OH$. Other members of the Ce group, especially La, are usually present; varieties with as much as 8% Y_2O_3 also are known. Th = up to 3.2%; minor U (0.004 to 0.066%) also may be present. Some Fe^2, Ti, and Be may be present; minor O and F substitute for OH, PO_4 for SiO_4, Na and K for Ca. Much allanite also is hydrated, and analyses commonly show more H_2O than is required in the above formula. Orthite is a synonym. A member of the epidote group. Parallel overgrowths of zoisite, clinozoisite, epidote, and even piedmontite are known (Fig. 2.49). In addition to metamictization, a hydrothermal alteration to an aggregate of bastnaesite, huttonite(?), hematite, and a pale yellow isotropic mineral has been found in allanite of the Elberton granites of northeast Georgia (Silver and Grunenfelder, 1957).

Occurrence.

1. As a widespread accessory mineral of acid to intermediate igneous rocks including granite (e.g., Ruby Mountains, Mont.; Medicine Bow Range, Wyo.; Wasatch Range, Utah; Humboldt Mountains, Nev.), granite aplite, granodiorite, syenite (Bancroft district, Ont.), feldspathoidal syenites and diorites (Smith et al., 1957) and some extrusive rocks, including rhyolite, trachyte, dacite, and andesite. The original discovery was made in granite from East Greenland. Occurs in miarolitic cavities in the Baveno, Italy, granite.

2. As an accessory mineral of such regional metamorphic rocks as biotite schist and gneiss, granite gneiss (Rio de Janeiro, Brazil), hornblende gneiss, hornblende-biotite gneiss, glaucophane schists and gneisses (Corsica), amphibolite, eclogite, kinzigite, lime-silicate gneiss, and migmatite (Black Forest, Germany).

3. In some pyrometasomatic marbles or skarns: Bastnaes, Sweden, with cerite; Essex and Orange Counties, N.Y.; Franklin Furnace, N.J.; Grand Calumet Island, Quebec. It is also found in calcareous ejecta from Mt. Vesuvius, Italy.

4. Very widespread in granitic and granodioritic pegmatites (only a few of the many localities may be listed). In numerous deposits with many other radioactive species in the Iveland and Evje districts, southern Norway, including, among others, Tveit, Dalane, Ivedal, Birketveit, Mölland, Frikstad, and Landsverk. Also in Norway at Garta in masses 50 to 100 kg, at Sjaen, Kragerö, and many other localities. In Sweden at Ytterby, Finbo, near Falun (crystals up to a foot long), Skeppsholm, Skuleboda (beryllian), and in central Roslagen (in tonalite pegmatite). Widespread in Greenland: in granites in the Egedesminde and the Godthaab districts and in granite pegmatites in the Frederikshaab and the Julianehaab districts. In Finland at Varala in Kangosala and in the Äva area. In the U.S.S.R. at Miask in the Ilmen Mts.; at Achmatoosk, Zlatoust district; and at Sliudiansky. Also at Striegau, Silesia; Criffel, Scotland; and other European localities.

With uraninite and gadolinite along the Black River, Union of South Africa, and at Milembule Village and localities near Ufipa, Tanganyika (estimated about a 50-ton reserve, McConnell, 1945). Widespread on Madagascar, in the

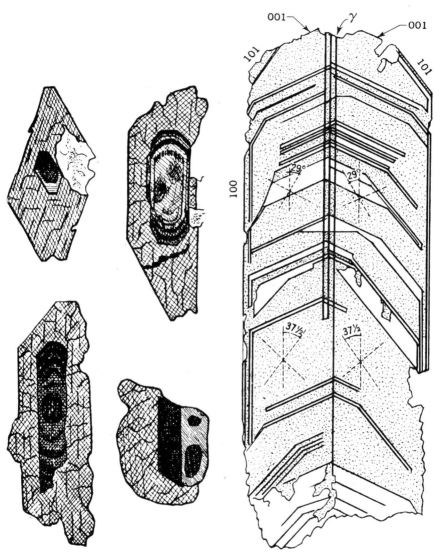

FIG. 2.49. Oriented overgrowth of epidote on allanite, Ilchester granite, Howard County, Md. (×100) (Hobbs, 1889).

FIG. 2.50. Twinned and complexly zoned allanite, syenite pegmatite, southern Norway (Brögger, 1890).

Lake Itasy region, southwest of Betroka, at Belamosima, at Sama, and other localities.

At Cooglegong and in the Woodstock pegmatite, Western Australia. In Japan at Hakata, Iyo Province; Shinden, Gifu prefecture; Tadati, Nagano prefecture; near Nagatejima, Noto peninsula (nagatelite = phosphatian allanite); Okuma, Ryozan, Husamata, Kozima-Ipponmatu, Harimiti, Siraiwa, Sirane, Nogisawa, and Iisaka (beryllian), Fukushima prefecture; Hiradani, Siga prefecture; and Oyama, Ehime prefecture.

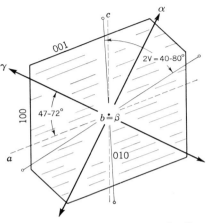

FIG. 2.51. Optical orientation of allanite.

Probably the most widespread radioactive mineral in Canadian pegmatites. In the Bancroft, Ont., district in many granitic and syenitic pegmatites, also in veins with pyroxene; in Quebec at several localities, and in British Columbia.

In the United States: Greenwich and Blueberry Mountain, Mass.; Mineville district, N.Y.; Chester County, Pa.; Amherst and Amelia Counties, Va.; near Taylorsville, Wilkes County, and in the Franklin-Sylva and Bryson City districts, N.C.; Wausau, Wis.; Baringer Hill pegmatite, Llano County, Tex. (one mass weighed 300 lb.); near Canon City, Fremont County, and on Trout Creek Pass, Chaffee County, Colo.; near Sheridan, Mont.; 10 mi northwest of Wheatland, Wyo.; Cerbat Range, Ariz.; and in California in Yosemite National Park, Tuolumne County, and at the Pomona Tile Quarry, San Bernardino County.

5. Rarely in placer deposits: a few beaches on South Island, New Zealand; Tobacco Root Mts., Mont.

Identification. Crystal habit, mixed isotropic-anisotropic character; low specific gravity, and low radioactivity are distinctive characteristics. Strongly resembles gadolinite but allanite is much more easily fused. Strongest x-ray lines (recrystallized in air): 2.95, 3.51, 2.68.

Gadolinite

Composition. $Be_2FeY_2Si_2O_{10}$. Ce-group elements usually are present, considerably subordinate to those of the Y group. Of the Y group, Y, Yb, Er, Dy, and Gd are usually the most abundant. Ho, Tb, Lu, Tm, and Eu are minor to absent. In the Ce group, Sa and Nd are commonly the most abundant. Minor amounts of alkalies, Mn, Mg, Fe^3 (due to oxidation?), and Al are present. Ca also occurs; and one type, calciogadolinite from Tadati village, Nagano prefecture, Japan, has 11.91% Ca. Most specimens contain Th ($ThO_2 = 0.14$ to 1.73%). U is rarely recorded, but usually is present in trace amounts or less than 1%. H_2O, present in small to large amounts, is secondary. The metamict type is spectacularly pyrognomic. Some Norwegian crystals have cores or partial cores of quartz-feldspar aggregates, like "shell" beryl and "shell" tourmaline. Coatings of tengerite occur on some specimens.

Occurrence. Almost exclusively a mineral of granite pegmatites; not a common species. One occurrence is known in an Alpine vein as small, deep green, translucent, complex crystals with quartz, adularia, albite, xenotime, and synchysite in the Val Alps, Switzerland. Also occurs very sparingly in the miarolitic cavities of the Baveno granite of Italy.

The more important pegmatitic occurrences are in the Baringer Hill, Tex., pegmatite in masses up to 200 lb.; Rockport, Mass.; Cotopaxi and Trout Creek Pass, Chaffee County, Colo.; in cerite pegmatites near Jamestown, as thin shells bordering cerite masses; Beaverbrook and Roscoe station, Jefferson County, Colo.; Devils Head, Douglas County, Colo.; and Aquarius Range, Ariz. In Canada in Loughborough Township, Ont., with euxenite.

Near Cooglegong, Western Australia, in three pegmatites and as alluvial pebbles. In 1913 these pegmatitic deposits yielded one ton of gadolinite. In the gravels, gadolinite is associated with allanite, yttrotantalite, and monazite. Also reported from Abydos, with cassiterite, polycrase, and mangano-columbite, from Bullock Well, Pilbara district, and from Payne's Find, 85 mi southeast of Yalgoo in the Lake Moore district.

In Japan at several localities, all pegmatites: Yamaguti village, Nagano prefecture; Tukano, Nagano prefecture; Tadati village, Nagano prefecture (calciogadolinite); Tenzin River, Siga prefecture; Shinden and Hirukawa, Gifu prefecture; and Otowadani, Kyoto prefecture.

In Namaqualand at Boksput. In Finland at Lövbole in the Kimito district. Widespread in Sweden at Ytterby (where it was first found); at Brodbo, Finbo, and Kårarfvet, all near Falun; Gustafsberg, Torsåker; in Dalarne at Österby, Karlberg, Svärdsjö, Bjursås, and Appelbo; Högsby, Kalmar; Nohl, Kongelf; and Taberg, Värmland.

Also relatively widespread in southern Norwegian pegmatites: on Hitterö at Rasvåg, Urstad, Veisdal, Medåsen, and Igeltjern; in the Ivedal district, especially from the Frikstad 7 deposit where a 500-kg mass was found and a total of 1,000 kg of gadolinite has been produced, forming an estimated 0.013% of the pegmatite; also in the same district at Fröysa, Rosås, Hiltveit, Ivedal, Birketveit, Nateland, Stöledalen, Birkeland, Kåbuland, Eptevand, Mölland, and Vådne; in the adjacent Evje district at Högetveit and As; in scattered localities including Malö, Grimstad; Haneholmen, Tvedestrand; Ranvik, Risör; Bandaksvand, Tördal, and Fyrrisdal in Telemark; Anneröd and Rygge, Moss; Halvorsröd, Råde; and Sörland, Östfold. Typical associates are fergusonite, euxenite, and thalenite. Gadolinite in Norway occurs in pegmatites rich in Y-group elements relative to Nb and Ta and also in Ca-Y-rich pegmatites, wherein it forms if Be is sufficient, and hellandite forms if Be is in insufficient supply.

Identification. Resembles allanite and chevkinite; the former is much more common and abundant; the latter is rarer. Gadolinite gelatinizes with HCl but fuses with difficulty; crystalline allanite does not gelatinize and is fused with ease. Chevkinite also fuses readily and yields a strong Ti reaction. Strongest x-ray lines (recrystallized in air): 4.75, 3.12, 2.82.

Chevkinite

Composition. A silicate of Ca, Fe, Ti, and rare earths, near (Fe^2,Ca) $(Ce,La)_2(Si,Ti)_2O_8$. Kauffman and Jaffe (1946) suggest $R^2R_2^3$ $(Si,Ti)O_6$. Some Y-group earths also are present. Some analyses show Mn, Mg, Be, Al, Na, Ta, Nb, F, Pb, Sn, and Fe^3. Small amounts of H_2O are secondary. ThO_2 up to 21%, generally much less and commonly 1% or less. UO_2 up to 3%. An alternative spelling is tscheffkinite.

Occurrence. A rare mineral in pegmatite and in rutile-ilmenite deposits. Occurs on Hat Creek, Nelson County, and in Bedford County, Va.; in the Aquarius Range, Mohave County, Ariz. (Kauffman and Jaffe, 1946). Also near Miask, Ilmen Mts., Urals region, U.S.S.R.; on Madagascar in both granitic and syenitic pegmatites near Tarendrika and Betroka; in Madras, India, on Kanjamalai Hill, Salem district; and on Ceylon in Sabaragamuwa Province. Occurs at Kobe-mura, Kyoto prefecture, Japan, in pegmatite with fergusonite, monazite, xenotime, and zircon; and in the Kogendo region of Korea. Also occurs as an accessory mineral in the Devil's Slide fayalite-quartz syenite near Stark, N.H. (Jaffe et al., 1956).

Identification. Resembles allanite and gadolinite. Distinguished by strong Ti test. Strongest x-ray lines (heated in air): 2.71, 3.21, 3.15.

Sphene

Composition. $CaTiSiO_5$. Isomorphous for Ca are Na, Ce, and La rare earth, Y rare earths, and minor Th; isomorphous for Ti are Fe^3, Al, and Nb; isomorphous for O are OH and F. Minor Fe^2, Mn, Mg, and Cr also may be present, and one variety is rich in Sn. Traces of Zr, Pb, Sr, V, Cu, Ga, Ta, and Ba have been detected. The ThO_2 content is usually considerably less than 1%, and many sphenes are nonradioactive. The radioactivity of numerous sphenes as determined by Larsen et al. (1952) and Hurley (1952) ranges from 2.6 to 260 α/mg/hr. Sphene from Wainui Inlet, N.W. Nelson, New Zealand, contains 0.28% ThO_2 (Hutton, 1950). Rare-earth-rich types have been called keilhauite or yttrotitanite. These varieties, which commonly are pegmatitic sphenes, may also be relatively rich in Th. Alters to a light yellow to white soft aggregate called leucoxene.

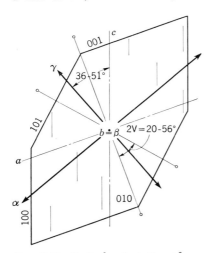

FIG. 2.52. Optical orientation of sphene.

Occurrence. A widely distributed accessory mineral in (1) intrusive igneous rocks, particularly in syenites, feldspathoidal syenites, monzonites, tonalites, granodiorites, less commonly in hornblende granites, diorites, and gabbros; (2) pegmatites, generally granitic with other radioactive rare-earth minerals (Norway) or with calcite, apatite, and zircon (Ontario, Canada); also in nepheline-syenite pegmatites (Langesund-fjord, Norway); (3) extrusive igneous rocks, especially phonolites; (4) metamorphic rocks including marble, skarn, granite gneiss, slate, mica schist, chlorite schist, talc schist, and amphibolite; (5) Alpine veins with adularia, smoky quartz, chlorite, and apatite; (6) sands and sandstones in the heavy detrital fraction.

Pegmatitic types are more likely to be somewhat more radioactive, although less usually moderately radioactive types also occur in other plutonic and metamorphic rocks, as well as in placers. Some noteworthy pegmatitic localities include Askerön ($2\frac{1}{4}$ kg obtained) and Sandö (10 kg obtained), southern Norway; Tangen and Sjäen on Kragerö, Norway, with allanite, columbite, uraninite, and uranothorite. In the Iveland, Norway, district in the Rosås, Birketveit, and Ljosland deposits. In East Greenland at Karra Akungnak, crystals up to 7 cm. In Finland at Nuolainniemi, Impilahti, with wiikite. On Madagascar, crystals occur at Ambalavaokely near Betroka and at Midongy. Fine pegmatitic crystals also occur at numerous places in Renfrew and Hastings Counties, Ont.; some very large. Also in the same area as a minor constituent in calcite-fluorite veins.

Identification. The form is characteristic, together with high relief, very strong birefringence, and extreme dispersion. Monazite has lower birefringence and is more strongly radioactive. Detrital grains of sphene resemble those of xenotime, cassiterite, or rutile, all of which are normally uniaxial.

Thalenite

Composition. $Y_4SiO_4O_{13}(OH)$. Considerable Th (up to 12% ThO_2) may substitute for Y; U is usually minor, up to about 4% UO_3, but usually less than 1%. Ce earths may also substitute for those of the Y group. Other elements that may be present in small, variable amounts include Ca, Mg, Fe^2, Mn, Na, Al, F, Pb, Zr, Ti, Sn, and He. Crystals may show zoning. Rowlandite may be a metamict variety; yttrialite appears to be thorian thalenite.

Occurrence. All varieties are very rare. Thalenite found at Österby and Åskagen, Värmland, Sweden, in pegmatites with fluocerite; also in pegmatites of the Iveland-Evje areas at Rosås, Ivedal, Stöledalen, and Högetveit; also at Sörland in Ostfold, and Hundholmen, Norway. Yttrialite from pegmatites near Iisaka, Japan, with thorogummite, fergusonite, and allanite. Both rowlandite and yttrialite from the Baringer Hill pegmatite, Llano County, Tex., with thorogummite, fergusonite, gadolinite, cyrtolite, and other radioactive species.

Identification. The relations of rowlandite and yttrialite to thalenite are not certainly determined. Thalenite is best determined by chemical analysis.

Uncommon Rare-earth Silicates

A great variety of rare-earth silicates, many of which are slightly to moderately radioactive, occur in nepheline-syenite pegmatites. In this group, Ce and the lighter lanthanons dominate over Y earths, and Th predominates greatly over U, which usually is absent or present only in traces. All of the species are exceptionally uncommon and are known chiefly from occurrences

TABLE 2.18. *Properties of the Th-bearing silicate minerals*

Mineral	Form	Color, Streak (S), Luster (L), Fluorescence (F)	Pleochroism	Indices and orientation	Cleavage and fracture	H	G
Allanite	Monoclinic. Metamict (more radioactive types), partly metamict or non-metamict. Euhedral, acicular crystals or needles elongated with *b*. Anhedra. (100) tablets	Dark brown to black. Alters to gray, green, red, buff. S pale to greenish brown, altered has brown or yellow brown. L vitreous to resinous, altered has dull to earthy	Absent (isotropic) or α = colorless, yellow, pink, yellow brown, dark brown, gray, green. β = yellow brown, red brown, dark brown. γ = yellow, green, brown, red brown, black brown	α = 1.690–1.791 β = b = 1.700–1.815 γ = 1.706–1.822 Indices and birefringence increase with Fe^3, Ti, and rare earths. Zoning common with outer zones usually lighter colored and with lower indices. (–) 2V = 40–80°, r > v distinct to strong, or r < v distinct. $\alpha \wedge c$ = 22–47°. Metamict types isotropic. n = 1.53–1.72 decreasing with hydration	(100), (001) poor. Irregular to conchoidal fracture	5.5–6 decreasing with alteration	3.9–4.2
Gadolinite	Monoclinic. Usually metamict. Anhedra and rough crystals, some prismatic	Black, dark green, brown altering to red brown or red. S greenish gray altering to red brown. L glassy, altering to earthy	None	Usually isotropic. n = 1.760–1.783. Also α = 1.695–1.80 β = 1.70–1.81 γ = 1.77–1.81 (+) 2V moderate to large, r < v strong or β = b, $\gamma \wedge c$ = 4–13°. Also (–) 2V = 0–35° (recrystallized, George, 1949)	None. Conchoidal to splintery fracture	6–7 (decreasing with alteration)	4–4.6

Chevkinite	Monoclinic. May be metamict. Some zoned with metamict rims. Rare crystals with simple forms. Madagascar material reportedly orthorhombic. Some contact twins on (001) (Jaffe et al., 1956)	Black. S dark brown. L vitreous to dull	None (isotropic) or α = nearly colorless. β = pale red brown. γ = dark red brown	Isotropic. n = 1.63–1.97. Also biaxial (−) 2V = small–78°. r > v marked. Also commonly biaxial (+) 2V = 80° α = 1.97 $\beta = b$ = 1.99 γ = 2.05 $\alpha \wedge c$ = 11–26°, also $\gamma \wedge$ elongation = 6.9°	Fracture irregular	5.5–6	4.33–4.72
Sphene	Monoclinic. Wedge-shaped euhedra with rhombic cross sections. Also pyramidal or elongated (c or a). (100) twins common, also multiple twins on (221) by shearing. Anhedral clusters. Detrital grains rounded, irregular, or euhedral	Brown, yellow, orange, gray, green, red, black. S white to pinkish. L resinous to adamantine	None or α = colorless, yellow, yellow brown. β = pink, yellow brown, yellow green. γ = pink, red orange, yellow, green, red brown	α = 1.840–1.950 $\beta = b$ = 1.870–1.970 γ = 1.943–2.093 Increasing Al and F decrease indices. (+) 2V = 20–56°, r > v extreme. $\gamma \wedge c$ = 36–51°. In zoned crystals outer zones have higher indices and larger 2V. Abnormal interference tints in sections normal to optic axes	(110) distinct. (100), (112) imperfect	5–5.5	3.4–3.56
Thalenite	Monoclinic. Strongly radioactive types metamict. (100) tablets, also prismatic and anhedral	Pink, red, or green altering to orange. S pale red to colorless. L vitreous	None	Isotropic. n = 1.725–1.758. Also α = 1.731 β = 1.738 $\gamma = b$ = 1.744 (−), 2V = 67–73°, r < v weak. $\beta \wedge c$ = 1–3°. Zoned crystals have cores of lower birefringence	Conchoidal to splintery fracture	5–6.5	4.2–4.6

TABLE 2.19. *Uncommon rare-earth silicates*

Name	Composition	Th or U content
Beckelite......	$(Ca,Ce)_2(Si,Al,Zr)(O,OH)_5$	(?)
Britholite.....	$(Ca,Ce)_2(Si,P)(O,OH,F)_5$	Up to 1–1.5% eU_3O_8
Cappelenite...	$Ba(Y,Ce,La)_6B_6(SiO_4)_3O_{12}(OH)_2$	$ThO_2 = 0.80\%$
Caryocerite...	A borosilicate of Ca, rare earths, Ta, and Th with OH and F	$ThO_2 = 13.64\%$. $UO_2 =$ trace
Cenosite......	$Ca_2(Ce,Y)_2Si_4O_{12}CO_3 \cdot H_2O$	
Cerite........	$(Ca,Ce)_3Si_2(O,OH,F)_9$	Weakly radioactive
Chinglusuite...	$Na_4Mn_5Ti_3Si_{14}O_{41} \cdot 9H_2O(?)$	$ThO_2 = 0.06\%$ but metamict
Hellandite....	$Ca_2(Ce,Y,Fe,Mn,Al)_6Si_4O_{19}(?)$	$ThO_2 = 0.62\%$
Johnstrupite...	A fluosilicate of Na, Ca, Ti, rare earths, and Zr	$ThO_2 = 0.79\%$
Lessingite.....	$(Ca,Ce)_2(Si,Al,P)(O,OH,F)_5$	Canadian material is radioactive?
Lovozerite....	$(Na,K)_2(Mn,Ca)ZrSi_6O_{16} \cdot 3H_2O(?)$	$Th = 0.50\%$
Melanocerite..	A borosilicate of Ca, rare earths, and Ta with OH and F (like caryocerite)	$ThO_2 = 1.66\%$
Mosandrite....	$NaCa_6Ce_2(Ti,Zr)_2Si_7O_{24}(OH,F)_7$	$ThO_2 = 0.34\%$
Perrierite.....	$(Ce,La,Ca,Th)_2(Ti,Fe^2)_2Si_2O_{11}$	$ThO_2 = 4.05\%$
Rinkite.......	Near $(Na,Ca)_{12}(Ce,Ti)_5Si_8(O,F)_{36}$	Th in small amounts
Rinkolite.....	$(Ca,Na)_{11}Ce_2(Si,Ti)_{10}O_{28}(F,OH)_8$	Radioactivity of the two:
Lovchorrite is richer in Ce		$Th = 0.41$–1.04%. $Ra = 0.25 \times 10^{-9}$–7.17×10^{-8}, $U = 2.00 \times 10^{-2}$–2.15×10^{-1}
Vudyavrite is an altered lovchorrite		$ThO_2 = 0.90$–2.06%
Steenstrupine..	A hydrous and fluorine-bearing phosphosilicate of Ce, La, Ca, Na, Mn, Fe^3, and Th with minor Nb, Be, Al, and traces of Pb, Mg, and K	$ThO_2 = 10.23$ (U.S.S.R.) $ThO_2 = 2.13$–7.09% (Greenland) Some types are metamict
Stillwellite....	$(Ca,Ce)(Si,Al,P)B(O,OH,F)_5$	$ThO_2 = 0.06$, $U_3O_8 = 0.67$
Thortveitite...	$(Sc,Y)_2Si_2O_7$	(?)
Törnebohmite	$Ce_3Si_2O_8OH$	Weakly radioactive
Tritomite.....	A fluorine-bearing borosilicate of Ca, rare earths, and Th	$ThO_2 = 8.58$–9.51%

at three groups of localities: (1) Narssarssuk and Kangerdluarssuk in southern Greenland; (2) the Langesundfjord area of southern Norway; and (3) the Khibina and Lovozero tundra areas of the Kola peninsula, U.S.S.R. Others occur in alkalic rocks near Mariupol, near the Azov Sea, U.S.S.R. A few of the silicates, especially those relatively rich in Y, e.g., hellandite, cenosite, and thortveitite, occur in granitic pegmatites of southern Norway. Another group is known from the contact metamorphic zone of alkali syenites, Kyschtym district of the Ural Mts., U.S.S.R. (lessingite, cerite, törnebohmite). The last two also occur in contact deposits in Sweden at Bastnäs and Norberg and near Jamestown, Colo., in pegmatite. Stillwellite is a contact metamorphic mineral at the Mary Kathleen deposit, near Mt. Isa, Queensland, Australia. Perrierite occurs in beach sands near Rome, Italy, derived from alkalic volcanic tuffs.

Minerals with Radioactive Impurities

There is a large and growing group of minerals that are found to be radioactive owing to the mechanical inclusions of other radioactive species, which in most cases are present in minute amounts and in grains too small for identification. See, for example, Frondel and Fleischer (1955), White and Stevens (1953), West and Benson (1955), Heinrich and Bever (1957). Only a selected few of the many references to such occurrences are given. Recorded minerals are (1) Sulfides: argentiferous galena, sphalerite, chalcopyrite, marcasite, pyrrhotite, pyrite (Narten and McKeown, 1952), bornite (Wedow et al., 1954B), molybdenite, urano-molybdenite reported (Derriks and Vaes, 1956) as occurring at Shinkolobwe, Belgian Congo. (2) Oxides and hydroxides: magnetite, ilmenite (Lovering, 1956), spinel, hematite (Vickers, 1953), goethite, limonite (Lovering, 1955; Barton, 1956; see also pages 529–531), psilomelane, columbite (Heinrich and Giardini, 1956). (3) Haloid: dark purple fluorites are commonly radioactive, usually owing to uraninite or thorite inclusions. Hess (1931) found radioactive purple fluorite from Wilberforce, Ont., to be free of microscopic inclusion and suggested it contained Ra, calling it radiofluorite, $(Ca,Ra)F_2$. Some fluorite probably has the composition $(Ca,U^4)F_2$, as that in Thomas Range, Utah (Staatz and Bauer, 1951A). Goddard (1946) found that the intensity of purple coloration and radioactivity increase together in Jamestown, Colo., fluorite. (4) Carbonates: calcite (Burbank and Pierson, 1953), malachite (Wedow et al., 1954B). (5) Phosphatesarsenates: pyromorphite, not uncommonly radioactive (e.g., Wright, 1950), probably owing to adsorbed Ra; mimetite; adamite. (6) Vanadates: corvusite (included rauvite(?), Frondel and Fleischer, 1955), volborthite, calciovolborthite, turanite; vanadinite. (7) Tungstate: scheelite. (8) Silicates: quartz (pitchblende(?) inclusions—Bueno, 1955), vesuvianite, scapolite (Haberlandt and Hernegger, 1947), sericite, biotite, chlorite, garnet (some isomorphous U(?), Ellsworth, 1932; Furcron, 1955), chrysocolla (Barton, 1956), hisingerite (Lang, 1952; Bowie, 1955).

• chapter three

RADIOACTIVE MINERAL
DEPOSITS—GENERAL

INTRODUCTION

Since the mid-1940s geologists of many countries have conducted an investigative program of unprecedented intensiveness on radioactive mineral deposits, particularly those of uranium. No other metal has ever received such concentrated geological and mineralogical attention. Not only have an enormous number of new individual deposits been found, but many of an entirely new geological character have been discovered and in regions whose geology previously had been regarded as incompatible with uranium concentration. Many of these new types were stumbled upon by untrained, Geiger counter–operated prospectors whose knowledge of uranium geology was insufficient to prejudice them against these "unfavorable" areas and who operated on the basis of "uranium is where you find it"—an adage turned aphorism.

The expanding geological horizon of uranium has thus revealed much about old and abundant new deposits, but the general characteristics of natural groups of occurrences are less well outlined. An attempt is made herein to describe such groups, as well as representative and unusual member deposits.

CLASSIFICATION

Several noteworthy attempts have been made to sort out the various kinds of radioactive mineral deposits and by correlating their mineralogical and geological characteristics to arrange them into groups that are representative of restricted environments of formation. Such genetic classifications focus attention both on the ways in which deposits are alike and also on their systematic differences, thus serving as a fundamental guide for exploration.

Both uranium and thorium are relatively abundant elements, both more

153

abundant than such long and widely used metals as Au, Ag, Hg, Bi, and Sb. Uranium, especially, also is widespread and is geochemically a persistent element, largely because of three factors:

1. Its isomorphism as U^{4+} with Th, Zr, RE, Ca, and Fe^2, so that it appears at least in small amounts in a variety of high-temperature complex oxides, silicates, and phosphates.

2. The wide stability range of uraninite, which may be precipitated in environments ranging from those of high temperatures and pressures (e.g., pegmatitic) to those of room temperature and atmospheric pressure.

3. The ease of oxidation of U^{4+} to U^{6+}, which forms the uranyl ion $(UO_2)^{2+}$, which itself may be further complexed (e.g., with CO_3^{2-}), leading, upon precipitation, to varied assemblages of low-temperature uranyl minerals; or decomposed and reduced to reprecipitate in the uranous form.

Thorium, less ubiquitous than uranium, nevertheless also is well distributed throughout a considerable P-T range, chiefly as monazite and thorite, monazite persisting as the chief radioactive resistate mineral of placer deposits. Thorium-bearing complex oxides, silicates, and thorianite, on the other hand, are formed predominantly in high-temperature deposits.

Among previous classifications of note are those of George (1949), Bain (1950), Lang (1952), Everhart (1954), Magakyan (1955), and Roubault (1955). Everhart, in two of his several papers (1954, 1956A), has tended toward a dual basis for classification, arranging deposits by genetic groups based on mineral association and inferred relative temperature of the depositional environment and further subdividing each group on the basis of the nature of the host rock. Certainly in some areas marked differences in the composition and in the kinds of openings of host rocks have exercised significant control on the form and even composition of their epigenetic deposits, as for example, the contrast between the deposits in the Todilto limestone and those in the Morrison sandstone in the Grants, New Mexico, district (pages 410–417). Probably one factor significant to the lack of vein deposits in such regions as the Colorado Plateau, Witwatersrand, and Blind River has been the ease with which solutions permeated clastic hosts of high transmissivity instead of being confined to fracture systems as they were in less permeable rocks. It is noteworthy that the various "sandstone-conglomerate" or disseminated types have geochemical and mineralogical counterparts in vein deposits (Table 3.1).

Classifications of uranium-bearing hydrothermal vein deposits have been presented by King et al. (1952), Everhart and Wright (1953), and Geffroy and Sarcia (1954). The latter recognize two main categories of productive uranium veins:

1. Extrusive type (Marysvale, Utah)
2. Intrusive type
    a. With Ag, Ni, Co, Bi
    b. With B.G.P.C. sulfides (pages 336–337)
    c. Fluoritic

TABLE 3.1. *Comparison of mineralogical and geochemical assemblages in selected stratiform disseminated replacement deposits and counterpart vein deposits*

Disseminated or replacement type			Analogous vein type		
Locality	Mineralogy	Geochemical assemblage	Locality	Mineralogy	Geochemical assemblage
Aravalli Range, northern Rajputana, India	Titanate (brannerite or davidite), copper sulfides	U-Th(?)-Ti-RE-Cu-S	Radium Hill, South Australia	Davidite, ilmenite, rutile, hematite, biotite	U-Th-RE-Ti-Fe
Blind River, Ont.	Uraninite, brannerite, thucolite, pyrite, other sulfides, sericite	U-Th-RE-Ti-Fe-S (Mo, Co, Au, Cu)	Chateau-Lambert, Haute-Saône, France	Brannerite, uraninite, pyrite, Cu sulfides, quartz, sericite	U-Th-RE-Ti-Fe-S (Mo, Cu)
Northern Rhodesia	Chalcopyrite, bornite, chalcocite, pyrite, pitchblende, Co minerals	Cu-Fe-S-U-Co (Ni, Se, Te, As)	Veins of the copper zone, Cornwall, England	Chalcopyrite, bornite, pyrite, pitchblende, quartz, fluorite	Cu-Fe-S-U (Co, Ni, As, F, Pb)
Serra de Jacobina, Brazil	Uraninite(?), gold, pyrite, quartz	U-Au-Fe-S	Placer de Guadalupe, Mexico	Uraninite, gold, pyrite, quartz, calcite	U-Au-Fe-S (Cu)
Unoxidized, low-vanadium, uranium-copper ores, Colorado Plateau	Uraninite, pyrite, chalcopyrite, bornite, chalcocite, galena, sphalerite	U-Fe-S-Cu-Pb-Zn (V, Se, Mo, Ag, Cd, Co)	Goldfields, Sask.	Uraninite, pyrite, chalcopyrite, pyrite, galena, hematite, calcite, chlorite	U-Fe-S-Cu-Pb (V, Se, Co, Ni, As, Ag, Zn)
Deposits in Todilto ls., Grants, N.Mex.	Uraninite, pyrite, fluorite, barite, calcite	U-Fe-S-F-Ba-Ca	Bauzot, Saône-et-Loire, France	Uraninite, pyrite, fluorite, barite, calcite, hematite	U-Fe-S-F-Ba-Ca (Mg, Pb)

155

Stocking and Page (1956) and Everhart (1956B) distinguish veins of five types:

Type *A:* Sooty pitchblende, some uraninite and pyrite; quartz and fluorite gangue sparse

Type *B:* Uraninite, iron and copper sulfides, galena, sphalerite, and molybdenite; quartz and fluorite abundant

Type *C:* Uraninite with Co, Ni, and Ag silver minerals in a dominantly carbonate gangue; minor quartz and barite

Type *D:* Uraninite, gold-bearing pyrite, quartz, and associated Pb, Co, and Ag sulfides

Type *E:* Uraniferous hydrocarbon and a variety of metallic sulfides in a calcite-barite gangue

It does not seem suitable to use the presence of sooty pitchblende as a criterion for defining a hydrothermal vein-type assemblage, since it has been found in many different assemblages. And in many deposits in which it has been noted it has been formed either by supergene alteration of normal uraninite, to which it gives way with depth, or probably also by late low-temperature hydrothermal alteration of older hard uraninite. Similarly, uraniferous hydrocarbons occur in a variety of vein types, in pegmatites, and in other deposits. It is doubtful that in most cases the deposition of hydrocarbon was genetically related to the formation of the vein as a whole (pages 525–528).

Lindgren (1933, p. 203) has summarized the problems attendant to classification as follows: "A genetic classification of deposits . . . is equivalent to the classification of really 'geological bodies' . . . and is, therefore, naturally beset with all the difficulties connected with an imperfect knowledge of geological processes." Although we possess growing knowledge of the conditions under which many radioactive minerals can be formed, the information in some cases is too general to define the environment with a precision that is of geological significance. This, together with the ambiguous nature of some of their characteristics, has led to considerable controversy over the origin of some deposits, particularly those of the Colorado Plateau, Witwatersrand, and Blind River. Although these three groups are generally alike in form, host rocks, extent, distribution, and relation to sedimentary features, and thus have been considered genetically as a unit by McKelvey et al. (1955), they differ markedly in mineralogy, geochemistry, and in their relation to tectonic features and to igneous intrusives and volcanic rocks.

The magmatic theory of origin of mineral deposits has led to the development of the widely accepted broad subdivisions of (1) magmatic, (2) pegmatitic, and (3) hydrothermal groups of deposits. Despite repeated attacks, the further subdivision of the hydrothermal group developed by Lindgren and others has remained usable and useful. As Mutch (1956, p. 677) has pointed out,

Probably the major weakness of Lindgren's classification . . . is the more or less general acceptance of the temperature and pressure conditions as ascribed to hydrothermal ore deposits formed at various elevations. . . . There appears to be little doubt that the deposits classed by Lindgren as epithermal, mesothermal and hypothermal are indeed representative of deposits formed at progressively deeper horizons; it is unfortunate that the names are based on a theoretical consideration rather than some less infallible descriptive term.

However, in the opinion of Sullivan (1954) the entire concept of hydrothermal solutions and hydrothermal ore deposits needs reexamination. Sullivan believes that thermal diffusion has been a major process in formation of ore deposits and that the melting point of an element is an index to the temperature at which the element becomes mobile or stationary. He has applied these ideas to speculation on the origin of such radioactive deposits as those of the Colorado Plateau and of the Rand-Rhodesia-Katanga (Sullivan, 1954). The weaknesses and inconsistencies of his arguments have received ample rebuttal from Wyman (1954) and from Krauskopf (1956).

GEOCHEMISTRY

The assemblages of elements accompanying uranium and thorium in the various main categories of deposits are summarized in Table 3.2. Although the assemblages for the various categories of deposits are distinctive, it is notable that some minor elements, e.g., Mo, Se, Ba, F, and P, are characteristic associates of uranium, considerably independent of the type of deposit.

Russell (1956) has analyzed spectrographically selected uranium ores from various types of United States deposits and compared them with barren host rocks. The trace element assemblage of the "sedimentary type" ores includes: Ag, As, B, Ba, Be, Cd, Cs, Co, Cr, Cu, Dy, Er, Ga, Gd, Ge, Li, Mo, Nb, Nd, Ni, Pb, Sc, Sn, Sr, Sm, U, V, Yt, Yb, Zn, and Zr. He concludes that a common mode of origin for these deposits is suggested by the similarity of the suite, despite differences in host rocks and ages.

In high-temperature deposits (pegmatitic, pyrometasomatic, and some hypothermal), U^{4+} and Th not uncommonly occur together in minerals, but in lower-temperature hydrothermal deposits they appear either in separate minerals in a single deposit or in entirely different deposits. The Shinkolobwe deposit contains considerable monazite which apparently was deposited after uraninite (Derriks and Vaes, 1956).

Figure 3.1 is an attempt to portray graphically the genetic interrelationships of the various major types of uranium deposits. Somewhat similar charts have been presented by McKelvey et al. (1955) and by Zeschke (1956).

Wright and Shulhof (1956) have demonstrated that sulfides coexisting with uraninite in vein deposits contain concentrations of uranium up to 10^4 times greater than in the same minerals in veins in nonuraniferous districts. This concentration may provide an index to the uranium concentration in the ore solutions.

THORIUM DEPOSITS

The minerals monazite, thorite, uranothorite, and thorogummite are rather widely distributed in radioactive hydrothermal deposits of several types. Thorianite and thorium-bearing complex oxides and silicates are relatively restricted in their occurrences. Monazite especially is a persistent pyrogenic

TABLE 3.2. *Assemblages of elements characteristic*

Deposit	Th	Ce	Y	Zr	Ta-Nb	Ti	Fe^2	Mg	Ca	Ba	Sr	Na	K	Al	Si	C
Granitic pegmatites	x	x	x	x	x	x	x		x						x	
Carbonatites	x	x		x	x (Nb)	x	x		x	x	x				m *	
High-temperature veins and replacement deposits	x		m			x	x	x	x				x	x	x	
Intermediate-temperature veins and replacement deposits							x	x	x	x		x	x	x	x	
Low-temperature veins							x	m	x	x			m	m	x	
Low-temperature disseminated deposits, chiefly in clastic rocks							x	m	x	m			x		x	x
Uraniferous phosphorites							m		x				m	m	x	
Uraniferous black shales							x		m					m	x	x

* m = minor or locally present.

and hydrothermal species, appearing as an accessory in granitic and other igneous rocks (pages 167–169); in pegmatites (page 216); in migmatitic deposits, e.g., Goldfields, Sask. (pages 222–223); in a few carbonatic vein deposits, e.g., Lemhi County, Idaho (page 249); in carbonatites and veins associated with carbonatites, e.g., Isoka, Northern Rhodesia (pages 234–235), Mountain Pass, Calif. (pages 241–243), and the Powderhorn district, Colo. (pages 240–241); in a few high-temperature veins, e.g., Hazelton, B.C. (pages 265–266); in xenothermal veins, e.g., Llallagua, Bolivia [1]; in mesothermal veins, e.g., Shinkolobwe, Belgian Congo (pages 292–293) and Steenkampskraal, Union of South Africa (pages 325–326); in mesothermal(?) lodes, e.g., Sub Nigel gold mine, Witwatersrand, Union of South Africa; in epithermal veins, e.g., Alpine "cleft" veins (Table 3.3); and in placers of all major types—river, beach, and consolidated (pages 494–519). The thorium content varies considerably, some epithermal and carbonatitic monazites being thorium-low.

Thorite and uranothorite likewise are relatively widespread geologically,

[1] Gordon (1939) reports this monazite to be thorium-free, but some will darken a photographic plate after long exposure (R. M. Denning, oral com.).

of major types of uranium deposits

CO₃	P	S	F	Cl	Cu	Pb	Zn	Cd	Mo	Au	Ag	V	Bi	Co	Ni	Cr	As	Mn	Se
	x																		
x	x	x	x	x															
m		x			m				m										
x		x	m		x	m			m	x	x		x	x	x				m
m		x	x		m	m	m		m							m			
x	m	x	m		x	m	m	m	m		m	x				m	m		m
x	x	m	x																
m	m	x	m																

occurring as rare granitic accessories (Jos Plateau, Nigeria) in pegmatites (pages 192–193), in veins associated with carbonatites (Mountain Pass, California, and Powderhorn district, Colorado), and in other veins.

Quartzose, feldspathic, or carbonate-rich hydrothermal veins that contain thorite, monazite, or both as the chief radioactive species are apparently relatively rare, at least as compared to pitchblende-bearing veins, and for this reason and also because their mineralogical assemblages are not known to be diagnostic of specific geological environments they are difficult to classify. Most, however, appear to fall into either the mesothermal group (Lemhi Pass district, Idaho-Montana) or in the epithermal group (Jamestown and Wet Mountains, Colorado). When sufficient data become available on the systematic variation of rare-earth elements in thorium minerals with their temperature of crystallization, it may be possible to use the composition of a monazite as a guide to the temperature of formation of the vein (Murata et al., 1953, 1957; Heinrich, 1957).

Commonly the thorium mineral is thorogummite (Frondel, 1956A), a variant of thorite in which tetrahedral groups of four OH ions substitute for SiO_4 tetrahedra. The mineral is very fine grained but definitely crystalline, i.e., not metamict. Apparently it is normally supergene, resulting from the polynucleic recrystallization of metamict thorite under low temperatures in

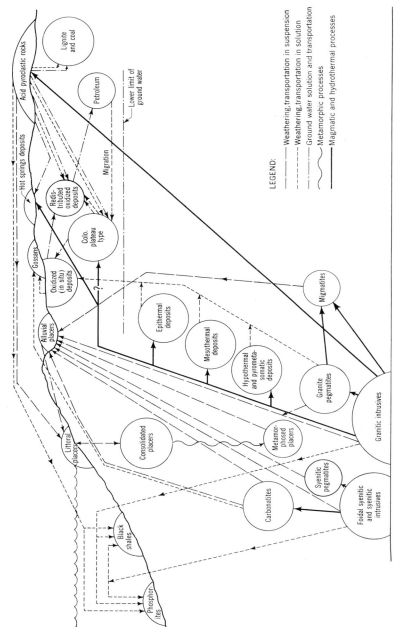

Fig. 3.1. Genetic interrelation of major types of uranium and thorium deposits.

LEGEND:

———— Weathering, transportation in suspension
------ Weathering, transportation in solution
—·—·— Ground water solution and transportation
〰〰〰 Metamorphic processes
━━━━ Magmatic and hydrothermal processes

Lignite and coal

Petroleum

Acid pyroclastic rocks

Lower limit of ground water

Hot springs deposits

Migration

Redistributed oxidized deposits

Gossans

Colo. plateau type

Oxidized (in situ) deposits

?

Alluvial placers

Epithermal deposits

Mesothermal deposits

Hypothermal and pyrometasomatic deposits

Granite pegmatites

Migmatites

Littoral placers

Consolidated placers

Metamorphosed placers

Carbonatites

Syenitic pegmatites

Granitic intrusives

Foidal syenitic and syenitic intrusives

Black shales

Phosphorites

the presence of sufficient water. It would be advantageous to determine if such "reincarnated thorite" resembles in its other chemical characteristics its ancestral thorite or if removal of rare earths and other isomorphous ions following metamictization aided in producing a more stable structure.

The vein assemblages are relatively simple in many cases. Quartz, carbonate, feldspar, barite, apatite, minor fluorite, iron and copper sulfides, and abundant hematite are characteristic. Hematization of wall rocks is common and may be intense. Considerable small-scale variations in thorium and rare earths characterize veins in some districts. Uranium usually is strongly subordinate or essentially absent. Thorium veins usually are related in distribution and in genesis to intrusive masses of alkalic igneous rocks. Table 3.3 summarizes the geology of some distinctive thorium vein deposits. Another example of a most unusual thorium-bearing type of deposit is represented by the zirconium veins in the Poços de Caldas region, Brazil, where thorium is present as an important vicarious element in baddeleyite and zircon (pages 327–329). Numerous thorium and rare-earth-bearing veins in gneiss have been reported over 240 sq km in an unspecified area in Brazil (MacFadyen and Guedes, 1956).

PROVINCES AND EPOCHS

There is evidence suggesting that certain petrographic provinces have characteristic radioactivities, just as others are distinguished by distinctive amounts of one or more nonradioactive elements. Acid igneous rocks of the Great Slave Lake area, the Great Bear Lake area, and other places along the western margin of the Canadian Shield are five times as radioactive as acid rocks from interior parts of the Shield in Ontario and Quebec (Keevil, 1943). Rocks from British Columbia and California were found to possess intermediate values of radioactivity. Similarly Senftle and Keevil (1947) have found some evidence for a regional distribution of uranium and thorium in North America.

Davidson (1951) has noted that regional radiometric surveys have outlined large areas of unusually high radioactivity in rocks of parts of Africa, Canada, and northern Michigan. A detailed geographic breakdown has been given by Birch (1954). Others who have attempted to define uranium-rich and uranium-poor igneous provinces, either on a geographical or petrological basis, include Senftle and Keevil (1947), Davis and Hess (1949), Asayama (1953), Adams (1954), and Coats (1956) (see pages 180–181).

Klepper and Wyant (1956) define a uranium province as a broad and generally indefinitely bounded area in which uranium deposits and uranium-rich rocks are relatively abundant; commonly the deposits are of several types and more than one age. They believe that the initial concentration of uranium in these broad areas occurred during development of the earth's crust. They suggest (Klepper and Wyant, 1955) the use of the province concept as an aid to large-scale prospecting. Nininger (1954) and Everhart (1956B) have advanced similar concepts of metallogenetic provinces rich in uranium.

Similarly the ages of many uranium deposits fall into one of three major groups: Laramide and Tertiary, Hercynian, and Precambrian; but certainly at least several epochs of uranium mineralization occurred during Precambrian time.

TABLE 3.3. *Examples of thorium veins*

Name and location	Geology	Host rock	Mineralogy	Reference
Copper Mt., 8 mi NW Twenty-nine Palms, San Bernardino County, Calif.	Mineralization along shear zones. Radioactivity up to 1.0 MR/hr. Zone traceable for 300 ft	Diorite and gneiss(?) intruded by fine-grained granite	Uranothorite, thorite, allanite; quartz, hematite, chlorite, magnetite, muscovite	Walker et al., 1956
Bear Lodge Mts., Crook County, northern Wyo.	Fe-Mn veins	Tertiary monzonite and syenite porphyry	$ThO_2 = 0.04-0.25\%$ RE_2O_3 up to 12.68%	Twenhofel and Buck, 1956
Milhollands Mill, Alexander County, N.C.	Vein up to 1 ft wide	Garnetiferous mica schist	Monazite (some complex crystals), quartz, quartz crystals, rutile, pyrite, muscovite, limonite pseudomorphs after siderite	Hidden, 1881
Salmon Bay area, northeast coast of Prince of Wales Island, Alaska	Narrow, steeply dipping veins 1 in.–2 ft thick, along fractures striking N to NW, with some wall rock impregnations	Silurian graywacke, sandstone, shale, and limestone breccia, cut by lamprophyric and alkalic Tertiary(?) dikes. Wall rocks hematitized	Thorite, monazite, parisite, and bastnaesite, in hematite-dolomite-ankerite gangue. Up to about 0.1% eU	Wedow et al., 1953: Matzko, 1955A

162

Location	Description	Host rock	Mineral composition	Reference
Mosher deposit, near Otter Rapids on Abitibi River, Pitt Township, 90 mi north of Cochrane, Ont.	Post-middle Devonian veins. Main vein about 1 ft wide, exposed at intervals for 240 ft	Precambrian gneiss intruded by granite and pegmatite	Thorium in appreciable quantities but mineral unidentified. Carbonate, quartz, pyrite, feldspar, muscovite, and hematite. 0.004–0.130% eU	Hogg, 1948; James et al, 1950; Lang, 1952
McLean Bay, southeastern shore Great Slave Lake, N.W.T., Can.	Two zones 10 and 6 ft wide within a 43-ft bed of dolomite containing concentric (algal?) structures	Kahochella fm., lower part of Great Slave group. Dolomite with interbedded quartzite	Much hematite; fine-grained monazite and pitchblende averaging 0.033% eU with Th:U = 5:1	James et al., 1950; Lang, 1952
Ogó mine, near São João da Chapada, Diamantina, Brazil	Quartzose vein	Diabase	Monazite, rutile, muscovite, quartz	Derby, 1900
Rangel Mts., Puna de Salta, Argentina	Quartz veins	?	Thorium-bearing, quartz, ± feldspar	Angelelli, 1956
Grimsel, Switzerland	Clefts (Alpine veins), low temperature	Granite	Monazite, xenotime, lanthanite, bastnaesite, autunite, calcite, ankerite, sphalerite	Beck, 1934
King's Bluff mine, Olary, South Australia	Small veins and vugs	Quartzite	Monazite, gold, quartz	Anderson, 1910
Duck Creek, Broadwater County, Mont.	Blebs and masses up to several lbs, disseminated near rhyolite dikes and sills	Precambrian argillite and phyllite	Thorite	Jarrard, 1957

The chief provinces that can be outlined readily are:

1. The Colorado Plateau and its surrounding "horseshoe" of vein deposits extending from the Black Hills at the northeast end through the Colorado Front Range, southwest and west through southern New Mexico and Arizona around the southern part of the Plateau, and thence north through Marysvale and into western Idaho (Sunshine mine) and eastern Washington (Everhart, 1956B). Includes disseminated deposits in sandstones and coals; mesothermal and epithermal veins, including some of thorium as well; carbonatite (Iron Hill); granitic pegmatites and contact deposits. Precambrian, Laramide, and Tertiary. Also phosphorites and black shales with syngenetic uranium, of Paleozoic and Mesozoic age.

2. A narrow belt along the southern and western margins of the Canadian Shield—Bancroft district, Blind River, Theano Point, west-central Manitoba, Goldfields, and Great Bear Lake (Lang, 1952). Granitic and syenitic pegmatites, vein-dikes, pyrometasomatic deposits, brannerite-pitchblende disseminated deposits, monazite-bearing migmatites, carbonatites or alkalic skarns, and mesothermal veins. Precambrian and Mesozoic.

3. A strip along the eastern side of Brazil, especially in two areas: (a) at the "hump" in Rio Grande do Norte and Paraiba, and (b) to the southeast in Bahia, Minas Gerais, Espirito Santo, and São Paulo (De Moraes, 1956). Granitic pegmatites, carbonatites, thorium veins, pitchblende-gold disseminations in conglomerate. Precambrian, early Mesozoic(?). Also Tertiary monazite placers.

4. A broad strip generally east-west across Central and Western Europe: Germany—Schmiedeberg, Erzgebirge, Wölsendorf, Wittichen; France—Vosges, Massif Central, Brittany; England—Cornwall; Portugal (Geffroy and Sarcia, 1954). Epithermal and mesothermal veins of Hercynian (and Alpine?) age.

5. A broad, discontinuous belt across southern Africa: Katanga, Belgian Congo; Rhodesia; Witwatersrand; eastern Africa; Mozambique; Madagascar. Pegmatites, migmatites, carbonatites, pyrometasomatic deposits, mesothermal veins, gold-pitchblende-thucolite disseminations in conglomerate. Precambrian, Mesozoic(?), Tertiary.

6. An area in northern, eastern, and southern Australia: Katherine—Darwin area, Northern Territory; Mt. Isa—Cloncurry region, Queensland; Broken Hill, New South Wales; Radium Hill and Mt. Painter, South Australia. Pegmatites, pyrometasomatic deposits, hypothermal and mesothermal veins and replacement deposits. Precambrian.

7. Probably in the Ferghana-Kara Tau region of U.S.S.R. Disseminations in sandstone, veins. Paleozoic and Tertiary(?).

• chapter four

SYNGENETIC DEPOSITS
IN IGNEOUS ROCKS

INTRUSIVE ROCKS

Uranium and Thorium Content

Some igneous rocks, especially those at or near the acid end of the series, normally are appreciably more radioactive than other rock types. The radioactivity of igneous rocks shows considerable variation, and many variations are systematic, relatable to chemical, mineralogical, petrographic, and structural features of the rocks; some variations are apparently nonsystematic. Factors that can be correlated with variation in radioactivity are:

1. SiO_2 content
2. Relative age in a consanguineous series
3. Position within a single pluton
4. Geographic or petrographic provinces (pages 161, 164)

Larsen et al. (1956) have demonstrated that the change in uranium content of successive members of a magma series is less systematic than is the change in major elements. This variability may stem from (1) diverse paths open to trace elements during magmatic differentiation, (2) differences inherent in traditional sampling techniques of igneous rocks, and (3) differences in post-crystallization histories of the rocks. The uranium and thorium contents of igneous rocks are functions not only of the initial content of these elements but also of the postcrystallization histories of the rocks, which have provided, in many cases, considerable opportunity for repeated changes in total uranium and thorium contents and also for changes in distribution of these elements among their various modes of occurrence in the rocks (Neuerburg, 1956).

Nearly all igneous rocks contain uranium in trace amounts (Evans and

165

Goodman, 1941); in silicic and silicic-alkalic types moderate concentrations have been discovered. Only a very few examples of silicic rocks contain in excess of 0.001 to 0.002% U, whereas some silicic-alkalic types are known to contain as much as 0.005 to 0.02% U. Various investigators have compiled average uranium and thorium contents for major igneous rock types (Table 4.1).

TABLE 4.1. *Average uranium and thorium contents of igneous rocks by groups for North America (adapted from data from Davis, 1947; Evans and Goodman, 1941; Keevil, 1938; Senftle and Keevil, 1947)*

Type	Uranium, ppm	Thorium, ppm
Ultramafic............	0.03	
Gabbroic.............	0.94–0.96	2.8– 3.9
Intermediate.........	1.4 –3.0	4.4–10.5
Granitic.............	2.8 –4.0	7.9–13.5

Keevil (1944) determined that the Th/U ratio for igneous rocks is between 3.0 and 3.5, and determinations on a larger number of samples show an average Th/U ratio of 3.4 for granitic rocks and 4.0 for intermediate rocks (Senftle and Keevil, 1947). Adams and Pliler (1956) report Th/U ratio is 2.5 to 5 for most igneous rocks and meteorites.

In igneous rocks radioactivity due to U and Th stems mainly from three sources:

1. Moderately radioactive accessory minerals
2. Weakly to very weakly radioactive essential minerals
3. Interstitial material along grain boundaries and in structural defects of minerals, which is in microscopically discrete but usually unidentifiable units or in submicroscopic phases

Some uranium and thorium also may be present in:

4. Fluid inclusions in minerals
5. Intergranular fluids

Substantial amounts of uranium and thorium are chemically so weakly attached that leaching of the pulverized rocks with dilute acid (either HCl or HNO_3) can dissolve significant fractions (Hurley, 1950; Brown and Silver, 1955) (Table 4.2). As much as 40% of the uranium of some rocks can be dissolved in this manner. Potassium may also contribute substantially to the radioactivity of some igneous rocks.

In a Hercynian granite from the Vosges Mountains, France, Picciotto (1950) has shown that 54% of the total radioactivity emanated from accessory miner-

TABLE 4.2. *Distribution of uranium and thorium in granite from Essonville, Ontario* (*Brown and Silver,* 1955)

	Mineral abundance, wt. per cent	Uranium, ppm	Thorium, ppm
Quartz......................	24	0.130	
Plagioclase................	20	0.204	
Perthite...................	52	0.218	0.410
Magnetite.................	0.4	2.57	
Apatite....................	0.02	90.5	
Sphene....................	0.4	303	5375
Zircon....................	0.04	2650	2170
Composite rock........................		2.74	41.88
Acid-soluble material (micrograms element per gram rock)......		0.90 (29%)	17.55 (42%)

als, 28% from essential minerals (quartz, biotite, and feldspar), and 18% from concentrations along grain boundaries and fractures.

The acid-leachable fraction is derived principally from (a) interstitial material, and (b) metamict accessory minerals, especially allanite. Other contributors to this fraction are some partly soluble accessories such as apatite and radioactive ions adsorbed on weathering products such as limonite. The interstitial material is believed to result from precipitation following a period of considerable mobility of uranium and thorium ions; such periods may occur during the deuteric stage, during hydrothermal or metamorphic episodes, or during weathering. Hurley (1950) has suggested that the leachable part may have resulted from supergene enrichment, since surface samples of tested granite contained larger leachable fractions than subsurface samples. The radioactive elements are not the only ones leached; other major extractable elements are Ca, Fe, Al, Si, P, and K, and minor Na, Mg, Ti, and Mn (Table 4.3).

Neuerburg et al. (1956) have found that generally the relations between uranium content and leachability and petrology are apparently random. In homogeneous outcrops, uranium content and leachability vary erratically; in heterogeneous outcrops, their variation is nonasymmetric. Geologic processes acting during and after crystallization rather than the bulk composition of the magma appear to have exercised the dominant control on the variation of uranium content and uranium leachability.

Radioactive Minerals

Primary accessory minerals mainly responsible for the bulk of the radioactivity of granitic and intermediate rocks are: zircon (Fig. 4.1), sphene (Fig.

TABLE 4.3. *Gross chemical composition of leaches in 1M HNO$_3$, at room temperature (Brown and Silver, 1955)*

Rocks from	Total solids, mg/100 g	Weight, per cent								
		SiO$_2$	Al$_2$O$_3$*	Fe$_2$O$_3$	MgO	CaO	Na$_2$O	K$_2$O	P$_2$O$_5$	TiO$_2$
Southern California	470	10	15	27	0.5	22	1.3	14	8.3	1.1
Georgia I	540	4	16	15	—	41	0.9	5.6	17	0.2
Georgia II	310	6.8	17	15	—	35	1.7	4.9	19	0.5
Montana	110	7.4	19	45	1.9	14	3.2	6.9	2.6	
Ontario	150	3.4	20	47	1.2	12	3.1	8.4	5.3	

* Includes rare earths.

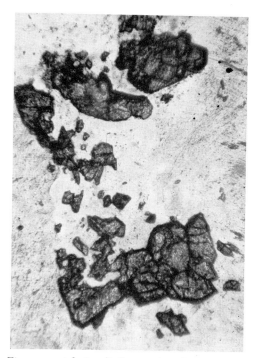

Fig. 4.1. Zircon crystals in alkalic granite, Quincy, Mass. ($\times94$).

4.2), apatite, allanite, xenotime, and monazite. Others, rarely present, but in some cases strongly radioactive, are uranothorite (White and Stevens, 1953), thorianite (at Mafufu, Belgian Congo), euxenite (Mackin and Schmidt, 1956), thorite, pyrochlore, chevkinite (Jaffe et al., 1956), fluorite (Wedow et al., 1954B), bastnaesite (Smith and Cisney, 1956), and possibly davidite (Walker et al., 1956). Other possible contributors are hematite, pyrite, columbite, ilmenite, and rutile, and in alkalic rocks rare zirconium and cerium silicates. Although uraninite has been reported as an accessory mineral of intrusive igneous rocks, it has not been demonstrated to be primary. The uranium and thorium contents of the minerals of various granites are summarized in Table 4.4. In many rocks, high radioactivity is associated with clusters of mafic minerals, e.g., biotite in granites or riebeckite in alkalic granites, largely because radioactive accessory minerals commonly are abundantly associated with mafic constituents.

The uranium and thorium contents of any one mineral species in a particular rock may vary greatly from grain to grain or within single grains. Radioactive zoning in zircon has been noted by Brotzen (1952) (Fig. 1.6*a*); nonsystematic uranium-thorium variations were described by Von Buttlar and Houtermans (1951); and Neuerburg (1956) states that uranium in minor accessories may vary depending on the nature of the host mineral that includes the accessory species.

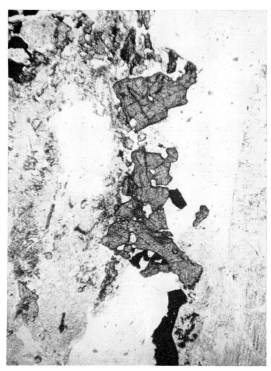

Fɪɢ. 4.2. Sphene in granite, northwestern Yellowstone Park, Wyo. ($\times$35).

Zircon, because it is widely distributed, relatively abundant, and generally radioactive, is the cause of the major part of the radioactivity of granitic igneous rocks. In some cases, however, much of the radioactivity of zircon itself apparently stems from unidentified radioactive inclusions (Fig. 2.48), as for example in a zircon of a post-Cretaceous monzonite intrusive of the Lower Yukon–Kuskokwim Highlands region, Alaska (White and Killeen, 1953). There is a distinct tendency of zircon from a specific igneous rock to display an over-all uniform fluorescence (Foster, 1948). Hayase (1953) has found that in the Tanakamiyama and Mikumo granites of the Siga prefecture, Japan, zircons that are both colored and of low birefringence show more radioactivity. Low birefringence in zircon is associated with structural damage preceding metamictization in more highly radioactive types. He also found that smaller and rounded zircons are more strongly radioactive than larger, better-formed crystals. A difference in radioactivity of as much as ten times may appear in metamict and non-metamict zircon from the same rock (Larsen and Phair, 1954).

Coppens (1950) has found that 60 to 70% of the radioactivity of such rocks as granites, granulites, gneisses, and mica schists stems from four different types of inclusions in minerals:

TABLE 4.4. *Radioactivity and uranium and thorium contents (ppm) in minerals of various igneous rocks*

Mineral	I *		II, α/mg/hr	III, avg. U	IV, α/mg/hr
	U	Th			
Quartz............	0.13 ± 0.01	—	0.17	2.2	1.5
Plagioclase......	0.20 ± 0.02	—	0.23	1.6	
Perthite (orthoclase or microcline)......	0.22 ± 0.03	0.410 ± 0.008	—	1.9	1.9
Biotite (± chlorite).........	—	—	0.39	5.7	48.9
Hornblende......	—	—	0.78	18.0	
Pyroxene........	—	—	—	3.7–7.7	
Zircon..........	2650 ± 40	2180 ± 20	401	1367	14,000
Sphene..........	303 ± 5	2205	266	196	8
Apatite.........	90.5 ± 1.3	—	56.2	67	710
Magnetite.......	2.57 ± 0.04	—	0.61	7.1	13
Allanite........	—	—	3600	180	
Monazite........	—	—	4000	820	
Xenotime.......	—	—	—	6630	
Muscovite.......	—	—	—	8.0	1.5
Epidote.........	—	—	—	32	213
Garnet..........	—	—	—	6.0	3.58
Fluorite.........	—	—	—	3.5	

* I = Granite, Monmouth Township, Haliburton County, Ont. (Tilton et al., 1955.)
  II = Lakeview tonalite, Southern California batholith. (Larsen and Keevil, 1942; Larsen et al., 1952.)
 III = Rocks of the Southern California batholith. (McKelvey et al., 1955.)
 IV = Ayer granite-migmatite, Chelmsford, Mass. (Keevil et al., 1944.)

1. Those with a high uranium content
2. Those with a high thorium content
3. Those with a weak uranium content
4. Those with a weak thorium content

Apparently inclusions with U-Th combined are rare.

Davis and Hess (1949) have suggested that nearly all of the radioactivity of ultramafic rocks is in a small amount of deuteric minerals, kaemmerite, talc, tremolite, and serpentine.

Geochemistry

Uranium in unaltered igneous rocks occurs as U^4. The U^4 and Th^4 ions are concentrated in late magmatic fractions and in accessory minerals largely because their relatively large ionic radii hinder their entrance into the structure of most of the common essential silicates. Other factors governing the distribution of uranium and thorium are their low initial concentration in magmas and their high valence (to which the size of their ionic radii is in part related). Although the high activation energy of migration (E-value) of uranium and thorium results in a tendency for their ions to become crystallographically fixed in the early or main stage of magmatic crystallization, the low concentration of the two elements prevents the precipitation of phases in which they are the principal constituents. As a result uranium and thorium appear chiefly either as isomorphous trace or minor elements in early crystallizing accessory minerals (coordination differences prevent their substitution for Ca in plagioclase or pyroxene), or they are concentrated in residual fluids to crystallize finally in the pegmatitic or hydrothermal stages.

It also appears from leaching studies that some uranium and thorium ions remain in solution until the very last crystallization stage, being finally deposited as weakly attached films on surfaces of essential mineral grains (McKelvey et al., 1955). However, not all interstitial leachable uranium and thorium can be ascribed to a late igneous stage.

Variation in Calc-Alkalic Series

In a series of igneous rocks that are genetically related and within a few million years of the same geological age, certain broad characteristics persist despite systematic variations in composition and wide variations in texture. A well-studied example of a consanguineous magma series from a petrographic province is the Southern California Middle Cretaceous batholith (Larsen, 1948), which is as much as 75 mi wide and over 1,000 mi long. The rocks range from gabbro (oldest) through successively younger tonalites and granodiorites to minor granite (youngest), with an SiO_2 range of from 40 to about 75%. Variation diagrams of the major elements fall on or near even characteristic curves. In contrast the content of radioactivity shows considerable scattering, although the curves rise markedly toward the SiO_2-rich end of the diagram (Fig. 4.3) (Larsen and Keevil, 1947).

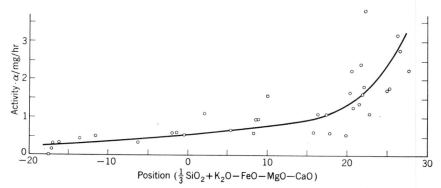

Fɪɢ. 4.3. Variation diagram of radioactivity in rocks of the southern California batholith (Larsen and Keevil, 1947; *Geol. Soc. Am.*).

A markedly different idea on uranium concentration has been advanced by Emmons et al. (1953), who have found abnormally large amounts of radioactivity and radioactivity induced thermoluminescence associated with some lamprophyres, particularly along their contacts. They regard lamprophyres as derived from the immediate walls of their host rocks, formed by the accumulation of deuteric-type material, principally late alkalic solutions derived from the exsolution of feldspars, modified by selectively resorbed mafic material. They suggest that trace amounts of uranium halides from granites gather with this alkalic fluid and drain into fractures to form radioactive lamprophyres, the uranium halides being precipitated as pitchblende upon contact with oxygen-bearing water.

In New Hampshire, lower Paleozoic strata are intruded by igneous rocks of four Paleozoic magma series, each of which consists of rocks that range from gabbro, diorite, or tonalite to granite (Billings and Keevil, 1946). Average radioactive values increase progressively toward the granitic end of each series, which is three to four times as radioactive as the mafic end. The White Mountain magma series (Mississippian?) is twice as radioactive as the other three, and its rocks are much more radioactive than similar rocks from elsewhere in North America.

In the Elzevir batholith, a composite batholith 50 mi northwest of Kingston, Ontario, Ingram and Keevil (1951) found that radioactivity increases progressively with differentiation:

	$\alpha/mg/hr$
Pegmatite	2.98
Aplitic granite	1.69
Red granite	1.56
Syenite	1.30
White granite	0.93
Gray granite	0.65
Diorite	0.20

Experimental data indicate that acidic magmas, which contain more uranium and thorium than basic magmas, retain relatively more uranium and thorium than do intermediate magmas in the same region (Senftle and Keevil, 1947).

Comparison of Calc-Alkalic and Alkalic Rocks

Although in a consanguineous calc-alkalic series the highest radioactivity generally correlates with highest SiO_2 content (and youngest age), in some alkalic series the SiO_2 content varies erratically with age, whereas uranium and thorium increase with decreasing age (Larsen and Phair, 1954). Silica-poor lamprophyres may contain relatively large amounts of uranium. Alkalic granites and alkalic syenites normally possess several times the average radioactivity of calc-alkalic granites. One of the high-alkali granites of New Hampshire, the Conway biotite granite (Billings and Keevil, 1946), contains about twice (9 ppm U) the average radioactivity of "normal" granites (4 ppm U). The quartz-bostonite dikes of the Colorado Front Range (Phair, 1952) contain an average of 33 ppm U and average 120 ppm eU. The albite-riebeckite granite of Nigeria averages 260 ppm eU. Other albite-riebeckite granites in Vermont, the Pikes Peak region of Colorado, the San Francisco Mountains of Arizona, and Alaska also are especially radioactive (Everhart, 1951), as is a Precambrian alkalic granite of Egypt (Schurman, 1956).

Rocks in which cerium earths and zirconium are relatively concentrated, i.e., in syenites and nepheline syenites and especially their pegmatitic derivatives, as a rule contain considerable quantities of thorium and are relatively low in uranium (pages 217–222).

In all series that have been carefully studied (calc-alkalic, sodic, or potassic), in which fractional crystallization apparently was the dominant process of differentiation, the trends are similar (Larsen et al., 1956): uranium is enriched in the youngest rocks, these being usually high in Si and K, and low in Ca and Mg, and maximum enrichment occurs in late, extreme differentiates very poor in Ca. Intermediate rocks in a series are the most variable; there is little or no overlap between granitic and gabbroic differentiates in any one series. In series whose differentiation was controlled primarily by processes other than fractional crystallization, local geologic conditions probably influenced the uranium content of each of the magmatic fractions.

Variation in Single Plutons

In a single pluton, peripheral parts generally show a distinctly higher radioactivity than do the central parts, and there may be a definite but not necessarily uniform increase in radioactivity from center to margin (Slack, 1949; Ingram and Keevil, 1951; Slack and Whitham, 1951; Gross, 1952). Around the Round Lake batholith near Kirkland Lake, Ontario, radioactivity increases regularly from south to north owing to the northward plunge of the batholith and the presumed migration of radioactive elements toward the upper surface (Slack, 1949). The outer parts of the Bourlamaque batholith, a simple granodioritic batholith 60 mi east of Noranda, Quebec, have a radioactivity six times the central part (Ingram and Keevil, 1951). Bodies under 2 mi in width generally show poor radioactive differentiation. In the larger members of the Elzevir batholith, a composite batholith 50 mi northwest of Kingston, Ontario, each is more radioactive marginally than centrally (Fig. 4.4). In two granites of the Siga prefecture, Japan, the marginal facies are more radioactive than central parts, and the stock-type granite is more radioactive than the batholithic type (Hayase, 1953).

A few determinations of radioactivity of deeper samples indicate a decrease in radioactivity with depth (Ingram and Keevil, 1951). Hurley (1950) found that deep-seated samples of granites from a Butte mine and from the Adams Tunnel in Colorado are less radioactive than near-surface samples of other granites and also contain less acid-leachable radioactivity.

Gross (1952) has found that in some batholiths radioactivity is concentrated in parts marked by faults or fractures, i.e., low-pressure areas, particularly where these are mineralized. If these are absent, the radioactivity is marginally concentrated. The low-pressure areas of high radioactivity are accompanied by higher than normal amounts of silica, zirconium, and heavy metals, all of which are ascribed to deposition from late solutions.

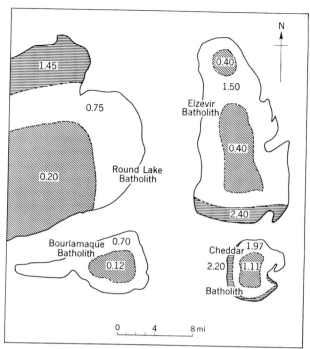

Fɪɢ. 4.4. Distribution of radioactivity in four Precambrian batholiths in eastern Ontario and western Quebec. Radioactivity values in α/mg/hr (Slack, 1949; *Am. Geophys. Union*).

Several types of luminescent phenomena (fluorescence, cryoluminescence, and thermoluminescence) may occur in minerals of rocks that are marginal to certain intrusive igneous bodies and to hydrothermal ore deposits (Mc-Dougall, 1954). Thermoluminescence in altered wall rocks close to intrusives is apparently closely related to radioactivity introduced during emplacement of the intrusive body.

At the head of Serpentine Creek, Seward Peninsula, Alaska, a Mesozoic or Tertiary granitic stock contains four facies: normal granite, pegmatite, fine-grained felsic dikes, and mafic tabular dikelike masses. The last three, which are all younger than the normal granite, also are more radioactive than the normal granite, with the pegmatitic type the most radioactive, averaging 0.009% eU (Moxham and West, 1953).

In the Rock Corral area, San Bernardino County, California, radioactive quartz monzonite contains as much as 0.009% eU, attributable chiefly to allanite and zircon. However, biotite-rich inclusions, consisting of 7% allanite, 5 to 6% magnetite, 3% apatite, 1% sphene, 1% zircon, 74% biotite, and 8% feldspar, contain as much as 0.03% eU. The xenoliths are usually less than 100 sq ft in extent (Moxham et al., 1955). Xenoliths of abnormally radioactive migmatized biotite schist occur in Precambrian granite on the southwest flank of the Wind

Fɪɢ. 4.5. Radioactive biotite schist xenolith (left of hammer) in Precambrian granite of southwest flank of Wind River Mts., near Boulder, Wyo. Pegmatite dike cuts both granite and schist.

River range near Boulder, Wyoming (Fig. 4.5). However, the xenoliths do not contain any notable concentrations of any of the common radioactive accessory minerals.

The more mafic border phases of the Boulder Creek batholith, Colorado, contain as much as 14 gU/ton, whereas the felsic interior parts, 12 mi away, contain but 2 to 4 gU/ton (Larsen et al., 1956). Rocks of the intermediate zone range from 5.3 to 7.8 gU/ton. In the floor of Grand Coulee near Steamboat Rock, Washington, a phase of a granite is exposed that includes biotite-rich schlieren containing 0.001% U (McKelvey et al., 1955). Doubtless the radioactivity of some intrusive masses has been modified by the assimilation of either low- or high-radioactive wall rocks. In the granodioritic laccolith of Malka River in the northern Caucasus, U.S.S.R., radium is most abundant in the upper parts of the intrusive, apparently independent of the rock type (Soloviev, 1936).

Variations of radioactivity in single plutons thus may be ascribed to:

1. Deposition of abnormally large amounts of radioactive elements by late-stage solutions (deuteric or hydrothermal) along marginal phases or along marginal fracture or fault zones.

2. Concentration of radioactive pegmatites marginally.

3. Peripheral assimilation of wall rocks of variable radioactivity.

4. Supergene enrichment of radioactive elements derived from eroded higher parts of the intrusive.

Examples

Calc-Alkalic Rocks

Large crystals of sphene up to ⅞ in. long and ⅝ in. wide occur in microcline-bearing tonalite and granodiorite in the San Jacinto Mountains, California. The euhedra, which include quartz and andesine grains, constitute 1 to 3% of the typical rock and locally as much as 5 to 10%. The crystals are distinctly radioactive, registering up to 0.01% eU_3O_8. Although Webb (1939) suggests that the sphene has been introduced, the evidence is not compelling. In the Rock Corral area, San Bernardino County, California, quartz monzonite intrusive masses contain as much as 0.009% eU, chiefly due to thorium-bearing allanite and zircon (Moxham et al., 1955). Well-defined anomalies were recorded over a quartz monzonite intrusive (Fig. 4.6), which is about 10,000 sq ft in area and which is anomalous only to the extent of 0.003% eU with respect to adjacent rocks.

Along the Upper Porcupine River, northeastern Alaska, rhyolitic dikes associated with a granitic intrusive, a few miles north of Porcupine, contain

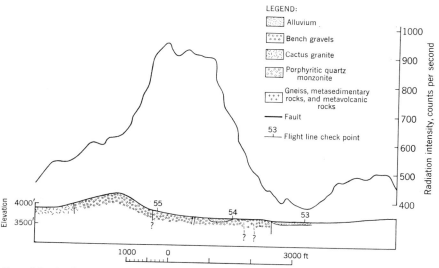

LEGEND:

[image] Alluvium

[image] Bench gravels

[image] Cactus granite

[image] Porphyritic quartz monzonite

[image] Gneiss, metasedimentary rocks, and metavolcanic rocks

—— Fault

53
⊥— Flight line check point

FIG. 4.6. Geologic section and radiation intensity profile across Rock Corral area, San Bernardino County, Calif. (Moxham et al., 1955; *U.S. Geol. Survey*).

about 0.006% eU in radioactive biotite, hematite, and pyrite and an unidentified calcium-uranium phosphate (White, 1952A). Granite of Mesozoic(?) age in the Miller House–Circle Hot Springs area, east-central Alaska, contains 0.005 to 0.007% eU, due to the allanite, zircon, and radioactive garnet and sphene. Sulfides, cassiterite, and uraniferous fluorite, malachite, and topaz have apparently been introduced hydrothermally (Wedow et al., 1954B). In the Ruby-Poorman district, Ruby Quadrangle, central Alaska, two small granite bodies in the Long area, about 30 mi south of Ruby, contain an average of 0.005% eU, due chiefly to disseminated uranothorite and to a lesser extent to sphene, allanite, and zircon (White and Stevens, 1953).

McKelvey et al. (1955) found that of twelve granitic bodies in Montana, Idaho, Washington, and Oregon, two contain abnormally high amounts of uranium, and one of these is rich in biotite schlieren. In all bodies the only radioactive minerals are zircon and allanite.

In Normand Township, 44 mi northwest of Grand'Mère, Quebec (Lang, 1952), abundant allanite in crystals up to 3 in. long is exposed in a cliff of coarse-grained reddish granite. Three samples yielded up to 0.25% eU_3O_8, and one contained 0.05% U_3O_8 and 0.50% ThO_2.

The average radioactivity of Canadian granites is 0.003% eU_3O_8 (Robinson, 1955B). In the Canadian Shield, red granites are commonly more radioactive than gray ones (due to more potassium?). A granite in the Parry Sound area of Ontario contains 0.01% eU_3O_8, 70% of which is removed by hot HCl leaching. In the Bancroft-Wilberforce area many dikes, which are coarse-grained but only locally pegmatitic, are abnormally radioactive. Some are granitic, others syenitic. Their radioactive minerals are uraninite and uranothorite, with minor cyrtolite and allanite. Uranothorite, which varies from yellow to black, partly envelops uraninite. Peristerite albite is a common constituent; locally calcite, pyrrhotite, or pyrite are abundant. Those dikes in carbonate-rich country rocks have developed pyroxene skarns near their walls and adjacent to xenoliths. The radioactive elements are usually concentrated in parts rich in magnetite, sphene, zircon, and pyroxene.

Alkalic Rocks

In the Central City district, Colorado, quartz-bostonite porphyries, silicic end members of a predominantly sodic series, contain 33 ppm U and 120 ppm eU (Larsen and Phair, 1954). All members of the series are markedly radioactive (Phair, 1952). The rock types with their average radioactivities are listed in their sequence of intrusion:

	Avg. % U
1. Monzonite porphyry............	0.002–0.007
2. Quartz bostonite..............	0.014
3. Quartz-bostonite porphyry.......	0.007–0.014
4. Bostonite....................	0.004–0.007

Most of the radioactivity appears to stem from zircon, the percentage of eU increasing with the percentage of ZrO_2. Phair (1952) has suggested that the pitchblende-bearing vein deposits of the Central City district were deposited

FIG. 4.7. Weakly radioactive zoned allanite in nepheline syenite, Miask, Ural Mts., U.S.S.R. (×35).

from solutions derived from a quartz bostonitic mass at depth and further enriched in uranium by leaching of other bostonitic rocks encountered en route upward.

In New Hampshire biotite granite (Conway type) of the White Mountain Magma series, an alkalic leucogranite containing albite, apatite, zircon, sphene, allanite, and fluorite averages 13 ppm eU and 9 ppm U. McKelvey et al. (1955) report an anorthoclase trachyte porphyry in the Eureka Quadrangle, California, that contains 0.008% U. Bostonite from Sussex County, New Jersey, contains 22 ppm U (Butler and Schnabel, 1956).

Pyrochlore-bearing alkalic rocks occur at several places in the world. In southern Norway pyrochlore, which appears chiefly in syenite and nepheline-syenite pegmatites, also occurs in normal syenitic and nepheline-syenitic rocks with polymignite, zircon, sodian orthoclase, hornblende, ± nepheline and magnetite. Polymignite is the oldest mineral, being bent, broken, and recemented by later minerals. Polymignite-pyrochlore rocks occur at Fredericksvärn, and pyrochlore rocks in the gneissic border syenites near Lillegården. In the Ilmen Mountains, Urals, U.S.S.R., pyrochlore occurs as black octahedra with zircon in coarse biotitic syenite.

Certain phases of albite-riebeckite granite from the Kaffo Valley, the Darowa district, the Kigom Hills, the Teria district, and the Shere Hills, Nigeria, are abnormally radioactive largely due to their pyrochlore content. The rocks also contain quartz, albite, perthite, and riebeckite as primary constituents and accessory zircon, topaz, cryolite, thomsenolite, astrophyllite, and thorite. In the Kaffo Valley (Beer, 1951) a deposit of 195 acres averages 0.012% U_3O_8 and 0.26% $(Nb,Ta)_2O_5$. The pyrochlore contains 3.1% U_3O_8 and 3.3% ThO_2. Similar rocks are reported in the French Sudan. Columbite-bearing granites of the Jos Plateau, Nigeria, also contain zircon, monazite, and thorite (John and Paulo, 1954; Williams et. al., 1956).

EXTRUSIVE ROCKS

As with intrusive rocks, the uranium and thorium contents of calc-alkalic extrusive rocks are proportional generally to the potassium and silicon contents or with the amounts of felsic minerals. Basalts have 0.6 to 1.1 ppm U; some dacites have four times as much, and obsidians with 15 ppm U are known (Adams, 1954). An average of 5.6 ppm has been indicated for volcanic glasses. In the alkalic series of Cripple Creek, Colorado (Larsen and Phair, 1954), the older latitic phonolite, which is richer in silica, is poorer in uranium and thorium than the younger phonolites, which are richer in nepheline and poorer in silica. Thus, in this series at least, radioactivity follows the previously stated rule of increasing with decreasing age. Thorium is about three times as abundant as uranium. The uranium content has been found to vary directly with the order of extrusion in the lavas of Lassen Park, California (Adams and Saunders, 1953; Adams, 1955).

There is some suggestion that volcanic and hypabyssal rocks may average slightly higher in radioactivity and uranium content than their plutonic equivalents (Larsen and Phair, 1954), but in general, differences between plutonic and extrusive rocks of the same clan are small to absent (Neuerburg, 1956). In some volcanic rocks abnormal radioactivity occurs in xenoliths, e.g., in Tertiary lavas of Little Gallinas Canyon, Black Range, New Mexico. Cherty xenoliths contain 0.068 and 0.016% U (Lovering, 1956).

The radioactivity probably results chiefly from such accessory minerals as zircon, sphene, allanite (Fig. 4.8), apatite, and fluorite, all of which have been identified as accessory constituents in rhyolites, quartz latites, trachytes, and dacites. Betafite has been identified in volcanic ash at Ndale near Fort Portal, Uganda (Davidson, 1956C). In the San Juan, Colorado, volcanics zircon is low in radioactivity, usually not over 100 α/mg/hr (Larsen and Phair, 1954). Monazite, perrierite, and thorite are the chief radioactive species in alkalic-potassic tuffs around Rome, Italy (Ippolito et al., 1956). In the rapidly solidified lavas of Mt. Lassen, California, radioactive material is randomly distributed in plagioclase, pyroxene, hornblende, biotite, and glass, and strongly radioactive accessory minerals are absent (Rogers and Adams, 1956).

Coats (1955) has shown that regional variations in uranium content in rhyolitic and dacitic rocks are nonrandom in nature, with rocks of the Shoshone province (northern Nevada, southeastern Idaho, northwestern Utah) having the highest mean uranium content. Rocks from the Ute province to the south and the Pacific Coastal province of Tertiary volcanic rocks have lower values. Similar types of variations occur for Sn, Be, Nb, Pb, and F. Processes suggested as offering some explanation of these systematic differences are subcrustal transport of sialic material and repeated generation and progressive upward migration of palingenetic magmas.

The radioactivity of tuffaceous rocks is of particular interest because of the possible genetic relation of such rocks to underlying deposits of uranium derived from them by supergene leaching (pages 447–451). The White River group (Oligocene) and the Arikaree formation (Miocene) in North and South Dakota and eastern Montana show appreciable radioactivity and in some areas contain uranium minerals, especially replacing fossils (Denson, 1955). The maximum determined uranium content is 0.003%, with an average of about 0.0015%. About 0.04% V also is present. Waters from these formations also contain uranium and significant concentrations of As, Cu, P, V, and Mo. Uraniferous lignites and carbonaceous shales occur in many localities unconformably below remnants of the volcanic rocks that cap buttes and escarpments.

On La Ventana Mesa, Sandoval County, New Mexico, uraniferous coals of the Mesaverde formation (Late Cretaceous) were probably once covered by

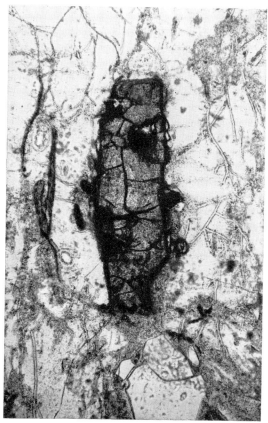

FIG. 4.8. Partly metamict allanite phenocryst in pitchstone, Meissen, Saxony (×66).

the Pliocene(?) Bandelier tuff, which contains about 0.003% U and which has been suggested as a source for the uranium in the coal (Cannon and Starrett, 1956). The uranium of coal, shale, and carbonaceous limestone of the Bear River formation (Early Cretaceous) in the Fall Creek area, Bonneville County, Idaho, is believed to have been derived from mildly radioactive, silicic, Tertiary volcanics that were formerly overlying (Vine and Moore, 1952). These contain 0.004% eU but less than 0.001% U.

About four miles south of Coaldale in Esmeralda County, Nevada, a welded rhyolitic tuff that averages 0.008 to 0.009% eU contains radioactive veinlets, pods, joint coatings, and matrix of a breccia pipe. The veinlets contain autunite and phosphuranylite. The uranium mineralization may have been derived from the volcanic rock itself or may have been introduced hydrothermally from unrelated sources (Duncan, 1953).

Disseminations and veinlets of various secondary uranium minerals (commonly autunite) occur in acid volcanic and tuffaceous rocks along fractures and as disseminations at various localities in several Western states. For example, in California they occur at the Rosamond prospect, Kern County, in Miocene tuff; at the Goldenrod claim, Kern County, in dacite that carries 0.006% eU and 0.001% U; and on the Stillwell property in tuff, Kern County (Walker et al., 1956). Although much of the mineralization occurs near faults, the solutions may have been supergene, collecting uranium from the volcanic rocks. At Topaz Mountain, Utah, autunite and opal with minor fine-grained dark purple fluorite occur in rhyolite.

In Wyoming, deposits of the Gas Hills area in the Wind River formation, deposits of the Pumpkin Buttes area in the Wasatch formation, and deposits in the Miller Hill area are regarded by Love (1952, 1954A, 1954B) as having been formed from uranium leached from formerly overlying White River tuff (pages 424–425). Similarly in the White River Badlands, Pennington County, South Dakota, uranocircite in the Chadron formation (Oligocene) is thought by Moore and Levish (1955) to have resulted from precipitation from ground water that leached uranium from the volcanic ash of the overlying Brule formation, also of Oligocene age, which contains on the average about 0.001% U.

In the Trunkey district of New South Wales a large body of fresh trachyte shows radioactivity of 12 times background, and similar occurrences have been found elsewhere in Australia (Sullivan, 1955). The over-all grade of betafite-bearing volcanic ash at Ndale, near Fort Portal, Uganda, does not exceed 0.01% U_3O_8 and 0.04% ThO_2.

ECONOMIC SIGNIFICANCE

The possibility of igneous rocks serving as long-range, large-scale, and low-grade sources of radioactive elements has been investigated by Brown and Silver (1955) who conclude:

1. A substantial fraction of the uranium, thorium, and certain other elements in igneous rocks can be removed by leaching with dilute acid.

2. More energy can be obtained from an average granite in the form of uranium and thorium than is required for processing the rock.

3. Although the costs of processing average granite are prohibitively high at the present time, a number of igneous bodies that possess higher than average concentrations of leachable uranium and thorium might be processed competitively in the near future.

4. There is sufficient uranium and thorium in the igneous rocks of the earth's crust to power a highly industrialized world economy for a very long period of time.

5. Solely from the point of view of availability, no nation needing uranium and thorium in quantity need be deprived of supplies of these elements.

The amount of leachable uranium in an igneous rock may also be of practical importance in identifying that rock as a source from which uranium has been removed, possibly deposited elsewhere in economic concentrations (Neuerburg, 1956).

• chapter five

RADIOACTIVE PEGMATITE DEPOSITS

GEOLOGICAL CHARACTERISTICS OF PEGMATITES

Introduction

Uranium and thorium minerals are widespread and common minor constituents of granitic, syenitic, and foidal syenitic pegmatites in many pegmatite districts. Although the occurrences of radioactive pegmatite minerals are very numerous and markedly variable in the details of their geology and mineralogical associations, few pegmatites, upon detailed exploration, have been found to represent significant sources of radioactive ores. Instead, most pegmatites have proved scientifically important chiefly in providing fine specimens of otherwise rare radioactive mineral species, and also, unfortunately, have served to elevate the hopes of the geologically untrained prospector.

Because pegmatites are exceedingly abundant in some terrains underlain by metamorphic and intrusive igneous rocks, and because many contain at least small amounts of numerous different, weakly to highly radioactive mineral species, they are, in many "hard rock" areas, the most common type of radioactive mineral deposit encountered. It has been estimated that in Canada over one thousand pegmatites are known to carry radioactive minerals, and within the United States there are probably at least that many in the numerous widely scattered districts. With the exception of the Colorado Plateau area, more radioactive mineral occurrences have been found in pegmatites within the United States than all other types of deposits combined. This is probably also true for the Canadian Shield, certainly for its southern part.

Most pegmatites approach the general composition of granite (including quartz monzonite and granodiorite). However, pegmatites of syenitic, nepheline-syenitic, dioritic, and other types also occur but are much less common. Some of these also contain radioactive minerals, particularly those of syenitic and nepheline-syenitic composition. In general, however, uranium minerals tend to

184

occur more commonly in granitic pegmatites, whereas thorium minerals tend to be more common in pegmatites of syenitic and nepheline-syenitic composition.

Distribution and Occurrence

Pegmatites, which commonly occur in swarms or well-defined groups, are essentially confined to hosts of intrusive igneous rocks and high- to intermediate-grade regional metamorphic rocks. The swarms are consanguineous with large plutons or batholiths of acid igneous rocks to which the pegmatites are related in time, geochemical and mineralogical features, position, and origin.

In many districts a zonal distribution of pegmatites about batholithic masses has been deciphered (Heinrich, 1948B). Gevers et al. (1937), for the pegmatites of Namaqualand, were able to recognize three classes of pegmatites, based on their positions with respect to the parent batholithic intrusive, a grouping found applicable in other districts:

1. Interior pegmatites—those within the interior of the batholith
2. Marginal pegmatites—those concentrated in the batholith along its margins
3. Exterior pegmatites—those outside of the batholiths, usually concentrated close to the intrusive contacts

This regional zoning may be of considerable significance in prospecting pegmatites for economic concentrations of rare minerals, for pegmatite masses occurring in one zone differ from those in another in abundance, size, shape, internal structure, and mineral content.

Pegmatites may be very small, ranging in thickness from only a few inches to many hundreds of feet. Some are a foot or less in length, whereas some others may extend for several miles. Some have been mined to depths of several hundred feet, and others have been bottomed within a few tens of feet of the surface. In general, most pegmatites show neither the strike nor the down-dip extent of hydrothermal veins, or the general persistence of ordinary granitic dikes.

Internal Structure

It has long been recognized that some pegmatites show internal differentiation into distinctive rock units (Hitchcock, 1833), but it was not until about 1940 that these units began to be investigated systematically and to be mapped in detail. The results of numerous studies (summarized in Heinrich, 1948B; Cameron et al., 1949; Jahns, 1955) have led to a widely applicable classification of internal units:

1. Zones: Complete or incomplete, successive shells of contrasting mineralogy and/or texture, which reflect to a considerable extent the shape and over-all structural features of the pegmatite body itself.
2. Secondary units: Units formed after the crystallization of most or a large part of the pegmatite and superimposed on the zonal structure.

In the ideal case, zones occur as concentric layers around a central unit or core. These units are primary, in that they represent original elements of the pegmatite formed by successive stages of crystallization from the walls inward. Recent usage has brought about the following nomenclature for zones: (1) The

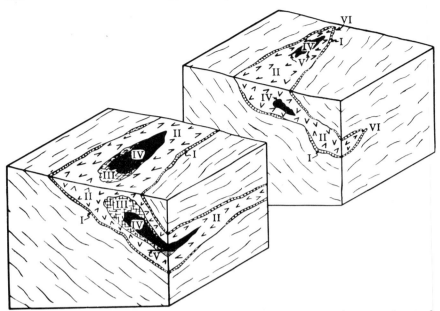

Fɪɢ. 5.1. Lensoid, moderately dipping pegmatite sill showing distribution and attitude of zones. I = border zone, II = wall zone, III = intermediate zone, IV = core, V = apophyse from core, VI = plunging keel of pegmatite.

thin outermost selvage, or *border zone*, commonly is too narrow to be mapped. (2) The next zone inward is the *wall zone*, which is usually relatively thick and well developed and may contain concentrations of economically important minerals. (3) Next follow *intermediate zones*, which may range in number from one to three, rarely more; the innermost is usually referred to as the *core-margin zone*. (4) The central unit is the *core* (Fig. 5.1).

Geological characteristics of zones and the zonal pattern reflect the shape and attitude of the pegmatite, particularly where the body is vertical or steeply dipping. Thus zones strike, dip, and plunge in conformity with the pegmatite as a whole. In many bodies, however, certain zones may be imperfectly developed, at least in any one horizon under immediate observation; zonal structure must be considered in three dimensions. In pegmatites that are relatively flat-lying, cores may be displaced laterally, particularly toward the hanging wall side, and other zones likewise tend to show an asymmetric development.

The following features are characteristic of zones: (1) In a general way their shape and attitude repeat the structural features and the shape of the pegmatite as a whole. (2) In many deposits their arrangement gives a rough bilateral symmetry to the pegmatite. (3) The grain size of minerals in zones increases from the margins toward the center of the pegmatite. (4) Zones are composed principally of common rock-forming minerals. (5) Zones tend to become increasingly simple in mineral content from margins toward core, many of which are mono- or bi-mineralic. (6) Zones tend to become more siliceous toward the core; cores consist principally of quartz or of quartz in combination with microcline. Common mineralogical assemblages in zones are shown in Table 5.1. Minerals that appear in more than one zone show systematic compositional variations (Heinrich, 1953B).

TABLE 5.1. *Mineral compositions in a typical sequence of pegmatite zones. For a more detailed representation see Cameron et al.* (1949)

Zone	Essential minerals	Accessory minerals
Border zone..................	Plagioclase, quartz, ± muscovite	Black tourmaline, garnet, magnetite, microcline
Wall zone....................	Quartz, plagioclase, microcline, ± muscovite, ± biotite	Black tourmaline, garnet, beryl, apatite
Outer Intermediate zone........	Microcline, quartz	Sodic plagioclase, muscovite
Inner Intermediate zone........ (core-margin)	Quartz, microcline, sodic plagioclase, ± muscovite, ± biotite	
Core.......................	Quartz	

Secondary units are of three main kinds: (1) fracture-filling veins; (2) replacement masses whose development was controlled by fractures or by zonal contacts; (3) partial replacements of a zone or of several zones, rarely complete replacement of a zone or of several zones (Fig. 5.2).

General characteristics of secondary units are: (1) In shape and in attitude they are to a considerable extent independent of the external structural features of the pegmatite. (2) They may be crosscutting and their distribution tends to destroy any zonal symmetry that may have been present. (3) Grain size within them is irregular and shows no systematic relationship to the distance from the pegmatite contact. (4) They may display marked evidence of replacement, such as coronas, concentric structures, relicts, veins, pseudomorphs, and solution vugs. (5) Many may be referred in their initial development to fracture or zonal contacts. (6) Their mineral compositions may be complex, and rare minerals may be developed, at least locally, in abundance. (7) There is no relationship between the composition of the individual secondary units and their position within the pegmatite. In uncommon examples, fracture fillings that transect outer zones originate as offshoots from inner zones (Fig. 5.1–V).

The development of secondary units in pegmatites appears to be dependent upon the initial presence of a zonal structure. No important examples have been found of pegmatites that show a major development of secondary structural units in which remnants of an older, well-developed zonal structure cannot also be detected. Many secondary units appear to have been formed as

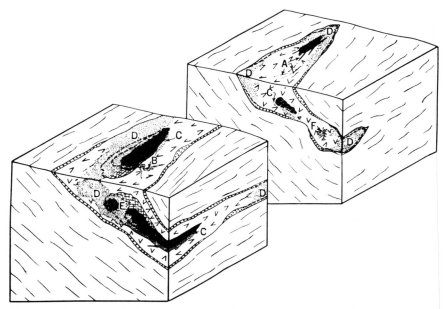

FIG. 5.2. Pegmatite of Fig. 5.1 with secondary units superimposed on zonal structure. A = fissure veins; B = fracture-controlled replacement body; C = small replacement body localized along footwall of core; D = major replacement body concentrated in footwall half and along keel of pegmatite, replacing parts of several zones; E = core relict; F = radial replacement aggregate.

the result of replacement or of deuteric reaction between freshly crystallized zonal pegmatite and generally highly subordinate amounts of residual, volatile-rich magmatic fluids or hydrothermal solutions, which were developed under closed system conditions as the end products of the fractional crystallization of the pegmatite magma itself. Thus in their development such solutions are related to the pegmatite in the same way as the pegmatitic magma is related to the batholithic magma.

CLASSIFICATION

The grouping of pegmatites by means of the presence or absence of internal structural units provides a basis both for a sound genetic classification and for intelligent prospecting and systematic mining. On the basis of the types of structural units they contain, there are three main classes of pegmatites: (1) homogeneous or *unzoned*, (2) *zoned*, and (3) those in which secondary units are superimposed on a zonal structure, i.e., structurally *complex* pegmatites.

Within a district all three types of pegmatites may be present. Usually complex pegmatites are most strongly developed in the exterior group of pegmatites, are less well developed in the marginal group, and rarely or not at all in the interior group. In general, however, complex pegmatites are few in number and the volume of rock that their secondary units represent is small, commonly less than 5% of the individual pegmatites and 1% or less of the total pegmatite rock in the district.

RADIOACTIVE MINERALS IN PEGMATITES

Mineralogy

The radioactive mineralogy of pegmatites has been summarized by Page (1950A) and earlier by Ellsworth (1932). The number of radioactive species found in pegmatites is very large, but it is necessary to distinguish between those formed as the result of pegmatitic processes, both magmatic and hydrothermal (hypogene minerals)—the "primary" radioactive pegmatite minerals— and those resulting from supergene processes, formed as the result of alteration and redistribution by meteoric or ground waters—the "secondary" radioactive pegmatite minerals.

The oxides are represented chiefly by uraninite, although thorianite occurs rarely. Most of the radioactive complex (multiple) oxides have been found in pegmatites, with the possible exception of davidite. Indeed, for most representatives of this mineral group, pegmatites are the principal type of deposit in which they occur. Monazite and xenotime, especially the former, represent the phosphates, and of the silicates, thorite, allanite, zircon, sphene, and gadolinite are relatively widespread.

Most of the brightly colored uranyl minerals are doubtless the result of the supergene alteration processes, but the possibility that some of these may be formed under late-stage, low-temperature, hydrothermal conditions cannot be dismissed for some deposits. Representative of this class are the mixture gummite, many hydrous uranyl oxides, a few uranyl carbonates and sulfates, many uranyl phosphates, rare uranyl arsenates, and many uranyl silicates, including uraniferous opal. Autunite, torbernite, and uranophane are especially widespread. Uranyl vanadates are rarely, if ever, formed.

Some of the New England pegmatites are noteworthy for their content of supergene radioactive minerals, including gummite-type alterations (Fig. 2.2). Pegmatites near Spruce Pine, North Carolina, also have yielded fine specimens of gummite, clarkeite, radioactive opal, and other supergene uranyl minerals.

In Portugal and Spain, pegmatites that contain uranyl minerals lie in the peripheral area of a large granitic mass extending from the northwest corner of Portugal southeastward, along the east side of the Sierra D'Estradella. The most important occurrences are between Sabugal and Guarda, Portugal; others are in Spain. The quartz-rich pegmatites occur chiefly just outside of the granite in surrounding schist and are usually ½ to 1 m thick. Some occur in granite. Two parallel swarms have been recognized. One dike is 15 km long, but some are not over 800 m long. The uranyl minerals include autunite, torbernite, sabugalite, and meta-uranocircite, which occur chiefly in the kaolinized wall zones of the pegmatites. Other pegmatite constituents are potash feldspar, sodic plagioclase, muscovite, cassiterite, wolframite, pyrite, arsenopyrite, and chalcopyrite.

In many cases, particularly for the gummitic type, the alteration has taken place essentially in situ. Autunite, torbernite, and other uranyl minerals also may show conspicuous development as fracture coatings, formed at various distances from hypogene uranium-bearing species, indicating redistribution of uranium under supergene conditions.

Thucolite doubtless also results from processes unrelated to the formation of the pegmatite itself (page 522).

Radioactive minerals occur in all three structural types of pegmatites—unzoned, zoned, or complex. Each type tends to have its own distinctive radioactive mineral assemblage with a characteristic distribution within the pegmatite. The more common radioactive mineral species found in pegmatites fall into one of several groups which occur characteristically (Table 5.2).

TABLE 5.2. *Occurrence of main hypogene radioactive minerals of pegmatites*

Mineral	*Principal occurrences*
Oxides:	
Uraninite	a. Unzoned pegmatites
	b. Wall and intermediate zones of zoned pegmatites
	c. Quartzose fracture fillings in complex pegmatites
Complex oxides (niobates, tantalates):	
Fergusonite-formanite	Core-margin or other replacement units in complex pegmatites: clevelandite or sugary albite type, biotite-rich type
Samarskite-yttrotantalite	
Euxenite-polycrase	
Eschynite-priorite	
Microlite	Lepidolite-rich replacement units in complex pegmatites
Phosphates:	
Monazite	a. Wall zones of zoned pegmatites
	b. Replacement units of complex pegmatites
Silicates:	
Thorite	a. Unzoned pegmatites
	b. In replacement units of complex pegmatites
Allanite	Wall zones of zoned pegmatites
Zircon	
a. Ordinary	a. In unzoned pegmatites or outer zones of zoned pegmatites
b. Cyrtolite	b. In replacement units of complex pegmatites
Gadolinite	In core-margin or fracture-controlled replacement units in complex pegmatites
Sphene	
a. Ordinary	a. In unzoned pegmatites
b. Yttrotitanite	b. In core-margin replacement units in complex pegmatites

Exomorphic Radioactive Minerals

In some districts where intrusion and crystallization of pegmatitic magma have been accompanied by marked exomorphic effects, various radioactive minerals have been formed metasomatically within wall rocks close to pegmatite contacts. Uraninite occurs in the wall rocks about some pegmatites in the Gordonia district, north of the Orange River, South Africa. Near California Gulch, Sheridan, Montana, a pegmatite rich in allanite locally has an altered wall-rock selvage of allanite and epidote. Monazite occurs in the wall rock of the Deake pegmatite in Mitchell County, North Carolina (Hidden, 1881). Some of the Ceylon pegmatites contain abundant sphene, and near Balangoda this mineral forms as much as 40% of the wall rock immediately adjacent to the pegmatite.

Production and Grade

Radioactive pegmatite minerals rarely occur in sufficient quantities to be of economic importance as sources or potential sources of uranium or thorium. In the past the pegmatites of Madagascar have been the only pegmatitic sources of significant amounts of radioactive minerals, and from these only several hundred tons of complex oxide minerals have been produced. Mining of a pegmatite in the Evje district after World War II by the Norwegian government yielded several tons of uraninite. In general, production in other districts of the world has been by-product to mica or feldspar mining and has resulted in specimen amounts, several to several hundred pounds or up to a few tons. However, with the discovery of the unzoned uraninite-uranothorite type of pegmatite in southern Ontario and elsewhere, it seems probable that some groups of these pegmatites will be mineable solely for uranium and will prove to be sources of moderate size.

In the Centre Lake deposits, Cardiff Township, Haliburton County, Ontario, pegmatites of the unzoned type containing uraninite and uranothorite yielded assays of 0.024 to 0.117% U_3O_8 over widths of 4 to 29 ft (Satterly and Hewitt, 1955).

Other results reported by the Geological Survey of Canada (1953) for various Canadian pegmatite deposits include: (1) Ontario, 0.001 to 0.044% U_3O_8 (15 samples); 0.10 to 0.31% U_3O_8 (5 samples); (2) Charlebois Lake, Sask., 0.04 to 0.20% U_3O_8 (5 samples); (3) Lac la Ronge, Sask., 0.03 to 0.15% U_3O_8 (10 samples); 0.162 to 0.372% U_3O_8 (5 samples).

The relatively fine grained pegmatite dikes and sills of the Charlebois Lake area, Saskatchewan (Mawdsley, 1955) have grades reported as follows: No. 1 body—1,090 tons per vertical ft averaging 0.075% U_3O_8; No. 2 body—1,640 tons per vertical ft averaging 0.08% U_3O_8.

McKelvey (1955) reports 0.1% uranium in a mineable pegmatite in the Colorado Front Range. On the other hand, the uraninite content of the intermediate zones of the Hyatt and Big Boulder pegmatites in Larimer County, Colorado, is estimated to be of the order of 0.000x% (Thurston, 1955).

UNDIFFERENTIATED PEGMATITES

General

Because of their poor record as commercial sources of other pegmatite minerals, undifferentiated or unzoned pegmatites have been largely dismissed as

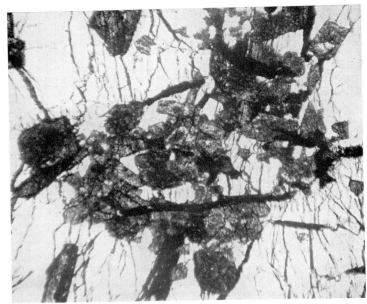

FIG. 5.3. Zircon (high relief, gray), allanite (high relief, dark gray), and columbite (narrow opaque blades) in sheared quartz-feldspar pegmatite, Monmouth
Township, Haliburton County, Ont. (×35).

potential economic sources of radioactive minerals. Work during the early
1950s in southern Ontario, largely by Satterly and Hewitt (Satterly, 1955;
Satterly and Hewitt, 1955) and also by Bateman (1955) has demonstrated
the widespread occurrence of unzoned or poorly zoned radioactive pegmatites
in that region, and the results of an extensive prospecting and exploration
program have indicated that some groups of these pegmatites constitute ore.
In contrast, at the time that the first general summary on uranium in pegmatites was prepared (Page, 1950A), little information was available on this type
of deposit, which appears to represent the most economically significant kind
of radioactive pegmatite.

Radioactive undifferentiated (unzoned, nonsegregated, or "simple") pegmatites are characterized by:

1. Shape usually is irregular, in some cases lenticular
2. They may occur in swarms or belts of considerable extent
3. The grain size may be uniform or variable; commonly the rock has been
called pegmatitic granite ("alaskite")
4. Regularly distributed zones are absent; if units of contrasting petrology
are present, they are irregular in size, shape, and structure and occur commonly
along the strike
5. Not uncommonly wall rock fragments, schlieren, and xenocrystic clots
are present. Wall rocks may be injected and migmatized

6. The chief radioactive minerals are uraninite and uranothorite with sphene, zircon, and allanite as accessories

7. The chief radioactive species may be roughly concentrated in shoots, some along the contacts, but they are not confined to a particular lithologic unit

8. Although generally granitic in composition, some bodies are in part or wholly syenitic. Graphic granite is rare

Although this type of deposit is best known from numerous examples in the Bancroft, Ontario, area, similar deposits have been found in the Charlebois Lake and Foster Lake areas of Saskatchewan (Mawdsley, 1955), and near Idaho Springs, Colorado.

Haliburton-Bancroft Area, Ontario

In the Haliburton-Bancroft area of southeastern Ontario, pegmatites and closely related deposits, which are exceedingly abundant in Grenville metasediments, are of several different types:

1. Granite pegmatites
   a. Markedly zoned (McDonald pegmatite)
      Radioactive minerals include euxenite-polycrase, pyrochlore-microlite, allanite, cyrtolite, and rarely uraninite (Fig. 5.3)
   b. Unzoned or very poorly zoned
      Uraninite and uranothorite are the main radioactive species
2. Syenite pegmatites
   a. Corundum-bearing, no radioactive minerals
   b. Uraninite- and uranothorite-bearing
3. Nepheline-syenite pegmatites
   Well zoned to poorly zoned. Cyrtolite is the chief radioactive mineral
4. "Vein-dikes"
   Zoned tabular deposits with a syenite pegmatite outer phase and a pronounced calcite-fluorite-apatite central phase containing uraninite (pages 217–221)

The zoned granitic pegmatites and the "vein-dikes" have long been recognized as sources of radioactive minerals in this area, the former for specimens; some of the latter from time to time are mined for uraninite. Recent prospecting for radioactive deposits in the district has led to discovery of several areas in which radioactive, unzoned to poorly zoned pegmatites occur abundantly.

The undifferentiated pegmatites show the characteristics listed in the previous section and are of two types (Satterly and Hewitt, 1955)—felsic (Dyno and Faraday properties) and mafic (Centre Lake). The felsic type is poor in biotite, hornblende, and pyroxene, but may have abundant magnetite. They are characteristically of granitic composition, with the textures and grain size of pegmatitic granite.

The mafic type is rich in biotite or hornblende, or in pyroxene where contaminated by wall rocks rich in calcium. Wall-rock assimilation is common, and exomorphic effects such as lit-par-lit injection and metacrysts are marked. The dikes may grade from quartzose granitic to granitic to syenitic. The mafic minerals may be concentrated in crystals or clusters near the walls. The textural evidence of replacement indicates a complex, multiple metasomatic origin.

Uraninite, the principal radioactive mineral, occurs as disseminated grains less than 1 mm across or in granular concentrations along walls, in association with hornblende or biotite. Uranothorite may occur irregularly distributed. Fluorite, calcite, molybdenite, tourmaline, garnet, pyrite, pyrrhotite, and chalcopyrite are accessories. Umangite and anatase also have been noted.

Pegmatites at Centre Lake, Cardiff Township, which are typical of this class, occur in a ½-mi north-northeasterly trending belt of paragneisses, bounded on the west by granite and granite gneiss and on the east by marble. The belt has been intruded by a swarm of pegmatite dikes and sills in a zone 500 to 1,000 ft across and several miles long. Individual syenitic and granitic dikes which strike north, dip 50°E, and are offset to the east, are 10 to 30 ft thick and several hundred feet long. They consist of coarse red peristerite feldspar with a narrow pyroxene-rich zone near the hanging wall and a thicker similar foot wall zone, both of which are rich in uraninite. The central parts are less radioactive. Many of the dikes show bands, gradational along the strike but fairly sharply defined across the strike, of such lithologic units as granite pegmatite, injection gneiss, leucogranite, gneissic pegmatite, and quartz-pyroxene rock.

Most of the uraninite is associated with mafic minerals which are related to wall-rock type: hornblende- and pyroxene-rich parts occurring where dikes intersect Ca-Mg paragneisses. The close relation of the uraninite with fractures and sulfides suggests that it is not a primary constituent but may have been introduced as a late pegmatitic constituent (Bateman, 1955). At the Faraday property one high-grade lens consists of magnetite in quartzose granite pegmatite; the other is a magnetite-pyroxene pod in a granite pegmatite (Satterly and Hewitt, 1955). Coatings of secondary uranium minerals such as uranophane are not uncommon.

ZONED URANINITE PEGMATITES

In zoned pegmatites, uraninite occurs in outer zones but not in the core. It may be a constituent of border and wall zones (Lac la Ronge, Saskatchewan) or of an intermediate zone (Hyatt pegmatite, Colorado, Fig. 5.4). In some zoned pegmatites that also contain replacement bodies, uraninite occurs in these secondary units (Bedford, New York; Haddam Neck, Connecticut), but it is not always certain that the uraninite itself is of replacement origin. In the Bob Ingersoll No. 2 dike, Black Hills, South Dakota, uraninite occurs in a quartz-cleavelandite-muscovite lens localized along the contact between quartz-albite and perthite-quartz pegmatite. In the Ruggles pegmatite, New Hampshire, uraninite appears in quartzose fracture fillings but also locally in a core-margin unit.

The uraninite is commonly in small crystals, but in the Ruggles deposit it

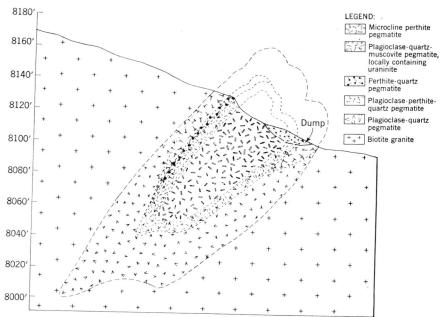

FIG. 5.4. Cross section of Hyatt pegmatite, Crystal Mt. district, Colo. Uraninite occurs locally in plagioclase-quartz-muscovite unit (Thurston, 1955; *U.S. Geol. Survey*).

forms three-dimensional dendrites (Fig. 2.2). Other radioactive associates usually are not common, but allanite, zircon (cyrtolite), monazite, and xenotime may be present. Thus the assemblage is characterized geochemically by: high U; low to very low Th; Zr and Ce earths present but usually low; Y earths uncommon; Nb-Ta rare to absent.

In some pegmatites thucolite has replaced uraninite, in some cases pseudomorphously. Ellsworth (1931, 1932) has described a pegmatite in Conger Township, Parry Sound district, Ontario, in which uraninite crystals occur in the mica-rich parts of the feldspathic outer zones. A little calciosamarskite was found, as were allanite and cyrtolite. Thucolite partly replaces uraninite or surrounds it. Davidson and Bowie (1951) have found that the thucolite is heterogeneous and contains inclusions of a uraninite-thorianite mineral.

PEGMATITES WITH RADIOACTIVE COMPLEX OXIDE MINERALS

Probably the most widespread type of radioactive pegmatite is that in which the radioactivity obtains chiefly from one or more species of the complex oxides, usually occurring with such other radioactive minerals as monazite, cyrtolite, metamict allanite, and gadolinite, and less commonly with such species as uraninite, xenotime, yttrialite, sphene, chevkinite, and thorite. Probably the most widespread complex oxide minerals are euxenite and

TABLE 5.3. *Selected examples of deposits or districts in which zoned or complex pegmatites contain uraninite*

Location	Structure	Radioactive minerals	Occurrence	Abundance	Reference
Northern Karelia, U.S.S.R.	Quartz cores, feldspathic intermediate zones and wall zones with oligoclase; local albitization	Uraninite, allanite, zircon, xenotime, monazite. Supergene uranium minerals. Thucolite	Uraninite in wall zone of quartz-oligoclase-biotite, with tourmaline and garnet	At least 5 uraninite pegmatite deposits: Panfilova Varaka, Sinjaja Pala, Louchsk region, Chitoostrov Island, Cernaja Salma	Fersman, 1940; Grigoriev, 1935; Borisov, 1937
Central Serbia, Yugoslavia	Microcline-quartz-beryl cores, wall zones of quartz, feldspar, tourmaline	Uraninite, monazite. Supergene uranium minerals	(?)	In several small lenses	Ristic, 1956
Gaya district, and Kodarma area, Bihar, India	Micaceous wall or core-margin zones, quartz cores. Albitized core-margin units	Uraninite, monazite, allanite, zircon. Supergene uranium minerals	Uraninite associated with segregations of biotite	In several deposits	Roy et al., 1939; Holmes et al., 1950
Bedford, N.Y.	Strongly albitized replacement units with scalloped, radially arranged albite-quartz-muscovite masses	Uraninite, allanite, cyrtolite. Supergene uranium minerals	Apparently in albitized unit~	Uncommon	Agar, 1933
Hyatt pegmatite, Crystal Mt. district, Larimer County, Colo.	Perthite core with an inner intermediate (core-margin) zone of plagioclase-quartz-muscovite rock	Uraninite. Supergene uranium minerals	In inner intermediate zone only	$0.000x\%$ in two pegmatites	Page, 1950; Thurston, 1955; Heinrich, pers. obs.

196

Location	Zoning/Structure	Minerals	Association	Abundance	Reference
Ruggles pegmatite, Grafton, N.H.	Intermediate zones, perthite core	Uraninite. Supergene uranium minerals	Associated with late veins and irregular bodies of quartz in perthite core and in pods in part of a perthite-quartz-plagioclase intermediate zone	Locally abundant	Shaub, 1938; Cameron et al., 1954; Heinrich, pers. obs.
Branchville, Redding, Conn.	Asymmetrically(?) zoned. Quartz core overlain by cleavelandite, and cleavelandite-spodumene units grading upward into cleavelandite-quartz rock	Uraninite, cyrtolite	Cyrtolite in margins of core and cleavelandite unit. Uraninite in spodumene-cleavelandite unit	Uncommon	Cameron et al., 1954; Heinrich, pers. obs.
Rock Landing Quarry, Haddam Neck, Conn.	(?)	Uraninite. Supergene uranium minerals	(?)	Only one mass found. Largest piece $6 \times 7 \times 10$ cm	Ingerson, 1938
5 mi east of Hunter Bay, Lac la Ronge, Sask.	Border, wall, 3 intermediate zones, plagioclase-quartz-muscovite core	Monazite, uraninite, allanite, zircon	Uraninite (1) in border and wall zone and (2) in late fracture fillings. Monazite and allanite in border zone and fracture fillings. Zircon in wall zone	Uraninite locally abundant in cubes up to 1.25 in.	Mawdsley, 1954; Ford, 1955
Upper Catatumbo River, Colombia	Zoned(?) with replacement units(?) containing cassiterite, green and red tourmaline, lepidolite, and fluorite	Uraninite	(?)	(?)	Codazzi, 1927
Between San Javier and Merlo, Sierra de Comechingones, Cordoba, Argentina	Apparently zoned	Uraninite, supergene uranium minerals	Uraninite associated with muscovite, garnet, and triplite	"Disseminated masses" have 0.3–0.4% U_3O_8	Angelelli, 1956
Hornachuelos, Sierra Morena, Spain	Zoned	Uraninite, brannerite, supergene uranium minerals	(?)	(?)	Alia, 1956

FIG. 5.5. Fracture-controlled sheets of biotite with smaller books of muscovite normal to the sheets and intergrown euxenite and monazite crystals, all within quartz-microcline core, New Mölland pegmatite, Iveland district, Norway.

samarskite; less common are fergusonite and polycrase; rare are yttrotantalite, betafite, priorite, eschynite, and ampangabeite. In some cases uraninite may be a conspicuous member of the assemblage, as at Lukwengule in the Uluguru Mountains, Morogoro district, East Africa, where pegmatites contain uraninite in cubes up to $3.5 \times 2.5 \times 2$ cm partly altered to rutherfordine, associated with eschynite, monazite, samarskite, and euxenite.

Characteristics of this type of pegmatite are:

1. They commonly form as bodies of moderate size with well-defined walls.
2. They have a well-developed zonal structure with quartzose or feldspathic cores.
3. Many show some evidence of postmagmatic crystallization mineralization, most of which falls into one of two categories:

    a. Large radiating to subparallel sheets of biotite, up to many feet long, that have formed along closely spaced fractures cutting across the fabric of the pegmatite. These fracture-controlled masses occur mainly within intermediate zones, in the outer parts of cores, or in both (Fig. 5.5). In some cases the fractures are curving, even sigmoidal (Fig. 5.6). Thin films of albite and quartz may also occur with the biotite, and in some cases the rock between the sheets is replaced by albite and muscovite. The radioactive complex oxides occur as crystals, grains, and pods intergrown with the biotite or close to the fractures. Monazite is a common associate. Examples of this type of control are found in pegmatites at Ytterby, Sweden, in the Iveland district, Norway (Fig. 5.5), and in Chaffee County, Colorado.

b. The radioactive specimens occur mainly in secondary units rich in albite, either cleavelandite or fine-grained ("sugary") albite, which may also contain microcline remnants, quartz, and in some cases abundant muscovite. Radial fractures and hematite halos are conspicuous around the crystals of radioactive species. Such rock units are transgressive across the pegmatitic fabric or even across zones, and are commonly well developed along keels of the pegmatite or keels of cores, along footwall sides of flat-lying cores, along rolls in contacts, or marginal to fracture systems. Examples are found in pegmatites of the Petaca district, New Mexico, at Baringer Hill, Texas, and around Kragerö, Norway.

Fig. 5.6. Curving, subparallel fracture-filling biotite sheets with intergrown fergusonite and gadolinite in quartz core, Ytterby pegmatite, Island of Ytterby, Sweden. Pegmatite first mined for quartz in 1756. In 1788 Lt. Arrhenius found the mineral gadolinite here, in which Johann Gadolin, professor of chemistry at the University of Åbo, Finland, first found the compound earth, "yttria," from which individual rare-earth elements were later isolated.

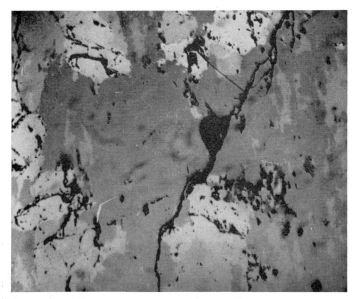

Fɪɢ. 5.7. Samarskite, Lonesome pegmatite, Petaca district, N.Mex. Note inhomogeneity; at least four metallic phases present as well as inclusions and veinlets of gangue (black). Reflected light (×60).

4. In some cases the radioactive species occur in masses or crystals of exceptional size, and locally they may be very strongly concentrated. Rarely are the grains uniformly disseminated through the units. The aggregate tonnage, however, in any one body or even in the district is usually very small.

Geochemically this type is characterized by: moderate to high U, with or without low to moderate Th (note, however, the exceptionally high Th assemblage in pegmatites of the Balangoda district, Ceylon, Table 5.5); high Nb-Ta (± Ti); moderate rare earths, either Ce or Y earths (note Iisaka, Japan, Table 5.5); and moderate to low Zr.

In some districts more elaborate mineralogical classifications of these multiple assemblage, radioactive pegmatites are possible. Björlykke (1937A) for the Kragerö district, southern Norway, suggests the following grouping:

1. Ca-rich granitic pegmatites
   a. Hellandite-gadolinite
   b. Fergusonite-betafite
   c. Betafite
2. Ca-poor granitic pegmatites
   a. Thalenite-gadolinite
   b. Fergusonite
   c. Euxenite (or samarskite)
   d. Columbite

Björlykke (1935) believes that the pegmatites in the Iveland district, Norway, and most of their radioactive species are magmatic in origin. Certainly the bulk of the pegmatite rock is magmatic, and fracture-controlled material is greatly subordinate. Moreover, in many other districts there occur pegmatites that contain such species as euxenite or samarskite in rare, scattered grains in pegmatitic rock (zones) that show little or no evidence of replacement or of fracturing. However, such pegmatites do not normally contain local *concentrations* of these species.

PEGMATITES WITH MICROLITE

Pegmatites that contain concentrations of microlite show not only a zonal structure but in most cases have well-developed secondary units. Microlite is commonly associated with pegmatitic rock rich in lithium minerals and some type of secondary albite. In many cases microlite occurs directly within large masses or pods of fine-grained lepidolite. Notable examples of this type are the Harding mine near Dixon, New Mexico, and the Brown Derby pegma-

FIG. 5.8. Sugary albite replacement unit (*lower left*), with finely banded "line rock" containing yttrotantalite along footwall side of quartz core (*right and upper half*), Rare Earth pegmatite, Aquarius Range, Ariz.

TABLE 5.4. *Selected pegmatites or pegmatite districts of the United States characterized by an assemblage of complex oxides and other radioactive minerals*

Location	Structure	Radioactive minerals	Occurrence	Abundance	Reference
Spruce Pine district, N.C.	Well zoned. Granodioritic to granitic. Some replacement units and fracture fillings	*Uraninite, samarskite,* cyrtolite, monazite; euxenite(?). Supergene uranium minerals	In albitized parts; in some cases associated with sulfides. Samarskite also in fracture fillings of quartz, albite, microcline, and sulfides at the McKinney mine	Local concentrations in only about half a dozen pegmatites	Ross et al., 1931; Ross, 1937; Cameron et al., 1949; Heinrich, 1950
Chaffee, Park, and Fremont Counties, Colo.	Well zoned. Quartz-rich cores. Large subparallel aggregates of biotite sheets at core margin in some	*Euxenite, monazite,* allanite, gadolinite, ilmenite, cyrtolite	In fracture fillings and replacement units of small size associated with albite, fluorite, and muscovite. Also with fracture-controlled biotite	Locally abundant in about 10 deposits	Heinrich, 1948A; Heinrich and Bever, 1957
Petaca district, Rio Arriba County, N.Mex.	Well zoned; quartz cores; core-margin replacement units rich in muscovite and albite	*Monazite, samarskite* (Fig. 5.7), columbite, uraninite and its alteration products	In albite-rich replacement units	Widespread in small amounts. Monazite in 83%, samarskite in 58% of deposits studied	Jahns, 1946; Heinrich, pers. obs.

Location	Description	Minerals	Occurrence	Remarks	References
Aquarius Range, Mohave County, Ariz.	Well zoned. Quartz cores. Some with footwall replacement units rich in sugary albite and banded (Fig. 5.8). Some fracture fillings	*Euxenite, yttrotantalite, monazite,* gadolinite, chevkinite, columbite	Chiefly in core-marginal albitic replacement units. Some gadolinite in veins filling fractures, with quartz, albite, wolframite	Widespread in the district. Several tons of yttrotantalite reportedly produced from one deposit	Heinrich, pers. obs.; Cameron et al., 1949
Baringer Hill, Llano County, Tex.	Well zoned. Quartz core with microcline-rich core-margin zone. Red albite forms secondary units in which large biotite masses up to 4 ft across occurred	*Allanite,* one mass weighed 300 lb; *gadolinite,* masses up to 200 lb; *cyrtolite,* fergusonite, yttrialite, uraninite polycrase,	In albitized core marginal parts. Closely associated with fracture-controlled biotite, ilmenite, sulfides, and fluorite	Mined for rare-earth minerals from 1887–1907; now under water	Hess, 1908; Landes, 1932
Cada Mts., San Bernardino County, Calif.	Upper coarse quartz-feldspar zone; lower granitic wall zone. Fracture-controlled biotite plates in both	Cyrtolite, betafite	Between plates of fracture-controlled biotite and in albitized potash feldspar	Rare	Hewett and Glass, 1953
Nuevo, Riverside County, Calif.	Quartz core, outer graphic granite zone, core-margin unit with schorl and cleavelandite	*Monazite, cyrtolite,* xenotime, samarskite	Along platy fractures in core-margin unit and core	In accessory amounts	Murdoch and Webb, 1954; Jahns, 1954

Fɪɢ. 5.9. Workings beneath footwall of quartz-microcline core of McDonald pegmatite, Bancroft district, Ont.

tites in the Quartz Creek district of Gunnison County, Colorado, in which microlite occurs chiefly as minute grains disseminated throughout pods and tabular secondary units rich in fine-grained lepidolite (Fig. 5.10).

Not uncommonly, more than one type of microlite may be present, the varieties differing in Ca-Na, Nb-Ta, U, Th, and OH-F. At Donkerhuk, South-West Africa, Reuning (1933) recognized seven paragenetically and chemically distinct varieties of microlite. In the Harding pegmatite, a second type of microlite (hatchettolite) occurs in a unit consisting of corroded, rounded plates of spodumene in a quartz-albite-microcline-muscovite matrix.

Other radioactive minerals may also occur in microlite-bearing dikes but usually are not common and rarely appear in the lithium-rich units. These include mainly monazite, euxenite, and slightly radioactive columbite-tantalite. In some deposits the niobium and tantalum for the microlite appear to have been obtained by hydrothermal destruction of columbite-tantalite (Guimarães and Belezkij, 1956) and calcium from the conversion of oligoclase to albite.

Pyrochlore-microlite also appears in the Bancroft district, Ontario, in some zoned pegmatites that do not contain lithium (e.g., McDonald mine—ellsworthite). The mineral is closely associated with masses of calcite in the dikes, and it has been suggested that in a calcium-rich environment pyrochlore would form instead of euxenite, which is the radioactive niobate present elsewhere in the dikes and in dikes free of calcite.

Microlite-bearing pegmatitic units are characterized geochemically by: high Li; relatively high Ca and Nb-Ta; low to moderate U; low to absent Th; Ce and Y earths absent to traces; Zr absent.

ALLANITE PEGMATITES

Pegmatites with relatively abundant allanite normally have the following characteristics:

1. Fair to well-developed zonal structure
2. Absence or near absence of secondary pegmatitic units
3. Tonalitic, granodioritic, and syenitic as well as granitic compositions represented; biotite and/or hornblende may be abundant
4. Some related genetically to allanite-bearing granites or diorites. At Nynie-Izets, Ural Mountains, U.S.S.R., allanite pegmatite grades into allanite granite
5. Allanite is the principal or commonly the only radioactive mineral, or other radioactive species are few and uncommon
6. Allanite commonly occurs in outer zones or marginal parts of the pegmatite, and in some cases also in the adjacent altered wall rock. Associates are biotite in outer zones or even epidote in altered wall rock
7. Allanite from these deposits commonly shows a relatively low order of radioactivity, unlike that of allanite associated with pegmatites containing a

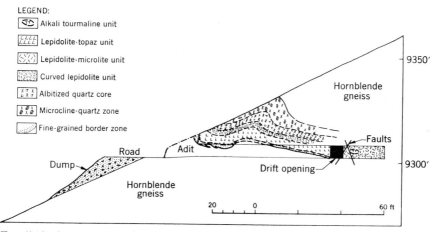

Fig. 5.10. Cross section of Brown Derby No. 1 pegmatite, Gunnison County, Colo. Quartz-microcline core is displaced to hanging wall and is albitized on footwall side. Footwall units are rich in lepidolite (adapted from Hanley, Heinrich, and Page, 1950; *U.S. Geol. Survey*).

TABLE 5.5. *Selected foreign pegmatites or pegmatite districts characterized by an assemblage of complex oxides and other radio-active minerals*

Location	Structure	Radioactive minerals	Occurrence	Abundance	Reference
McDonald mine, Monteagle Township, Ont.	Well zoned. Quartz-microcline core. Pods of calcite-sulfide-plagioclase rock along footwall side of core	*Cyrtolite, sphene, pyrochlore* (ellsworthite), allanite, uranothorite(?), uraninite(?)	Cyrtolite and pyrochlore abundant along foot-wall side of core, associated with secondary calcite pods (Fig. 5.9). Allanite in wall zone	Abundant. Allanite up to 2 ft	Hewitt, 1955; Heinrich, pers. obs.
Minas Gerais, Brazil	Well zoned, generally symmetrically, also asymmetrically in flat-lying bodies. Quartz-microcline and quartz cores. Core-margin albitization, concentrated on footwall side of core in asymmetrically zoned deposits	*Zircon, samarskite,* polycrase, euxenite, fergusonite, *monazite, xenotime, uraninite,* columbite	(?)	Widely distributed; locally abundant: Divino de Uba; Ribeirao de Santa Clara, Pomba; Machado; Rio Branco district; Sabinopolis; Santa Maria de Ita-bira; Itamarandiba; Nova Era; Antonio Dias and many other localities	Leonardos, 1936; Pecora et al., 1950; Florencio, 1952; de Moraes, 1956
Western and southern boundaries of Swaziland	(?)	Yttrotantalite, priorite, monazite, allanite	(?)	In pegmatites mined for cassiterite	

Locality	Structure	Minerals	Associations	Remarks	References
Gordonia district, Cape Province, Union of South Africa	Zoned, also albitized. Some wall zones rich in biotite	*Uraninite*, fergusonite, gadolinite, cyrtolite, euxenite, sphene, zircon, allanite	Uraninite and euxenite associated with abundant biotite in wall zones. Some uraninite in adjacent wall rocks	Uraninite up to 7 cm on edge	Mountain, 1931; Behrend, 1933
Ribaue-Alto Ligonha district, Mozambique	Zoned and albitized	*Samarskite*, allanite, monazite, zircon; possibly gadolinite and euxenite	(?)	Samarskite in 3 pegmatites; 8 tons produced	Bandy, 1951; Hutchinson and Claus, 1956; Cavaca, 1956
Madagascar	Zoned. Chiefly in the potash-type pegmatites, i.e., those not strongly albitized	Fergusonite, samarskite, ampangabeite, *euxenite*, priorite, *betafite*, allanite, chevkinite, uraninite, thorite, *monazite*, xenotime(?), zircon, pyrochlore, microlite	Little information. Some in core-margin units rich in biotite. Associated with native Bi and its alteration minerals	20 tons betafite from Ambatofotsy; one group weighed 104 kg. Allanite in crystals up to several kg. Widely distributed in numerous pegmatites. Locally abundant	Lacroix, 1923; Turner, 1928
Iveland, Setesdal, Norway	Well zoned. Quartz ± microcline cores. Fracture-controlled units rich in biotite, muscovite, albite are subordinate features (Fig. 5.5)	Gadolinite, *allanite*, cyrtolite, fergusonite, yttrotantalite, sphene, *euxenite*, samarskite, betafite, microlite, uraninite, thorite, *monazite*, xenotime	Some radioactive rare-earth minerals found in or closely associated with fracture-controlled biotite-muscovite units	Gadolinite in masses up to 500 kg. Allanite up to 100 kg. One dike mined for uraninite	Björlykke, 1935, 1937B; Heinrich, pers. obs.
Kragerö and adjoining coastal areas, southern Norway	Well zoned. Quartz-feldspar cores cut by cleavelandite veins	Sphene, *euxenite*, thorite, *allanite*, *cyrtolite*, betafite, thalenite, gadolinite, fergusonite, yttrotantalite, samarskite, polycrase, cenosite, *monazite*, xenotime	Generally associated with marginal, albitized parts of cores	Widely distributed in many deposits; in very large masses in some	Brögger, 1906; Brögger et al., 1922; Björlykke, 1937A; Heinrich, pers. obs.

TABLE 5.5. *Selected foreign pegmatites or pegmatite districts characterized by an assemblage of complex oxides and other radioactive minerals* (Continued)

Location	Structure	Radioactive minerals	Occurrence	Abundance	Reference
Ytterby, Sweden	Zoned. Quartz core. Fracture-controlled biotite sheets in core and margins (Fig. 5.6)	Fergusonite, yttrotantalite, gadolinite, cyrtolite, allanite, xenotime	Associated with fracture-controlled biotite masses	Most rare minerals found from 0–25 m of depth	Holmquist, 1910; Heinrich, pers. obs.
Slyudyanka, Khamar-Daban Range, U.S.S.R.	(?)	*Betafite*, allanite, zircon	Single crystals of betafite in massive quartz (core?), clusters in feldspar	Only accessory in two parts of a deposit. Allanite 800 kg, in crystals $30 \times 4 \times 3$ cm	Shimkin, 1949
Bortchovotchnii Range, Transbaikalia, U.S.S.R.	(?)	Euxenite, allanite, cyrtolite, three varieties of monazite	(?)		Fersman, 1940
Near Ulan Bator, northern Mongolia	Zoned. Feldspar-quartz cores	Samarskite, zircon, allanite, sphene	Associated with biotite-magnetite-rich parts	(?)	Fersman, 1940
Balangoda area, Ceylon	Zoned with quartz cores	*Monazite, zircon, thorianite, allanite, xenotime,* eschynite, chevkinite, gadolinite, sphene, baddeleyite, thorite, *fergusonite,* samarskite, uraninite	(?)	Widely distributed. 2 types: (a) with monazite in gneisses; (b) with monazite and other radioactive minerals in khondalite	Wadia, 1943; Wadia and Fernando, 1945

Location	Description	Minerals	Occurrence	Abundance	References
Ishikawa prefecture, Iwaki Province, Japan	Zoned. Quartz-feldspar cores	Monazite, xenotime, zircon, allanite, euxenite, samarskite, fergusonite, ishikawaite, sphene, uraninite	(?)	120–130 pegmatites	Harada, 1948; Japan Geol. Survey, 1956
Naegi-Machi, Nakatsugowa, Gifu prefecture, Japan	Lensoid to irregular pegmatites; vugs common	Fergusonite, monazite, allanite	In vugs	Area 6 × 8 km	Japan Geol. Survey, 1956
Iisaka, Fukushima prefecture, Japan	Feldspathic cores or core-margin zones	Xenotime, cyrtolite, yttrialite, radioactive yttrian apatite, fergusonite, beryllian allanite, tengerite, microcrystalline uraninite, thorogummite	Some associated with biotite books	Locally abundant	Harada, 1948; Japan Geol. Survey, 1956
Sui-chung district, South Manchuria	Well zoned. Quartz core. Core-margin albitized microcline unit	Euxenite, fergusonite, samarskite, betafite, allanite, thorogummite, zircon	Associated with albite, late quartz veins and biotite laths in core-margin unit	(?)	Kuno, 1946, 1950
Wodgina, Western Australia	Strongly albitized; asymmetrically zoned(?)	Gadolinite, pilbarite, monazite, euxenite, microlite, thorogummite	In coarsely albitized unit of dike 4–5 ft thick, with quartz and biotite on both sides of a 15-ft central unit of quartz and fine-grained albite	Locally abundant	Simpson, 1912, 1928
Cooglegong, Western Australia	(?)	*Monazite, gadolinite,* allanite, yttrotantalite, tantalian euxenite, fergusonite		Several tons gadolinite produced; monazite in 100-lb masses	Simpson, 1912

TABLE 5.6. *Selected examples of pegmatites or pegmatite districts characterized by microlite*

Location	Structure	Radioactive minerals	Occurrence	Abundance	Reference
Brown Derby pegmatite, Gunnison County, Colo.	Flat-lying, asymmetrically zoned; several cleaveland-ite-lepidolite-rich units beneath core	Monazite, euxenite, columbite Microlite	In wall zone. In fine-grained lepidolite unit, 104 × 60 × 3 ft	0.35–1.03% microlite with 4.09% $UO_2 + UO_3$	Hanley et al, 1950; Page, 1950A; Heinrich, 1956B; Staatz and Trites, 1955
Harding pegmatite, Taos County, N.Mex.	Flat-lying, asymmetrically zoned. Lepidolite-rich pods beneath lath-spodumene zone	Microlite	Largely restricted to lepidolite pods	Abundant	Jahns and Wright, 1944; Jahns, 1951; Heinrich, pers. obs.
Pidlite pegmatite, Mora County, N.Mex.	Zoned. Quartz core, and 3 secondary composite units one of which consists chiefly of lepidolite	Monazite, euxenite Microlite	Wall zone Secondary lepidolite unit	Uncommon. Local concentrations; disseminations	Jahns, 1953; Heinrich, pers. obs.
São João del Rei, Minas Gerais, Brazil	Rudely zoned, albitized. Spodumene-rich units	Microlite	Closely associated with spodumene. Some replaces tantalite	Known reserve of microlite is 2,500 tons	Guimarães and Belezkij, 1956; Heinrich, pers. obs.
Rio Grande do Norte and Paraiba, Brazil	Zoned with secondary units. Spodumene-rich	Microlite Cyrtolite, euxenite, samarskite	Alteration of tantalite. Outer zones(?)	(?)	De Almeida et al., 1944; Pough, 1945
Donkerhuk, South-West Africa	Zoned. Feldspar-rich core. Some replacement	Microlite, 7 varieties	In replacements of tourmaline crystals	(?)	Reuning, 1933
Greenbushes, Western Australia	Albitized spodumene-rich pegmatite	Microlite, thorite	(?)	(?)	

Fɪɢ. 5.11. Allanite, some crystals slightly metamict, in feldspathic marginal part of Bivins Creek pegmatite near Sheridan, Mont. (×35).

complex oxide assemblage of radioactive minerals. Thus it usually is crystalline or only partly metamict. Exceptional to this is the Varala, Finland, allanite with 2.04% ThO_2

In the United States such pegmatites are widely distributed (Table 5.7). The well-known locality at Little Friar Mountain, Amherst County, Virginia, is probably of the complex radioactive assemblage type, for this allanite is largely metamict and zircon and fergusonite are associates.

Allanite-bearing pegmatites have the characteristic geochemical assemblage of: high Ca; low to very low Th; very low to trace U; high Ce earths; Y earths, absent to rare; absence of Nb, Ta, and Zr.

MISCELLANEOUS TYPES

Cerite Pegmatites

Fine-grained cerite, in irregular masses, occurs in the outer parts of small pegmatites related to the Precambrian Silver Plume granite in the Front Range

TABLE 5.7. *Examples of allanite pegmatites in the United States*

Locality	Structure	Other radioactive minerals	Character of allanite	Reference
Greenwich, Mass.	Pegmatite lens in Monson granodiorite	None(?)	Anisotropic $ThO_2 = 1.74\%$ $U_3O_8 = 0.12\%$	Marble, 1950
Blueberry Mt., Woburn, Mass.	Zoned pegmatite in granodiorite	Sphene, thorite	Partly metamict	Richmond, 1937
Mineville, Essex County, N.Y.	Quartz core(?)	None	5–6 in. crystals, masses up to 200 lb	Ries, 1897
Deep Creek No. 1 pegmatite, Bryson City, N.C.	Sheared quartz-microcline-oligoclase pegmatite	None	Partly metamict	Heinrich, 1950
14 mi NW Wheatland, Wyo.		None(?)	$ThO_2 = 1.28\%$ $U_3O_8 = 0.02\%$	Wells, 1934

Albany, Wyo.	Feldspathic pegmatite	None(?)	In oat-shaped grains, zoned, coalescing to masses weighing several hundred pounds. Several tons produced	Hess, 1933B
Bivins Creek, Sheridan, Mont.	Zoned with quartz core; allanite in marginal parts	None	Slightly metamict; in bladed aggregates corroding feldspar (Fig. 5.11)	Heinrich, pers. obs.
Kingman, Ariz.	In wall zone of pegmatite with microcline-rich core	None	In pods, lenses, and thick crystals Very abundant	Heinrich, pers. obs.
Long Gulch, Yosemite Natl. Park, Calif.	"Simple" pegmatite	Sphene	Slightly metamict	Hutton, 1951C
Pacoima Canyon, Los Angeles County, Calif.	Apparently not zoned. Quartz-microcline cut by swarms of biotite plates. West end rich in oligoclase, biotite, and hornblende, the last in crystals up to 3½ × 4 × 1 ft	Zircon crystals with hollow cores up to 8 in. long. Uranothorite	Crystals up to 18 × 10 × ½ in. long, strongly fractured and distorted, not metamict	Neuerburg, 1954; Patchick, 1955

TABLE 5.8. *Examples of foreign allanite pegmatites*

Locality	Structure	Other radioactive minerals	Character of allanite	Reference
Bancroft district, Ont.	Unzoned to poorly zoned granitic and syenitic pegmatites	Uraninite in some	Weakly radioactive; very wide-spread	Lang, 1952; Heinrich, pers. obs.
Central Roslagen, Sweden	Tonalitic pegmatite cutting gabbro	None	Isotropic	Lundegårdh, 1944
Ava area, Åland Islands, Finland	Distinctly zoned with quartz-feldspar cores	None	Associated with biotite; crystals up to 3×5 cm. 0.53% ThO_2	Kaitaro, 1953
Var la, Kangasala, Finl nd	Zoned; biotite-rich	None	Crystals and anhedra; fresh and "altered"; $ThO_2 = 1.98$–2.56%	Lokka, 1935, 1950
Macedonia, Yugoslavia	Unzoned(?). Sodic plagioclase, quartz, microcline, muscovite	None	"Radioactive epidote" with 110–3250 ppm U, no thorium or rare earths. Crystals up to 1 m long	Ristic, 1956

214

Location	Geology	Associated minerals	Remarks	Reference
Northern Saltytchia, Dnepropetrovsk region, Ukraine; also northwest of Shitomar, U.S.S.R., 15-km belt	Allanite in marginal parts of pegmatites. Considerable magnetite in some bodies	None(?)	Lamellar structure; abundant	Lukashev, 1937
Svyatoy Noss, Transbaikalia, U.S.S.R.	Zoned with quartz cores; granitic and tonalitic with hornblende and biotite	None	Crystals up to 2 cm; 3.5% ThO_2; very abundant	Eskola, 1921
Michalkovo, Central Rhodope range, U.S.S.R.	Gneisses, tonalitic pegmatite	None	Elongated crystals up to 3 cm long	Kostov, 1940
Luluabourg, Belgian Congo	Monzonitic "affinity"	None	Fairly abundant	Ball and Shaler, 1914
Milembule, Kisi, Koanga Hill, and Singiso River, at Ufipa, Tanganyika	(?)	None	Very abundant; 50 tons reserve at Kisi; 0.83% ThO_2	McConnell, 1945
São Bento, Santa Cruz, Rio Grande do Norte, Brazil	Allanite concentrated marginally	Polycrase(?), monazite, rare euxenite(?)	5–10 cm long; $ThO_2 = 0.14$–0.89%; $U = $ nil	Argentière, 1957

near Jamestown, Colorado (Goddard and Glass, 1940; Hanson and Pearce, 1941; Hanley et al., 1950). The radioactivity of the dikes stems from the narrow veinlets of allanite bordering the cerite, small disseminated grains of uraninite, and monazite in veinlets. Other rare-earth minerals are törnebohmite and bastnaesite. In addition to these and the usual pegmatite minerals, there also are present epidote, fluorite, pyrite, and chalcopyrite. Cerite is also reported from the Villeneuve pegmatite, Papineau County, Quebec (Ellsworth, 1932), in which the radioactive assemblage also contains uraninite (the chief radioactive mineral), monazite, and zircon.

Monazite Pegmatites

Although monazite usually appears as a member of the radioactive assemblage of pegmatites characterized by a group of complex oxide minerals, in some pegmatites it is the sole important radioactive species, e.g., Mars Hill, North Carolina, or with xenotime—Steinbauer, Styria (Meixner, 1938). In the Western Altai, U.S.S.R., accompanying monazite are xenotime, zircon, allanite, and sphene. In the Rainbow pegmatite, Solo district, 12 mi southeast of Baker, San Bernardino County, California, monazite and thorite are the radioactive species. A pegmatite near Bandolier Kop, Zoutpansberg district, Northern Transvaal, contains inclusions of apatite-rich rock rimmed by monazite (Janisch, 1926).

Zircon Pegmatites

Radioactive pegmatites characterized mainly by zircon show a low order of radioactivity. Zircon also occurs abundantly in some syenitic pegmatites (southern Norway) and has also been found in gabbroic(?) pegmatite, consisting of calcic plagioclase, hornblende, and biotite 2 mi north of Mellen, Wisconsin (Wilcox, 1936). The zircon is in needles up to $7\frac{1}{4} \times \frac{1}{8}$ in. in size.

Examples of occurrences in granitic dikes include:

1. Quanah Mountain, Wichita Mountains, Comanche County, Oklahoma (Larsen et al., 1953; Busch, 1956). The pegmatite cuts the Quanah granite. The zircon is in pyramidal crystals as much as 30 mm long, which show alternating crystalline and metamict zones, the latter markedly richer in uranium.

2. At the Jones and Freeman deposits, near Green River, Henderson Co., North Carolina, 30 tons mined before 1889. The Jones pegmatite also contains allanite and altered sphene (xanthitane).

3. Cheyenne Mountain, Colorado (Cross and Hillebrand, 1885), in massive quartz with some microcline. Pegmatite also contains rare fluorides (cryolite, pachnolite, etc.). Zircon is also a widespread constituent of other pegmatites in the Pikes Peak region.

4. Köflach, Styria (Meixner, 1938).

5. At Tagashet, Bolshoe and Menshoe Hills, Bec-Detlovskai, 100 km north of Minusinsk, U.S.S.R., occur 57 pegmatites containing potash feldspar, albite, quartz, arfvedsonite, ordinary zircon, and thorian-rare-earth zircon (malacon) (Michailov, 1937).

Sphene Pegmatites

Pegmatites with a low order of radioactivity that stems mainly from sphene occur in Renfrew County, Ontario. The sphene is concentrated near the walls of the dikes, which also contain smoky quartz, microcline, plagioclase, hornblende, biotite, scapolite, and molybdenite. On Turners Island in Lake Clear, Sebastopol Township, syenitic pegmatites have yielded beautiful crystals of sphene (over one foot long), zircon (nearly a foot across), and apatite (up to 700 lb). The dikes also contain calcite, scapolite, biotite, pyroxene, hornblende, and feldspar.

Weakly radioactive sphene is a widespread pegmatite mineral occurring in many different associations. More strongly radioactive sphene (yttrotitanite) is characteristically associated with an assemblage of complex-oxide radioactive species.

RADIOACTIVE SYENITIC PEGMATITES

Syenitic pegmatites are relatively uncommon, but in a few districts are known to contain small amounts of various radioactive minerals: Larvik area, and Langesundfjord area, Norway (Brögger, 1890), gradational to nepheline-syenite pegmatites—pyrochlore, polymignite, zircon (Fig. 2.44), thorite, and xenotime; Haliburton-Bancroft area, southern Ontario (Satterly and Hewitt, 1955), gradational into unzoned granitic pegmatites—uraninite, uranothorite and minor sphene, allanite, and zircon, e.g., Blue Rock Cerium mines, Monmouth Township, Haliburton County. Only the last district contains deposits of economic significance for uranium.

The syenitic pegmatites of the Wausau area, Marathon County, Wisconsin, are locally associated with nepheline-syenitic and granitic pegmatites; these owe their radioactivity to thorogummite, thorian cyrtolite, allanite, and pyrochlore. The zircon-bearing granitic pegmatites are the most radioactive (Vickers, 1956C.).

CALCITE-FLUORITE-APATITE VEIN-DIKES

Essentially unique radioactive mineral deposits of the highly diversified assemblage that occurs in the Haliburton-Bancroft area, Ontario, are the tabular to lenticular fissure fillings known variously as syenite pegmatite (Spence and Carnochan, 1930), calcite-fluorite vein-dikes (Ellsworth, 1932), calcite-fluorite pegmatites (Lang, 1952), and calcite-fluorite-apatite veins (Satterly and Hewitt, 1955). The deposits have been the subject of considerable study and controversy. The Richardson deposit near Wilberforce, one of the best known, was discovered in 1922 and was explored also in 1929 to 1931, 1933, and again in 1947 to 1949 (Rowe, 1952). Four major properties expose occurrences of this general type (Satterly and Hewitt, 1955). The deposits occur in a variety of Grenville metasedimentary rocks, banded gneisses, syenitized gneisses, and syenite, which are cut by syenitic and granitic pegmatites. The deposits range in thickness from 1 to 12 ft; some are concordant, others discordant. Their geological and mineralogical characteristics are:

Fᴵɢ. 5.12. Calcite-fluorite-apatite vein, Cardiff Uranium Mines, Ltd., Cardiff Township, Haliburton County, Ont. Banded structure, light calcite, dark fluorite in bands and blebs (Satterly and Hewitt, 1955; *Ontario Dept. Mines*).

1. Tabular to lenticular and discontinuous fissure fillings. Some of the longer bodies split locally around wall-rock masses

2. Commonly zoned or well banded (Fig. 5.12)

3. Grain size ¼ to 3 in.

4. Outer zones contain chiefly oligoclase, microcline, antiperthite, and hornblende. Cavities lined with feldspar crystals occur locally

5. The central unit, consisting primarily of calcite, fluorite, and apatite, shows strongly granulated textures, shears, and flowage features as well as brecciated wall-rock xenoliths

6. Much of the fluorite is purple to nearly black (Fig. 5.14); some of it, near uraninite, is fetid. The brown to dark red apatite forms crystals whose long axes are parallel with the shear zones

7. Minor constituents are biotite, sphene, scapolite, magnetite, tourmaline, hematite, pyrrhotite, pyrite, chalcopyrite, and molybdenite

8. The chief radioactive mineral is a high-thorium (11 to 13% ThO_2) and rare-earth-bearing uraninite which occurs in cubes, some of large size (Fig. 2.1), chiefly in the central calcite-fluorite-apatite rock, but also in lesser amounts in the feldspathic outer units. Other rare radioactive constituents are pyrochlore, allanite, and zircon

In the Richardson deposit, which has been traced at intervals for 3,100 ft, the zoning consists of (Heinrich, pers. obs.; Rowe, 1952):

1. A thin, fine-grained border zone of equigranular red oligoclase-microcline

rock with accessory magnetite, uraninite, biotite, hornblende, zircon, sphene, tourmaline, apatite, fluorite, and younger calcite.

2. A wall zone of red oligoclase antiperthite crystals 1 to 4 in. in size which are euhedral where projecting into the calcite-fluorite-apatite core (Fig. 5.13). Inclusions of uraninite, magnetite, zircon, tourmaline, and fluorite are present.

3. An intermediate hornblende zone which is commonly discontinuous, missing, telescoped with the wall zone or core, or present only on one side of the core. Some hornblende crystals are over 6 ft long.

4. The core of calcite, fluorite, and apatite, banded and granulated, with fragments of other zones present as inclusions. Uraninite and magnetite are widespread accessories (Fig. 5.14). Calcite-fluorite veinlets project into outer zones.

In some deposits the outer feldspathic zones are absent, and the entire fissure filling consists of calcite-fluorite-apatite rock (Fig. 5.12).

Although uraninite is locally a conspicuous constituent (Fig. 2.1), exploration has shown that the deposits probably cannot be mined for uranium alone. In the Richardson deposit the U_3O_8 content of samples ranged from 0.006 to 0.12% (Lang, 1952). However, uraninite may be recovered as a by-product to fluorite mining.

The various theories of origin have been summarized by Rowe (1952):

1. The deposits are pegmatites with an important late hydrothermal stage (Ellsworth, 1932)

2. The deposits represent a limestone lens intruded and metasomatically altered by syenite

3. The metasomatic alteration and replacement of amphibolite by high-temperature hydrothermal solutions containing Si, CO_2, F, B, U, and Th (favored by Rowe, 1952)

Rowe's theory, which was applied exclusively to the Richardson deposit, loses much of its argument with the recognition that other similar deposits occur in wall rocks other than amphibolite and that all deposits do not have outer zones of the Richardson type. The deposits are closely associated with syenite intrusive masses, and the writer believes that the deposits are essentially derivatives of syenitic magmas formed in the early stages (outer zones) as syenitic pegmatites and in the later stages as high-temperature hydrothermal veins, *under open-system conditions.* The euhedral nature of the oligoclase crystals that project coreward suggests that the central parts of the deposits were open channelways. Orientation of apatite crystals in the cores points to flowage in these channelways. The later hydrothermal fluids, which at the Richardson deposit precipitated mineral material to fill the central pegmatite channelway, elsewhere followed fractures cutting other rocks, where the pegmatitic stage had not been present. The deposits are perhaps analogous to the syenitic pegmatites and veins of the Bearpaw Mountains, Montana (Pecora, 1942, 1948, 1956; Heinrich, 1949) (page 241), which have a strongly developed carbonate-sulfide phase (calcite, rare-earth carbonates, pyrrhotite, pyrite, galena, and chalcopyrite). In some deposits sanidine and aegirine are concentrated marginally with central fillings of calcite that corrodes the feldspar. Pecora (1948)

FIG. 5.13. Wall zone of red oligoclase antiperthite crystals, footwall side of calcite-fluorite-apatite core, Richardson deposit, Wilberforce, Cardiff Township, Haliburton County, Ont.

FIG. 5.14. Uraninite grain in fluorite with minor calcite (clear). Halo of dark purple color in fluorite envelops uraninite. Richardson deposit, Wilberforce, Ont. (×66).

has described these deposits as the alkalic counterparts of telescoped and xenothermal quartzose veins.

RADIOACTIVE NEPHELINE-SYENITIC PEGMATITES

Most of the weak radioactivity associated with some of the uncommon nepheline-syenitic pegmatites stems from various silicate minerals that may contain thorium in small amounts. Some complex oxides and phosphates also may be present. Rare-earth minerals, especially of the Ce group, and zirconium minerals may be associated.

The radioactivity of these dikes in the classic Langesundfjord area of southern Norway (Brögger, 1890; Siggerud, 1956) stems from assemblages of the following species: allanite, zircon, sphene, perovskite, tritomite, melanocerite, thorite, pyrochlore, xenotime, and apatite (Fig. 5.15). The nepheline-syenitic pegmatites of southern Greenland contain in small amounts the radioactive minerals rinkite, lorenzite, steenstrupine, and thorian apatite.

In the Khibina and associated plutons of nepheline syenites and related rocks

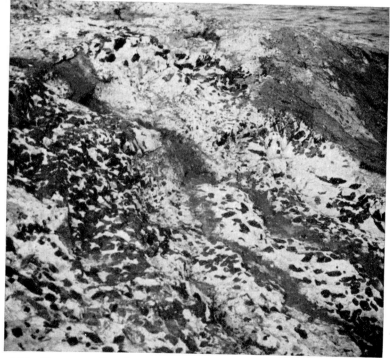

Fig. 5.15. Hanging-wall side of nepheline-syenite pegmatite, Island of Låven, Langesundfjord, Norway, in ditroite, *upper right*. Thin border zone of fieldspar and magnetite, *upper right;* wall zone contains anorthoclase, nepheline, aegirine (dark crystals), fluorite, zircon, and mosandrite.

in the Kola Peninsula, U.S.S.R., the mineralogically famous pegmatites contain minerals of low radioactivity, including lovchorrite, rinkite, loparite, vudyavrite, yuksporite, steenstrupine, sphene, and zircon. Nepheline-syenitic and syenitic pegmatites occurring in the Ilmen Mountains, Urals, U.S.S.R., contain pyrochlore, eschynite, chevkinite, and zircon (Panteleyev, 1938). The nepheline-syenite pegmatites of the Bancroft, Ontario, region are mineralogically relatively simple, but some contain cyrtolite.

MIGMATITE DEPOSITS

In several places in the world, regional metamorphic rocks have been so thoroughly injected or migmatized that the resulting hybrid, consisting of scarcely distinguishable pegmatitic bands and coarse granitic layers and stringers together with bands of injected, recrystallized, or metasomatically altered regional metamorphic rocks, may have a relatively uniform content of radioactive minerals and is mineable as a whole. This type of deposit has been referred to by Lang (1952) as pegmatitic schist or migmatite deposit. Some deposits in the Haliburton-Bancroft district of southern Ontario (Satterly and Hewitt, 1955) are essentially of this type. Some of the finer-grained pegmatitic deposits of the Charlebois Lake area, Saskatchewan, appear to be dominantly migmatitic in nature. They grade from granite pegmatite through quartz-biotite rock to biotite-molybdenite bands with disseminated uraninite (U:Th = 10:1), minor thorite, cyrtolite, thucolite, sphene, monazite and accessory sulfides and tourmaline (Robinson, 1955B).

In the Herb Lake region of Manitoba a contact zone between pegmatites and metasediments is reported to have a grade of 0.15 to 0.20% U_3O_8 for widths of 10 to 15 ft over a length of 850 ft (Can. Geol. Survey, 1953). Migmatitic deposits, consisting of alternating bands of pegmatite, biotite schist, and biotite gneiss occur at the East Found group, 10 mi east of Rennie, and the Triangle and West Found groups along Trans-Canada Highway at mileage 101, Manitoba (Lang, 1952). The radioactive minerals are uraninite, thorite, and cyrtolite. On the Triangle–West Found property the zone, 600 ft wide, has been traced for 10 mi along the contact of a mass of gneissic granite. Radioactivity of 8 times background occurs over small areas underlain chiefly by pegmatite but also by biotite gneiss and schist along pegmatite contacts.

Lang (1952) also reports migmatite deposits have been found north of the East Arm of Great Slave Lake and in the Black Lake area of Saskatchewan. Robinson (1955B) reports that in the Beaverlodge area, Saskatchewan, many bands of migmatite formed in gneisses of the Tazin group are radioactive owing to monazite, uraninite, thorite, cyrtolite, and sphene. Microcline and molybdenite also have been formed in the migmatitic layers. Intervening bands are not radioactive. One type of this migmatite consists chiefly of biotite with monazite euhedra which locally make up as much as 25% of the narrow segregations.

Somewhat similar deposits have been recorded by Davidson (1949, 1956D) from southern Travancore, India, where a medium-grained biotite-monazite schist bordering a pegmatite injection zone is reportedly of sufficient grade to be mined. Mineralization extends over 100 ft intermittently for nearly a mile, with samples containing nearly 18% monazite. Thorite also occurs in migmatitic deposits along the Southern Rhodesia–Union of South Africa border with euxenite and allanite in zones of mixed pegmatite-migmatite. Davidson (1956C) reports that the interior of Sierra Leone is underlain by many migmatites rich in high-thorium monazite, especially south of Kenema.

The distinction between pegmatite deposits and migmatite deposits in some districts is rather arbitrary, and in some other districts pegmatitic and pyrometasomatic deposits likewise intergrade.

I was gratified to be able to answer promptly, and
I did. I said I didn't know.

Mark Twain

• chapter six

CARBONATITES AND RELATED DEPOSITS

GENERAL

Definition and Characteristics

Carbonatites are carbonate-silicate rocks containing mainly calcite or less commonly dolomite, rarely ankerite, rhodochrosite, or siderite, and lesser amounts of a variety of silicates, oxides, and other minerals, originally deposited from a carbonate-rich fluid (Pecora, 1956). Once regarded as relatively rare, within the last few years they have been found in many new occurrences, particularly in eastern Africa and Brazil, largely because of their newly recognized importance as large-scale potential sources of niobium, of the cerium-group rare-earth elements, and of by-product radioactive elements, especially thorium. Some are also sources or potential sources of apatite, magnetite, barite, vermiculite, and in some areas even of $CaCO_3$ for portland cement. Production of pyrochlore concentrates averaging 50% Nb_2O_5 has been begun from the Fen, Norway, deposit (Björlykke, 1955).

Carbonatites have the following general characteristics:

1. They occur with and are genetically related to complexes of feldspathoidal or quartz-free intrusive igneous rocks, i.e., those undersaturated in silica and rich in sodium (rarely rich in potassium): particularly various nepheline syenites (foyaite, microfoyaite, shonkinite, pulaskite, juvite, and malignite); to a lesser extent syenites; feldspar-free nepheline intrusive rocks (ijolite, urtite, melteigite, and turjaite [1]); dikes and minor intrusives of trachyte, phonolite, and nephelinite; lamprophyric dikes of alnoite, monchiquite, and nepheline basalt;

---

[1] The nomenclature of the feldspathoidal rocks is confusing and has been inconsistent. Von Eckermann's systematization (1948) helps to separate the rocks and

224

and minor to major masses of ultramafic rocks including jacupirangite, pyroxenite, and rare dunite. The complexes, usually roughly circular in plan, range in size from less than a mile to several miles across.

2. They commonly form the lower part of the necks of some explosive-type volcanoes and also occur as cone sheets, dikes, and breccia zones. A notable exception to this form is the Sulphide Queen carbonatite mass at Mountain Pass, California, which is unique in some other respects as well. The carbonatite masses do not exceed about three square miles in area, and as Pecora (1956) has pointed out, their exposed area shows no relation in size to that of the complex.

3. Many occurrences of carbonatites with their associated alkalic rocks are surrounded by a contact metasomatic aureole of country rocks (commonly gneisses, schists, and granite) altered to syenites (both leuco- and melasyenites) by the action of alkalic solutions. These metasomatic syenites are called fenites, and the alteration process is called fenitization.

4. Many carbonatites show flow structure through parallelism of biotite, alkali amphiboles, apatite, rutile, orthoclase, etc. Locally the structure may be highly contorted. Some types are brecciated or contain or are associated with feldspathic breccias and agglomerates of explosive volcanic origin. If the carbonatite occurs as a central plug, it usually shows well-developed ring structure and commonly is circular to ellipsoidal in plan. The ring structure results from a combination of concentric flow structure in the carbonatite, ring dikes or cone sheets around the neck, and zonal fenitization in the wall rocks.

Mineralogy

Carbonatites are characterized geochemically by relatively high concentrations of the elements P, Cl, F, Ti, Zr, Nb, Ce-group, S, Ba, and Sr and appreciable concentrations of Th and lesser U. Their characteristic mineral assemblages include:

Sulfides: pyrite, pyrrhotite, Pb and Cu sulfides, rarely molybdenite
Fluorides: fluorite, sellaite
Phosphates: apatite, isokite, monazite

will aid in following the literature on carbonatite occurrences:

Rocks	% Na-orthoclase	% Nepheline	% Pyroxene
Pulaskite	70–90	0–5	10–15
Juvite	40–50	45–50	0–10
Pyroxene juvite	30–45	35–45	10–30
Foyaite	25–35	25–35	25–40
Malignite	20–30	15–25	40–55
Ijolite	—	40–60	60–40
Melteigite	—	15–25	65–75

Ti minerals: titanian magnetite, ilmenite, brookite, anatase, rutile, leucoxene, sphene, perovskite, betafite

Nb minerals: pyrochlore, columbite, betafite, perovskite, titanian magnetite, rutile

Zr minerals: zircon, baddeleyite

Ba and Sr minerals: barite, strontianite, strontian calcite

Ce minerals: monazite, pyrochlore, perovskite, synchisite, parisite, bastnaesite, sahamalite, other rare-earth carbonatites, allanite, cerite

In addition various silicates are widespread, including orthoclase, albite, alkali amphiboles and pyroxenes, phlogopite-biotite (or vermiculite), olivine, monticellite, chondrodite, melilite, and serpentine. Magnetite, hematite, and manganese oxides likewise are common. Cassiterite has been noted. Late quartz and chalcedony are abundant.

The nomenclature of carbonatites has been rendered needlessly complex. Relatively pure calcitic carbonatite = sövite. Dolomite-apatite carbonatite = rauhaugite. A dike rock of relatively pure calcitic carbonatite = alvikite. A dike rock of dolomitic carbonatite = beforsite. Impure or hybrid carbonatites are: kåsenite = sövite with a low percentage of silicate minerals of the ijolite-melteigite rock series; hollaite = sövite with a high percentage of silicates;

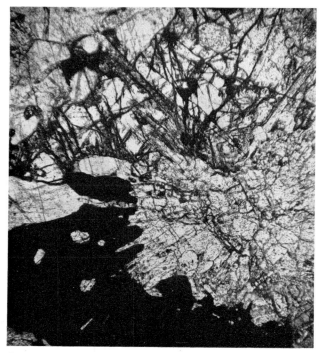

Fig. 6.1. Radioactive perovskite (knopite) (opaque) with apatite (needles of moderate relief) in calcite in sövite, Langörsholmen, Alnö Island, Sweden ($\times 35$).

ringite = a sövite-fenite hybrid; hortite = a sövite-melasyenite hybrid. The proportion of calcite to dolomite varies widely, but in general calcite is more abundant and calcitic carbonatites are more common.

The radioactivity stems chiefly from pyrochlore and monazite in most occurrences, with zircon, baddeleyite, allanite, perovskite, and sphene also contributing. At Mountain Pass, California, monazite, thorite, and bastnaesite are the chief radioactive species, and at Iron Hill, Colorado, monazite, thorite, thorogummite, and xenotime are responsible for the radioactivity. At Oka, Quebec, the radioactive minerals are pyrochlore and betafite (Rowe, 1955A).

Pecora (1956) has pointed out that carbonatites are of two mineralogical types which may intergrade: one, the more common apatite-magnetite type, associated with feldspathoidal rocks, and the other the rare-earth carbonate-phosphate type, associated with more silicic alkalic rocks.

Origin

The origin of carbonatites is in considerable dispute. Formerly many were regarded as large transported xenoliths of limestone or marble. Most are now recognized as being of intrusive origin, but, as pointed out by Turner and Verhoogen (1951, p. 341), "To admit the intrusive igneous origin of carbonatites is not the same thing as admitting the existence of carbonate magmas of similar composition." The main theories advanced to account for their origin are:

1. Recrystallized and metasomatized xenoliths of limestone or marble, rafted into position by rising magma or injected in the solid state by plastic flow.
2. Deuteric (or hydrothermal) replacements of country rocks or of intrusive rocks by carbonate-rich fluids derived from alkalic magmas.
3. Crystallization and repeated replacement of igneous minerals in an alkalic magma in presence of a fluid phase rich in CO_2, followed by intrusion of the partly crystallized liquid or by plastic flow of solid material.

Pecora (1956) has discussed the various theories in considerable detail. He concludes that a carbonatitic magma is less likely to exist than carbonate-rich solutions containing an unusually high concentration of dissolved material at elevated temperature and pressure. Such concentrated liquid solutions should be capable of a variety of high-intensity geochemical activities and upon release of pressure would be a source of CO_2 gas. Agard (1956), however, regards the formation of carbonatites as occurring under conditions of very high pressure and fairly low temperature.

Some carbonate rock bodies listed as carbonatites are not truly so, being nonintrusive in origin. Such masses, which may show many of the textural and mineralogical features characteristic of intrusive or "true" carbonatites, are probably best distinguished as alkalic skarn rocks, representing metasomatized xenoliths of limestone or marble (Pecora, 1956). The carbonate bodies at Oka, Quebec, and in the Garnet Mountain–Aquila Ridge area, Ice River, British Columbia, are apparently of this type. Others may also prove to be after their structural relations are deciphered in detail, for intrusive carbonatites are nor-

Fig. 6.2. Silicate sövite, Alnö Island, Sweden. Calcite with clusters of biotite and pyroxene.

mally the youngest units in the intrusive sequence, whereas masses of alkali skarn are the oldest, being preintrusive in age.

EUROPE

Sweden

Alkalic intrusives and related carbonatites occur over an area 3 mi in diameter on Alnö Island near Sundsvall in northern Sweden. Von Eckermann (1948) has determined that a series of explosions from three foci of different depths fractured the Archean metamorphic complex, permitting intrusion of alkalic cone sheets, ring dikes, and radial dikes. The outer intrusives are generally mafic alkalic rocks; those of the intermediate zone consist primarily of felsic alkalic rocks; and the core (largely underwater) consists of sövite. Surrounding the complex is a zone of fenite grading outward into fractured and iron-stained migmatite. Perovskite (Fig. 6.1) and pyrochlore occur in the sövite, but apparently only in specimen amounts. The knopite contains 0.04% U_3O_8, 3.00% ThO_2; dysanalyte 0.01% U_3O_8, 0.08% ThO_2; perovskite 0.01% U_3O_8, 0.24% ThO_2; and pyrochlore 0.00, 0.03% U_3O_8, 0.15, 1.31% ThO_2 (von Eckermann and Wickman, 1956). Sövite, alvikite, and beforsite of different types also occur as dikes. The sövites contain calcite with apatite, biotite, and pyroxene in varying amounts (Fig. 6.2). Dikes of various alkalic rocks and barite-fluorite veins also cut the complex.

Norway

The Fen area in Telemark, Norway, is an alkalic complex of 4 sq mi intrusive into Precambrian granitic rocks which have been altered along the contact to alkalic syenites (fenite and mafic fenite) (Brögger, 1921). The outer zone of the complex consists chiefly of ijolite and melteigite around a carbonatite core (sövite) which forms about half the complex. Carbonate rock also forms veinlike bodies. The carbonatite contains chiefly calcite with subordinate to trace amounts of dolomite, manganophyllite, biotite, chlorite, hornblende, tremolite, sphene, magnetite, pyrite, apatite, barite, niobian perovskite, and pyrochlore (Fig. 6.3). Yellow brown to deep brown pyrochlore occurs in octahedra modified by (100), up to 6 to 8 mm on edge. It contains about 2% rare earths. In some places, sövite grades into hematitic sövite (rödberg), consisting of calcite impregnated by fine-grained hematite, with some magnetite, pyrite, apatite, chlorite, and minor pyrochlore. These rocks are, in turn, transitional to carbonate iron ores. A monthly production of 15 tons of concentrate was reported by Björlykke in 1955.

In northern Norway calcite-bearing pegmatites (albite-ringites and canadite) and oligoclase pegmatites (plumasite) cut the mafic intrusive complex in the Seiland area. Radioactive zircon occurs in the albite-ringite type; fergusonite in the plumasite type (Barth, 1927).

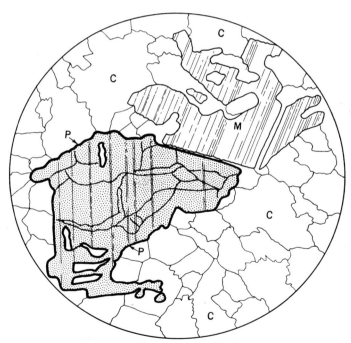

FIG. 6.3. Pyrochlore (P) with manganophyllite (M) in calcitic (C) sövite, Hydro Quarry, Fen area. Norway (Brögger, 1921) (×25).

Fɪɢ. 6.4. Pyrochlore (opaque) with radial apatite cluster in calcitic sövite, Schelingen, Kaiserstuhl, Baden, Germany (×35).

Germany

Alkalic rocks, both intrusive and extrusive, occur in the Kaiserstuhl, a group of low mountains, northwest of Freiburg in Baden. The rocks are mainly breccias and lavas (phonolite, nepheline basanite, nepheline tephrite) with intrusive ijolite, essexite-gabbro, and monchiquite. Carbonatite occurs as nodules containing melanite and apatite in alkalic rocks, as dikelike masses cutting the vent breccia, and as a mass nearly a square mile in size near the center of the complex. Dark red to cherry-red pyrochlore (koppite) occurs in carbonate rock (Fig. 6.4) as crystals faced by (111) and (110) and in spinel twins about 3 mm in size. It contains 176.5×10^{-12} g Ra/g and is associated with niobian perovskite, biotite, forsterite, apatite, and magnesioferrite.

U.S.S.R.

Carbonate veins associated with feldspathoidal rocks have been described from the following localities in the U.S.S.R. (Pecora, 1956): Turkestan; near Mariupol; and at Kola.

AFRICA

General

In Africa many carbonatites occur in close proximity to rift valleys and are considered genetically related to them (James, 1956). They tend to stand up as isolated hills, because the alkalic rocks resist weathering to a greater extent than the granitoid gneisses that they penetrate. The radioactivity of the deposits stems chiefly from thorium, especially in pyrochlore (0.83 to 4.5% $eThO_2$; U_3O_8 is low, <0.01%), and from daughter elements of uranium adsorbed on limonite. The monazite is generally thorium-poor (Davidson, 1956B). The carbonatites and alkalic complexes in Uganda and Kenya are Middle to Late Tertiary; those in Nyasaland and Mozambique are regarded as Mesozoic(?); Lulu Kop and others in South Africa may be Precambrian.

Uganda

Along the eastern border of Uganda are four eroded volcanic centers (Davies, 1947, 1954): Sukulu, Tororo, Bukusu, and Sekululo, ranging in diameter from about 2 to 5 mi. All breach granite and generally show the following concentric arrangement of rocks:

1. Unaltered granite (outermost)
2. Granite with sodic hornblende
3. Granite converted to syenite and mafic syenite (fenites)
4. Mixed alkalic rocks: ijolite (predominating), melteigite, nepheline syenite, urtite, pyroxenite, and dunite
5. A band of magnetite-apatite-phlogopite rock
6. A zone of garnet, wollastonite, and tremolite with anatase and pyrochlore
7. Carbonatite containing magnetite, hematite, pyrite, fluorite, apatite, phlogopite, and pyroxene

At Tororo a pipe of agglomerate occurs as well, but the magnetite-apatite band is missing. Here the carbonatite mass is 1½ mi long north-south. Eluvial soils are rich in apatite and pyrochlore. The Bukusu mass is 5×4.5 mi and dikes of carbonatite also are present. The magnetite belt here is ¼ to 1¾ mi wide and contains 15 to 16% perovskite ($ThO_2 = 0.16$, $Ce_2O_3 = 1.46$, La_2O_3, etc. = 1.79), 3 to 8% leucoxene, and 76 to 82% titaniferous magnetite (Broughton et al., 1950).

In the Sukulu group the carbonatite is 2.5 miles across. Soil from the magnetite zone contains 90% apatite, 5% quartz, 2% iron oxides and ilmenite, 3% remainder of pyrochlore (0.37 to 2.86% ThO_2), baddeleyite, zircon, tremolite, anatase, and perovskite. Soil reserves to 20 ft are estimated to contain 85,000 tons of pyrochlore (Davidson, 1956D). The carbonatite with the highest percentage of pyrochlore is a tangential dike (Williams, 1952). Presumably this is the deposit described by MacKay and Schnellmann (1956) as having reserves of apatite-pyrochlore ore in excess of 200 million tons, also containing recoverable magnetite, zircon, and baddeleyite.

Carbonatite surrounded by ijolite is known at Lokupoi in the Elgon Chain, southern Karamojo, and carbonatite also is known at the site of the Toror volcano in the same area.

Kenya

Carbonatites that have been described occur at (1) Jombo (Mrima) in the Mombasa-Kwale area, in the extreme southeastern corner of Kenya (Baker, 1953); (2) at Ruri and Homa Mountain in western Kenya; and (3) at Usaki

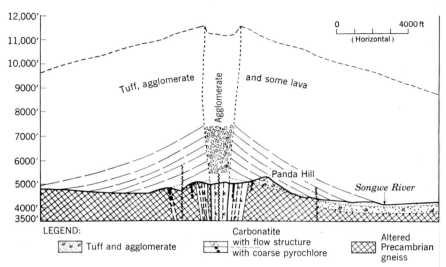

FIG. 6.5. Reconstruction of volcano overlying Mbeya carbonatite, Tanganyika. $c =$ carbonatite (Fawley and James, 1955; *Econ. Geol.*).

near Homa Bay, Kavirondo, in south Nyanza. Six separate major alkalic and carbonatite ring complexes beside two minor vents are known in the Kavirondo rift valley (McCall, 1956).

Jombo, a hill rising a thousand feet above the plain, has three satellic centers within a 10-mi radius—Mrima, Kiruku, and Nguluku. Carbonatite is minor, the complexes consisting chiefly of nepheline syenites, their mafic relatives, and silicified agglomerates. Lateritic iron-manganese ores occur locally. Baker (1953) detected radioactivity 2 to 3 times background at Mrima and Kiruku, later found to be due to large amounts of eluvial monazite (0.4% ThO_2) and pyrochlore.[1] Reserves of soil are reported to be as much as 42 million tons, containing 0.7 to 2.7% pyrochlore (Davidson, 1956D).

At Homa Mountain (Saggerson, 1953) and Ruri Hills the soil mantle contains pyrochlore and a member of the euxenite-polycrase series. Homa Mountain is a multiple-centered carbonatite complex of ring dikes and cone sheets.

In the Homa Bay area (Pulfrey, 1944, 1950) several carbonatite bodies up to a mile long have crude annular or plug shapes. They are associated with ijolite, alkalic dikes, and locally fenitized country rock; contain melanite, vesuvianite, aegirine, phlogopite, magnetite, and apatite; and are cut by younger iron-bearing carbonatites.

---

[1] The first record of Mrima Hill was made by a Greek named Basiles who sailed down the east coast of Africa in 60 A.D. and found the Arabs there using boats built entirely without nails, the planks being held to the ribs with rope. These boats are reportedly used today, because the Arabs believe that near the powerful magnetism of Mrima Hill, nails will be drawn out and the craft will collapse and sink.

Tanganyika

At Mbeya (Panda) Hill near the southwestern border of Tanganyika on the edge of the Rukwa Trough is a central carbonatite plug and an outer carbonatite ring with a discontinuous zone of fenitized Precambrian gneiss between (Fawley and James, 1955). An explosion vent breccia of gneiss is cemented by carbonate (Fig. 6.5). Both carbonatite bodies as well as calcitic and dolomitic dikes carry pyrochlore. Accompanying minerals are apatite, zircon, fluorite, magnetite, pyrite, pyrrhotite, amphibole, phlogopite, and lesser amounts of columbite, sphene, cassiterite, hematite, ilmenite, galena, barite, olivine, chlorite, and vermiculite. Pyrochlore forms grains generally 1 mm or less, exceptionally greater than 5 mm in size. The larger may be embayed and carry inclusions of calcite, apatite, fluorite, and iron oxide. The pyrochlore is variable in color: pale yellow, olive, black, or cores of red; and in composition: $eThO_2 = 0.17$ to 2.45%; one analysis gave 0.025% U_3O_8. Davidson (1956D) suggests an average of 1% ThO_2, with a possible annual production of 5,000 tons of pyrochlore. A reserve of 45 million tons of pyrochlore-bearing carbonatite averaging about 0.3% Nb_2O_5 has been proved.

Pyrochlore also is reported at Ngualla, north of Lake Rukwa in the Chunya district.

Nyasaland

Dixey et al. (1937) described carbonatites in southern Nyasaland at Chilwa Island, Tundulu, Songwe, Kangankunde, and at Muambe (Mozambique), grouping them, their alkalic associates, and similar rocks at over a dozen other localities (no carbonatites) into the Chilwa series. Some 30 ring structures were known by 1951. All form prominent hills 700 to 1,400 ft high (Fig. 6.6). The carbonatite plugs that generally form the cores (¼ to 4 mi) of the vents are associated with orthoclase breccias (Fig. 6.7). The pipes usually are roughly circular to ellipsoidal. Associated alkalic rocks are syenites, nepheline syenites, ijolites, phonolites, and nephelinites with surrounding fenitized gneiss. Ring structures and flow structures are well developed (Garson, 1955).

Typical carbonatite is commonly even-grained (0.5 mm), cream, pinkish, and dark brown, and mottled to banded, consisting chiefly of calcite and lesser siderite, ankerite, and rhodochrosite (Smith, 1953). Other constituents are apatite, orthoclase, quartz, pyrite, magnetite, rutile, anatase, zircon, fluorite, barite, biotite, synchisite, florencite(?), and pyrochlore. The pyrochlore is in colorless octahedral and cubo-octahedral grains, 0.4 to 1 mm in size, containing 0.13% eU_3O_8. Composite samples have 1.0% ThO_2, and soil reserves are

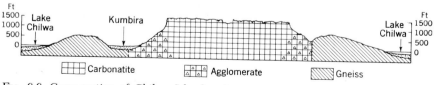

Fig. 6.6. Cross section of Chilwa Island carbonatite, Nyasaland (Dixey et al., 1937; *Nyasaland Geol. Survey*).

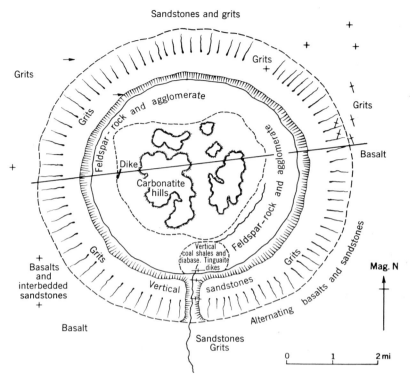

Fɪɢ. 6.7. Sketch map of Muambe carbonatite, Mozambique (Dixey et al., 1937; *Nyasaland Geol. Survey*).

estimated at 45 million tons with less than 2 lb pyrochlore per cubic yard (Davidson, 1956D).

On Kangankunde Hill the mineral association is a green Ce-rich monazite, synchysite, sphalerite, pyrochlore, barite, strontianite, apatite, and manganese minerals. A rich apatite zone containing pyrochlore and synchysite occurs at Tundulu. Chilwa Island carbonatite also is locally rich in pyrochlore with small fluorite deposits.

Northern Rhodesia [1]

Nkumbwa Hill, 1,000 ft high, 15 mi east of Isoka in the northeastern corner of Northern Rhodesia, is a carbonatite plug punched through Precambrian gneisses and granite (Reeve and Deans, 1954). The carbonatite ($\frac{3}{4} \times \frac{1}{2}$ mi)

---

[1] The Detroit News of March 31, 1957, reports a novel technique for locating radioactive carbonatites in Africa: "Aging elephants, it seems, drift instinctively to any radioactive spring or mineral lode, there to soak up rays that soothe aching joints. Over the years they have beaten paths from all parts of Africa to these therapeutic sites. This discovery was made here by P. L. A. O'Brien, senior geologist at the Geological Survey Department at Lusaka. O'Brien followed a centuries-old elephant track to a group of strange rock formations. There he found three 'pipes' or outcroppings of thorium, tantalum and columbium, all highly radioactive."

is dolomitic, locally ankeritic and sideritic; some parts are manganiferous, others silicified. Other minerals are apatite, forsterite, phlogopite, pyrite, quartz, barite, sellaite, ilmenite, aegirine, riebeckite, arfvedsonite, and isokite ($CaMgPO_4F$) (Deans and McConnell, 1955). Minerals of economic significance are monazite and pyrochlore. The former is green, cryptocrystalline, and almost nonradioactive. Pyrochlore occurs in carbonatite, eluvial material, and transported soils as pale yellow octahedra, <10 μ to 1 mm in size, containing 0.1% $eThO_2$. Grades of the different materials are:

	Per cent pyrochlore
Carbonatite	0.01–0.36
Residual soil	0.37–0.90
Transported soil	0.01–0.66

Southern Rhodesia

In Southern Rhodesia, carbonatites have been found by Mennell (1946) at Shawa and Dorowa in the upper part of the Sabi Valley. At Shawa a carbonatite core is partly enclosed in a crescent of ijolite-jacupirangite-dunite and an outer ring of syenite-shonkinite (fenite?), all in granite. The complex is 4 mi across. Separating the carbonatite from the alkalic rocks is a screen of serpentinite containing veinlets of magnesite. The dolomitic carbonatite, which shows flow structure, contains magnetite and apatite.

The Dorowa Hills carbonatite is enclosed in syenite, pyroxenite, nepheline syenite, and urtite-ijolite, the complex measuring 1×2 mi. The dolomitic carbonatite, locally ferruginous, contains phlogopite(?), asbestiform amphibole, and masses of magnetite-apatite rock.

Although no niobium or radioactive rare-earth minerals are reported, the deposits are so similar to others that contain such minerals that further investigation probably will reveal their presence.

At Chishanya in the Sabi Valley Swift (1952) found a carbonatite mass bordered by alkalic rocks. Local magnetite-apatite concentrations are present.

Transvaal

Radioactive and rare-metal minerals are found in two carbonatite masses, the larger about ½ sq mi in size, at Phalaborwa (Palaboro), northeastern Transvaal (Strauss and Truter, 1951A,B; Hiemstra, 1955). They include zircon, baddeleyite, and uranothorianite (60% ThO_2). Other constituents are magnetite, abundant apatite, orthoclase, diopside, phlogopite, olivine, chondrodite, chalcocite, bornite, and chalcopyrite. The carbonatite at Lulu Kop (Loolekop) is a hill 300 ft high surrounded by a zone of shonkinite-pyroxenite, an outer zone of syenite, all in granite (Shand, 1931). The country rocks are Precambrian gneisses. Lead isotope ratios in the uranothorianite indicate a probable age of more than two billion years, which is much older than most other African carbonatites are thought to be (Davidson, 1956D).

In Sekukuniland in eastern Transvaal a foyaite stock intrudes Bushveld red granite and encloses a carbonatite mass $1 \times ¾$ mi, fringed by ijolite (Strauss and Truter, 1951A,B). Magnetite, apatite, pyrite, serpentine, and crocidolite occur in the carbonatite (Shand, 1921). Fenite occurs marginally.

Other Occurrences

Breccia pipes, locally strongly impregnated with calcite, magnesite, barite, silica, and limonite, are represented by the Saltpetre Kop group, Sutherland district, and the Geitsi Gubib (Gross Brukaros Mountain), South-West Africa. The Pretoria Saltpan, a craterlike structure 25 mi north of Pretoria, exposes, in addition to granite blocks, blocks of norite, alkalic syenite, and dolomitic breccia containing magnetite. Also in South-West Africa at Kalkfeld, southwest of Otavi, iron ore occurs in a carbonatite or in a skarn rock near the center of a craterlike ring structure chiefly underlain by nepheline syenite. Another ring structure with foyaite is at Okorusu, south of Otavi. Ijolite, reportedly with associated carbonatite, occurs at Songo, Sierra Leone. All of these structures appear to be similar to pyrochlore and monazite-bearing carbonatitic deposits found elsewhere in Africa and thus deserve additional detailed investigation for these minerals.

BRAZIL

At least 14 radioactive alkalic complexes are known in Brazil and several are known to contain carbonatites. The chief radioactive mineral is pyrochlore.

Jacupiranga, São Paulo

At Jacupiranga in São Paulo an alkalic complex, $4\frac{1}{2} \times 6$ mi, intrudes Algonkian(?) granodiorite and schists. In the southern part a carbonatite core, 800×300 yd, forms a hill in the center of a jacupirangite-pyroxenite mass that grades into ijolite to the west and in other directions into nepheline syenite (Fig. 6.8). Alkalic dikes are numerous, and the surrounding country rock has been fenitized. The carbonatite contains 12% apatite, commonly in coarse clusters, 4% magnetite, and vermiculite, monticellite, serpentine, pyrite, zircon, perovskite, baddeleyite ("brazilite," Hussak, 1895), and pyrochlore. The average composition of the carbonatite is 51% CaO, 3.4% MgO, 3.2% Fe_3O_4, 5.2% P_2O_5, and 0.2% SiO_2 (Leonardos, 1956).

Registro, São Paulo

About 60 km northwest of Jacupiranga, in the drainage of the Guaviruva River, is an occurrence in Serrote, halfway between Juquiá and Registro. A hill of nepheline syenite about 100 m high and 1 km in diameter is surrounded by a belt of apatite-rich rock 10 to 50 m across and further out by pyroxenite. The dark red eluvial cover contains barite, limonite, magnetite, vermiculite, and a radioactive mineral.

About 1 km distant is Morro do Ferro, composed of peridotite, magnetite veins, and surficial iron-rich material ("canga"). The third hill, the highest, known as Serrote, is underlain by apatite rock, barite veins and, in depth, by dolomitic carbonatite (Leonardos, 1956).

Another occurrence of magnetite-rich soil similar to that of Jacupiranga is

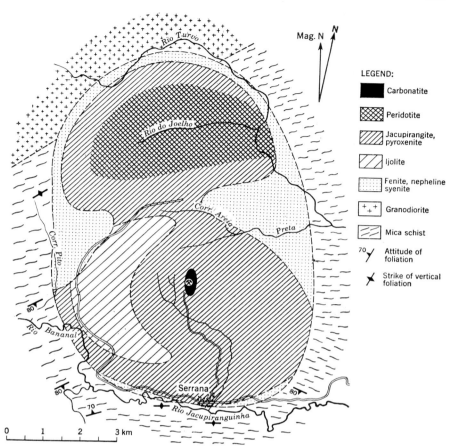

Fɪɢ. 6.8. Map of the alkalic complex and carbonatite of Jacupiranga, São Paulo, Brazil (after G. C. Melcher, Leonardos, 1956).

LEGEND:

- Carbonatite
- Peridotite
- Jacupirangite, pyroxenite
- Ijolite
- Fenite, nepheline syenite
- Granodiorite
- Mica schist
- 70⟋ Attitude of foliation
- ⟋ Strike of vertical foliation

Sarapui, about 15 km from Piedade on the Piedade-Juquiá highway, in the state of Rio de Janeiro.

Ipanema, São Paulo

On Araçoiaba Hill, at Ipanema, about 100 km north of Juquiá, occur dikes of decomposed jacupirangite and other sodic subsilicic rocks cutting phyllites and marbles of the Algonkian Acungui series. The dikes are sheared and marginally brecciated. Magnetite and apatite are abundant and other constituents of the thick eluvial soil are aegirine, hastingsite, chalcedony, vermiculite, barite, and zircon (Derby, 1891; Leonardos, 1956).

Araxá, Minas Gerais

At Araxá in Minas Gerais reserves of pyrochlore-bearing eluvial material are estimated to exceed 3 million tons with 3 to 14% Nb_2O_5 to a depth of 3 m.

The complex consists of malignites and related rocks, barite veins, carbonatite, and dolomitic carbonatite dikes containing a blue sodic amphibole (Leonardos, 1956). The surficial material is a reddish-brown aggregate of barite, magnetite, hematite, limonite, pyrochlore, apatite, and containing also blocks of "canga" (magnetite crystals cemented by limonite). The apatite-bearing material is estimated at 100 million tons (Leonardos, 1956).

About 45 km south of Araxá, at Antas, occur masses of titaniferous magnetite in a perovskite-rich rock of the jacupirangite type. Other occurrences have been noted about 10 km from Araxá on the Antas road and at Pinto on the Cachoeirinha estate (Leonardos, 1956).

Anitapolis, Santa Catarina

White, coarsely crystalline carbonate rocks in contact with nepheline rocks occur locally at Anitapolis and contain tremolite, apatite, biotite, and magnetite. The alkalic rocks include ijolite, pyroxenite, larvikite, and types rich in magnetite and apatite (Leonardos, 1956).

Other Occurrences

Jacupirangite-type rocks rich in magnetite and vermiculite and containing perovskite have been found at Catalão, Goyaz (Hussak, 1894). The soil also contains apatite, quartz crystals, and chalcedony masses.

Other occurrences of radioactive alkalic centers are known at Salitre, near Patrocinio, where alkalic ultramafic rocks contain titaniferous magnetite and perovskite. Radioactive niobium mineralization also is reported at Corrego Bebedoura in Minas Gerais. Guimarães (1947) and de Freitas (1956) have summarized the occurrences of alkalic rocks in Brazil.

CANADA

Quebec

Niobium-thorium deposits occur in alkalic intrusive rocks and alkalic calcitic skarns near Oka, Quebec (Rowe, 1955A), west of Montreal. The alkalic complex is part of the Monteregian petrological province extending for about 150 mi east from Como, Vaudreuil County, to Big Megantic Mountain, Compton and Frontenac Counties (Dresser and Denis, 1944). At Oka, a Precambrian inlier consisting mainly of anorthosite, gabbro, gneiss, quartzite, and marble has been intruded by a complex of ijolite, melilite rocks, and lamprophyres. The intruded marble has been metasomatized to apatite-biotite-magnetite, soda pyroxene-calcite, and monticellite skarns; both the marbles and intrusive rocks have been altered to biotite-rich metasomatic rocks. The minerals of economic interest are (1) niobian perovskite which occurs chiefly in altered alkalic rocks, (2) pyrochlore (Th-bearing) which occurs in skarn and is the principal Nb mineral (Fig. 2.10), (3) betafite (Th-bearing) which appears in the biotite replacement rocks, and (4) niocalite, a new Nb-Ca silicate, found in skarn (Nickel, 1956). By 1957, over 100,000,000 tons of niobium ore had been developed (to 500 ft) (Maurice, 1957).

Ontario

Uranoan pyrochlore occurs at the Newman and nearby deposits, on and near the Manitou Islands, Lake Nipissing. The ore-bearing breccia lenses occur in a circular zone of mixed carbonate rocks, light- and dark-colored alkalic silicate rocks (Rowe, 1954; Gill and Owens, 1956). This zone, which is up to 1,200 ft wide, separates a central pluton of "diorite" from intruded Precambrian quartz-feldspar gneiss and Ordovician limestone and conglomerate (Birds Eye and Black River formations). The rocks of the contact zone consist of varying amounts of potash feldspar, acmite, biotite, soda-amphibole, calcite, and minor pyrite, magnetite, hematite, apatite, fluorite, monazite, and locally disseminated uranoan pyrochlore (Fig. 2.9). The main ore zone shows repeated brecciation and is cut by pegmatites, lamprophyres, calcite-fluorite veins, and faults of small displacement.

The Newman deposit is mainly underwater, having been traced by drilling for 1,100 ft east from Newman Island. Another small lens occurs on the southwestern end of Great Manitou Island, and three still smaller lenses have been found on Calder Island. By 1955, 5,431,000 tons of ore, averaging 0.53% Nb_2O_5 and 0.039% U_3O_8 after 10% dilution, had been outlined (Rowe, 1955B).[1]

Pyrochlore carbonatite deposits have also been discovered (1) 7 mi northeast of Nemegos Station (50 million tons, 0.26% Nb_2O_5); (2) at Nemogosenda Lake (two deposits—20 million tons, 0.5% Nb_2O_5, and 15 million tons); (3) at Beaucage Mines near North Bay (Jones, 1957).

British Columbia

The Ice River igneous complex, an asymmetrical laccolith composed of several types of feldspathoidal rocks including urtite and nepheline-sodalite syenite, is exposed in the southern part of Yoho National Park. In the Field area around the northwest part of the complex, near Aquila Ridge and Garnet Mountain, the enclosing fossiliferous Cambrian limestones and limestone xenoliths have been metasomatized by the addition of Na, K, Nb, and Zr, resulting in the formation of several extensive alkalic skarn zones containing pyrochlore and other radioactive minerals (Allan, 1914).

UNITED STATES

Arkansas

At Potash Sulphur Springs, 6 mi west of Magnet Cove in Hot Springs County, soil overlying a complex of nepheline syenite, mafic alkalic rocks, and carbonatite locally contains up to 0.24% Nb in yellow pyrochlore (Kaiser, 1956). Magnet Cove is a similar but larger alkalic complex which also contains carbonatites as a 4,000- $\times$ 500-ft mass and as dikes. The central carbonatite contains nepheline-syenite xenoliths altered to diopside-vesuvianite aggregates. Rutile and niobian perovskite deposits occur in the complex; brookite deposits occur

---

[1] Indian tribal legend says the islands are cursed, telling of braves who made war paint from a red oxide found there and later died of a bone disease!

in quartzite (Devonian and Mississippian) near the contacts; pyrochlore has not been found (Fryklund et al., 1954).

Gunnison County, Colorado

Thorium deposits in the Powderhorn district are closely associated with the Iron Hill stock of alkalic rocks (Larsen, 1942; Larsen and Cross, 1956), which includes, from oldest to youngest, central dolomitic carbonatite (Fig. 6.9), melilite rock (uncompaghrite), pyroxenite of several types, ijolite, soda syenite, nepheline syenite, and nepheline and quartz gabbro. Carbonate veins cut rocks of the stock. The carbonatite, a mass of about 2 sq mi, is generally massive with a local, steeply plunging lineation resulting from apatite streaks along shear planes (Wallace and Olson, 1956; Olson, 1956; Olson and Wallace, 1956). Other minerals of the carbonatite are phlogopite, magnetite, aegirine, pyrochlore, and sodic amphibole. The stock is pre-Jurassic in age and intrudes Precambrian igneous and metamorphic rocks.

The thorium deposits are of three types: (1) mineralized shear zones, (2) banded carbonate veins, and (3) weakly radioactive zones in the stock carbonatite. Uranium is low to absent, the radioactivity being due almost entirely to thorium and its derivatives—the average of 45 samples is more than 0.3% ThO_2, with a selected sample from the Little Johnnie vein (Fig. 6.10) containing more than 4% ThO_2. The chief radioactive species are thorite and thorogummite and, to a lesser extent, monazite. The two major types of deposits are compared in Table 6.1. In the carbonatite stock nontabular radioactive bodies occur in two places, containing rare-earth apatite, mica, and magnetite. Rare-

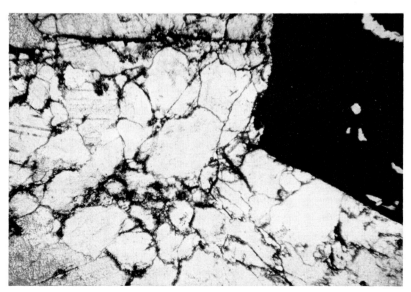

FIG. 6.9. Carbonatite, Iron Hill, Gunnison County, Colo. Pyrite crystal (opaque) in granular dolomite, with interstitial limonite ($\times 35$).

TABLE 6.1. *Comparison of two types of radioactive deposits, Powderhorn district, Gunnison County, Colorado* (Olson and Wallace, 1956)

Deposit	Size	Attitude	Minerals	Host rock	Rare earths
Mineralized shear zones	<1–18 ft wide; few 10s–many 100s ft long. Little Johnnie probably 3,500 ft long (Fig. 6.10)	Steep to vertical dip. Variable strike	Quartz, iron oxides, alkali feldspar, thorite or thorogummite, ba ite, carbonate, apatite, pyrite, galena, xenotime, monazite, rutile, tourmaline, fluorite	Precambrian metamorphics	Richer in Y earths
Carbonate veins	Several in.–15 ft wide; few feet to 3,500 ft long	Crude radial arrangement with respect to carbonatite	Dolomite; also calcite, ankerite, siderite; apatite, pyrite, chalcopyrite, sphalerite, galena, fluorite, quartz, opal, alkali feldspar, phlogopite, amphiboles, pyroxenes, barite, bastnaesite, cerite(?), synchisite(?)	Cut rocks of the complex mainly	Richer in Ce earths

earth apatite and perovskite occur in the pyroxenite of the stock, and niobian brookite in gabbro on the Little Johnnie claim.

Montana

Several dikelike bodies of calcitic rock up to 18 in. thick and also containing biotite, pyrrhotite, pyrite, galena, barite, and rare-earth carbonates (burbankite and calkinsite) occur at the head of Big Sandy Creek, Bearpaw Mountains, Montana, in association with larger syenitic pegmatites that contain calcite-feldspar cores (Pecora, 1942, 1948, 1956; Pecora and Kerr, 1953; Heinrich, 1949). Small amounts of apatite, magnetite, and uranoan pyrochlore are present (Pecora, pers. com.).

Unusual carbonate veins along the West Fork Bitterroot River, Ravalli County, Montana, contain strontian calcite; variable amounts of barite; the ore minerals columbite, ancylite, and monazite; and allanite and fersmite.

San Bernardino County, California

Rare-earth carbonate rocks, locally radioactive, occur as veins and carbonatite masses genetically associated with Precambrian, potash-rich granite, syenite, and shonkinite that intrude a Precambrian metamorphic complex in the Mountain Pass district, California (Pray and Sharp, 1951; Olson and Pray, 1954; Olson et al., 1954). Carbonate veins, which are most abundant in and near the

FIG. 6.10. Little Johnnie vein, Iron Hill area, Gunnison County, Colo. (contacts indicated in dashed lines).

southwest side of the largest shonkinite-syenite stock, are as much as 20 ft thick and 600 ft long but are generally less than 6 ft thick, and many are only 1 ft thick or less. The Sulphide Queen carbonatite mass, an irregular northwest-bending body, is the largest (2,400 × 700 ft) (Fig. 6.11), being more than 10 times the sum of the areas of all other exposed carbonate veins. The third type of deposit consists of mineralized shear zones several feet thick. Much of the carbonatite is foliated from the orientation of barite grains and streaks. The principal minerals are carbonates, including calcite, ankerite, dolomite or siderite, and barite, strontian barite, barian celestite, quartz, bastnaesite, and parisite. Minor minerals are aegirine, crocidolite, chlorite, biotite, phlogopite, muscovite, allanite, sphene, monazite, magnetite, hematite, galena, pyrite, chalcopyrite, tetrahedrite, bornite, aragonite, fluorite, strontianite, apatite, thorite, cerite, and sahamalite. Secondary constituents include goethite, wulfenite, malachite, azurite, and cerussite. An estimate of the average composition of carbonate rock is (Olson et al., 1954):

Carbonates	60%
Barite	20%
Rare-earth fluocarbonates	10%
Quartz, other silicates	10%

Very slightly radioactive bastnaesite, the principal rare-earth mineral, constitutes 5 to 15% of much of the Sulphide Queen mass and locally exceeds 60%. Thorite in small grains occurs chiefly in mineralized shear zones and in some carbonate veins. Monazite (ThO_2 = 1 to 3%) occurs mainly in dolomitic parts of the Sulphide Queen body and in some carbonate veins (Jaffe, 1955). The radioactivity of the deposits results almost entirely from thorium and its decay products. In the Sulphide Queen mass, ThO_2 ranges from 0.01 to 0.16% and is relatively uniform. Vein samples range from 0.004 to 0.55% eU, with more than 2% ThO_2 in some but no more than 0.020% U.

The Sulphide Queen body probably represents the world's greatest concentration of cerium metals. Barite can be produced as a by-product, and thorium is a potential by-product. It is estimated that the inferred reserve for the district exceeds 25 million tons of rock containing 5 to 10% rare-earth oxides, 20 to 25% barite, and a small fraction of 1% ThO_2. Cerium is the preponderant rare-earth metal; lanthanum and neodymium are next in abundance; praseodymium and samarium are less abundant. The geologically potential reserve of the district may exceed 100 million tons containing more than 10 billion lb of rare-earth oxides.

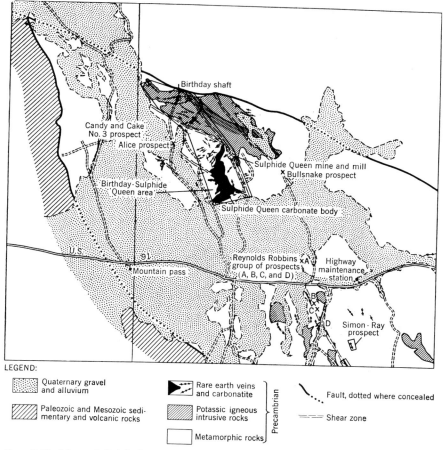

LEGEND:

Quaternary gravel and alluvium

Paleozoic and Mesozoic sedimentary and volcanic rocks

Rare earth veins and carbonatite

Potassic igneous intrusive rocks

Metamorphic rocks

Precambrian

Fault, dotted where concealed

Shear zone

Fig. 6.11. Map of Sulphide Queen carbonatite body, Mountain Pass, San Bernardino County, Calif. (Olson et al., 1954; *U.S. Geol. Survey*).

• chapter seven

PYROMETASOMATIC AND OTHER HIGH-INTENSITY HYDROTHERMAL DEPOSITS

PYROMETASOMATIC DEPOSITS

General

Pyrometasomatic deposits of radioactive minerals are uncommon. In fact, few representatives of this group were known until recently, when the intensive search for radioactive materials determined that both uranium and thorium may occur in pyrometasomatic deposits of various types and that in some cases such deposits are sufficiently mineralized to warrant detailed attention and sampling. A few are mineable, and several are probably major discoveries. The major subtypes are:

1. Pyrometasomatic deposits of thorianite-uraninite in marble or metapyroxenite near contacts of granitic, syenitic, or pegmatitic intrusives
2. Allanite deposits in contact marbles, commonly around pegmatites, in some cases in skarns with other cerium-earth minerals
3. Metasomatic monazite deposits
4. Pyrometasomatic magnetite deposits, usually with pitchblende, but also containing other radioactive minerals
5. Molybdenite-pitchblende contact deposits
6. Uraninite-copper deposits
7. Oxidized contact deposits in which the original radioactive minerals are not certainly known, having been strongly altered to such species as autunite or zeunerite

Another distinctive type of pyrometasomatic deposit is exemplified by

244

the alkalic skarns formed around or near alkalic subsilicic rocks. These characteristically contain such minerals as pyrochlore, monazite, and beta-fite, and because of their close mineralogical and geological similarities to carbonatites are considered under that section (pages 238–239).

Thorianite-Uraninite Deposits

Bancroft Region, Ontario

The deposits consist of radioactive zones in marble as lime-rich amphibo-lite ("metapyroxenite" of Satterly and Hewitt, 1955), near contacts of granitic, syenitic, or pegmatitic intrusives. In the marbles, skarn minerals such as diopside, tremolite, scapolite, epidote, phlogopite, and sphene are commonly developed, especially sugary diopside and euhedral phlogopite. Others are pyrite, pyrrhotite, garnet, chondrodite, graphite, and molybdenite. The calcite has recrystallized with a salmon-pink color. The radioactive min-eral is uranoan thorianite or thorian uraninite ($ThO_2 < 25\%$). Traces of thorite and such rare-earth minerals as monazite, allanite, lessingite, and melanocerite also have been found (Robinson, 1955B). The radioactive zones are irregular in size, shape, and distribution.

In the lime-rich amphibolites, radioactive deposits of thinly tabular form appear to have been developed along faults or shear zones. Common con-stituents are coarse biotite, diopside, scapolite, feldspar, apatite, calcite, and fluorite. The usual radioactive mineral is uraninite; some deposits have pyrochlore, the two species rarely occurring together. Uranothorite as disseminated euhedra has been formed in a few deposits of irregular shape.

Pyrometasomatic deposits of these two closely related types are known in Canada at some nine localities in Cardiff, Monmouth, Faraday, and Dun-gannon Townships, Ontario, and in Grand Calumet and Huddersfield Townships, Quebec (Satterly and Hewitt, 1955; Robinson and Sabina, 1955).

Other Deposits

Similar deposits have been noted outside of Canada, although not so commonly. At Easton, Pennsylvania, thorian uraninite occurs in serpentin-ite at the contact of pegmatite with limestone. At the Stalin's Present prospect, 11 mi northeast of Oreana in the Humboldt Range, Nevada, uraninite occurs as scattered grains in a dark green layer, 4 to 10 in. thick, consisting of diopside, epidote, chlorite, quartz, and hornblende cut by smoky quartz-calcite stringers (Anderson and Waddell, 1952; Lovering, 1954). The layer (0.042 to 0.060% U) trends north, dips steeply east, and is enclosed in a light gray granite which contains thin gummite frac-ture coatings.

Placers in Ruby Creek, Nixon Fork district, west-central Alaska, carry secondary uranium minerals and thorianite, possibly derived from a con-tact zone between monzonite and limestone (White and Stevens, 1953).

Uranothorianite deposits occur on Madagascar in a north-south arc 150 km long and 30 to 40 km wide from Fort Dauphin north to the Mandare

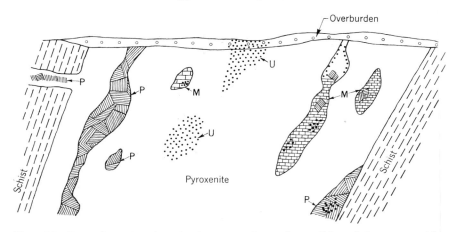

Fig. 7.1. Uranothorianite deposits in pyroxenite and xenoliths of impure marble, Madagascar. P = phlogopite, M = marble xenoliths with calcite, wernerite, anorthite, and uranothorianite, U = disseminations of uranothorianite in pyroxenite (Hésairie and Noizet, Roubault, 1956).

River basin (Roubault, 1956). The deposits occur in masses and lenses of pyroxenite interlayered with Precambrian schists. They contain urano-thorite in concentrations of disseminated grains in the pyroxenite itself and in association with lensoid masses of calcite-wernerite, phlogopite, or an-orthite enclosed in the pyroxenite (Fig. 7.1). Both eluvial and alluvial placer deposits are also known.

Contact Allanite Deposits

Allanite is a relatively widespread mineral in pyrometasomatic deposits, and in some it is sufficiently abundant to produce considerable radioactiv-ity. Usually it is associated with other radioactive or nonradioactive cerium-earth minerals, and in some examples uraninite is also present.

The Whalen mine, at the head of Holmes Gulch, Hidden Creek area, Nixon Fork district, west-central Alaska, is near the contact of monzonite with a large xenolith of roof pendant of Upper Cretaceous limestone (White and Stevens, 1953). The contact-metamorphosed limestone con-tains 0.005 to 0.5% eU but only 0.002 to 0.004% U; most of the radioactiv-ity is due to thorium. The radioactive minerals are allanite, parisite, zir-con, sphene, and hematite. Other constituents are calcite, quartz, kyanite, and scheelite. The heavy concentrate, which makes up about 25% of the limestone, consists of 98% allanite.

On Grand Calumet Island in Quebec, allanite in subparallel plates up to 3 to 4 in. across occurs with hematite, quartz, biotite, fluorite, and apatite in a contact zone between gneiss and sedimentary rocks.

In the contact zone of alkalic syenites in the Kyshtymsk district, Ural Mts., U.S.S.R., allanite occurs with cerite, bastnaesite, lessingite, and törnebohmite (Silberminz, 1929).

Two allanite-bearing skarn deposits are known in Sweden, one at Bastnäs, Riddarhyttan district, and the other at the Östanmossa mine, Norberg. Both contain cerite (Geijer, 1921, 1927). At Bastnäs cerium-earth minerals occur in narrow skarn bands in marble associated with banded quartz-specular hematite ores. The skarn is rich in actinolite (Fig. 7.2), and also contains quartz, magnetite, chalcopyrite, bismuthinite, molybdenite, linnaeite, and the rare-earth minerals cerite, allanite, törnebohmite, fluocerite, lanthanite, and bastnaesite. The allanite is only weakly radioactive.

At the Östanmossa mine, magnetite aggregates and skarn minerals replace dolomitic marble. The skarn consists of felted tremolite-actinolite with diopside, andradite, norbergite, chondrodite, clinohumite, chalcopyrite, pyrite, molybdenite, bismuthinite, and fluorite. The rare-earth minerals are cerite, allanite, and magnesian allanite (both non-metamict).

Mary Kathleen Deposit, Queensland

The Mary Kathleen, an essentially unique uranium deposit about halfway between Mount Isa and Clancurry in northwestern Queensland, Australia, consists of a radioactive garnetized zone in a folded and faulted series of calc-silicate beds (Corella beds) between two granites, all of Lower Proterozoic age (McAndrew and Scott, 1955; Sullivan, 1955; Matheson and Searl, 1956). The

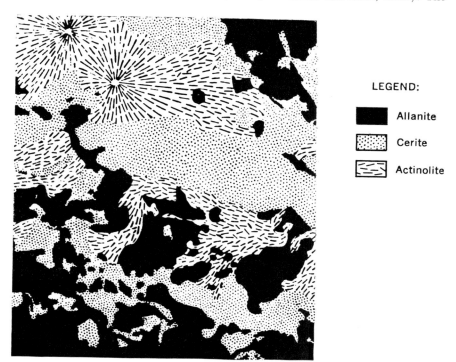

LEGEND:

■ Allanite

▨ Cerite

▨ Actinolite

Fig. 7.2. Allanite-cerite-actinolite skarn. Bastnäs, Riddarhyttan district, Sweden. (Geijer, 1921; *Swedish Geol. Survey*).

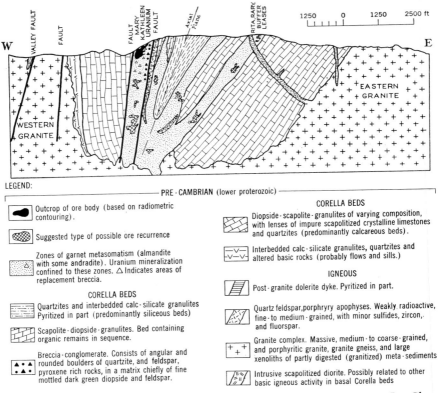

LEGEND:

────────────────────── PRE-CAMBRIAN (lower proterozoic) ──────────────────────

Outcrop of ore body (based on radiometric contouring).

Suggested type of possible ore recurrence

Zones of garnet metasomatism (almandite with some andradite). Uranium mineralization confined to these zones. △ Indicates areas of replacement breccia.

CORELLA BEDS

Quartzites and interbedded calc-silicate granulites Pyritized in part (predominantly siliceous beds)

Scapolite-diopside-granulites. Bed containing organic remains in sequence.

Breccia-conglomerate. Consists of angular and rounded boulders of quartzite, and feldspar, pyroxene rich rocks, in a matrix chiefly of fine mottled dark green diopside and feldspar.

CORELLA BEDS

Diopside-scapolite-granulites of varying composition, with lenses of impure scapolitized crystalline limestones and quartzites (predominantly calcareous beds).

Interbedded calc-silicate granulites, quartzites and altered basic rocks (probably flows and sills.)

IGNEOUS

Post-granite dolerite dyke. Pyritized in part.

Quartz feldspar,porphryry apophyses. Weakly radioactive, fine- to medium-grained, with minor sulfides, zircon, and fluorspar.

Granite complex. Massive, medium- to coarse-grained, and porphyritic granite, granite gneiss, and large xenoliths of partly digested (granitized) meta-sediments

Intrusive scapolitized diorite. Possibly related to other basic igneous activity in basal Corella beds

FIG. 7.3. Diagrammatic cross section of the Mary Kathleen area, Mount Isa–Cloncurry district, Queensland, Australia (Matheson and Searl, 1956; *Econ. Geol.*).

deposit occurs between two steeply dipping north-trending shears on the west flank of a north-south syncline, overturned to the east. The Corella beds, which consist of interlayered quartzites, impure marbles, siliceous and calcareous granulites, and some mafic igneous rocks, are cut by quartz-feldspar porphyry apophyses, quartz veins, and postgranite diabase dikes.

The mineralized rock is a mushroom-shaped mass formed by garnetization of diopside granulite and some breccia-conglomerate along the contact of impure marble (west) and breccia-conglomerate (east). The main ore body is an irregular unit, as much as 450 ft across, with mineralization controlled by joints. Typical ore contains allanite replacing garnet-diopside-apatite rock, with abundant minute grains of pitchblende disseminated through the allanite and locally sulfides and rare-earth minerals such as stillwellite, caryocerite, and rinkite. Pyrite, pyrrhotite, and chalcopyrite occur widely disseminated and also as irregular masses. Molybdenite and galena are rare.

Oxidation is strong to 50 ft resulting in gummite, uranophane, and betauranophane, and continues partly to 120 ft. Below 120 ft the uraninite grains have primary halos of "amorphous silica," fluorite, apatite, calcite, pyrite, or arrojadite. The allanite itself is not substantially radioactive.

The deposit is regarded as having been formed by replacement at high temperature by solutions derived from the granitic masses (Matheson and Searl, 1956).

Similar deposits occur at the south end of the Mary Kathleen syncline, the Elaine Dorothy, and 2½ mi southeast on the Rita leases.

Metasomatic Monazite Deposits

Monazite deposits of an unusual type occur in an area just north of the Salmon River between North Fork and Shoup, Idaho, in northern Lemhi County. They consist of monazite-bearing carbonate layers in micaceous schists and gneisses of Beltian age (late Precambrian), cut by rhyolitic and pegmatitic dikes. Some of the latter contain minor monazite, allanite, and thorite(?). Barren quartz veins also penetrate some layers. The gneissic complex, previously mapped as granite of the Idaho batholith, may represent an injected border zone (Trites and Tooker, 1953). Carbonate lenses occur in at least three horizons that trend generally northwest and usually dip at moderate to steep angles southwest. They consist of calcite in places stained by hematite, and locally also of actinolite, barite, siderite, pyrite, magnetite, ilmenorutile, garnet, zoisite, apatite, and monazite. Some layers are offset by faults for a few tens of feet, and larger offsets may explain their discontinuity (Abbott, 1954).

Honey-colored monazite occurs as fine to coarse porphyroblastic crystals and aggregates and as irregular masses. Concentrations are in zones 1½ to 6 ft thick, some of which are at least 300 ft long. Microscopically the thorium-low monazite appears as subhedra to euhedra replacing calcite and actinolite, apparently one of the latest minerals to crystallize. Abbott (1954) has suggested that clastic monazite, originally deposited in the associated arenaceous Belt sediments, was decomposed during metamorphism, with migration of liberated rare-earth and thorium ions to the carbonate layers where they were reconstituted to monazite. It seems more likely, however, that in view of the presence of the typical assemblage of the silicates actinolite, garnet, zoisite, of the oxides magnetite, specularite, and ilmenorutile, and also of pyrite and barite, that the deposits are metasomatic in origin. New data indicate they probably are veins similar to those to the north in Montana (page 241).

Radioactive Magnetite Deposits

Uranium, usually as uraninite but locally as uranothorite, has been found in several occurrences south from the western Adirondacks to North Carolina (Walthier, 1955). The radioactive zones, which show a slight preference for the footwall section of magnetite ore, are stained red by hematite, and occur usually in gneiss. In one deposit bordering magnetite ore, uraninite is confined to chlorite-hornblende-magnetite layers in drag-folded gneiss and is concentrated as pencil-shaped shoots of good grade, several feet across along axial parts of the folds parallel to the regional plunge.

Uraninite is associated with pyrite in low-grade magnetite ore along the footwall contact between magnetite lenses and granite at the Miles Standish mine near Warwick, New York.

At the Phillips pyrite mine, Putnam County, New York, uraninite is associated with magnetite and hornblende in a basic pegmatite that passes through a footwall ore zone consisting of pyrrhotite, pyrite, magnetite, and a little chalcopyrite in a hornblende-pyroxene-feldspar gangue.

Rare-earth-bearing apatite containing 0.15% ThO_2 and 0.32% U_3O_8 occurs in magnetite ore at the Old Bed and Smith mines, Mineville, New York (McKeown and Klemic, 1953, 1956; McKelvey, 1955). Fine-grained monazite, bastnaesite, and hematite rim and vein some apatite.

Irregular bodies of quartz-hematite-magnetite-feldspar rock containing doverite (Smith et al., 1955), xenotime, bastnaesite, leucoxene, and lesser amounts of zircon, sphene, chevkinite, and monazite occur associated with Precambrian magnetite ore bodies at the Scrub Oaks mine, Morris County, New Jersey. The doverite contains 1.62% ThO_2 and the rare-earth ore contains 0.009% U and 0.062% Th.

Radioactive hydrocarbon-uraninite complexes (thucolite) were discovered many years ago in several iron-rich skarn deposits in Sweden (Davidson and Bowie, 1951). Thucolite occurs at Norberg and Dannemora (ash averages 3% U_3O_8), at the Eriks mine (12% ash with 0.8% U_3O_8, and at the Lilla Kallmore mine (13% ash with 7% U_3O_8).

Some radioactivity has been detected in ferruginous metamorphic rocks in the Paroo Creek area, north of Mount Isa, Queensland, where appreciable radioactivity was noted in Precambrian magnetite quartzites at several localities (Connah, 1954).

The contact metamorphic magnetite deposit at Schmiedeberg, Germany, also contains uraninite and has been cited as an example of a pyrometasomatic uraninite deposit (Palache et al., 1944). However, the uraninite occurs where younger veins intersect massive magnetite ore along a sedimentary-granite contact (Bain, 1950).

Lone Mountain Deposit, New Mexico

A uraniferous pyrometasomatic magnetite-hematite deposit in Permian sedimentary rocks near the margin of the Lone Mountain monzonite stock of Laramide age, 11.5 mi N. 30° E. of Carrizozo, Lincoln County, New Mexico, contains 0.015 to 0.031% U (Walker and Osterwald, 1956B). The ore consists chiefly of magnetite, with lesser hematite, pyrite, chalcopyrite, sphalerite, covellite, quartz, chlorite, marcasite, gypsum, hydrated iron oxides, metatorbernite, torbernite(?), and an unidentified uranium mineral. The deposit, a tabular mass 100 ft long, up to 6 ft thick, and parallel to the bedding, was formed by replacement of a limestone bed in a section consisting largely of rock gypsum. Adjacent to it is an aureole, up to 6 ft thick, of marmorized limestone, gypsum, epidote, actinolite, and minor specularite, pyrite, chalcopyrite, phlogopite, and fluorite. Most of the uranium (exclusive of the secondary uranium minerals) is dispersed in the iron oxide minerals—rather uniformly in magnetite, locally in hematite.

The deposit is considered by Walker and Osterwald (1956B) to be relatively low-temperature (300 to 500°C or slightly higher), metasomatic in origin, with uranium, in part formed in magnetite as a coprecipitate during coagulation of a hydrosol of ferrous hydroxide in a mildly alkaline environment. The criteria and reasoning for such an origin have been shown to be dubious and inconsistent (Krauskopf, 1956).

Radioactive Molybdenite Deposits

At Azegour in the Haut-Atlas of Guedmioua, Morocco, uraninite, which is closely associated with hematite, occurs in a molybdenite-bearing garnet-rich tactite (Von der Weid, 1941; Permingeat, 1952A,B). The gangue minerals are calcite, dolomite, ankerite, garnet, wollastonite, vesuvianite, actinolite, chlorite, quartz, fluorite, and some barite. The ore assemblage also includes pyrrhotite, pyrite, chalcopyrite, marcasite, a little hematite, scheelite, and minor magnetite (after hematite), native bismuth, linnaeite, niccolite, tetrahedrite, galena, and sphalerite. Uraninite lies between garnet grains, and locally in the interior of molybdenite crystals. It is replaced by pyrite and subordinate sphalerite (Ramdohr, 1955A).

At the Bou-Azzer deposit at Tichka, southern Morocco, anhedral grains of brannerite a few millimeters across occur with gray quartz with molybdenite, other sulfides, calcite, and clay minerals (Jouravski, 1952; Pabst, 1954). Cobalt minerals also are known. The molybdenite deposits of Tichka, which also contain bismuthinite, pyrite, tetrahedrite, chalcopyrite, and galena, occur in association with garnetiferous skarns, marginal to a granitic intrusive, and thus resemble in many ways the molybdenite deposits of Azegour.

Uranium mineralization, probably as uraninite, occurs with copper, molybdenum, and some gold at the Larap deposits of the Philippine iron mines in the Paracale-Mambulao district, Camarines Norte, Philippine Islands (Clemente and Reyes, 1956). Although the distribution of the uranium appears to be somewhat irregular, some assays as high as 1.5% U_3O_8 have been reported. The ore contains magnetite, molybdenite, chalcopyrite, pyrite, apatite, and mica.

Uraninite-Copper Deposits

Bisbee, Arizona

Uraninite occurs in the Copper Queen block of the Bisbee, Arizona, porphyry copper deposits. This is made up of Precambrian rocks, Paleozoic sediments, and the Sacramento Hill rhyolite porphyry which was emplaced prior to deposition of Lower Cretaceous strata and altered and mineralized after deposition of these strata (Bain, 1952). The uraninite is localized along slip planes that are part of a fracture-shear system related to the Dividend fault which bounds the Copper Queen block on the north. Hematite flakelets and quartz crystals accompany the micron-sized cubes of uraninite, which is the oldest mineral to form, followed successively by a pyritic phase, a galena-sphalerite phase, a quartz-carbonate phase, and, last, a copper sulfide phase. The uraninite has an age of 104 ± 6 m.y., corresponding to the end of the Lower Cretaceous. The deposit has been placed in the pyrometasomatic group by Lindgren (1933).

Moonta-Wallaroo District, South Australia

The Moonta-Wallaroo copper district, on the east shore of Spencer Gulf, South Australia, was discovered in 1860; and its radioactive hydrocarbon complex was found in 1906 (Radcliff, 1906). A Precambrian complex is successively overlain by Cambrian conglomerates and limestones and by Tertiary limestones. The schists and phyllites are cut by mafic and felsic dikes and by later Precambrian granite and its pegmatites. The replacement lodes, localized along shear zones, strike south of east, dipping steeply. Some are several thousand feet long and were mined to depths of several thousand feet. They were oxidized to 150 ft, and beneath the oxidized zone showed secondary sulfide enrichment. The ores consist of chalcopyrite, bornite, and pyrrhotite with traces of galena, sphalerite, ferberite, and scheelite. Gangue constituents are quartz, carbonate, apatite, fluorite, tourmaline, amphibole, pyroxene, scapolite, and the hydrocarbon compound.

Mawson (1944) states the hydrocarbon occurred chiefly in lodes across the main bornite ore bodies at several levels, accompanied by smoky quartz. Relatively large amounts were removed and burned. The complex is light gray in reflected light and sooty to pitchy black in hand specimens, which are traversed by irregular fractures. Specimens assay from 0.9 to 5.0% eU_3O_8. According to Davidson and Bowie (1951), the hydrocarbon is isotropic, nonpleochroic, and the radioactive constituent (probably pitchblende) forms discrete inclusions less than 1 μ in size, closely associated with slightly larger inclusions of covellite and chalcopyrite. Inclusions of arsenopyrite, pyrite, and especially bornite are also present. Some of the bornite appears to replace hydrocarbon. Radiometric analysis of 348 bore samples from the Moonta tailings dumps assayed between 0.03 and 0.05% U_3O_8 lb/ton.

Lindgren (1933) has classed the deposit as being of liquid magmatic origin, but more likely it is pyrometasomatic, from its structure and mineral assemblage.

Oxidized Contact Deposits

The oxidized contact deposits of the Mount Spokane area, Washington (pages 534–536), occur in shear zones along a granodiorite contact, but their primary phases are so poorly known that an exact genetic designation is not yet possible. They may be contact deposits in their position without being pyrometasomatic.

Near the southern edge of the Reese River district, 3 mi south of Austin, Lander County, Nevada, uranium mineralization occurs along fractures and faults in both a Jurassic(?) quartz monzonite body and host Cambro-Silurian low-grade metasediments, near their contacts (Thurlow, 1956A). Roof pendants near the contact contain disseminated mineralization. The fracture zones, which trend east-west and are vertical or dip 50° N., contain chiefly quartz and sericite with minor Au, Ag, Cu, and Fe minerals. Uranium occurs in autunite and metatorbernite. The veins form conspicuous reef outcrops in the intrusive, but are inconspicuous in the metasediments, which are mainly quartzite and phyllites and subordinate hornfels and silicified limestone. The highest concentration of uranium minerals occurs in a fracture zone in metasediments near the contact.

On Boulder Creek near Deer Lodge in Granite County, Montana, uranium values up to 0.06% U_3O_8 have been obtained from skarn and graphitic shale near the Brooklyn mine, formerly a small Zn-Pb-Cu-Ag producer from ores in limestone garnetized at the contact of a porphyry dike.

At Brooks Mountain, Seward Peninsula, Alaska, metazeunerite occurs in a contact deposit in the marginal parts of altered granite with hematite, pyrrhotite, arsenopyrite, scheelite, cassiterite, bismuthinite, tetrahedrite, chalcopyrite, fluorite, calcite, and siderite. It appears as disseminated flakes along joints in bright red hematite in altered, vuggy pegmatitic granite in quartz-tourmaline veins (West and White, 1952). Bordering the granite is a nonradioactive tactite zone in marmorized limestone characterized by Ca and Mg silicates, sulfides of Fe and Cu, Fe oxides, and B, Sn, and W minerals.

HYPOTHERMAL DEPOSITS

In hypothermal deposits, uranium and thorium are closely associated, appearing in the minerals davidite, brannerite, and thorian uraninite. Ilmenite, hematite, magnetite, molybdenite, and pyrite are relatively common metallic associates; huebnerite, arsenopyrite, cobaltite, and cassiterite have been found in some examples. The gangue usually consists in large part of high-temperature silicate assemblages.

A unique radioactive deposit, classified by Lang (1952) as a diorite pegmatite, occurs at the Rex group, on the south shore of Stark Lake, 130 mi east of Yellowknife. Six deposits fill steeply dipping north and northwest fractures in a diorite stock. The dominant mineral is coarse, fibrous actinolite with lesser calcite, magnetite, apatite, fluorite, and uraninite. This assemblage does not represent a dioritic pegmatite but possibly a high-temperature hydrothermal deposit.

Criteria for distinguishing between hypothermal and pyrometasomatic deposits are not always sharply defined, and the nature of the host rock may be a more important factor than the *P-T* environment in some cases.

Davidite Veins

South Australia

The Radium Hill deposits, 60 mi southwest of Broken Hill, which were found in 1906, were worked intermittently for Ra until 1915, yielding 350 mg of $RaBr_2$ from 95 tons of concentrates. A complete exploration program began in 1944, and by 1954 the mine was prepared for full-scale production.

The mineralization occurs along fractures in Archean metasediments and igneous rocks a mile or more east of the major McDonald Hill fault (Parkin and Glasson, 1954). The locally extensively granitized gneisses and quartzites were intruded by (1) an early sill of somewhat metamorphosed amphibolite, (2) a later transgressive amphibolite, and (3) several types of pegmatite of which a sodic aplitic variety may be genetically related to ore deposition. In the gneisses, folds with steeply dipping limbs have east-northeast axial directions and pitch usually at a low angle.

The main lodes, which are slightly arcuate in plan, are along fractures and faults on the southeast limb and near the axis of a flat-pitching anticline. They strike in two main directions, N. 57° E. and N. 47° E., with dips ranging from 30 to 70° SE. for the first set, and from vertical to steep for the second. These directions correspond to axial plane cleavage and bedding foliation in the metasediments. Three major and five smaller lodes have been found, as well as many other minor occurrences. The smaller occur to the southeast along the axial zones of drag folds. The three main lodes are 100 ft apart, extending along the strike for several thousand feet.

The typical lode begins as a sericitic shear in banded gneiss along which biotite-quartz augen are segregated. Next appear scattered clusters of iron and titanium minerals, with or without uranium, in the form of ilmenite, rutile, and hematite (nodular or spotted ore). Where initial fracturing or brecciation was more intense the lodes are thicker and better developed as coarse-grained intergrowths of bronze biotite, pinkish quartz, ilmenite, rutile, hematite, and davidite. Davidite is concentrated mainly centrally within or about the thicker parts. Some secondary carnotite appears along fractures and grain boundaries. In one variant the rock is intensely silicified, biotite is essentially absent, and davidite is much more variable in distribution.

At splits, one branch may develop rich ore, whereas the other remains low grade. Splitting, narrowing, and variation in uranium values are closely related to premineral vertical transcurrent (strike slip?) faults that have disturbed the channelways, cutting them obliquely. The channels also are cut at nearly right angles by normal faults that dip about 45°.

The mineralization is younger than most igneous activity and is regarded as developing in the stages:

1. Replacement of sericitic shear rock along overthrust fault lines by quartz-biotite-hematite-ilmenite mineralization
2. Intrusion of rare-earth pegmatites (salmon-pink and glassy-white feldspar) containing allanite and xenotime
3. Movement along the shears causing brecciation of the pegmatites and their biotization
4. Intrusion of amphibolites along faults
5. Introduction of clear quartz stringers containing davidite together with formation of irregular bright red feldspar replacements. Davidite also developed extensive intergrowth with the earlier ilmenite-hematite complexes

By the lead isotope method the davidite is 1,730 m.y. old.

Davidite veins also have been discovered at Houghton and in the Crockers Well area, where discoveries at Mount Victoria have been proved to justify mining. Allanite occurs with davidite at the Victoria Hut prospect.

Mozambique

Davidite has been found at numerous localities over about 300 sq mi in the Mavuzi district, 20 to 50 km north of Tete, Mozambique (Davidson and Bennett, 1950; Bannister and Horne, 1950; Kerr and Holland, 1951; Coelho, 1954). The discovery site is on the Mavuzi River, a tributary of the Zambezi. The sequence of rock units is:

1. Precambrian(?) gneisses, schists, marbles, and granites
2. Noritic gabbro. An intrusive body 80 × 30 mi
3. Basic dikes along north-trending shears in 2
4. Syenite dikes, granite pegmatite, and quartz veins transecting 2
5. Karoo sediments overlying 1 to 4
6. East-west mafic dikes of Tertiary(?) age

According to Cavaca (1956) the syenite-granite intrusives (4) are probably Tertiary in age. The norite varies greatly in grain size. Some coarse anorthositic phases are present; other parts have been intensively sheared and metasomatically altered to epidiorite. Roof pendants of marble and schist are enclosed.

The mineralization is in the main intimately associated with shear zones, the largest of which (at Mavuzi) is about ½ mi long and 5 to over 40 ft wide. Along these shears the fine-grained norite has been converted to gneissic epidiorites commonly showing augen structure, in which feldspar has been extensively scapolitized, and the coarser norite converted to streaked hornblende gneisses (Fig. 7.4). Davidite is associated with three distinctive types of gangue:

1. Scapolite-calcite type, the commonest type at the Mavuzi mine. The minerals are early, massive white quartz in veins 2 to 3 ft wide; scapolite in bands up to 2 × 50 ft; diopside which may surround quartz masses as reaction rims; calcite-dolomite in bodies up to 50 ft long and 3 ft wide; pyrite, pyrrhotite, chalcopyrite, molybdenite, rutile, sphene, magnetite, davidite, ilmenite, golden-brown apatite, and traces of siderite and tourmaline. Davidite in scapolite is enclosed in a halo of red color. Postmineralization movements have sheared scapolite, plastically deformed calcite, oriented molybdenite flakes, and shattered rutile and davidite. Postshearing veinlets of quartz cut earlier minerals.

2. Pyroxene type. Davidite occurs in coarse-grained lenses, some tens of feet long and a few feet wide, consisting of predominant diopside, in crystals

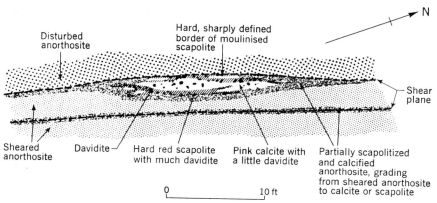

FIG. 7.4. Map of typical shear zone in anorthosite, mineralized with davidite, scapolite, and calcite, Mavuzi, Tete, Mozambique (Davidson and Bennett, 1950; *Mineral. Mag.*).

an inch to a foot across, granular to prismatic pink scapolite, and veinlets of vermiculite. These lenses are in a metasomatic aureole of scapolite and hornblende with minor biotite, apatite, and tourmaline. Locally quartz and calcite appear, indicating transitions to type 1.

3. Fine-grained plagioclase-calcite type. Davidite occurs in calcite which is minutely intergrown with sodic plagioclase, the aggregate forming veins up to a foot wide and usually less than 20 ft long in scapolitized norite. The larger bodies contain considerable calcite; albite predominates in the smaller. Quartz and tourmaline are accessories.

At Mavuzi, 53 tons of hand-cobbed davidite, many individual crystals of which exceeded a foot in diameter, were obtained from a small open cut, but ore at the 100-ft level underground proved noneconomic. The ore assayed from 7.5 to 8% U_3O_8. This occurrence was the richest found. The numerous others are smaller, with patchy distribution of davidite. At Matema allanite is abundant. Other occurrences of note are at Inhatobue, Nhaondue, Catipo, and Capangula.

The deposits have been characterized variously as magmatic (segregation) or as late magmatic replacements. They are epigenetic and hydrothermal, formed at high temperatures. They were formed during the latter stages of a period of shearing that followed emplacement and complete solidification of the noritic mass. McKelvey et al. (1955) suggest a genetic relationship to the gabbroic intrusive, similar to ilmenite deposits associated with anorthosite. However, the presence of uranium and thorium in davidite, of molybdenite, tourmaline and very abundant quartz in several generations, argues strongly against a derivation of the ore solutions from the noritic magma. Some of the carbonate masses may represent metasomatized marble xenoliths. In some places the norite is cut by syenitic and pegmatitic dikes, the latter in some places injected lit-par-lit into the sheared epidioritic norite. Davidson (1949) believes that the mineralization has been introduced into the basic rocks "by gaseous emanations" from underlying granites. The crude Pb-U age is 565 m.y., which is roughly the age of the Katanga mineralization.

India

In the uranium belt of the tightly folded zone of the Aravalli range in northern Rajputana, a uranium titanate of brannerite-davidite affinities occurs with copper minerals in Archean phyllites and younger schists and coarse granite (Wadia, 1956). The grade ranges from 0.04 to 0.46% (U?).

Brannerite Deposits

United States

Brannerite forms small prismatic crystals at the California mine, a high-temperature quartzose vein once mined for molybdenite, south of Mount Antero, Chaffee County, Colorado (Adams, 1953). The locally vuggy vein, which cuts the Pomeroy quartz monzonite stock, contains quartz, molybdenite, beryl, pyrite, huebnerite(?), tourmaline, fluorite, rutile, sericite, and secondary molybdite. It is 1½ to 3 ft thick, strikes N. 72 to 75° E., is nearly vertical, and has a probable length of 1,000 ft. It is genetically related to Tertiary pegmatites in granite on and around Mount Antero and White Mountain that contains beryl, phenakite, bertrandite, fluorite, topaz, and other minerals, some occurring as fine crystals in miarolitic cavities.

Tests on vacuoles in beryl and fluorite with the assumption of a formational cover of 10 km indicate that beryl crystallized at about 315°C close to the lower limit of Lindgren's (1933) hypothermal range, and the beryl tested was of the late-stage type from a vug.

Brannerite occurs as slender prisms in minor amounts in quartz veins ¼ in. to 1½ ft thick that traverse late Mesozoic quartz monzonite along closely spaced subparallel sheeting joints in the canyon of the West Walker River, 7 mi south of Coleville, Mono County, California (Pabst, 1954). The vein material is 95% massive milky quartz, with minor smoky quartz, clear quartz crystals, muscovite, magnetite, pyrite, chalcopyrite, calcite and trace amounts of biotite, orthoclase, epidote, hornblende, garnet, tourmaline, zeolites, molybdenite, and bismuthinite. Although the veins are said to be mesothermal, the silicate-mineral assemblage, the presence of molybdenite and bismuthinite, and the genetic relation to nearby pegmatites and aplite which have the same accessory suite also along sheeting joints, indicate that they are probably hypothermal.

Hewett et al. (1957) have described an unusual occurrence of brannerite in the San Bernardino Mountains, San Bernardino County, California. The mineral occurs as lenticular or roughly spherical nodules in a granite gneiss (Precambrian?). The smaller nodules (1 to 20 g) are sheathed in biotite and generally lie along the foliation. The larger (up to 200 g) are along thin shear zones across the foliation which also contain rutile, biotite, and sodic plagioclase. Brannerite replaces biotite.

France

In the molybdenite deposit of Château-Lambert (Haute-Saône), Vosges, France, brannerite occurs as uncommon, thin prismatic crystals, 2 to 3 cm long, that are fractured and healed by quartz (Branche et al., 1951). It appears in grayish-white vein quartz of a greasy luster, commonly covered by brown ferruginous coating. Near the surface it is altered to a soft, fine-grained, white to light yellow material, probably anatase. It is accompanied by cubo-octahedral crystals of uraninite, 0.2 mm across. The presence of the modifying octahedral faces probably indicates low-thorium uraninite.

The deposit consists of two veins in pegmatites, striking northwest and west-northwest, cutting a dioritic endomorphic facies of the Ballon granite (Geffroy and Sarcia, 1954). The mineralization, which included alteration of the pegmatitic feldspar to sericite and biotite to chlorite, consists of two phases:

1. Molybdenite, quartz, feldspar, brannerite
2. Chalcopyrite, pyrite, bornite, tetrahedrite, fine-grained quartz, uraninite

Some scheelite also is present.

Australia

A thorian brannerite with nearly 13% ThO_2 ("absite") occurs as irregular grains and narrow veinlets replacing late Precambrian quartz monzonite and granodiorite along a breccia zone at Crockers Well, South Australia, west of Radium Hill. Rutile-bearing quartz veins contain brannerite crystals 5 to 10 cm across.

Deposits 20 mi north of Mount Isa, Queensland, consist of brannerite disseminated in carbonate beds and lenses.

Blind River, Ontario

General

One of the most important uranium districts of the world in terms of future production and reserves is the Blind River area (Algoma district) in Ontario, on the north side of the north channel of Lake Huron, about halfway between Sudbury and Sault Sainte Marie. In Canada the district, which measures about 30×40 mi, is second only to the Lake Athabasca region in its economic significance. Although the ores are generally of low grade, the location of the area and the low acid consumption in ore treatment help to reduce production costs. Radioactivity was discovered in the area in 1949, but assays proved disappointing. Credit for opening the district belongs to Franc R. Joubin, who determined through drilling that, although surface values were low, large tonnages of mineable rock existed below the leached outcrops, and who in four weeks during the summer of 1953 directed a secret, wholesale claim-staking operation that was climaxed on July 11, 1953, with the recording of about 1,400 claims. The boom thus begun exploded in the staking of an additional 8,000 claims. About 50 companies are actively interested in the area and by June, 1955, about 50 diamond drills were at work. At the same time, mill construction was in progress on four properties, with total capacity of 12,500 tons/day. By the end of 1955 indicated reserves of ore had mounted to 50 million tons, and the estimated potential for the district had reached 300 million tons. In 1958, 11 mines will be delivering more than 34,000 tons/day.

Geology

The chief geological units of the district are (Collins, 1925; Abraham, 1953):

3. Intrusives

   Diabase, gabbro, and diorite (Keweenawan). Diabase dikes near the Nordic deposit are postore. Granitic rocks of the Killarney type intrude all rock types except olivine diabase dikes. The Cutler granite batholith which crops out on Lake Huron south of the Pronto mine is the largest younger intrusive recognized

2. Huronian metasediments, weakly metamorphosed

   f. Lorrain quartzite

   e. Gowganda formation, conglomerate, quartzite, graywacke, unconformity(?)

   d. Serpent quartzite, impure quartzite, 1,100 ft thick

    c. Espanola formation, limestones and graywackes, 500 to 900 ft thick. Lowest member is the Bruce limestone

    b. Bruce conglomerate, 50 ft thick

    a. Mississagi quartzite formation, 750 to 4,500 ft thick, commonly 1,500 to 3,500 ft thick. South of the Murray fault it thickens to about 12,000 ft (Units *a* to *d* were assigned by Collins to the Bruce series, *e* to *f* to the Cobalt series)

1. Pre-Huronian basement complex of

    b. Granite and granite gneiss with

    a. Greenschist, diabase, and gabbro xenoliths

    The ore-bearing formation is the Mississagi, consisting of quartzite, arkose, graywacke, argillite, boulder conglomerate, and quartz-pebble conglomerate. In some parts of the area a threefold subdivision of the formation is useful: (*c*) upper quartzite, (*b*) intermediate graywacke-argillite, 100 to 800 ft, (*a*) lower quartzite, 0 to 1,300 ft. The chief mineralized rock is the fluvatile quartz-pebble conglomerate (McDowell, 1957), although some mineralization is in a red arkosic quartzite where the conglomerate is absent, and some is in the regolith or transition zone along the unconformity between pre-Huronian and Mississagi. A boulder conglomerate consisting of boulders and cobbles of quartz, granite, gneiss, and greenstone in a graywacke matrix commonly lies along the pre-Huronian contact. Where the lowest unit (*a*) is thin, quartz-pebble conglomerates can occur at any horizon within it, as in the Quirke Lake trough where two or more beds occur from 50 to 100 ft above the unconformity; where this member is thick, the conglomerates are restricted to the basal 100 ft.

    Figures on ore reserves have been increasing each year since exploration began: late 1955, 30 million tons; 1956, in excess of 100 million tons; 1957 for the Quirke Lake—Elliot Lake zones alone (Roscoe, 1957), 320 million tons. The average grade of the ore bodies ranges from 0.07 to 0.133% U_3O_8.

    The Mississagi quartzite has been folded into a reversed S, facing west, with an outcrop length of over 80 mi. The northern limb dips 25 to 30° S.; the intermediate limb dips 16° N.; and the southern rim dips 10 to 16° S. The northern syncline (Quirke Lake trough) plunges west at about 5°, and the southern anticline (Otter-Montgomery anticline) also plunges westward (Joubin, 1955A,B; Young et al., 1955; Holmes, 1956) (Fig. 7.5).

    Some faulting has affected the Mississagi formation, particularly those parts that were deposited on the undulating peneplain overlying hard massive granitic rocks rather than soft schistose xenoliths where most of the ore bodies occur. Some transverse faults (Webbwood and Montgomery) cross the middle limb, and the north limb has been cut by a zone of strike faults (Quirke fault) probably of reverse nature between Whiskey and Quirke Lakes (Joubin, 1954). The faulting and fracturing are largely postore, although near Magog Lake radioactivity has been detected adjacent to shear zones, and in one place fault-zone breccia is mineralized (Joubin and James, 1956A). The major structure is truncated on the south by the Murray fault, and as the southern anticlinal limb of the Mississagi approaches the fault its dip steepens to vertical. South

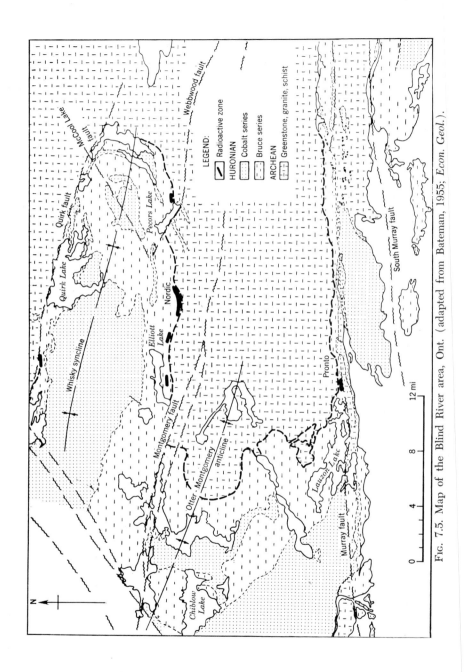

Fig. 7.5. Map of the Blind River area, Ont. (adapted from Bateman, 1955; *Econ. Geol.*).

260

of the fault the formation dips steeply northward, indicating that the fault has intersected a tight anticline.

Mineralization

The conglomerate beds are 5 to 25 ft thick, may be more than 7,000 ft long, and are known to extend down dip for more than 6,000 ft. They occur singly or in series separated by strata of arkose. The range in constituents of the mineralized conglomerate is:

$$
\begin{array}{ll}
\text{Quartz pebbles} \dots\dots\dots\dots & 40\text{--}65\% \\
\text{Sulfides (mainly pyrite)} \dots & 2\text{--}8\% \ (\text{locally } 25\%) \\
\text{Sericite-chlorite} \dots\dots\dots & 5\text{--}20\% \\
\text{Matrix quartz} \dots\dots\dots\dots & 15\text{--}25\%
\end{array}
$$

The pebbles, which are rather uniform in size, measuring 1 to 1¾ in. across, consist of white to gray glassy quartz (95%), pink to buff quartz, gray to black chert, jasper, quartzite, and, in the basal conglomerates, a few fragments of underlying rocks. Cross-bedding is common; normal bedding ranges from thick to thin to absent; coarse grains are more rounded than nearby fine ones. Such features indicate that the conglomerates were oligomictic shallow-water gravels deposited above the lower limit of wave action along beaches, bays, and bars.

The matrix consists chiefly of (1) quartz, sericite, chlorite, and pyrite; (2)

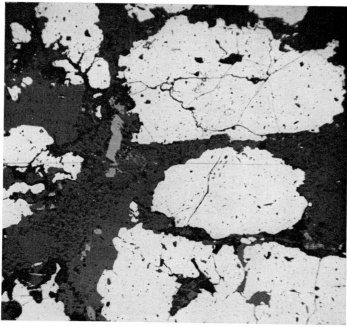

Fig. 7.6. Anhedral pyrite (white), and uraninite (medium gray) in quartz-sericite gangue (dark), Mississagi conglomerate, Pronto deposit, Blind River, Ont. Reflected light (×44).

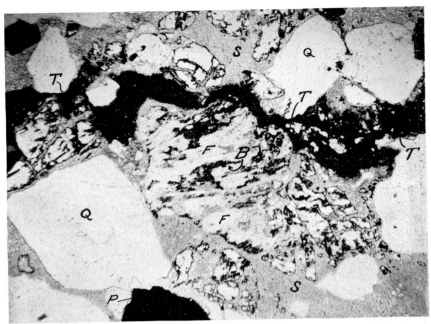

Fig. 7.7. Radioactive ore, Pronto, Blind River, Ont. Grains of quartz (Q), altered feldspar (F), and pyrite (P) in sericitic matrix (S), cut by thucolite veinlet (T) and containing brannerite and uraninite. Brannerite needles (B) replace feldspar (×35).

the radioactive minerals brannerite (Nuffield, 1950), monazite, uraninite, and thucolite; (3) other sulfides including pyrrhotite, molybdenite, cobaltite, chalcopyrite, galena, sphalerite, and marcasite; and (4) other minerals—gold, hematite, rutile, anatase, titanian magnetite, zircon, feldspar, and scheelite. Pyrite is euhedral, anhedral, or fills fractures in the quartz pebbles (Fig. 7.6). Gold values are low and erratic, 0.02 to 0.03 oz/ton. All the radioactive minerals except two reported pitchblende stringers occur as discrete grains, averaging 100 μ in diameter, many angular, with some uraninite fragments fitting together as jigsaw puzzle pieces, recemented by younger sericitic matrix (Traill, 1954). Some sooty pitchblende also occurs, but all uraninite specimens tested by the Canadian Geological Survey (Robinson, 1955B) contain thorium, between 6 and 10% (Traill, 1954). The relative abundance of radioactive minerals varies widely, brannerite predominating in most areas, pitchblende or monazite in some others (Fig. 7.7). The angular to subrounded brannerite grains are largely altered, rimmed, or impregnated by secondary anatase and thorogummite.[1] The alteration mixture has undergone enrichment of Th relative to U. The ores contain rare earths, especially yttrium in significant amounts, and Er, Gd, Nd, Ce, Sm, Dy, and La also have been detected. Some of the uraninite euhedra have cores replaced by quartz. Ore matrix material rich in

[1] Strong heating in the absence of air produces the brannerite pattern.

sericite usually also has high uranium values. High uranium values occur in matrix rich in pyrite, but pyrite-rich matrix is not necessarily rich in uranium. There is no variation in values correlatable with folds, faults, or metamorphic intensity. The thicker and more radioactive parts of the conglomerate occur in a north-south zone in which a series of northwesterly trending belts may have been localized along channels in the pre-Huronian surface scoured in softer greenstone.

Lesser but important radioactive mineralization also occurs in two finer-grained rocks—a gray feldspathic quartzite ("grit") and in red albitite.

The grits are gray, dark green, and black, relatively fine grained rocks with scattered larger angular quartz and feldspar particles as much as ¼ in. across. In some hand specimens, irregular tongues of reddish-brown material are present. The radioactivity apparently stems from an unidentified earthy pale yellow mineral, widely disseminated in minute anhedra.

Microscopically the rock shows such extensive sericitization that its original nature is difficult to determine. It consists chiefly of fine-grained sericite which includes relict patches of (1) detrital quartz aggregates and (2) aggregates of interlocking subhedral albite crystals with minor quartz. Intergrown with the sericite is a subordinate amount of biotite (pleochroic pale buff to light brown) in somewhat coarser flakes.

The entire aggregate is cut by veinlets of (1) albite and quartz, (2) sericite, (3) sericite and biotite, and (4) carbonate. The sequence of mineral formation is:

1. Detrital quartz, feldspar, trace zircon
2. Albitization, some general, some in veinlets with minor quartz
3. Extensive general sericitization especially inward from grain contacts, along with minor biotite formation. Some sericite veins with comb structure and central biotite. Some biotite is later than the sericite
4. Formation of carbonate veinlets

The radioactive mineral is found in semitranslucent aggregates of irregular outline and variable size. Some of it is closely intergrown with hematite-limonite. It appears white to yellowish white in reflected light (leucoxene?). Pyrite is not present, but some small black opaque grains may be uraninite.

The red albitite is aplitic in texture and locally markedly sheared, with the development of considerable chloritic material and local quartz and calcite along the shear planes. Quartz is not conspicuous megascopically. Under the microscope the rock is seen to consist of an interlocking aggregate of 90 to 95% albite (Ab 91) in subhedra and euhedra of variable grain size. Euhedral apatite is a minor accessory. Quartz is subordinate to absent. Sericitization is minor, but the mica is present as grain-boundary replacements, and with chlorite and hematite as thin ramifying veinlets and larger irregular patches. Hematite is abundant as clusters of coarse plates and grains, and throughout the feldspar as tiny, uniformly distributed specks. Pyrite is absent. The rocks resemble closely in many ways the hydrothermal hematitic oligoclasite commonly associated with many pitchblende deposits in the Goldfields region, Saskatchewan

(Conybeare and Campbell, 1951). The radioactive mineral is similar to that in the gray grits.

The albitites occur above the basal grits, occupying the stratigraphic position normally taken by the radioactive conglomerates. They grade up into normal green quartzite, and their color is most intense at the base. Radioactivity in general increases with intensity of red coloration. The zone ranges from several inches to 14 ft thick.

Ore bodies are large: the Quirke body is 7,000 ft long and known to extend down dip 3,400 ft; the Nordic body measures 4,000 ft in length and 2,200 ft down dip. Many average about 10 ft thick, ranging from 7 to 40 ft. U_3O_8 ranges from 2.0 to 2.5 lb/ton or 0.11 to 0.16%, locally as high as 2.5%. The ore body at Pater Uranium also contains 1.53% Cu and 0.11% Co. At Nordic Lake a drill hole to 2,000 ft intersected 6.5 ft of conglomerate averaging 0.08% U_3O_8, including a 3-ft layer, with 0.12% U_3O_8. Exploration has been extended to 4,200 ft, and to the west the ore horizons will be deeper than 5,500 ft.

The abundance of pyrite in the ore has yielded much H_2SO_4 under weathering, and outcrops have been leached of uranium values to depths of 70 ft.

Joubin (1954) has pointed out that, although the ores are strikingly uniform, a few regional variations are apparent:

1. A gradual increase in pyrrhotite and a decrease in pyrite from the south through the middle, to the north limbs
2. A slight increase in Th from the south, through the middle to the north limbs
3. The appearance of trace amounts of Mo, Co, and Ni, and of U in thucolite in north-limb ores

Origin

Minerals most probably of detrital origin are feldspar, zircon, and magnetite. The sulfides and uraninite are hydrothermal, and probably much of the sericite has been introduced. The monazite has been reported as detrital; much of it occurs in rounded grains, but crystal faces have been observed on a few fragments. The grains also vary widely in color: pale yellow, gray green, orange, and brown.

It has been suggested that the brannerite is of detrital origin, largely because of its alteration to anatase, but it remains to be shown that such alteration is strictly the result of original weathering, for it is apparently not uniform. The brannerite is said to have "detrital characteristics," but in the only important brannerite placers known (Idaho), the mineral appears as relatively large pieces and crystal fragments and has not traveled far. Clearly the Blind River brannerite, even if detrital, is not derived from pegmatites in which it characteristically forms relatively large individuals. Vein brannerite forms minute, slender crystals that are exceedingly fragile, and in the upper parts of such deposits, are altered to soft anatase. That such material could long withstand the abrasive action indicated by the characteristics of the oligomictic conglomerate seems unlikely, a conclusion supported by Traill (1954). Since in the formation of the conglomerates, weathering was sufficiently rigorous to allow only quartz pebbles to remain over a lithologically complex basement, it is unlikely that pyrite, uraninite, and brannerite could persist concomitantly (Bateman, 1955). The anatase-thorogummite alteration also may be related to metamictization of the brannerite, and since it varies from grain to grain, it is probably nonsedimentogenic. Thorogummite may well be a low-temperature hydrothermal alteration mineral in this and some other of its occurrences. It also has been suggested that the uraninite is a replacement of detrital brannerite (Robertson, 1955; Robertson and Steenland, 1957), yet the uraninite contains up to 10% ThO_2, whereas only a trace of thorium is reported in brannerite, and Th is enriched in its alteration products.

The ore deposits nearly always are localized by sedimentary structures and petrologic features but some crosscutting uraninite mineralization has been noted (Joubin, 1954), which some investigators have ascribed to groundwater redistribution. Such seams, up to ⅛ in. wide, show some colloform structure and are flanked by hematitized wall rock. Strouth (1955) reports some uranium mineralization with chalcopyrite in fractures in diabase, also noted by Joubin (1954), just north of the area. Other evidence supporting a hydrothermal origin include the high U/Th ratio; the Fe/Ti ratio; the abundant pyrite; the euhedral nature of much uraninite; the many resemblances of the ore, in metal content (Co, Cu, U), to other deposits in the Cobalt–Sault Sainte Marie region (Joubin, 1954); and the presence of ore in an albitized zone at the base of the formation. Age determinations on uraninite can be interpreted to indicate that the ores are probably not older than Paleozoic (Stieff et al., 1956). The present evidence supports a hydrothermal origin for both the uraninite and the brannerite. Relatively high temperature conditions of deposition are suggested not only by its presence, but also by the presence of up to 10% ThO_2 in the uraninite, and by the presence of pyrrhotite, cobaltite, and scheelite. As long as the sedimentary hypothesis is invoked, exploration will follow beds of Mississagi age; consideration of the hydrothermal theory will direct equal attention to channelways in other petrologically similar formations.

At the present time data are inadequate to resolve the genetic argument, but as stated by Joubin and James (1956A, p. 613) ". . . hydrothermal fluids have been present and active in and near the uraniferous conglomerates and have undoubtedly affected their present distribution and form." The inadequacies of the arguments of the placeristic hypotheses have been effectively summarized by Davidson (1957) who demonstrates that these ideas require radical departure from actualistic principles.

Molybdenite-Uraninite Deposits

Several deposits in British Columbia, particularly in the Bridge River and Hazelton camps, have features characteristic of high-temperature deposits (Stevenson, 1951; Lang, 1952; Robinson, 1955B). These deposits are characterized by molybdenite and gold-bearing cobalt sulfarsenides in important amounts and by the presence of uraninite in crystals instead of botryoidal masses. The deposits are well-defined lenticular veins. The Victoria (Hazelton) and Little Gem and Index (Bridge River) are in fractures in granodiorite along the eastern zone of the Coast Range belt of Jurassic-Cretaceous batholiths. The

Molly deposit (south of Nelson) is in sheeted zones in granitic rocks related to the Nelson batholith of similar age in the southeastern part of British Columbia.

At the Victoria deposit, uraninite occurs as microscopic grains in a vein a few inches to 4 ft wide with a gangue predominantly hornblende. At the Little Gem, lenses 2 to 10 ft wide contain microscopic grains of uraninite in a gangue of chiefly chlorite and allanite. Other constituents in the coarse-grained, usually rudely banded gangues are apatite, orthoclase, quartz, monazite, and younger chlorite, sericite, and carbonates. Metallic minerals include gold and molybdenite at all the properties listed above; arsenopyrite, cobaltite, cobaltian loellingite, and skutterudite at the Little Gem and Victoria deposits; and pyrrhotite, pyrite, and chalcopyrite at the Index and Molly. Scheelite also is reported at the Molly (Lang, 1952). Five specimens from the Molly ranged from 0.047 to 0.13% eU_3O_8.

Spectrochemical analysis of the zoned allanite, which is only marginally isotropic, failed to detect U or Th, yet the mineral forms pleochroic halos in iron silicate. The uraninite, which is widely disseminated as minute euhedra or as clusters and chains of closely packed crystals, crystallized early. It shows zoning with HNO_3 etching and alteration to gummite. The monazite also is radioactive.

At the Emerald mine, 6 mi southeast of Salmo, an important tungsten source in World War II, uraninite occurs as a local accessory with scheelite. Other minerals are molybdenite, pyrrhotite, chalcopyrite, pyrite, and quartz (Thompson, 1951).

The deposits are assignable to the hypothermal group on the basis of (1) their position in the batholiths; (2) the euhedral nature of the uraninite; (3) the gangue assemblage, particularly of orthoclase, hornblende, allanite, biotite, and apatite; (4) the contemporaneity of the uraninite with this early gangue; and (5) the abundant associated molybdenite.

At Carcoar, New South Wales, uraninite and uranyl minerals are associated with Co-Mo-Cu mineralization. Near Pambula, New South Wales, traces of uraninite and uranyl minerals occur in Mo-Bi pipes in granite.

Copper-Uraninite Veins

The pitchblende deposits of the Carrizal-Alto district in the northern part of the Department of Freirina in north-central Chile (Flores, 1942; Everhart and Wright, 1951, 1953; McKelvey et al., 1955), which were large copper producers in the early part of the nineteenth century, belong to Lindgren's group of hypothermal copper-tourmaline deposits. Several were worked to depths of over 1,000 ft. One of the most important mines was the Socavan, 15 mi from Peña Blanca. Here the vein is 6 ft wide and yields ores averaging 18% Cu. Oxidized ores extended to 150 ft, below which chalcopyrite is the chief ore mineral.

The quartz veins, which are tensional fractures that trend N. 60° E. in diorite of the Andean batholith (Cretaceous), contain tourmaline, actinolite, magnetite, molybdenite, and arsenopyrite, suggesting depositional temperatures up to at least 500°C. The paragenetic sequence is: (1) magnetite, chalcopyrite;

(2) hematite, pitchblende; (3) molybdenite, pyrite, cobaltite; (4) arsenopyrite; (5) niccolite; (6) chloanthite; (7) bornite, chalcopyrite; (8) calcite. Other gangue minerals are epidote and chlorite. Hematite has been introduced into the adjacent wall rocks. The pitchblende forms scattered small pods and veinlets replacing and cutting magnetite and hematite. The mineralization is believed to be of Tertiary age.

At Sarimsakli in the Kara-Mazar Range, along the border of Uzbekistan and Tadshikistan, U.S.S.R., a 1-m quartz-pyrite vein in granodiorite contains pitchblende(?) with arsenopyrite, wolframite, bismuthinite, chalcopyrite, sphalerite, and galena. The granodiorite has been impregnated with uranyl minerals. The ore contains 0.12 to 0.2% U (Kohl, 1954).

Giant Quartz Veins

The giant quartz veins of the Northwest Territories, Canada (Kidd, 1936; Lang, 1952) occur between Great Bear and Great Slave Lakes, at intervals from near the mouth of the Coppermine River to Ral, some 350 mi. One has been described at Odjick Lake, 125 mi east of Hottah Lake, and an apparently similar vein has been reported at Bathurst Inlet on the Arctic coast, 250 mi east of Great Bear Lake. Examples occur at Hunter Bay, 30 mi northeast of Port Radium, and in the Marian River region, 100 mi northwest of Yellowknife. These are large replacement stockworks of quartz stringers and silicified wall rocks, generally occupying major faults, many of which trend northeast. They are several hundred feet wide and can be traced for several miles, some up to 10 mi. Locally some contain small amounts of pitchblende, specular hematite, and a second generation of quartz stringers as streaks and pods along fractures or fracture intersections. The younger quartz shows crystal faces into cavities and alternating milky and clear zones. Traces of pyrite, chalcopyrite, and other copper minerals may be present. Chlorite occurs in granite at their contacts. In some cases, lenses of hematite and pitchblende occur in the wall rocks.

The Giauque deposit, 97 mi northwest of Yellowknife, contains a general zone of the fractures about 25 ft wide extending down the center of the vein for 2,200 ft (James et al., 1950). The fracture-filling material yields fairly high assays, but the fractures are so erratically distributed that values across significant widths are low. These deposits at best are potential sources under large, low-grade operations. A determination of the thorium content of the pitchblende would be of considerable assistance in classifying the veins more readily in the absence of a significant suite of accessory minerals.

Uraninite-Uranothorianite Veins

A relatively large area in eastern Serbia, Yugoslavia, is underlain by a metamorphic complex, cut by mafic intrusives, and overlain by Paleozoic sediments, the whole intruded by Carboniferous granite. The granite shows all degrees of cataclasis, up to mylonitization, with accompanying chloritization, sericitization, and kaolinization. Uraninite and subordinate uranothorianite in grains 10 μ to 2.3 mm occur disseminated through the granite and are concentrated in cataclastic zones (Ristic, 1956). The uraninite, which is both anhedral and euhedral-cubic, also contains thorium.

Uraniferous Cassiterite Deposits

In central Malaya, torbernite and autunite, probably from the supergene alteration of pitchblende, occur in quartz stringers that carry cassiterite. Uranium mineralization is known at three mines about 10 mi from Frasers Hill.

In Queensland, Australia, small amounts of pitchblende occur in cassiterite-bearing veins and pipes. In the New England district of New South Wales uranyl minerals occur along fractures in granitic rocks, associated with Sn-W-Pb mineralization and in one case with beryllium minerals.

At the Miyoshi mine, Haratsu, Kurashiki, Okayama prefecture, Japan, zeunerite occurs in quartz veins 10 to 20 cm wide in granite, greisenized at vein contacts. The veins contain wolframite, cassiterite, and minor molybdenite, arsenopyrite, and chalcopyrite (Japan Geological Survey, 1956).

Some say that the Northern Lights are the glare
of the Arctic ice and snow;
And some that it's electricity, and nobody
seems to know.
But I'll tell you now—and if I lie,
may my lips be stricken dumb—
It's a mine, a mine of the precious stuff
that men call radium.

"The Ballad of the Northern Lights"
Robert Service

• chapter eight

MESOTHERMAL DEPOSITS

GENERAL

INTRODUCTION

Among the mesothermal deposits are most of the richest uranium deposits of the world and many of those that have been and are among the world's most productive uranium veins, e.g., Shinkolobwe, Great Bear Lake, and Goldfields. Included are the only deposits containing large reserves of grade exceeding 0.1% uranium and the only deposits that have produced large tonnages of grade as high as 0.5% uranium (McKelvey, 1955).

TYPES

Mesothermal uraniferous vein deposits are of two main types: the classic Ni-Co-Ag type (Bastin, 1939) and its minor variations, and the pitchblende-pyrite type, which may be accompanied by gold and sulfides of Pb, Cu, and Ag. Analogous to the first type of vein deposits are the disseminated Rhodesian copper deposits, which locally contain significant uranium; and counterparts to the second type are the disseminated deposits of the Witwatersrand. A third less common type of radioactive mesothermal deposit is represented by monazite or thorite veins.

A more elaborate subdivision of uraniferous veins of the Ni-Co-Ag category has been presented by Schneiderhöhn (1955), who, in his Ag-Co-Ni-Bi-U association, recognizes seven uraniferous subtypes:

1. Fluoritic, baritic, Ag- and Bi-bearing, cobalt veins (Wittichen type)
2. Baritic, Ag- and Bi-bearing, cobalt-nickel veins (Schneeberg type)
3. Calcitic, quartzose, cupriferous, cobalt-nickel veins
4. Baritic cobalt veins (cobalt Rücken, Richelsdorf)
5. Quartzose uranium veins (Shinkolobwe)

269

6. Quartzose, argentiferous cobalt-bismuth veins (Joachimsthal)
7. Calcitic cobalt-nickel veins (Schmiedeberg)

MINERALOGY

Many of the veins contain a gangue chiefly of carbonate—calcite, dolomite, or siderite, rarely magnesite or rhodochrosite. Some are siliceous, generally with coarse quartz; chalcedony is rare or late. Still others combine quartz and carbonate. Hematite is very common and may be abundant, conspicuously coloring the carbonate or quartz and impregnating the walls. Chlorite is widespread in some deposits. Barite and fluorite are rare. Pyrite is common, but marcasite and arsenopyrite or loellingite are unusual.

Many deposits contain appreciable amounts of the precious metals—Au, Witwatersrand, Placer de Guadalupe; Ag, Coeur d'Alene, Schneeberg; and Pt metals, Goldfields, Shinkolobwe. The silver occurs native, as sulfides, or less usually as sulfosalts.

Base metals that may be present in significant amounts are Bi, Cu, Pb, Co, and Ni. Of lesser importance are Zn and Mo. Bismuth is represented by native bismuth or bismuthinite, rarely as wittichenite. Chalcopyrite is by far the most widespread copper mineral, with bornite and secondary chalcocite and covellite locally abundant in some deposits. Tennantite is uncommon.

The greatest mineralogical variation is shown by Co and Ni: recognized are niccolite, cobaltite, gersdorffite, glaucodot, skudderudite, Ni-skutterudite, smaltite, chloanthite, safflorite, rammelsbergite, maucherite, polydymite, millerite (rare), and at Shinkolobwe and in the Mansfeld Rücken the sulfides, vaesite, cattierite, and siegenite.

Selenium is represented abundantly at Shinkolobwe by Co-Ni sulfides-selenides and to a lesser extent in the Goldfields area by Cu and Pb selenides. Tellurium occurs at Shinkolobwe as melonite. Vanadium as nolanite is locally abundant in several deposits in the Goldfields area (Robinson et al., 1957).

Uraninite (var. pitchblende) is the usual radioactive mineral. It is thorium-low, but rare earths may be present in that of some deposits (Placer de Guadalupe). Distinctive amounts of Zr and Mo have been detected in some Front Range pitchblendes. The unit cell is intermediate in size, $a_0 = 5.413$ to 5.440 (Berman, 1955), generally greater than those of Colorado Plateau pitchblendes, and less than those of pegmatitic pitchblendes. This indicates a moderate U^{4+}/U^{6+} ratio, characteristic of pitchblende formed neither at low nor high temperatures.

Other radioactive species are rare, although uraniferous hydrocarbon is an ore constituent in the Rand deposits and also occurs elsewhere, e.g., Goldfields. Monazite is abundant locally in the Shinkolobwe deposit, which also contains a urano-molybdenite. Coffinite is largely absent in this group, but has been found with uraninite in the Copper King deposit, Larimer County, Colorado (page 302). Oxidation may be deep, and because of the presence of S, As, P, and the various metallic elements, the assemblage of uranyl species can be complex and highly variable.

The pitchblende is usually spherulitic-botryoidal, although at Shinkolobwe colloform uraninite has not been found, and here it is granular to euhedral, in cubic crystals.

The spherulitic texture with radial-concentric structure and its modification, spheroidal or pellet, and its aggregate forms, botryoidal, framboidal, and in part colloform, as it occurs in uraninite, generally is regarded as formed by coagulation and crystallization of colloidal sols. The common presence of irregular radial syneresis fractures filled with later sulfides and gangue minerals and confined to the spherulites, results from internal stresses developed upon shrinkage. Everhart and Wright (1951) suggest that, since coagulation of a colloid depends largely on the presence of a suitable electrolyte, spherulitic pitchblende may be either early or late in the paragenetic sequence, relatively variable in its temperature of deposition. Robinson (1955A) points out that early Goldfields pitchblende is largely colloform and late pitchblende is granular.

WALL-ROCK ALTERATION

Wall-rock alteration is widespread and may be intense. Epidote, chlorite, pyrite, and calcite may be introduced. Sericitization and argillization are common, but silicification is much less so than in epithermal deposits. Scapolitization (Erzgebirge) and skarn development (Great Bear Lake) also have been noted. Pitchblende has been introduced into wall rocks of some vein deposits of the Colorado Front Range, Cornwall, and the Erzgebirge.

Hematitic alteration of various types is a feature characteristic of many mesothermal vein deposits and their wall rocks, commonly as very fine grained hematite impregnating and pigmenting in wholesale fashion both wall rocks and carbonate or quartz gangue. In some districts (Goldfields, Canada; Myponga, South Australia—Campana et al., 1953), a characteristic alteration consists of the development of replacement masses of hematitic oligoclasite (page 307). The abundant association of uranium and hematite has suggested that if uranium is transported as the uranyl ion, it may be precipitated as the result of the oxidation of iron according to the equation:

$$3H_2O + 2Fe^{2+} + (UO_2)^{2+} \rightarrow Fe_2O_3 + UO_2 + 6H^+$$

This goes to completion at 25°C at pH values greater than about 4.0 (McKelvey et al., 1955).

ENVIRONMENT OF DEPOSITION

The most common hosts are metamorphic rocks of sedimentary ancestry. In some districts veins also occur in granitic intrusives, in their marginal parts. However, at Schneeberg, veins extending into granite were barren. Strong structural control of mineralization is obvious in most districts but is not apparent or conspicuous in some, e.g., Witwatersrand, Rhodesia. Well-defined fracture systems (Erzgebirge), faults (Goldfields, Great Bear Lake), nappe structure (Shinkolobwe), and contacts between dissimilar rock types, especially along dikes (Montreal River, Placer de Guadalupe), have served to localize mineralization.

That open space filling has been widespread is indicated by abundant crustification, breccia fillings, and vugs. Wall-rock replacement by ore minerals generally is minor or absent. The ore shoots are localized along steeply dipping vein parts in contrast to barren "flats" (Joachimsthal); where fractures cut layers of brittle rock (Wood mine, Central City); where fault zones cut layered metamorphic rocks rather than porphyry (Great Bear Lake); along minor shears in a major fault system (Martin Lake, Goldfields); and along intersections of cross faults with axial plane shears (Darwin, Australia). Veins may show multiple reopening and intramineralization brecciation. The unique Gunnar deposit, Goldfields, Canada, is a breccia pipe in altered granite. Breccia and foliation-plane replacements also occur in deposits of the Darwin area, Australia.

Although the valence state of uranium in hydrothermal solutions is not definitely known, laboratory experiments have shown that uranium may be transported in solution as the uranyl ion, $(UO_2)^{2+}$, and precipitated by reduction to uraninite, UO_2, with Fe^{2+}, H_2S, and SO_2 (Gruner, 1953; Miller and Kerr, 1954). As pointed out by McKelvey et al. (1955), precipitation of pitchblende may result from decreases in temperature, pressure, or both, or from reaction with wall rocks. Since wall-rock alterations are so characteristically well developed, such reactions apparently have been of considerable significance in effecting precipitation, particularly for veins rich in carbonate. It has also been suggested that carbon, in the host rocks of such deposits as those of Rum Jungle, has been important as a reductant, but if this carbonaceous material was graphitic at the time of uranium deposition, it was probably ineffective as a reducing agent.

ZONING IN DISTRICTS [1]

Zonal distribution of pitchblende deposits in several Front Range districts has been described by Leonard (1952), where he believes the pitchblende-bearing veins are confined to the zone transitional from a core of gold-pyrite veins and a marginal zone of Pb-Zn-Ag veins. This view has been disputed by Sims and Tooker (1956), who find a clustering of the uraniferous deposits. Pierson et al. (1952) report that in the Lower Uncompahgre district, Colorado, uraniferous deposits occur close to the boundary between a pyrite-gold-base metal core and an outer silver-lead-zinc zone.

In Cornwall, England, uranium appears chiefly in the copper zone. At Joachimsthal the vertical zoning is described as upper silver ore, intermediate cobalt-nickel ore, and lowermost uranium ore. In the disseminated Rhodesian copper ores, the highest uranium values occur on the edge of the copper zone (page 298). Regional zoning in variations in copper and cobalt also has been noted in the Katherine-Darwin area, Australia.

[1] The germ of the concept of zonal distribution of various types of ores was expressed as early as 1798 by Robert Townson in *Philosophy of Mineralogy*, pp. 103–104. "Further, there is not only a relative antiquity or seniority between the veins, but likewise between different kinds of ore and vein-stones. Tin, molybden, tungsten, and wolfram are amongst the most ancient, then uranite and bismuth: these are never found in the stratified rocks. Then gold and silver. Quick-silver, copper, lead, and zink, have each been formed at many different times. Cobalt and kupfer nickel are of later formation."

Ni-Co-Ag AND ALLIED TYPES

UNITED STATES

Caribou Mine, Boulder County, Colorado

The Caribou deposit near Nederland, Colorado, contains the Radium vein characterized by minerals of the Ag-Ni-U assemblage. The mine has been worked for silver and lead at various times since 1869. Veins occur along two fracture sets that strike east and northeast dipping 70 to 90° N. or NW. across the north-south axis of the Caribou stock, a late Cretaceous intrusive ranging from quartz monzonite to gabbro (Ridland, 1950; King, 1952; Moore and Cavender, 1952; Wright, 1954).

On the 1,040-ft level of the mine the Radium vein branches east from the No Name vein, which strikes N. 50° E. The Radium vein strikes east and dips 70° N. to 80° S. Pitchblende occurs between 875 and 1,075 ft. Much of it occurs as sooty powder mixed with pyrite and clay gouge, usually as a streak, 1 to 6 in. wide, along the footwall of the vein, which splits apophyses here and there across to the hanging wall. Hard botryoidal pitchblende occurs as irregularly distributed lenses up to a foot long. The larger of two shoots measures 200 ft vertically and 70 ft horizontally.

The alteration halo, up to 4 ft thick, contains early epidote, chlorite, calcite, and pyrite replacing mafic minerals, intermediate montmorillonite and kaolinite replacing feldspars, and youngest sericite and quartz adjacent to the vein and sericite beyond the argillized zone. Uranium also has diffused out into the wall rocks as far as the limits of hydrothermal alteration.

Vein minerals were deposited in the following sequence:

1. Quartz, calcite, and siderite, followed successively by pyrite, chalcopyrite, sphalerite, and galena
2. Brecciation
3. *a.* Gersdorffite and chalcedony
   b. Pitchblende
   c. Sphalerite, chalcopyrite, argentite, proustite, and native silver

The chalcedony and silver minerals suggest ". . . relatively low temperatures . . . probably not higher than the low temperature portion of the mesothermal range" (Wright, 1954, p. 164).

Black Hawk District, New Mexico

The Black Hawk district, 13 mi west-southwest of Silver City in Grant County, New Mexico, has been the source of silver ore valued at more than one million dollars. Precambrian gneissic tonalite, which intrudes metasediments and orthogneisses of the Bullard Peak series, is itself cut by Precambrian granite and by a Laramide stock and dikes of monzonite porphyry and other rock types.

The deposits are narrow, persistent fissure veins containing the Ag-Ni-Co-U assemblage of minerals—argentite, native silver, millerite, niccolite, skutterudite, nickel-skutterudite, bismuthinite, pitchblende, and sphalerite in a carbonate gangue (calcite, dolomite, siderite, and ankerite), with lesser barite and quartz. The seven radioactive deposits are in a northeast belt 600 ft long and 1,500 ft wide, nearly parallel with the southeastern margin of the Twin Peaks monzonite stock (Gillerman and Whitebread, 1956). Some post ore faults cut the veins.

The pitchblende forms grains 2 mm or less across in veins generally a foot or less wide but which may swell to 3 to 10 ft. Ore shoots are lensoid. Specimens from dumps assay 0.07 to 0.24% U_3O_8.

Coeur d'Alene District, Idaho

Uraninite mineralization occurs between the 2,900- to 3,700-ft levels in the footwall of the Sunshine vein in the Coeur d'Alene district of northernmost Idaho, a district noted for Ag-Pb production from sideritic veins. The Sunshine vein strikes west-northwest and dips 60 to 80° SW. parallel with the axial plane of the Big Creek anticline in the Belt series (latest Precambrian), cutting the Wallace formation near the surface, continuing through the St. Regis formation, and probably extending into the Revett quartzite. The anticlinal limb has been crumpled. Early uraninite-bearing veinlets up to 4 in. thick are lopped off by irregular low-angle faults, but some younger veinlets follow the fault planes. Shear zones carrying pitchblende veinlets are erratically distributed over a width of 200 ft (Thurlow and Wright, 1950; Everhart and Wright, 1953; Kerr and Robinson, 1953). Some uraniferous zones show parallel ribbons of white quartz and siderite with bordering bands of pyrite-pitchblende. As much as a foot from the veins, hematite has been introduced into the sericitized quartzite.

The disseminated pitchblende occurs mainly as spherulites up to 10 μ across replacing vein jasper, quartzite breccia pieces, and wall rock, usually in or with pyrite-jasper veinlets. Locally pitchblende occurs as streaks in siderite veins. Kerr and Robinson (1953) regard these occurrences as representing recrystallized fragments, mechanically transported, whereas Thurlow and Wright (1950) regard some pitchblende as younger than tetrahedrite and replacing it. It seems difficult to explain all pitchblende-siderite occurrences by reworking of transported older pitchblende or reopening of pitchblende veinlets.

Similar mineralization at the Crescent mine on Big Creek, but at a level about 3,000 ft higher, indicates that the lateral extent of the uranium mineralization is at least 2 mi. Although the Coeur d'Alene silver mineralization generally has been regarded as genetically related to monzonitic intrusives of early Tertiary age, an age determination on Sunshine pitchblende has yielded a Precambrian age of 750 ± 50 m.y. (Kerr and Kulp, 1952). It is not certain whether the tetrahedrite-siderite veins constitute a later phase of the Precambrian mineralization or a much younger separate phase.

CANADA

Great Bear Lake Area, Northwest Territories

General Geology

The east shore of Great Bear Lake is underlain by Precambrian rocks of four main ages

(?)	4. Mafic sills and dikes
	b. Late quartz diabase
	a. Early diabase, locally amygdaloidal
Late Proterozoic	3. Hornby group: sandstone, conglomerate
(Jolliffe, 1952)	2. Diorite, granodiorite, granite
Middle(?) Proterozoic	1. *b.* Cameron Bay sandstone, arkose,
Early Proterozoic	quartzite, conglomerate
(Jolliffe, 1952)	*a.* Echo Bay group: tuffs, flow rocks, argillite, quartzite, dolomitic limestone

In general even the older rocks of the area show only mild metamorphism and gentle structures. Early Proterozoic rocks lie in belts trending chiefly north to northwest. Late Proterozoic beds are flat-lying and but little disturbed. Widespread faults that trend generally north to northeast are later than the folding and displace rocks of all the units, although some of the diabase dikes have been displaced only slightly. Many faults are branching; some are represented by shear and breccia zones up to several hundred feet across. Giant vertical quartz stockworks, some of which are more than 1,000 ft wide and 10 mi long, are conspicuous in the central and southern parts of the region and are known to extend all the way to the southeastern shore of Coronation Gulf. Several are localized along major faults along which repeated movement has led to dominantly lateral separations of as much as 8 mi (Jolliffe, 1952).

Uranium mineralization of the Ag-Co-Ni type with Bi and Cu is in veins and stockworks along fractures, shear zones, and faults cutting early Proterozoic, granitic rocks, and early diabase. Some of the giant quartz veins also contain small amounts of pitchblende (page 267). Apophyses of some of the late diabase dikes cut pitchblende-bearing veins, and these dikes also have not been subjected to the hematitic alteration which accompanies the uranium mineralization. It is not certain whether the deposits are related genetically to the granitic intrusives or are much younger. Mineralogically complex deposits show three stages of mineralization, the last of which, consisting of quartz, carbonate, and chalcopyrite, occurs in small veins locally cutting the young diabase. The uranium mineralization occurred in the interval between the intrusions of the two types of diabase (Collins et al., 1952), but probably closer to the time of intrusion of the younger diabases. The age of the mineralization is 1,400 ± 50 m.y. (Collins et al., 1954).

Uranium mineralization was first found in the area in 1930 by Gilbert Labine and E. C. St. Paul, marking the discovery of one of the world's major uranium areas. Production began in 1933, halting in 1940. To a large extent radium from the Eldorado mine broke the Belgian monopoly based on the rich Congo deposits. With the development of nuclear fission weapons, the shares of the Eldorado Gold Mining Company were acquired by the Canadian government, and the Eldorado mine was reopened in 1942.

The main deposits within the Great Bear Lake area are

1. The Eldorado mine, on the east shore of Great Bear Lake, just south of the Arctic Circle
2. Contact Lake mine, 9 mi southeast of the Eldorado mine

Eldorado Mine

Veins at the Eldorado mine cut folded layers of the Echo Bay group (Kidd, 1932A,B; Spence, 1932A,B; Jolliffe and Bateman, 1944; Lang, 1952). The Echo Bay group has been divided into four main units (Murphy, 1948), the lower three of which are most widespread near the mine:

4. Andesitic flows, 3 types, separated by tuffs
3. Feldspar porphyry, largely intrusive
2. Cherty metasediments, banded tuff, banded limestone (2 and 3 together are about 1,500 ft thick)
1. Massive tuff, 500 ft thick

Granite is exposed along the lake shore and granite apophyses have been encountered in the western workings. The fold axes strike north-northeast, and the folds plunge slightly to the north.

The ore deposits range from narrow veins, of high grade, to stockworks 40 ft across, only partly ore grade. They occur along four of five roughly parallel fault zones (Nos. 1, 2, 3, and 5), at irregular intervals (Fig. 8.1). Individual veins widen from 1 in. to 10 ft, but locally, because of marginal stringers, ore bodies are as much as 15 ft across. Ore shoots are 50 to 700 ft long and have been mined vertically for 600 ft (Murphy, 1948). They tend to be concentrated around the ends of feldspar porphyry sills but occur almost exclusively in stratified rocks or along sections of the fault zones occupying stratified rocks—early diabase contacts. Where fault zones cross porphyry, mineralization ceases within short distances. Silver-nickel ore ceased to be important below a few hundred feet, and pitchblende changes from colloform near the surface to massive at depth (Lang, 1952).

Hematitic wall-rock alteration is prominent, especially within 4 to 5 ft of the vein, where the rocks are converted to a very fine grained jasperoid of quartz, hematite, magnetite, sericite, chlorite, and carbonate. Coarse skarn masses of amphibole, epidote, apatite, magnetite, and carbonate with lesser garnet, feldspar, chlorite, and pyrite are locally and irregularly developed in the metasediments.

Some of the veins are banded, locally with vugs and wall-rock inclusions. Some are laced by faults, others are strongly brecciated. They consist mainly

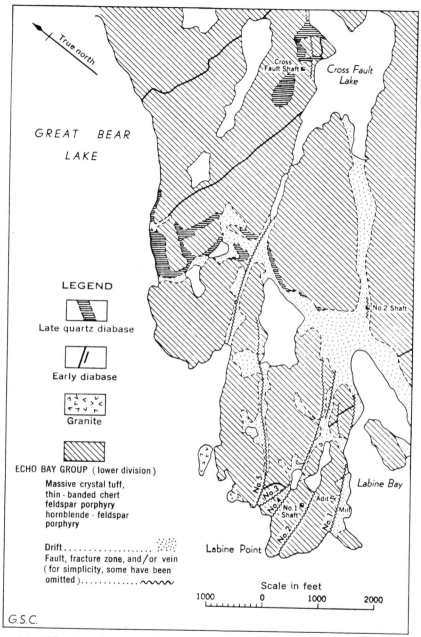

GREAT BEAR LAKE

Cross Fault Lake

Cross Fault Shaft

True north

LEGEND

Late quartz diabase

Early diabase

Granite

ECHO BAY GROUP (lower division)

Massive crystal tuff,
thin - banded chert
feldspar porphyry
hornblende - feldspar
porphyry

Drift . . . .

Fault, fracture zone, and / or vein
(for simplicity, some have been
omitted) . . . .

No.2 Shaft

Labine Bay

No.5
No.3
No.4
No.1 Shaft
No.2
No.1
Adit
Mill

Labine Point

Scale in feet

1000   0   1000   2000

G.S.C.

Fig. 8.1. Eldorado mine area, Great Bear Lake, Northwest Territory, Canada (Jolliffe and Bateman, 1944; *Geol. Survey Canada*).

277

of quartz, carbonate, hematite, and minor chlorite. In the No. 1 vein zone, which is markedly banded, Murphy (1948) distinguished four main stages of mineralization:

1. Massive quartz with seams of chlorite, minor carbonate, and pyrite.
2. Banded quartz-hematite, some cherty, with vugs containing crystals of carbonate, hematite, quartz, and chalcopyrite.
3. Narrow bands, interlaced stringers, and lenses of sulfides, arsenides, bismuth, silver, pitchblende, and calcite, chiefly in the cherty parts of the quartz-hematite veins. These minerals may occur intergrown or in separate stringers.
4. Small veins and vug fillings of quartz, carbonate, and chalcopyrite, later than the younger diabase.

Kidd and Haycock (1935) distinguished four characteristic types of mineralization:

1. Pitchblende, quartz, safflorite-rammelsbergite; minor glaucodot, polydymite, gersdorffite, hematite, molybdenite
2. Quartz, smaltite-chloanthite, bismuth, skutterudite, cobaltite
3. Dolomite, Pb, Zn, Cu sulfides
4. Ferruginous rhodochrosite, Cu and Ag sulfides, native silver

Not all types are present in all four mineralized zones.

Although pitchblende forms solid bands or lenses up to 1 ft across and 40 ft long and masses as much as several feet across, it commonly appears as veinlets and lenses a few inches wide or as disseminated aggregates. It occurs as (1) botryoidal and spherulitic structures (Fig. 2.5), which show syneresis cracks filled by quartz, carbonate and sulfides, brecciation, and various degrees of replacement by carbonates and sulfides; (2) cellular forms arranged in disconnected annular or linear structures; and (3) dendrites of skeletal cubes. The pitchblende is low both in ThO_2 ($<0.01\%$) and rare earths, $(Ce,Y)_2O_3 = 0.94$ to 1.4% (Marble, 1939). The primary pitchblende ($UO_2:UO_3 = 10:2.2$) is partly replaced by a softer pitchblende ($UO_2:UO_3 = 10:100$) (Kidd and Haycock, 1935). Some reworking of the primary pitchblende also is suggested by the range in results of age determinations—600 to 1,400 m.y. (Robinson, 1955B).

The temperature of the solutions declined considerably during the four depositional stages: high initial temperatures are indicated by early massive quartz, molybdenite, and specular hematite. Types 2 and 3 are typical mesothermal assemblages, and the vein structures—banding, brecciation (Fig. 2.7) and some vugs—also are characteristic. Type 4, with rhodochrosite, native silver, hessite, argentite, stromeyerite, and jalpaite, indicates cooler terminal temperatures, either conditions indicative of the upper part of the mesothermal or lower part of the epithermal zones. The general sequence of precipitation of the principal heavy metals is: U, Ni, Co, Zn, Pb, Cu, Ag. The upper silver ores are regarded generally as hypogene except by Murphy (1948), who believes they are products of secondary enrichment.

Supergene uranyl minerals are uncommon, but becquerelite, curite, vandendriesscheite, uranophane, zippeite, and liebigite have been identified or reported (Palache and Berman, 1933; Lang, 1952; Frondel, 1956B).

Mineralization very similar to that at the Eldorado mine occurs on the Echo Bay claims, which adjoin the Eldorado property on the northeast, and on the El Bonanza property 6 mi southwest of Port Radium on the east shore of the lake.

Contact Lake Deposit

The Contact Lake mine has been a small producer of native silver and minor pitchblende (Furnival, 1939; Lang, 1952). Quartz-carbonate veins occur along fracture and shear zones in granodiorite intruded by granite 500 ft to the southwest. The three zones trend north of east. No. 1, the western, is as much as 5 ft wide, and has been traced for 1,100 ft underground. The granodiorite walls are altered to hematite and chlorite. Four main stages of mineral deposition have been recognized (Furnival, 1939):

1. Magnetite-hematite
2. Gray quartz
3. White, finely banded comb quartz
4. Carbonate with Ag-Co-Ni-Bi-U minerals, in which pitchblende is the earliest, and native silver (hypogene, with minute amounts of Hg) is the last

About thirty different hypogene minerals have been identified. In 1938 to 1939, nearly 7,000 lb of U_3O_8 reportedly was produced (James et al., 1950).

Similar mineralization is reported at the Bell claims, between Contact Lake and Bay 66 of Great Bear Lake, 10 mi southeast of the Eldorado mine.

Other Deposits

Radioactive sulfide mineralization with cobalt occurs at the Pitch 27 and 28 claims on the northeast corner of Hottah Lake about 60 mi south of the Eldorado mine. Silver-pitchblende or copper-pitchblende mineralization also is reported from some six other properties, and many other radioactive or pitchblende occurrences are known in the region (Lang, 1952).

ARGENTINA

San Santiago Mine, La Rioja

The San Santiago deposit, worked for nickel in the 1850s, is 280 km by road northwest of Chilecito near the Chilean border at about 7,500 ft. The vein, which strikes N. 65° E. and dips 50 to 65° NW., cuts quartzite of a Precambrian metasedimentary complex. Tertiary disturbances have resulted in closely spaced fractures, generally at right angles to the plane of the vein (Angelelli, 1956). The eastern part is offset 10 m by faulting, and locally some vein minerals are brecciated. The vein, several centimeters thick, contains dominant gangue of calcite in two generations, a pink, which was deposited with niccolite and pitchblende, and a white, associated with pyrite, chalcopyrite, sphalerite, and galena. Pitchblende appears as thin films and grains disseminated in niccolite. Wall rock is pyritized and penetrated by niccolite and calcite stringers. Average grade at depth is 8% Ni and 0.70% U_3O_8.

La Niquelina Mine, Sierra de Santa Victoria

La Niquelina mine is in Tuctuca district, on the east slope of the Sierra de Santa Victoria near the Bolivian border, above 13,500 ft. The deposit consists of three veins that strike N. 30 to 40° W. and dip 70° NE. to nearly vertical in Cambro-Ordovician beds of slate and along their contacts with quartzite. The veins range in thickness from several decimeters to over a meter, consisting of niccolite, galena, sphalerite, chalcopyrite, pyrite, and pitchblende in a quartz-siderite gangue. Wall-rock breccia pieces are common. Pitchblende forms fine stringers, especially in niccolite-impregnated quartzite (Angelelli, 1956).

EUROPE

Cornwall, England

Pitchblende in Cornwall occurs principally (1) in fissure-filling veins in or near the granite, which are younger than the associated main tin and copper lodes, e.g., St. Anstell group, and (2) as a late accessory mineral within tin and copper lodes, (*a*) filling fissures produced by widening of the original lodes, (*b*) in small veins across the lodes, or (*c*) along the intersections of the older lodes with cross fissures, e.g., St. Just, St. Ives, East Pool (Penrose, 1915; Dines, 1930; Everhart and Wright, 1951, 1953; Davidson, 1956A).

In the Cornwall district, folded Lower Devonian slates ("killas") and greenstones have been intruded, along an east-west line, by five main post-Carboniferous granite plutons around which the cassiterite veins are clustered. Preceding vein formation, a series of east-northeast-trending granite porphyry dikes ("elvans") was intruded into both slate and granite. The older tin-copper lodes, which are simple or composite, trend generally northeast. The vein systems are zoned (Davison, 1927), with successive diagnostic assemblages downward or toward the granite of (1) galena, sphalerite, pyrite, fluorite, siderite or ankerite, and quartz; (2) sphalerite, pyrite, and chlorite; (3) chalcopyrite, bornite, sphalerite, pyrite, fluorite, and chlorite; and in or near granite of (4) cassiterite, arsenopyrite, wolframite, tourmaline, quartz, and feldspar. Also found are scheelite, molybdenite, bismuthinite, magnetite, and specularite. Along the tin lodes, granite has been tourmalinized, silicified, and kaolinized. In greenstones, axinite, pyroxene, garnet, and some tourmaline have been developed. In some cases, an outermost lowest-temperature zone of hematite, pyrolusite, manganite, and rhodochrosite has been recognized.

Pitchblende was known in the deposits before 1815, probably at least by 1805 (Phillips, 1816), and both it and its supergene alteration products, principally autunite, torbernite, and zippeite and rarely bassetite and uranospathite (James, 1945; Rumbold, 1954; Frondel, 1954), are widespread. Uranium ores are known to have been mined from (1) Wheal Owles, St. Just; (2) Wheal Trenwith and Wheal Providence, St. Ives; (3) East Pool and Agar, Illogan; (4) South Terras mine, St. Stephen; and (5) St. Austell Consols, St. Stephen; especially from 2 and 4 (Robertson and Dines, 1929; Dines, 1930; James, 1945). Several other occurrences are described by Davidson (1956A).

The vein in the South Terras deposit (Radium or Green Jim lode), the

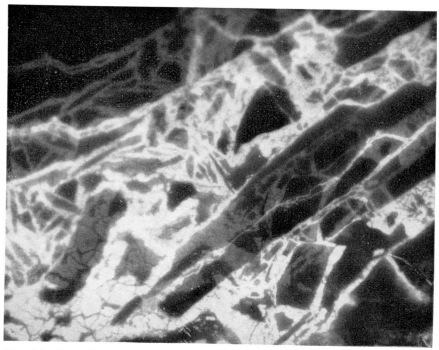

Fig. 8.2. Autoradiograph of pitchblende veinlets in brecciated quartzose gangue, Cornwall, England (Ward's Nat. Sci. Establishment).

only lode in which uranium minerals formed the principal ore, was discovered in 1873 and mined for uranium between 1878 and 1900, 1906 and 1909, 1913 and 1914, 1920 and 1921, and 1923 and 1927 (Gregory, 1946). It strikes N. 10° W. across the earlier tin-copper lodes, dips 10 to 30° SW., is 2 ft thick on the average, and contains coarse comb quartz and inclusions of slate. It was traced for 1,000 ft along the strike. To the south, it splits and pinches out against a granite dike. The pitchblende was chiefly in marginal stringers, with the oxidized uranium minerals to a depth of 60 ft, and chalcopyrite, pyrite, arsenopyrite, galena, and traces of smaltite, niccolite, and barite. The pitch-blende-bearing part of the vein varied from a knife-edge to 8 in. thick and was traced to a depth of about 900 ft. In 1952 to 1953, drilling by the Geological Survey of Great Britain failed to locate any significant new ore.

At the Trenwith mine, pitchblende impregnated slate and greenstone wall rocks to as much as 40 ft from the lode. The vein here strikes east-west, dips very steeply north and the pitchblende is a late fracture-filling mineral along walls in the copper-bearing parts of the lode, forming lenses 2 to 12 in. thick at intersections with cross fractures. In some deposits pitchblende also occurs as disseminations in slate. Secondary uranium minerals have been found along joints in kaolinized granite and slaty wall rock in the oxidized zone.

In ore specimens, pitchblende appears with clear quartz as thin stringers and irregular lenses cutting brecciated gangue (Fig. 8.2) stained by hematite and rich in fine-grained quartz. Some lenses are locally vuggy, showing botryoidal surfaces. Apparently no thorium determinations are available. Nevertheless, the associated minerals, the zonation, and the age of the pitchblende veins relative to the tin lodes, point definitely to the mesothermal environment of deposition.

It is estimated that from the district as a whole 300 tons of U_3O_8 has been produced. In recent years the South Terras mine has been reexamined and the deposit drilled, but although several small masses of ore were discovered, none was large enough to warrant reopening.

France

Rabasse, Hérault

Uranium mineralization at the Ceilhes mine, Rabasse, in Hérault, south of the Massif Central, is regarded as transitional between hypothermal and mesothermal (Geffroy and Sarcia, 1954). The deposit is a replacement of Cambrian limestone, containing galena, sphalerite, pyrite, auriferous arsenopyrite, bismuth minerals, niccolite, rammelsbergite, and pitchblende. The pitchblende appears as skeletal residuals in the nickel minerals.

Kruth, Haut-Rhin

At Kruth in the Thur Valley, Vosges, pitchblende occurs in a nearly vertical vein that strikes N. 70° W. across porphyritic granite. The mineralization consists of barite, quartz, fluorite, pyrite, marcasite, chloanthite(?), loellingite, chalcopyrite, tennantite, bornite, chalcocite, covellite, galena, sphalerite, and hematite. Three types of veins are recognized (Geffroy and Sarcia, 1954):

1. Veins of botryoidal pitchblende
2. Banded veins with 1 to 3 mm marginal "garlands" of pitchblende and central purple fluorite bands
3. Brecciated veins containing pitchblende cockades, red quartz, barite, and sulfides

The deposits are somewhat similar to those at Wittichen in the Black Forest, Germany (Roubault, 1956), but appear to be transitional between epithermal and mesothermal.

Erzgebirge

General

The Erzgebirge, a famous and ancient mining region of Saxony (Eastern Germany) and Bohemia (Czechoslovakia), includes the mining centers of Joachimsthal (Jáchymov), Johanngeorgenstadt, Annaberg, Eibenstock, Schneeberg, Freiberg, Marienberg, Niederschlag, and others. It forms part of a low mountain chain extending across central Germany to the Carpathian Mountains, serving as a natural boundary between Saxony to the north and Czechoslovakia to the south. Although deposits of the region have been mined mainly for Pb, Ag, Co, Ni, and Bi, uranium minerals, chiefly pitchblende and various supergene alteration products, occur widely and have been mined at Joachimsthal and to a lesser extent at Johanngeorgenstadt, Annaberg, and Schneeberg.

The discovery of silver deposits at Freiberg in 1170 initiated mining in the region, which spread gradually over the entire Erzgebirge and has lasted with some interruptions for nearly eight centuries. Silver lodes were found at Annaberg in 1492. In the middle of the eighteenth century activity was renewed because of the use of cobalt blue as a ceramic coloring agent. During the nineteenth century, many deposits yielded chiefly cobalt and bismuth, with by-product silver.

It was from ore mined at Joachimsthal that Pierre and Marie Curie first succeeded in isolating radium. One kilogram of pitchblende of 60% U_3O_8 will yield 0.333 mg $RaBr_2$, for which the pitchblende ores were first mined. Previously pitchblende had been employed to a small extent in the production of uranium pigments (after 1850). Until the discovery of the Belgian Congo deposits, the Erzgebirge pitchblende was the foremost source of radium. Joachimsthal had yielded approximately one-twelfth of the world's uranium production prior to World War II, but by the end of World War I most of the mines in the region had been shut down. By 1936, 100 g of Ra had been secured from Czechoslovakian ores.

In accordance with the Yalta and Potsdam agreements, the western Erzgebirge and its uraniferous deposits were turned over to Russian occupation, although originally captured and occupied by American forces in 1945. The Soviet-controlled Vismut Corporation was established to mine uranium from the deposits and proceeded on the basis of techniques such as sealed camps, police control, forced labor battalions, and an incentive program based on food rations.[1] It has been stated that as many as 100,000 workers were employed by the Russians, although this figure seems excessive (Frohberg, 1950). The uranium mined at peak operation may have reached 3 to 4% of the world's production.

Regional Geology

Mineral centers in the Erzgebirge lie along only two lines, which intersect at Joachimsthal: a northwesterly zone from Schneeberg through Johanngeorgenstadt to Joachimsthal, and a north-south zone from Freiberg through Marienberg, Annaberg, Niederschlag, Joachimsthal, and Schlaggenwald. The area around the intersection is underlain by Precambrian paraschists and Paleozoic phyllites and slates into which has been intruded the Eibenstock granite pluton of late Paleozoic age, exposed along its northwest-southeast axis for about 25 mi and over a width of 5 to 15 mi. Surrounding the pluton is a zone of progressive contact metamorphism in which the slates and phyllites have been transformed to spotted hornfels, andalusite hornfels, and quartzites. The granite bodies occur in the two belts trending nearly normal to Variscan folds. In late Tertiary time, faulting was accompanied by widespread vulcanism, yielding predominantly basalts and phonolites and their dikes.

[1] See, for example, Soviet operation of uranium mines in Eastern Germany, East European Fund, Inc., Research program of the U.S.S.R., mimeo. ser. No. 11, 1952.

The ore deposits, which are genetically related to the Paleozoic granites, include:

1. Pyrometasomatic Fe-Cu deposits
2. Sn-W veins
3. Pyritic Pb veins
4. Veins of Ag-Co-Bi-U minerals
5. Veins with Fe and Mn oxide minerals

The Ag-Co-Bi-U veins have been the most important economically. Generally these fissure veins are best developed in the metamorphic rocks, becoming barren as they enter granite, but at Schneeberg in the Weisser-Hirsch mine, pitchblende also occurs in veins in granite. The veins follow two main sets of fractures and to a lesser extent faults: one group striking north to northeast, and a second trending northwest to west, parallel with the Variscan fold axes.

Many of the deposits consist of several parallel veins, which also may show multiple reopening. Their length ranges from several hundred feet to about 2 mi, and the thickness averages ½ to 2 ft. Silver ores were most abundant in the upper levels, with Co-Ni-Bi ores predominating in intermediate levels and pitchblende most abundant in lower levels.

The veins are characterized by a complex suite of minerals. Silver is represented by native silver, argentite, stephanite, the ruby silvers, and rarer sulfosalts; cobalt and nickel mainly by niccolite, smaltite, safflorite, and chloanthite; and bismuth by native bismuth and bismuthinite. Galena, sphalerite, chalcopyrite, and pyrite also are present. The gangue consists chiefly of quartz, jasper, calcite, dolomite, other carbonates, barite, and fluorite. Pitchblende, the chief uranium mineral, is confined essentially to veins with a gangue of reddish dolomite.

Oxidation has increased the complexity of the assemblage: horn silver, bismutite, beyerite, uranyl oxides (uranosphaerite), carbonates (liebigite, schroeckingerite, voglite), sulfates (zippeite, uranopilite, johannite), phosphates (autunite, torbernite, meta-uranocircite, saléeite, fritzcheite), arsenates (metazeunerite, uranospinite, troegerite, walpurgite), and silicates (uranophane, beta-uranophane, cuprosklodowskite).

Pitchblende forms thin seams, streaks, and irregular patches within dolomitic or dolomitic quartzose veins or rarely along microfractures in schistose wall rock (Fig. 8.3).

Joachimsthal

Joachimsthal,[1] in Bohemia, is about 2½ mi east of the Eibenstock batholith which cuts the Joachimsthal schist. The veins form two separate systems: a north-south (Midnight), and an east-west (Morning), the latter continuing without disturbance, but the former veins individually deflected (Jaffe, 1912; Kraus, 1916). The east-west system is older than the north-south, which in general carries the higher uranium values. Where veins of the two systems intersect pitchblende-rich shoots commonly have been formed. Vertical sections of

[1] Silver from this district was made into coins known as "Joachimsthaler," which was abbreviated to "Thaler" and served as the root word for dollar.

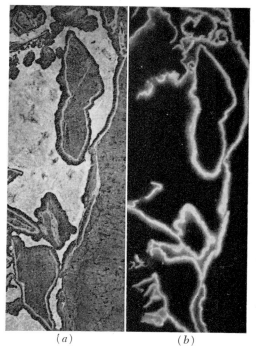

(a)   (b)

Fig. 8.3. (a) Pitchblende ore from Hildebrand vein, Joachimsthal, Erzgebirge, showing wall-rock fragments encrusted with quartz and pitchblende, in gangue of quartz and dolomite. (b) Autoradiograph of same specimen (Step and Becke, 1904).

veins are strongly mineralized in contrast to the barren, brecciated flat sections. Veins have been followed for 1½ mi and to a depth of 1,600 ft and are a few inches to 2 ft thick. Some veins transect granite at depth, where uranium mineralization is inferred to decrease.

Most of the uranium production has come from the Midnight veins, 0.1 to 1 m thick. Dolomite and calcite accompanying pitchblende have been colored red by finely disseminated hematite. Pitchblende forms irregularly distributed lenses and masses usually close to the schistose wall rocks, either adjacent to the walls or breccia wall fragments or separated from the walls only by a thin quartz seam. Some pitchblende impregnates the schists. Scapolitic wall rocks at the Edelleut mine contained 0.265% U_3O_8. Near veins muscovite is abundant in the wall rocks. Some of the Midnight veins show layering: (1) at the walls a thin quartz coating, (2) dolomite with pitchblende lenses, (3) central dolomite and arsenides. In general, pitchblende is younger than quartz and carbonate and some of the Co-Ni minerals and older than other Co-Ni and the Ag minerals.

With depth, the ores change from primarily Ag to Co-Ni and to U. Although this has been ascribed to thermal zoning, it may be related to the

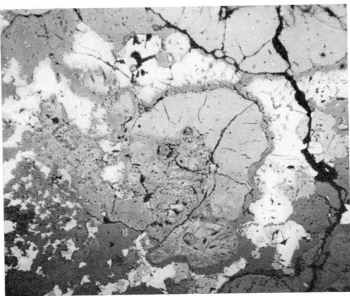

FIG. 8.4. Pitchblende spherulite with interstitial pyrite and Ni-Co minerals, Joachimsthal, Erzgebirge. Reflected light ($\times$44).

presence of different wall rocks (Bain, 1950), and richest pitchblende concentrations occur where veins cross marble interlayered with schist.

Between 1854 and 1914, 500 tons of 50% U_3O_8 pitchblende ore was produced. The radium production between 1909 and 1915 was 7.8 g, between 1915 and 1921, 13 g obtained from 110 tons of concentrate with 50% U_3O_8. Except for the rich Geister and Schweizer veins (0.6 to 1.16% U_3O_8), the ore averaged about 0.2% U_3O_8 (Kraus, 1916).

Schneeberg

At Schneeberg, Saxony, about 30 mi northwest of Joachimsthal, Ag-Co-Ni-Bi-U veins cut steeply dipping contact-metamorphosed schists and phyllites in a zone 3 mi wide between the Eibenstock batholith and the Oberschlema granite stock. The two vein sets intersect acutely, striking west-northwest and north-northwest and dipping steeply. Individual veins average 2 ft thick, extend for as much as 1.8 mi, and have been worked to 1,600 ft. One type carries argentite, native silver, ruby silvers, nickel arsenides, and bismuth in a barite-fluorite-carbonate gangue. In 1477, a mixed argentite–native silver mass weighing about 20 tons was recovered at the St. George mine. The other type contains smaltite, chloanthite, niccolite, pyrite, bismuth, local silver, and pitchblende in a chert-calcite gangue. Silver ore in general prevailed at higher levels, Co-Bi ores with depth. Veins that extend into the granite become barren, although two veins contained significant pitchblende close to and into the granite for short distances. Production is estimated at 80 tons of pitchblende.

Johanngeorgenstadt

At Johanngeorgenstadt, in Saxony, 12 mi northwest of Joachimsthal, deposits have yielded primarily Ag-Bi ores in contrast to the Ag-Co-Ni ores of Joachimsthal. The fissure veins occur in Precambrian and Cambrian phyllites contact metamorphosed to spotted schists by the Eibenstock granite, which was encountered at 1,200 ft (Viebig, 1905). Some of the persistent veins have been followed for more than 2 mi; they average less than 1 ft thick. The two intersecting vein systems trend northwest and east-northeast dipping steeply. Pitchblende shoots appear to be erratically distributed. Some of the wall rock has been impregnated by Ag, Bi, and U minerals, sericitized, and locally intensely silicified.

Here too pitchblende occurs closely associated with a reddish dolomitic gangue, which also contains quartz, chert, barite, fluorite, and rare calcite. The pitchblende forms crusts, bands, or botryoidal masses in a fine-grained galena-bismuth-chalcopyrite matrix. Veinlets of these minerals cut the pitchblende. Other minerals are sulfosalts of Ag and Bi, native silver, sphalerite, and rare Co-Ni minerals. Some veins are banded, others brecciated. Those entering granite become narrow and barren near the contact. The district is estimated to have been the source of 12 tons of pitchblende, of which 6.1 tons were produced in the period 1905 to 1907, much from the Vereinigt mine in the Fastenberg.

Other Deposits

One vein in the St. Viti mine at Durrnaul near Marienbad is reported to have contained a shoot with 100 to 150 tons of pitchblende. By-product pitchblende has been obtained from the rich silver veins at Annaberg.

In the contact-metamorphic magnetite deposit at Schmiedeberg (Meister, 1926), pitchblende occurs with martite close to the contact of the Riesengebirg granite, as veins, warts, and incrustations in and on hematite, on the margins of martite bodies. Some pitchblende lenses have been formed in adjacent silicified wall rock and altered hornblende schist. Calcite, coarse-grained and red, and quartz are the principal gangue minerals. Pitchblende follows boundaries between calcite grains and calcite breccia pieces. It is botryoidal with galena, ruby silvers, and covellite filling fractures, together with a second generation of pitchblende. Other ore constituents are chalcopyrite, bornite, covellite, niccolite, sphalerite, loellingite, violet fluorite (Hoehne, 1936), and vanadiferous muscovite (1.08% V_2O_3) (Jung, 1937). Some secondary uranophane and liebigite have been formed (Meixner, 1940A). The magnetite deposits are older and were transformed marginally to martite during the subsequent formation of pitchblende veins. At Breitenbrunn, northeast of Johanngeorgenstadt, is a similar occurrence, with veins of Zn-Cu minerals and minor pitchblende cutting contact magnetite ores.

Deposits at Freiberg, Saxony, are reported to have yielded 10 tons U_3O_8 from Ag-Co fissure veins in metasediments above a granite pluton. Other Czechoslovakian occurrences are at Pribram where the veins are concentrated along dikes cutting Ordovician graywacke. Small pods of pitchblende are contained in a 2- to 5 cm-footwall zone along the Johanni vein. Minor secondary uranium minerals also have been found in the Sn-W deposits at Zinnwald and Altenberg, and in the cassiterite deposits of Schönficht; pitchblende occurs in the cassiterite deposits of Schlaggenwald.

Mansfeld "Rücken"

The Mansfeld, Germany, Kupferschiefer (pages 490–491) is cut by fault fissures ("Rücken"), which have been mineralized by quartz-barite-carbonate vein material containing molybdenite, native bismuth, pyrite, maucherite, niccolite, chloanthite, cobaltite, wittichenite, Ni-Co selenides, pitchblende, and small amounts of chalcopyrite, bornite, manganite, galena, and sphalerite. The quartz is light smoky to amethystine; traces of anhydrite and fluorite also are present (Kohl, 1941; Kautzch, 1956; Messer, 1955). Secondary uranopilite, liebigite, and schroeckingerite are reported (Kohl, 1954). The pitchblende, which forms nodules, seams, and lenses as much as ½ in. thick, occurs chiefly in reddish carbonate and to a lesser extent in red barite. Uranium also appears in a radioactive solid hydrocarbon.

Some of the vein material is brecciated or shows banding in layers of calcite, barite, and quartz. The veins are generally regarded as hydrothermal in origin, the solutions stemming from a Variscan(?) granite mass discovered magnetically and intersected by boring at Dessau. Some investigators regard the vein fillings as entirely magmatic in origin; others believe that the ascending solutions dissolved ore and gangue material in the mineralized Mansfeld shale through which they passed. However, the veins and the shale do not contain entirely the same geochemical assemblage, nor are the elements present in the same proportions.

Black Forest

Since 1792, torbernite, autunite, and zeunerite have been known to occur at various localities in the Black Forest in Baden and Württenberg, Germany: Badenweiler, Leisberg near Baden-Lichtental, Eisenbach (Rappenloch mine), Wittichen (St. Anton and Sophia mines), Weiler near Geroldseck (Michael mine), Bühlhof in the Hinterhambachertal, Baden-Baden, and Reinerzau near Freudenstadt (Unverhofft Glück mine). Some of the occurrences are along fractures in granite, e.g., autunite in the Blue granite of Badenweiler, but most are associated with silver-nickel deposits. As early as 1840, Marignac determined that a smaltite specimen from the Sophia mine contained 15% U_3O_8 in the form of pitchblende (Kohl, 1954). Recent investigations by the Geologische Landesanstalt of Baden disclosed that many of the abandoned deposits in the Wittichen area are uraniferous and that the pitchblende commonly is intergrown with smaltite. Ore samples gave assays as high as 2.85% U, but most are less than 1%.

The veins are of the Ag-Co-Ni-Bi-U type with barite-fluorite-quartz gangue. In the Wittichen deposit, early fluorite and quartz were followed by barite, native silver, and bismuth, then by Ni-Co minerals, and last by fluorite, carbonate, and silver ores (Schneiderhöhn, 1955). They occur in granite which has been impregnated with smaltite and is cut by pitchblende veinlets up to

1 cm long. Some samples of wall-rock granite contain as much as 13% U (Kohl, 1954). The pitchblende, which forms botryoidal crusts, is relatively high in U^6. The veins, rarely mined for silver below 200 m, are worth further exploration for uranium.

AFRICA

Shinkolobwe Mine, Katanga, Belgian Congo

General

The Shinkolobwe (Kasolo) deposit, doubtless the largest single uranium deposit in the world and by far the most famous, is 20 km west of Jadotville and 20 km south of Kambove, in Katanga, in the southernmost part of the Belgian Congo near the border with Northern Rhodesia. Elisabethville is 80 mi to the southeast.

Copper deposits of the region were first recorded in 1902 by prospectors of Tanganyika Concessions, Ltd., but had previously been worked by natives. In 1915, a British army officer, Major Sharp, in the course of fixing concession boundaries, examined a rather inconspicuous ridge on which he noted copper-stained silicified outcrops. Very small pieces of a bright yellow material caught his eye, and two small trenches revealed the ore in place, analyses indicating that it consisted of uranium minerals.[1] Systematic geological studies and mining began in 1921. Production of radium from these rich ores ended mining operations in the small low-grade deposits of the Colorado Plateau, and the Shinkolobwe deposit had no serious rival as essentially the world's sole source of radium until the opening of the Eldorado mine on Great Bear Lake in 1933. Mining was suspended in 1936 when operations reached 57 m in the open cut and 79 m in the underground workings. In 1944, open-cut operations were reactivated, followed in 1945 by resumption of underground operations. During the 15-yr period of operations the deposit yielded 100,000 tons of radioactive minerals from 500,000 cu m of ore (Derriks and Vaes, 1956). Level 255 m represented the lowest underground workings in 1955. Shinkolobwe ore is treated at Olen, Belgium, where U, Pt, and Pd are recovered.

Although numerous papers on individual uranyl minerals have been published,[2] only two major contributions on the geology of the deposit have appeared—Thoreau and Du Trieu de Terdonck (1933) and Derriks and Vaes (1956).

[1] Buttgenbach (1947) notes an entertaining yarn published in an Anvers newspaper in 1928 in which a mythical Dutch expedition found the deposits through a tribe of natives who used the radioactive mud medicinally: " 'The secret of the extraordinary vitality and mysterious immunity of the natives against diseases was revealed: each, young or old, daily swallowed a certain quantity of this mud containing radium salts and used it on every occasion to dress sores and wounds.' " (Translation.)

[2] Summarized in Buttgenbach (1947).

Geology

The typical savannah region is characterized by low hills with scattered clumps of trees and tall grass and a thick soil cover revealing but a few deeply weathered outcrops. The area is underlain chiefly by folded and faulted sedimentary Precambrian rocks (Table 8.1) of the Katanga group consisting of the systems (descending): Kundelungu (800 to 2,500 m), the Grand Conglomerate and Mwashya (500 to 1,000 m), and the Schisto-Dolomitique. Mineralization occurs chiefly in the Mine series, in which silicification is a common feature; many of these strata also show the effects of low-grade metamorphism, containing talc and chlorite. There apparently is no unconformity between Kundelungu beds and older units.

Beds of the Mine series, the Mwashya system, and the Kundelungu system

TABLE 8.1. *Regional stratigraphy, Shinkolobwe, Katanga, Belgian Congo (adapted from Derriks and Vaes, 1956)*

System	Units	Petrology	Thickness
Kundelungu system	Upper	Not represented	
	Middle	Argillaceous shale and sandstone	Several m
		Silicified rock	Several m
		"Petit" conglomerate	60 m
	Lower	Sandstone and sandy shale	1,650 m
		Gray to red shale and intraformational conglomerate	900 m
		Kakontwe limestone and dolomite	Lensoid
		Gray-green shale	60 m
Grand Conglomerate and Mwashya systems	Grand Conglomerate	Poorly represented and not studied	More than 120 m
	Upper Mwashya		
	Lower Mwashya		
Schisto-Dolomitique system	Mine series	Chiefly dolomite and dolomitic sandstone with lesser chloritic shale, conglomerate	More than 75 m
		Dolomite, talcose dolomite, dolomitic quartzite, chert	60 m
		Magnesite	130 m
		Acicular dolomite	25 m
		Dolomitic micaceous shale and dolomite	30 m
		Siliceous dolomite	0–20 m
		Magnesite and siliceous dolomite	9 m
	R.A.T. group— (Roche argilotalqueuse)	Sandy, dolomitic shale, shale, and dolomite	More than 200 m

have been folded into a generally northwest-trending series of asymmetric anticlines and synclines. This arc, the Katanga synclinorium, is 200 mi long and as much as 65 mi across near its middle. In Rhodesia, the folds are generally simple and open, dipping usually less than 50°. Their axes trend and plunge northwest. In Katanga, northwest of the center of the belt, its trend swings westward and even slightly south of west; Shinkolobwe lies at this change in trend. Folding here is close and isoclinal. Westward folds are overturned to the north and northwest and are broken by thrusts. In some places so large a displacement is involved that the transported blocks have been termed nappes.

In the Shinkolobwe area, an irregular northeast-trending slice, consisting mainly of Mine series beds, dips southeast as a fold-fault wedge between synclinally folded Kundelungu strata both to the northwest and southeast. Longitudinal faults trending northeast further split the Mine series wedge, which is also segmented by cross faults that trend generally northwestward. These fault-bounded structural blocks within the Mine series wedge are referred to as spurs (Derriks and Vaes, 1956).

At the Shinkolobwe mine, where this wedge in contrast dips generally northwestward, three spurs are recognized at the surface, persisting downward to the 114-m level where they abut against the flat-lying front of a nappe (R.A.T. nappe) consisting of thick, overturned beds of dolomites and shales of the lowest unit in the Mine series (R.A.T. unit). At 150 m and below, the sequence of Mine series beds is continuous across the wedge except for minor cross-fault displacements. The juncture of the three blocks at the surface is marked by a pipelike breccia mass (Brèche de Remplissage), which continues to the lowest explored level. Below 114 m, it is first flanked and then at 255 m is surrounded by a lenticular mass of magnesite replacing dolomite.

Ore Deposits

Mineralization, both copper and uranium, is largely restricted in the Katanga to rocks of the Mine series. The primary copper sulfide deposits are mainly disseminations in dolomitic beds close to thrust faults. The exception is the Prince Leopold deposit at Kipushi, which is a pipelike replacement deposit in Mine series limestone extending up into Kundelungu beds (Bateman, 1950). Specimens of uranium minerals are listed from at least 13 localities, but veins of significant thicknesses occur only at Shinkolobwe and Kalongwe (Bain, 1950).

At Shinkolobwe the uranium minerals and their numerous associates occur as veins along fractures, bedding planes, joints, and minor faults; as breccia cement; as replacement masses and nodules; and as disseminated grains in chiefly dolomitic shale and siliceous dolomite. Individual veins lack continuity, but locally are so numerous that in aggregate they may appear as a stockwork. Veins range in thickness from a few centimeters to a meter. Some extend for only a meter or two, others are continuous for 10 m. The main faults are not mineralized but occupied by clay-talc breccias.

Mineralization to the 255-m level lies in the blocks and in the nappe between two major cross faults limiting the Shinkolobwe wedge to the east and west. Mineralization is particularly intense beneath the domelike structure formed by the front of the R.A.T. nappe, where minor faults and fractures are closely spaced. Beginning at about the 180-m level, uranium mineralization tends to shift eastward, although Co-Ni sulfides persist throughout. Below the 220-m level, uranium values tend to decrease in the central part of the wedge, and apparently here uranium disappears with depth. However, uranium mineralization continues as traces along the 50° west-dipping western boundary fault and in substantial amounts on both sides of the east-dipping eastern boundary fault.

Near the surface the ores consisted chiefly of oxidized minerals, but below the water table pitchblende and metallic sulfides predominate. The highest well-preserved sulfide vein was encountered at 79 m.

Mineralogy

The hypogene ores consist chiefly of uraninite, Co-Ni sulfides and selenides, with widespread molybdenite, pyrite, copper sulfides, gold, and monazite in gangues of dolomite, magnesite, chlorite, and lesser quartz (Table 8.2). Sulfides rich in selenium occur only below the dome of the R.A.T. nappe. Veins of selenium-free Co-Ni sulfides are relatively simple in mineralogical composition, whereas those rich in selenium are complex. Gold is relatively abundant in seleniferous veins, not in sulfide veins.

TABLE 8.2. *Hypogene minerals of the Shinkolobwe deposit*

U:
   Uraninite
   Urano-molybdenite (molybdate?)
Th-rare earth:
   Monazite
Sulfides-selenides-tellurides:

Co-Ni	Cu	Others
Cattierite *—CoS_2	Chalcopyrite	Molybdenite
Vaesite *—NiS_2	Bornite	Se-molybdenite
Ni-cattierite—$(Co,Ni)S_2$	Digenite	Pyrite
Co-vaesite $(Ni,Co)S_2$	Covellite	Galena
Se-vaesite	Umangite—Cu_3Se_2	Pd-sulfide(?)
Siegenite		Pentlandite (reported)
Se-siegenite		
Millerite		
Melonite—$NiTe_2$		

Native elements:
   Gold
   Copper (very rare)
Gangue:

Silicates	Carbonates	
Quartz (not common)	Calcite	Apatite (minor)
Chlorite	Dolomite	
Tourmaline (minor)	Magnesite	

* Kerr (1945).

Uraninite occurs as massive veins or in veins with Co-Ni sulfides. Also, outside of the uraniferous zones, Co-Ni mineralization may persist. Within the uranium-bearing zones the Ni:Co ratio is 3:1, whereas outside of these zones it shifts to 1:3. Below the 220-m level where uranium values diminish, Ni-Co minerals persist but are less abundant, especially Ni. Uraninite has not been found in cattierite veins.

Colloform pitchblende has not been recognized at Shinkolobwe. Cubic crystals are relatively common, especially in open fissures, or in wall rock, or embedded in vaesite, siegenite, monazite, or carbonates in veins. A few crystals as large as 4 cm on edge have been found. The crystals are corroded or veined by Se-vaesite, siegenite, Se-siegenite, gold, melonite, molybdenite, and monazite. A magnesium urano-molybdate in purplish elongated lamellae has been found on the 150-m level, formed by alteration of molybdenite associated with uraninite. Monazite is widespread, especially in brecciated rocks below the 114-m level.

The paragenetic sequence is (Derriks and Vaes, 1956):

Phase A. Magnesite

Phase B. Uraninite, pyrite

Phase C. Molybdenite, monazite, and chlorite; Se and Te in unidentified minerals, largely replaced by Co-Ni sulfides

Phase D. Quartz, cattierite-vaesite series

Phase E. Fracturing, dolomite

Phase F. Chalcopyrite

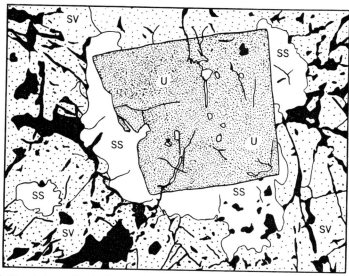

Fɪɢ. 8.5. Uraninite cube (U) in selenio-vaesite (SV), with partial replacement by selenio-siegenite (SS) initiated along the margins of the uraninite crystal. Reflected light ($\times$47) (after Derriks and Vaes, 1956).

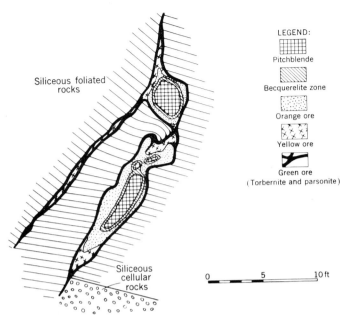

Fɪɢ. 8.6. Vertical section through a lenticular pitchblende vein, showing successive shells of uranyl minerals, Shinkolobwe, Belgian Congo (Thoreau and du Trieu de Terdonck, 1933).

Phase G. Hypogene transformations: cattierite-vaesite to siegenite with accompanying development of native gold from a gold selenide or telluride; melonite follows gold; chalcopyrite is altered to bornite, digenite, covellite, and umangite

Phase H. Supergene minerals

Supergene alteration resulted in the formation of most of the uranyl minerals (Table 8.3), essentially in situ. The lead in many of these species probably is radiogenic in origin. Some uranyl species have been precipitated by moving solutions at points away from their uranium sources, especially torbernite and metatorbernite. Kasolite occurs preferentially in dolomitic-graphitic shale, whereas torbernite is formed especially in cavities in siliceous dolomite. Autunite has not been found. Near-surface rocks with disseminated uranyl species are strongly silicified and cavernous.

Some of the veins near the surface show bands of various alteration minerals (Fig. 8.6), with a relict core of uraninite enveloped by successive zones of black ore (mainly becquerelite), orange ore (mainly curite), yellow ore (chiefly schoepite), and green ore (torbernite and parsonite).

The supergene ores are essentially of three main types:

1. Black ore, consisting mainly of the hydrous oxides, becquerelite and ianthinite, lesser schoepite and curite, relict uraninite, and minor sklodowskite and uranophane. Ianthinite alters to becquerelite

TABLE 8.3. *Supergene minerals of the Shinkolobwe deposit*

Minerals	Associated elements	Occurrence
Uranium:		
Hydrous oxides		
* Becquerelite	—	Surface, in situ
* Pb-becquerelite	Pb	Surface, in situ
* Billietite	Ba	Below 57 m
* Curite	Pb	Surface, in situ
* Epiianthinite	—	Surface, in situ
* Fourmarierite	Pb	Surface, in situ
* Ianthinite	—	Surface, in situ
* Masuyite	—	Below 57 m
* Richetite	Pb	Below 57 m
* Schoepite	—	Surface, in situ
* Vandenbrandeite	Cu	Surface, in situ
* Vandendriesscheite	Pb	Below 57 m
Phosphates		
* Dewindtite	Pb	Surface only, in situ
* Dumontite	Pb	Surface only, in situ
Metatorbernite	Cu	Redistributed, surface and below
* Parsonite	Pb	Surface only, in situ
* Renardite	Pb	Redistributed
* Saléeite	Mg	Redistributed
Torbernite	Cu	Redistributed, surface and below
Molybdate		
Mg-urano-molybdate	Mg	Below 57 m
Carbonates		
Rutherfordine	—	Below 57 m
* Sharpite	—	(?)
* Studtite	Pb	Below 57 m
Silicates		
* Cuprosklodowskite	Cu	Surface
* Kasolite	Pb	Redistributed
* Sklodowskite	Mg	Redistributed, surface only
* Soddyite	—	In situ and redistributed
Uranophane	Ca	Redistributed, surface(?) and below
Others:		
Wulfenite (alteration of molybdenite)		
Garnierite		
Black oxides of Co, Ni, Cu, and Mn (heterogenite → cobaltian wad)		
Quartz		
Cobaltian dolomite		
Aragonite		

* Denotes species found initially at Shinkolobwe.

2. Yellow-orange ore, little or no becquerelite or relict uraninite, curite very common and predominates in many cases, schoepite common, lesser soddyite and kasolite, uranophane more common than in black ores. This type of secondary ore corrodes and replaces black ore. The yellow to greenish-yellow variant contains chiefly schoepite with soddyite and uranophane; the orange variant consists mainly of curite with soddyite or uranophane; and the red-orange or red variant contains curite alone or curite plus kasolite. Both soddyite and kasolite replace curite

3. Zoned or striped ore, consisting chiefly of phosphates. Brown stripes are mainly parsonite, yellow dewindtite, and green torbernite

In a general way the paragenesis of the secondary minerals, although very difficult to decipher in detail, corresponds to the three ore types:

Stage 1. Hydrous oxides
      a. Ianthinite
      b. Becquerelite, schoepite, curite
Stage 2. Silicate stage
      Soddyite, kasolite, uranophane, sklodowskite
Stage 3. Phosphate stage
      a. Parsonite
      b. Dewindtite
      c. Torbernite
Stage 4. Minor recrystallized hydrous oxides, especially curite

Origin

The solutions rose chiefly along the eastern-bounding cross fault to approximately the present 150-m level where the channelways split, one group extending eastward at a low angle into the highly fractured rocks beneath the dome of the R.A.T. nappe, the other continuing upward below the impervious fault barrier separating the Mine series wedge from the overlying Kundelungu rocks into the fault blocks above the nappe (Fig. 8.7). The age of the uraninite is about 630 m.y., probably late Precambrian. The supergene alteration took place mainly at a time when the water table was much deeper; presently it lies at but 45 m.

Although granite is not exposed in the vicinity of the mine, post-Kundelungu granitic intrusives (Younger Granite) occur in the Katanga near the Rhodesian border, and at Muliashi, ore beds have been converted to amphibole-tourmaline-chlorite rocks. East of the Shinkolobwe mine, outcrops of highly altered igneous rocks, resembling trachyte, are exposed in shallow folds.

Derriks and Vaes (1956) view with some skepticism the generally accepted idea of essential contemporaneity of the Co-Ni-U mineralization and the much more widespread copper mineralization, pointing out: (1) that cobalt is uncommon in the copper deposits, Cu:Co = 6:1; (2) that copper is present only in minute amounts at Shinkolobwe; (3) that except for Kipushi the copper deposits are stratiform; Shinkolobwe mineralization is in veins; (4) that Ni, abundant at Shinkolobwe, is essentially absent in the copper deposits; (5)

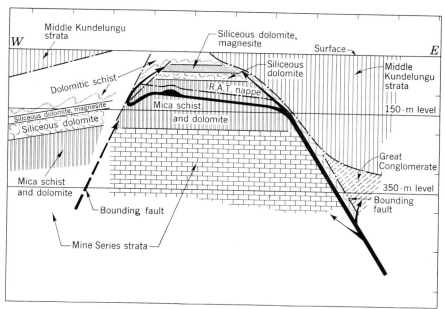

F_{IG}. 8.7. Longitudinal section of wedge of Mine series rocks with bounding faults, showing inferred directions of movement of uraniferous solutions, Shinkolobwe deposit, Belgian Congo (Derriks and Vaes, 1956).

that although uranium minerals occur in small amounts in some of the copper deposits, they occur as isolated masses and are not in the copper ores proper. Bain (1950) believes in a genetic relationship of the uranium and copper deposits, also supported by Turneaure (1955). Deposition from hydrothermal solutions took place under mesothermal conditions. Bain points out that even the copper mineralization in parts of the belt is influenced by fractures, and suggests that the minor uranium occurrences are related to Shinkolobwe in the same manner that Johanngeorgenstadt and other lesser uranium deposits of the Erzgebirge are related to Joachimsthal, the focus of the uranium mineralization. It has also been suggested that the Shinkolobwe ores represent a somewhat higher intensity, slightly earlier, and more restricted phase of the more general copper mineralization. Ideas on the interrelationship of the uranium and copper ores of the Katanga also bear significantly on consideration of the genesis of the Rhodesian copper ores (page 298), which likewise contain considerable cobalt and generally small amounts of uranium. It is also noteworthy that the relative abundance of selenium at Shinkolobwe is paralleled in the Goldfields district, Saskatchewan, but that at the former selenium is preferentially associated with Co-Ni, at the latter with Cu and Pb. Likewise, platinum metals are found in concentrations in both areas.

Schneiderhöhn (1955) regards the deposit as katathermal (hypothermal), deposited at high temperatures, probably with a pneumatolytic beginning.

Rhodesian Copperbelt

The Rhodesian Copperbelt, which covers 40×140 mi adjacent to the Belgian Congo, south and southeast of the Shinkolobwe mine, is the largest copper-producing district in the world, including five major mines: Roan Antelope, Nkana, NChanga, Mufulira, and Rokana. The host rocks are folded and weakly metamorphosed calcareous shales and arkoses of the Lower Roan formation, Katanga system, in which occur finely disseminated (0.06 mm) chalcopyrite, bornite, and chalcocite with minor pyrite and covellite. Minor elements include U, Co, Ni, Se, Te, As, and Sb. Cobalt as linnaeite and carrollite is present in significant amounts in parts of the Muliashi and Baluba deposits. Davis (1954) has shown that the disseminated ores may exhibit both lateral and vertical zonal distribution of Fe, Co, and Cu sulfides. The highest concentrations of U (as pitchblende) occur at the edge of the Cu zone where both Cu and Co values become uneconomic (Davidson, 1956B). In addition to the large disseminated deposits, e.g., Roan Antelope with over 100 million tons of 3.3% Cu ore (Davis, 1954), smaller but higher-grade veins, lenses, and pipes cut across the sedimentary strata. Nearly all of the Cu-Co ores are weakly radioactive (0.005 to 0.01% U_3O_8) but locally, as for example, in the Mindola section of the Nkana mine, uranium mineralization, without payable Cu values, is of economic significance.

The disseminated ore bodies are regarded by some investigators (Davis, 1954; Garlick, 1955) as syngenetic, possibly bacteriogenetic, modified by dynamothermal metamorphism. Arguments for an epigenetic origin have been summarized by Douglas (1955, 1956). Davidson (1956B) favors a hydrothermal origin, pointing to the similarity of the geochemical association to that at Shinkolobwe (Turneaure, 1955), and to the contemporaneity of the pitchblende age (about 612 m.y.) and that of a period of granitization in Tanganyika to the east. The S^{32}/S^{34} ratios fall within the magmatic, pegmatitic, and hydrothermal ranges, as well as within part of the biogenic range, and thus are inconclusive to determine whether the origin is hydrothermal-epigenetic or biogenic-syngenetic (Bateman and Jensen, 1956).

Weakly radioactive zones with sparsely disseminated uraninite occur at the Molly mine in Southern Rhodesia in the Sinoia district where copper minerals are disseminated through Precambrian arkoses in deposits similar to those of the Copperbelt (Davidson, 1956B).

PITCHBLENDE-PYRITE ($\pm$Pb, Cu, Ag SULFIDES) TYPE

UNITED STATES

Central City District and Adjacent Areas, Gilpin and Clear Creek Counties, Colorado

General Geology

In 1871, pitchblende was discovered for the first time in the United States in dump material from the Wood mine, Quartz Hill, near Central City (Pearce,

1875; Bruÿn, 1955). Before 1917 the district produced small amounts of pitch-blende as a radium source, and it is estimated that 110,757 lb of U_3O_8 has been obtained from the veins of the district, more than 98% from the Wood and Kirk mines (Armstrong, 1952). The area, which is in the Front Range mineral belt, is underlain by Precambrian metasediments and intrusives that are transected by Laramide faults and intruded by Tertiary dikes and stocks (Lovering and Goddard, 1950). The metasedimentary rocks include mainly biotitic and silli-manitic gneisses (Idaho Springs formation) and lesser lime-silicate gneiss and amphibolite (including Swandyke gneiss). Precambrian intrusives are quartz monzonite and granite gneiss, granodiorite, granite (Silver Plume), and peg-matites. The metamorphic layers have been deformed into northeast-trending folds with limbs of moderate dip.

Monzonites and bostonites are the most common types of Tertiary intrusives; others are granitic and granodioritic. Many of the quartz bostonite dikes are strongly radioactive, and are closely related spatially to pitchblende veins (Alsdorf, 1916; Phair, 1952).

Ore Deposits

The veins are fissure fillings along faults, mined chiefly for gold and silver but also containing copper, lead, zinc, and uranium ores. Numerous reports have recently appeared on the district (Wells and Harrison, 1954; Sims et al., 1955; Sims and Tooker, 1956; Merwin, 1956; Sims, 1956), on the adjacent Fall River area (Smith and Baker, 1951), and on individual deposits: King (1951B), Wood mine; Moore and Butler (1952), Drake (1957), Wood and Calhoun mines.

Some of the deposits in which pitchblende has been found are Alps, Belcher, Buckley, Calhoun, Carroll, Cherokee, German, Kirk, Leavenworth, Mitchell, Pewabik, Rara Avis, Wood, and Wyandotte. Metatorbernite occurrences have been studied at the Two Sisters and R.H.D. mines.

The oldest faults strike northwest and dip steeply north. Younger, less per-sistent sets trend successively northwest, east-northeast, northeast, and north-northeast, dipping steeply to moderately, with only small displacements. Most veins are a few hundred feet long and average a foot or less in thickness; some have been traced for a mile and to depths of nearly half a mile. Both individual fissure fillings and branching lodes are represented.

Successive alteration layers along the veins generally consist of an inner sericitized-silicified zone and an outer argillized zone of illite and montmoril-lonite (Tooker, 1955A,B, 1956). Kaolinite in the outer zone is of supergene origin.

Veins are of two main types: one with pyrite dominant, the other with sphalerite and galena; intermediate types also appear. The pyritic type con-tains mainly quartz and pyrite and lesser chalcopyrite and tennantite, with values chiefly in gold. The Pb-Zn ores also have minor pyrite and some local chalcopyrite and tennantite, with some veins rich in silver. Composite ores have been formed by reopening of pyritic veins and precipitation of galena and sphalerite; these have been the principal gold-producing deposits.

Pitchblende occurs in all three ore types but chiefly in the composite and

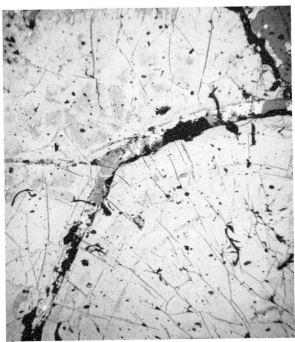

Fɪɢ. 8.8. Colloform pitchblende with pyrite along curving layers (selective replacement?) and in syneresis cracks, Wood mine, Central City, Colo. Note variation in reflectivity of pitchblende. Reflected light (×44).

Pb-Zn types, as pods and lenses usually no more than several inches thick and several tens of feet long (Sims and Tooker, 1956). In the Wood vein, pitchblende nodules and streaks occur on the footwall side within a gold ore shoot that rakes steeply west (Drake, 1955). The positions of gold ore shoots were controlled in a general way by the intersections of veins with brittle granitic layers (Armstrong, 1952). The known pitchblende ore shoots are small; the largest measures $1 \times 20 \times 50$ ft (Sims, 1955). The ore produced from the Wood and Kirk mines had an estimated average grade of 0.2% U_3O_8 (Armstrong, 1952).

Pitchblende occurs in veins that follow fractures trending northwest, west-northwest, east, or east-northeast, but not northeast (younger fractures). Veins tend to be wide and ore-bearing in quartz monzonite gneiss and pegmatite, but weakly mineralized to barren in biotite gneiss. Some calcium- or iron-rich wall rocks may have been chemically favorable hosts for pitchblende deposition in some of the Front Range deposits (Sims and Tooker, 1956), and in the nearby Fall River area pitchblende occurs in veins only along their intersections with garnet and quartzose lime-silicate rocks (Hawley and Moore, 1955).

The pitchblende ranges from hard, lustrous, colloform to soft, dull, sooty, fine-grained material (Fig. 8.8). Some is brecciated and veined by quartz. In oxidized parts of veins pitchblende has been altered mainly to torbernite, metatorbernite, and autunite, with minor kasolite, dumontite, and zippeite. The pitchblende, which contains unusual amounts of zirconium and molybdenum (Sims, 1955), was the first metallic mineral to crystallize; the pyrite stage was preceded by major fracturing; and base-metal minerals followed another period of reopening.

Metatorbernite, deposited from solutions that probably derived their copper and uranium from the pitchblende veins, replaces altered biotite-quartz-plagioclase gneiss and amphibolite wall rocks along vein margins in the supergene zone (Sims and Tooker, 1955). It is absent in other wall rocks. Torbernite also occurs in granite and pegmatite at distances from the vein deposits (King and Granger, 1952), indicating considerable local redistribution of uranium. Although a supergene origin for the torbernite appears more likely, ". . . it may be a primary mineral deposited directly from mineralizing fluids of different composition from those which deposited pitchblende" (Sims et al., 1955, p. 19).

The district is zoned with a pyritic vein–type core about 2 mi across, surrounded by a peripheral zone of veins of the Pb-Zn type. Between these is a transition zone containing composite-type veins. However the uranium deposits are locally clustered, and their distribution lacks correlation with the regional zonal pattern (Sims and Tooker, 1956), contrary to the earlier views of Leonard (1952).

The veins generally have been classed as mesothermal (Lindgren, 1933; Sims and Tooker, 1956; Sims, 1956), although a xenothermal classification has been advanced by Armstrong (1952) and suggested alternately by Leonard (1952). The mineralization is 55 to 70 m.y. old (Sims and Tooker, 1956), thus is early Tertiary. Phair (1952) concludes that the uranium solutions were derivatives of the cooling quartz bostonite magma at depth and were further enriched by solution of uranium from along quartz bostonite channelways, while passing to higher levels.

The uranium ore deposits of the district are small but generally high grade. Thus recovery is generally by-product to mining of precious metals and Pb-Zn ores. Since 1954, a few tons of uranium ore have been shipped from the district. At least one deposit of the secondary torbernite type, the Two Sisters mine, has substantial reserves of ore. Assays of selected samples of secondary ore may be very high (as much as 6.11% U), but averages are much lower (0.031% to 1.53% U) (Sims and Tooker, 1956).

In the adjacent Lawson-Dumont district, Clear Creek County, pitchblende occurs at the Jo Reynolds deposit in several veins in Precambrian Idaho Springs formation and Silver Plume granite cut by Tertiary bostonite dikes (Lovering and Goddard, 1950; King, 1951A; Harrison and Leonard, 1952; Merwin, 1956). The No. 2 vein is localized along a fault independent of Precambrian structures and has an ore shoot that trends N. 17° E., plunging 60° NE. Pitchblende, localized by transverse joints, occurs between the 900- to 1,050-ft levels. The vein also contains galena, pyrite, sphalerite, and some gold, chalcopyrite, tetrahedrite, silver sulfides, and sulfosalts in a quartz-siderite-hematite gangue.

At the Copper King mine in Larimer County, pitchblende and coffinite form veinlets and disseminations along faults and breccias in Precambrian skarn-type metasediments and in granite. The walls are chloritized and sericitized. The hematitic quartzose gangue contains less siderite and sparse pyrite, galena, copper sulfides, and molybdenite (Phair and Sims, 1954; Everhart, 1956B).

Jefferson County, Colorado

The several uranium deposits in the Golden Gate Canyon and Ralston Creek areas in northern Jefferson County occur along major Laramide fault and shear zones in Precambrian igneous and metamorphic rocks (Idaho Springs formation), especially hornblende gneiss, biotite schist, and pegmatite (Adams et al., 1953; Adams and Stugard, 1956A,B). The zones, which are occupied by carbonate-cemented breccia masses 1 to 5 ft thick, contain pitchblende, pyrite, pyrrhotite, chalcopyrite, tennantite, bornite, chalcocite, sphalerite, galena, emplectite(?), ankerite, calcite, hematite, quartz, adularia, chlorite, and barite. Ankerite is the most abundant cementing mineral. In part, the pitchblende is botryoidal in structure. Secondary species are covellite, copper carbonates, limonite, and the uranyl minerals, uranophane, uranopilite, autunite, torbernite, and metatorbernite. Along the breccia zones, hornblende gneiss wall rock has been severely bleached, involving replacement of hornblende by chlorite and plagioclase by sericite.

At several deposits in the Ralston Creek area high uranium values occur where the breccia veins cut garnetiferous biotite gneiss, and low values appear as they pass into overlying muscovite schist and underlying silicified hornblende and calc-silicate gneisses. The biotite gneiss is considered to have been a favorable host owing to its ability to supply abundant Fe^2 ions for uranium precipitation (Bird, 1956). Also the brittle nature of the gneiss led to the formation of an open breccia zone which is supplanted upward by a series of tight parallel slips, leading to impounding of upward-rising solutions.

Similarly in the Golden Gate Canyon district most of the known uranium occurrences appear where fault zones cross hornblende gneiss, a rock rich in Fe^2 (Adams and Stugard, 1956A,B).

The Schwartzwalder deposit is a northeast-trending siliceous vein cut by northwest fractures and occurs in silicified, sericitized, and slightly chloritized hornblende gneiss and mica schist of the Idaho Springs formation. In addition to quartz the gangue consists of ankerite and adularia with the metallic minerals pyrite, sphalerite, galena, copper sulfides, and minor molybdenum and manganese minerals (Everhart, 1956B). The radioactive species are pitchblende, and abundant secondary torbernite and autunite.

North Fork District, East-Central Idaho

At the Garm-Lamoreaux mine, about 10 mi north of North Fork, Idaho, Belt quartzite, schist, and phyllite are cut by a fracture zone that strikes N. 80° W. and dips 60 to 80° NE. (Trites and Tooker, 1953). The vein along the zone contains galena, gold, pyrite, quartz, goethite, torbernite, and autunite. Pitchblende also is present (Armstrong, 1954). Assays of samples range from 0.009 to 0.11% U. The Moon deposit, to the north on Blosche Gulch, is a gold-quartz vein that contains torbernite.

Other Occurrences

Numerous other minor occurrences of uranium, as pitchblende, have been described from base and precious metal vein deposits in Arizona (Wright, 1950; Everhart, 1956B), e.g., the Wallapai district, and in Colorado (Pierson et al., 1952). Of some economic and scientific interest is the Red Bluff mine in Gila County, Arizona, where fine-grained pitchblende, pyrite, and minor galena and copper sulfides are disseminated in dark bands and streaks in two favorable beds of the Precambrian Dripping Spring quartzite formation (Davis and Sharp, 1957). The mineralization is controlled by two fracture sets; one, dominant, is vertical and strikes N. 75° W., the other, minor, trends N. 20° E. (Everhart, 1956B). Diabase dikes occur nearby. The ore minerals have been largely secondary; metatorbernite, uranophane, and others are reported. Several hundred tons of ore were produced in 1952–1953.

CANADA

Montreal River Area, Ontario

Pitchblende (coracite), first reported from Theano Point in 1847 (LeConte, 1847), was rediscovered there by Robert Campbell in 1948, resulting in an extensive rush and in the staking of about 2,000 claims. By fall of 1951, activity had slackened. The area lies 70 mi north of Sault Sainte Marie in the Algoma district on the east shore of Lake Superior. It is underlain chiefly by Algoman(?) granite, granite gneiss, syenite, and pegmatite in which pre-Algoman mica gneisses, schists, and amphibolites occur as xenoliths. The Algoman(?) rocks are cut by Lower Keweenawan diabase dikes and locally overlain by basaltic flows (Middle Keweenawan) and by a few patches of conglomerate and sandstone (Upper Keweenawan) (Nuffield, 1950, 1956; Lang, 1952).

The numerous diabase dikes with which the pitchblende mineralization is associated trend generally west-northwest to northwest with a few trending east-northeast, and dip steeply. Some are more than 100 ft wide and traceable for several miles. They are generally altered to clinozoisite, chlorite, actinolite, antigorite, and quartz, and tend to weather out as trenches, especially along the shore of Lake Superior (Fig. 8.9). Pitchblende occurs as stringers and pods with hematite and calcite in fractures along diabase-granite contacts, which consist of abraded granite and diabase breccia fragments in a calcite-chlorite-hematite matrix. The fractures are up to 6 in. thick and may project into the granite for several feet. Most intersect the contact at low angles. Pyrite, galena, and clausthalite are minor associates of pitchblende (Fig. 8.10). Exposures of mineralized rock are coated by secondary yellow uranium minerals. The pitchblende-bearing fractures are erratically distributed along the diabase contacts, both horizontally and vertically, and are only locally abundant. At the Camray property the best zone, 110 ft long, averaged 0.034 to 0.037% U_3O_8

Fig. 8.9. Trench formed by weathering and removal of diabase dike in Algoman(?) granite, Theano Point, Montreal River district, Ont. Pitchblende mineralization is localized along footwall contact.

over 3 ft. At the Ranwick property a combined adit length of 302 ft assayed 0.039% U_3O_8. At the LaBine-McCarthy property the 12- to 15-in. brecciated mineralized zone is within a diabase dike, several feet from the south contact. Nuffield (1956) suggests a genetic relation of pitchblende and diabase. Of some 13 major occurrences that have been thoroughly explored, none has proved mineable.

Goldfields Region, Saskatchewan

History

The Goldfields region includes an area on the north shore of Lake Athabasca in northwestern Saskatchewan about 50 mi across, centering about Beaverlodge Lake. Gold was discovered in 1934, but operations ended in 1942. During gold development, pitchblende had been recognized at the Nicholson property by

F. J. Alcock in 1935, and thucolite was found at the Box mine. This led to further exploration of the area in 1944 to 1947 by the Canadian Crown Company, Eldorado Mining and Refining, Ltd., and the Canadian Geological Survey. General public prospecting was again permitted in 1948, and in 1949 the Saskatchewan government established 25-sq mi concessions which were sold to individuals and companies for exclusive prospecting rights to expire August, 1952. By 1952, some 300 sq mi was held as claims or concessions by seven main companies including Eldorado. Uranium in amounts of 0.05% U_3O_8 or more had been reported from 71 properties, and the total of individual occurrences was estimated at 2,400 (Lang, 1952). In June, 1953, the first production was shipped from Eldorado's Ace-Fay mine.

By fall 1957 the district had become a major world uranium producer with estimated production for 1957 valued at $54,000,000. Three mills are in operation—Eldorado, Gunnar, and Lorado—with a combined capacity of 4,000 tons/day. Major operations are: Black Bay Uranium, Cayzor, Athabasca Mines, Eldorado Mining and Refining, Gunnar Mines, Lake Cinch Mines, Lorado Uranium Mines, National Explorations, and Rix-Athabasca Uranium Mines (Can. Inst. Mining Met., 1957).

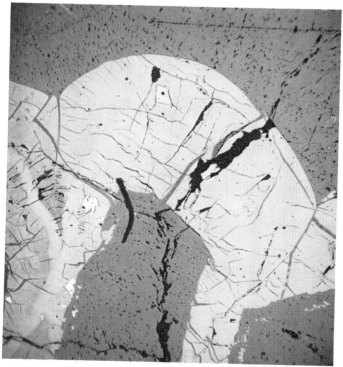

Fig. 8.10. Colloform pitchblende with inclusions of pyrite in calcite gangue. Note variations in reflectivity of the pitchblende. Ramwick property, Montreal River district, Ont. Reflected light ($\times$44).

General Geology

Table 8.4 shows the sequence of formations and their petrology (Buffam, 1951; Christie, 1953; Allen et al., 1954; Fraser, 1954; Hale, 1954; Tremblay, 1954, 1957). The Tazin group, 30,000 ft thick, consists of metasedimentary rocks, with subordinate amounts of metavolcanics. In places they grade into lit-par-lit gneisses resulting from the intimate intermingling of widespread granite, generally gneissic and containing Tazin xenoliths. Some quartzose granite masses are nonfoliated and very low in mafic minerals. Parts of the granite bodies have been altered metasomatically to quartz albitites containing variable amounts of chlorite, calcite, and sericite. The Tazin rocks are intruded by pegmatites and lamprophyre dikes, of postgranite age.

The slightly metamorphosed Athabasca series, clastic sediments and vol-

TABLE 8.4. *Formations in the Goldfields area, Saskatchewan (after Christie, 1953)*

Era		Formations and lithology
Proterozoic		Basic dikes
	Athabasca series	Basalt flows (a few sills) Arkose and sandstone Conglomerate
		Unconformity
Archaean or Proterozoic		Lamprophyre dikes
		Granite and granite gneiss; may contain inclusions of amphibolite and quartzite and bands of diopside or tremolite
		Intrusive contact
	Tazin group	Amphibolite Biotite schist or gneiss Garnetiferous gneiss Chlorite-epidote rocks
		Conglomerate Dolomite and dolomitic quartzite Ferruginous quartzite
		Quartzite

canics, occurs as remnants unconformably overlying older rocks or as down-faulted masses (Christie, 1953) (Fig. 8.11). Small dikes, monzonitic to gab-broic in composition, cut all other rocks in the area.

Foliation (and bedding) in the Tazin rocks strikes northeast except locally. The largest structure, the Martin Lake syncline, adjacent to the northwest part of Beaverlodge Lake, plunges 25° NE. To the southwest, an anticline near Milliken Lake, separated by granite, plunges 20° NE. Other major folds occur southeast of the syncline, and minor folds are common. Lineation is also well developed in Tazin rocks; boudinage structure occurs locally.

Three major faults are post-Athabascan in age. The Black Bay fault extends probably 25 mi, striking N. 35° E., and dipping 65° SE., and in general plac-ing granitic rocks on the northwest in contact with Athabasca rocks to the southeast. The St. Louis fault, 7 mi long, strikes N. 60 to 66° E. and dips 50° SE. from Beaverlodge Lake to Raggs Lake. The ABC fault, which probably represents the northwest-trending extension of the St. Louis fault, dips 40° SW., cutting off Athabasca rocks at the north end of the ridge separating Beaver-lodge and Martin Lakes. Broad zones of mylonites, flaser gneisses, and breccias, which have been developed in pre-Athabasca rocks flanking major faults, con-tain much hydrothermal quartz, hematite, calcite, and chlorite (Dawson, 1956).

Ore Deposits

Ore deposits containing pitchblende have been localized along fractures that cut all rock units. They include veins, tabular breccia zones, breccia pipes, and disseminations. Most commonly pitchblende occurs in narrow veins or stringers that fill tension fractures, but shears and faults also may be occupied. Essential vein constituents are hematite, calcite, chlorite, and pitchblende with minor pyrite, chalcopyrite, and galena; quartz is subordinate. Many veins show banding, comb-structure inclusions of wall-rock fragments, and coatings of colloform pitchblende over crystal terminations; a few have vugs. In some deposits postmineralization brecciation is conspicuous. In some parts of the area, it has been possible to relate the localization of pitchblende along frac-tures to deflections in strike or intersections (Hale, 1954). A deflection of the St. Louis fault 4,000 ft northeast of the Ace shaft has an ore body as much as 80 ft wide.

Wall rocks adjacent to the veins show conspicuous hematitic ("red") altera-tion, and vein carbonate likewise is colored red to brown (Dawson, 1951). Also commonly associated with the pitchblende deposits is a hydrothermal hematitic oligoclasite—a red, aplitic rock consisting chiefly of oligoclase with minor quartz, pennine, specularite, and calcite (Conybeare and Campbell, 1951). The plagio-clase crystals are euhedral to subhedral with irregular hematitic altered cores and clear fresh rims. Other constituents are interstitial. The oligoclasite occurs as lenses, particularly directly beneath the St. Louis fault, along or across the metamorphic foliation, replacing argillite, chlorite schist, granite gneiss, biotite gneiss, and mylonite.

Some of the veins also contain as local and usually minor associates of pitch-blende (Robinson, 1955A,B) (1) nolanite ($3FeO \cdot V_2O_3 \cdot 3V_2O_4$); (2) copper and lead selenides—clausthalite, klockmannite, umangite, berzelianite, com-

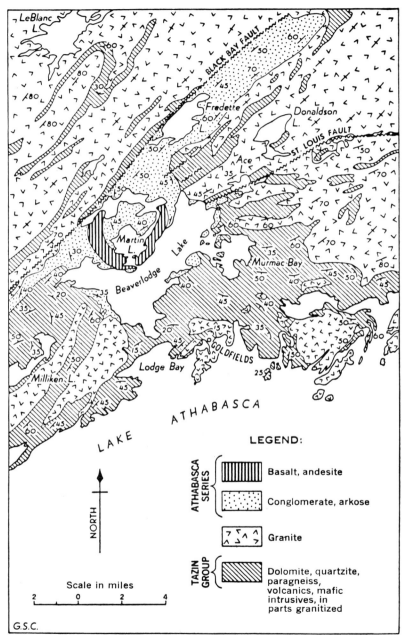

LEGEND:

ATHABASCA SERIES

| | Basalt, andesite |
| | Conglomerate, arkose |

| | Granite |

TAZIN GROUP

| | Dolomite, quartzite, paragneiss, volcanics, mafic intrusives, in parts granitized |

Scale in miles

2   0   2   4

NORTH

G.S.C.

FIG. 8.11. Generalized map of part of the Goldfields region, Saskatchewan (after Christie, 1953; Lang, 1952; *Geol. Survey Canada*).

308

monly with native copper; (3) Co, Ni, and Fe arsenides—arsenopyrite, niccolite, and rammelsbergite, pararammelsbergite, cobaltite, siegenite, ullmanite;
(4) native gold; and (5) hisingerite and a uraniferous hydrocarbon that lacks
thorium (Bowie, 1955). Other uncommon vein constituents locally associated
with pitchblende include copper sulfides (bornite, chalcocite, covellite), silver
minerals (silver, dyscrasite, proustite), iron sulfides (marcasite, pyrrhotite),
sphalerite, titanium oxides (rutile, anatase, ilmenite), and the nonmetallics
barite, ankerite, and dolomite. Native tin occurs in grains up to 1.5 mm across
in calcite in pitchblende ore at the Nesbitt-LaBine mine (Silman, 1954). Exceptional concentrations of the platinum metals (Pd up to 443 g/ton) in some
Athabasca ores (Hawley and Rimsaite, 1953) appear to have a rough relation
to the amount of gold present, in which they probably occur in solid solution.

The pitchblende is invariably low in thorium and rare earths. Some has been
regarded as metamict (Conybeare and Ferguson, 1950), but the x-ray effects
are ascribable to a very fine grain and oxidation of U^4 to U^6 (Brooker and
Nuffield, 1952). Some pitchblende grains disseminated through calcite are of

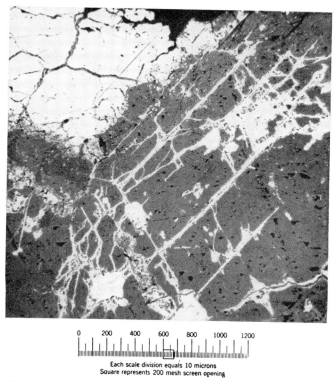

0   200   400   600   800   1000   1200

Each scale division equals 10 microns
Square represents 200 mesh screen opening

Fig. 8.12. Pitchblende ore, Goldfields district, Saskatchewan, Canada. Pitchblende
(light) in two generations. Upper left pitchblende has been corroded by calcite.
A later generation of pitchblende replaces calcite along cleavage directions (Robinson, 1955A; *Geol. Survey Canada*).

FIG. 8.13. Fine-grained pitchblende (black), chlorite, and hematite (dark) replacing brecciated calcite, Goldfields region, Saskatchewan (×35).

the order of 10^{-5} cm (Robinson, 1955A). Four main textural types of pitchblende are recognizable: colloform aggregates, interstitial or included anhedral forms, sooty or dusty aggregates, and euhedra. Some colloform pitchblende has been brecciated and recemented by other minerals, including anhedral pitchblende. Colloform types are peripherally banded, and in large part spherulitic, occurring as individual botryoids, as swarms of partly coalesced groups, as irregular rounded aggregates, and as wavy banded rims on early minerals or rock pieces. Radial syneresis fractures are common and may be filled by dusty hematite, calcite, chlorite, sulfides, and younger pitchblende. Outer zones may contain marked concentrations of inclusions of sulfides, calcite, or gold. Some botryoids have an intermediate layer of calcite, and calcite and sulfides also replace central parts of botryoids.

The anhedral pitchblende forms, with other species, cement in brecciated vein material, replaces calcite along cleavages (Fig. 8.12) zonally or pseudomorphously, or appears as elongated lenses or wisps in chlorite or other gangue species. Much anhedral pitchblende is minutely intergrown with hematite, calcite, chlorite, chalcopyrite, pyrite, and galena (Fig. 8.13).

The rare sooty variety is restricted to deposits where probable supergene alteration has taken place. Also rare are uraninite euhedra, largely restricted to crystals molded over or perched on comb quartz.

The pitchblende mineralization of the area is younger than the gold-quartz mineralization. Six overlapping phases of mineralization, not all represented in a single deposit, have been deciphered by Robinson (1955A), who notes numerous exceptions and local reversals of the idealized sequence (Fig. 8.14).

Uranyl minerals occur in outcrops and persist to about 1,000 ft in the Gunnar deposit and to 975 ft in the Ace mine. Species identified (Robinson, 1955A; Hogarth, 1951) are becquerelite, fourmarierite, masuyite, vandendriesscheite; the carbonates liebigite and studtite; the sulfates zippeite and uranopilite; the arsenate metazeunerite; the vanadate tyuyamunite, in two deposits that have nolanite; and the silicates cuprosklodowskite, sklodowskite, kasolite, and uranophane. Uranophane is the chief uranyl mineral (and an ore mineral) in the Gunnar deposit.

Age

Numerous radioactive age determinations based on lead-uranium and lead isotope ratios have been made on Athabasca pitchblende (Collins et al., 1952, 1954; Robinson, 1955A; Eckelmann and Kulp, 1956). The more recent results indicate apparent ages ranging from about 200 to 1,900 m.y., with two groups of ages well represented, 850 to 950 m.y. and 230 to 350 m.y. Pitchblendes of different ages show no systematic geological distribution.

Explanations for the tremendous spread on age determinations include:

1. An initial period of pitchblende deposition 1,900 m.y. ago with reopening and reworking over a long period of time, with two additional later periods of mineralization, the youngest in Paleozoic time (Robinson, 1955A)

2. An initial and single period uranium mineralization 1,900 m.y. ago, and two subsequent periods of lead exsolution, with variable lead fractions removed as pitchblende was recrystallized in the presence of solutions at temperatures

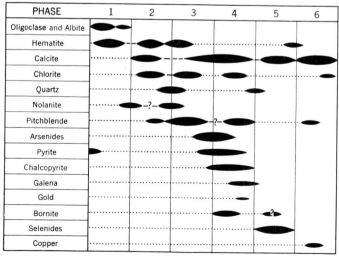

Fig. 8.14. Generalized paragenetic sequence of minerals in deposits of Goldfields region, Saskatchewan (Robinson, 1955A; *Geol. Survey Canada*).

between 150 and 300°C. Uranium leaching and radon leakage are inadequate to explain the anomalies in the apparent isotopic ages (Eckelmann and Kulp, 1956)

Origin

Mineral deposition is considered to have taken place at relatively shallow depths, chiefly between 250 and 350°C and over a vertical range of probably more than 2,500 ft. Thus the deposits are to be classed as upper mesothermal or leptothermal (Robinson, 1955A). The source of the mineralizing solutions is not known, but it is not likely that they are related to the late mafic rocks, whose distribution is not related to that of the pitchblende. Pitchblende veins follow fractures in diabase on the Aurora Uranium and Gold Mines, Ltd., property where abundant bladed rutile and apatite have been recrystallized along vein margins. At the Chum deposit, pitchblende veins also are younger than one generation of diabase. The mineralization, which was controlled by faults and fractures, took place largely in post-Athabasca time.

ABC Group (Nesbitt-LaBine)

The chief deposits at the ABC group, east of Melville Lake, occur in a shatter zone where a northeast fault in Tazin rocks swings tangentially against a major northwest fault that has down-faulted Athabasca rocks on its southwest side. The deposits consist dominantly of hematite (up to 50%) in at least three generations, with lesser pitchblende, pyrite, chalcopyrite, and traces of galena. The gangue constituents, quartz, calcite, and chlorite, are subordinate.

Ace and Fay Mines (Eldorado Mining and Refining, Ltd.)

The deposits extend for 6,000 ft along the St. Louis fault between Ace and Beaverlodge Lakes, largely within footwall rocks 200 ft or less below the plane of the normal fault which dips 50° SE. (Fig. 8.15). Footwall rocks are mainly Tazin chlorite-epidote schists, whereas hanging wall rocks are chiefly granite gneiss, which are highly sheared and chloritized near the fault. Two main ore bodies, relatively poor in sulfides, have been found, one near Ace Lake and the other 700 ft to the southwest.

Consolidated Nicholson Deposits

The Consolidated Nicholson properties of five separate deposits are on the north shore of Lake Athabasca, 2 mi east of Goldfields. The deposits consist of northwest zones of discontinuous veins along subparallel fractures and shears, chiefly in quartzite and dolomitic quartzite near contacts with hematitic quartzite breccia. The mineralization includes pyrite, Ni-Co arsenides, silver and silver sulfides, gold, nolanite (with platinum metals), tiemannite, copper sulfides, pitchblende, galena, calcite, and dolomite. Hisingerite with minute pitchblende inclusions and massive hematite occurs in one ore shoot, and much pitchblende is marginally replaced by thucolite. The No. 4 vein locally shows crude banding, vugs (one measured $20 \times 8 \times 12$ ft!), and wall-rock inclusions.

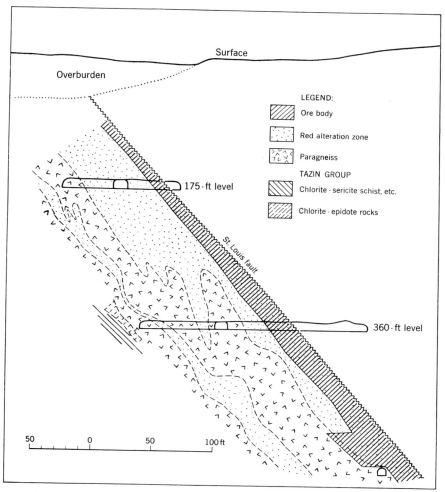

Fig. 8.15. Cross section of ore body, Ace mine, Goldfields region, Saskatchewan (R. B. Allen; Lang, 1952; *Geol. Survey Canada*).

Eagle Mine

Pitchblende veins with hematite cut mainly Tazin epidote-chlorite rocks in four subparallel northeasterly systems at the Eagle mine, near Eagle Lake, north of Beaverlodge Lake. Calcitic veins contain hematite, pyrite, chalcopyrite, bornite, and pitchblende that is botryoidal, anhedral, or forms selective replacements after zoned calcite. Quartzose veins contain chiefly hematite and pitchblende, both anhedral and euhedral. North of Hal Lake 1,500 ft west of the Eagle shaft pitchblende with selenide masses occurs in three small deposits in shear zones cutting granitized mafic rocks. Umangite is especially abundant, replacing pitchblende and altering to chalcomenite.

Gunnar Mine

The Gunnar deposit, on the south end of Crackingstone Peninsula, is a mineralized breccia pipe in a "syenite" mass—an albite granite in which quartz has been selectively replaced by calcite; chlorite also is present (Jolliffe, 1955, 1956; Evoy, 1956). Some ore also occurs in smaller adjacent syenite bodies. The main pipe plunges south at 45° for a known length of 1,400 ft with a maximum near-surface diameter of 450 ft. Between 250 and 350 ft, it changes in plan from a rough circle to a figure eight, the northern unit of which pinches out (Fig. 8.16).

The ore consists of finely disseminated pitchblende and uranyl minerals, chiefly uranophane. Much ore and wall rock is hematitized, and locally the ore is vuggy owing to removed calcite. Small amounts of pyrite, chalcopyrite, galena, and dolomite are present. The uranophane/pitchblende ratio varies without relation to the present surface. Uranophane persists to at least 1,000 ft and probably represents oxidation in place, without marked migration of uranium, in the absence of supergene waters charged with H_2SO_4 (essential absence of pyrite, abundance of calcite).

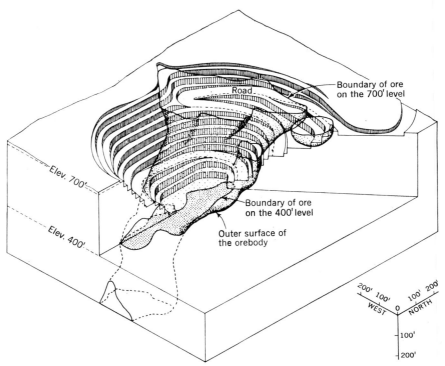

Fig. 8.16. Block diagram of Gunnar ore body, Goldfields region, Saskatchewan (Evoy, 1956; *Mining Eng.*).

Martin Lake Mine

Ore lenses at the Martin Lake mine, between Martin and Beaverlodge Lakes, lie along minor shears that dip parallel with major faults of a blocky system that intersects Athabasca rocks. The northeast-trending shear zones are mineralized chiefly in basalt, but little in arkose. Hematite and carbonate have been introduced into wall rocks. The lenses contain copper sulfides, selenides, native copper, two generations of pitchblende, barite, and calcite in four generations.

Rix Mine

At the Rix mine, which is northwest of the Black Bay fault and west-southwest of Uranium Ctiy, mineralization is localized across a wide transverse fault breccia (201 zone) (Joubin, 1955A). One ore type consists of a parallel system of calcite-pitchblende veins 1 to 5 ft across, in the hanging wall of the zone. These high-grade veins converge at about 300 ft into a zone up to 30 ft wide. Pitchblende is concentrated where veins intersect bands of pegmatite in amphibolite. The second type consists of lenses of brecciated oligoclasite adjoining the 201 zone, cut by stringers of calcite-pitchblende and crossed by mylonite bands. The lenses are up to 450 ft long, 350 ft down dip, and 35 ft thick, cutting hybrid gneisses.

Nisto Deposits, Black Lake, Saskatchewan

The Nisto deposits on the west side of Black Lake, east of Lake Athabasca, are mineralized fracture and shear zones, up to 2 ft wide and 600 ft long in Tazin group paragneisses and other metasediments and in gabbroic sills and dikes. The quartzose veins are in contrast to the Athabasca carbonate-rich types and contain pitchblende, chalcopyrite, galena, and hematite (Lang, 1952). Cobaltite and stibnite have been identified doubtfully.

PLACER DE GUADALUPE, EASTERN CHIHUAHUA, MEXICO

At Placer de Guadalupe, black fissile shales with interbedded sandstone and limestone of Upper Jurassic age are intruded by 4- to 8-ft porphyritic andesite dikes (Krieger, 1932; Reyna, 1956) that strike N. 70 to 80° W. and dip 65° S. to vertical. Along the hanging wall contacts between the dikes and the shales, metalliferous quartz-carbonate veins, 8 in. to 2 ft thick, parallel the dikes. The dikes are thoroughly altered hydrothermally to sericite, kaolinite, quartz, calcite, and pyrite. Vein apophyses cut both the dikes and the shales, and wall-rock pieces included in the veins are replaced by quartz, calcite, and metallic minerals.

The metallic vein constituents are pyrite, uraninite, gold, minor magnetite, and chalcopyrite. Uraninite forms euhedra and aggregates ranging in size from microscopic to an inch across. Some have cores partly replaced by pyrite. Uraninite is accompanied by gold, and enclosing calcite has been colored pink. The sequence of formation of the metallic minerals has been pyrite, uraninite, and gold. Above the water table uraninite has been leached out, leaving cavities containing wire gold and some uranophane. The uraninite is thorium-low ($ThO_2 = 0.05\%$) but contains 5 to 6% of rare-earth oxides. An age determination indicates that it was crystallized 36 m.y. ago, or in Oligocene time (Wells, 1930).

Uraninite has been found at a number of mines (especially at the La Virgen, Bolaños, and San Blas) in a northwest-southeast zone, 3 km long and 1.5 km wide. Veins richest in calcite contain highest gold and uranium values, whereas those rich in quartz are low grade. Although gold has also been found in small placer deposits in the sands and gravels of nearby arroyos, uraninite has not been recognized in these deposits.

EUROPE

Margnac, France

At Margnac in Limousin in the western Massif Central, mineralization consists of pitchblende impregnations in crushed and altered granite (Roubault, 1956). Richer mineralization occurs in irregular lenses separated by lower-grade rock. Pyrite, marcasite, galena, and locally abundant hematitized calcite are associated minerals. At the surface the deposits are represented by abundant disseminations of gummite and autunite. The deposits differ considerably from others in the Limousin area, e.g., La Crouzille, Le Brugeaud, which are definitely epithermal.

Weissenstadt, Bavaria, Germany

The Weissenstadt district in the Fichtelgebirge, northeastern Bavaria, a former source of tin, also has long been known for occurrences of torbernite and autunite along fractures and in quartz veins cutting the Fichtelgebirge granite. Around at least one of the torbernite-bearing fractures, the granite is markedly radioactive and contains, in addition to its usual accessories (magnetite, ilmenite, and zircon), wolframite, arsenopyrite, chalcopyrite, sphalerite, pyrite, and euhedral to subhedral crystals of thorium-low uraninite (0.1 to 0.3 mm) (Neuhaus, 1954). The rock contains 9 to 10 g U/ton.

Further investigations have disclosed numerous other torbernite-quartz veins and torbernite fracture coatings (Kohl, 1954). Torbernite is especially abundant at vein intersections and persists to at least 200 m.

Cuneo-Lurisia District, Italy

Uranium mineralization, occurring in the foothills of the Maritime Alps south of Cuneo and Mondovi about 60 mi west of Genoa, is in three zones of highly folded chlorite-sericite schists of Permian age (Nininger, 1954; Ippolito, 1956). The mineralization consists of small, irregular quartz-pyrite veins and lenses mainly localized in schistose layers near contacts with quartzite that forms a transition to Lower Triassic rocks. The lenses also contain chalcopyrite, hematite, calcite, carbonaceous material, pitchblende (generally sooty), torbernite, autunite, uranophane, and other uranyl species. Adjacent wall rocks have kaolinized feldspar and introduced pyrite and hematite.

The mineralization is believed to be premetamorphic and is regarded as ". . . due to an alteration brought about by metamorphism on enrichments of sedimentary origin" (Ippolito et al., 1956).

At Rio Freddo, pitchblende occurs at a depth of 10 to 15 m, beneath autunite mineralization. About 300 tons of ore contained 2 to 5% uranium.

TURKEY

Uranium minerals were discovered in the nineteenth century near Edirne (Adrianople) along the east branch of the Maritsa River just east of the Bulgarian border. The ore consists of pitchblende with calcite, chalcopyrite, galena, and some silver and secondary torbernite, liebigite, medjidite (a doubtful uranium sulfate—Smith, 1848), gypsum, and iron oxides.

KON-I-MANSUR MINE,
KARA-MAZAR MOUNTAINS, U.S.S.R.

Abnormal radioactivity is reported in the deposits of the Kon-i-Mansur mine near the Uzbekistan-Tadzhikistan border, where a complex vein system cuts andesite. Galena, pyrite, minor argentite, sphalerite, tetrahedrite, and rare chalcopyrite are present (Kohl, 1954).

AUSTRALIA

Darwin-Katherine Area, Northern Territory

Uranium deposits were discovered at Rum Jungle,[1] 60 mi south of Darwin, Australia, in September 1949, and the district is presently producing ore. Most of the deposits occur in the Brooks Creek group (Lower Proterozoic), consisting of metaconglomerates, quartzites, some black slates, and marbles, including a metalimestone reef breccia (Sullivan and Matheson, 1952; Fisher and Sullivan, 1954; Ward, 1954; Sullivan, 1955). The deposits, of which the White and Dyson are most important, occur on the southern flank of a north-south dome whose core is a granite complex 10 × 6 mi in plan (Fig. 8.17). They are in folded metasediments close to the abnormally radioactive granite. The Giant's Reef fault, which trends northeast across the southern end of the dome, places granite on the southeast in contact with metasediments to the northwest. In this block of metasediments, a major east-pitching drag fold has been overturned to the north. Axial plane shears parallel with the Giant's Reef fault have been developed in beds along the flanks of the fold. Later north- and north-northeast—trending faults offset the fold and the major fault. Fault planes of both age groups are locally occupied by quartz veins.

[1] *The New Yorker* of November 15, 1952, states, "There are a number of explanations of how Rum Jungle got its name. The most likely one is this: Back at the end of the last century the place was known simply as the Jungle. At that time a group of miners were digging for tin in the slate there, and a storekeeper used to go out from Darwin to supply them with the basic needs of life—tea, sugar, flour, meat, tobacco, and liquor. For a while, things went on well enough; then the ore petered out, and after a bit the storekeeper refused to extend the miners any further credit. Outraged, they broke into his storehouse one night and stole a barrel of rum. In their eagerness to get at its contents, the men shattered the barrel, and the liquor flowed down a slope and into a spring that fed a pool there. In the morning, the miners were discovered happily lapping up the miraculous tonic from the pool."

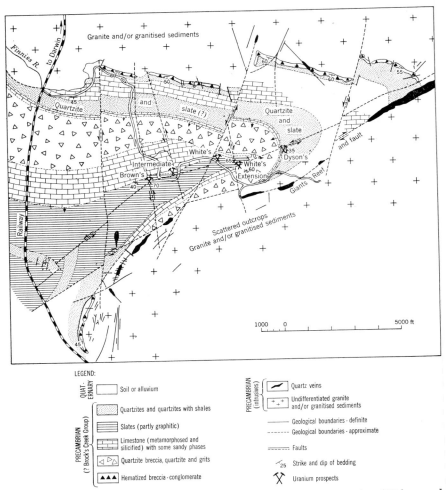

Fɪɢ. 8.17. Map of Rum Jungle area, Northern Territory, Australia (Fisher and Sullivan, 1954; *Econ. Geol.*).

The deposits, which occur chiefly in carbonaceous slate and graphitic schist and to a lesser extent in breccia and metaconglomerate (Crater prospect) are (1) replacements along bedding foliation and fracture cleavage near intersections of the cross faults with axial plane shears, (2) quartz veinlets across schist, and (3) replacements of breccia zones. Both copper-rich and copper-poor deposits are present. The primary mineralization consists of chalcopyrite, bornite, bournonite, pyrite, and uraninite. Traces of sphalerite, hematite, and bravoite(?) are reported. Chalcopyrite replaces uraninite and pyrite (Stillwell, 1952). Chalcocite and covellite appear near the water table. Oxidized ores, which may persist to a depth of 100 ft, consist of azurite, malachite, pseudomalachite, dihydrite, iron oxides, torbernite, and phosphuranylite. At Dyson's deposit, the chief oxidized mineral is saléeite (previously identified as autunite), and copper minerals are negligible. Major mineralization occurs at five groups of deposits extending along a line parallel to and northwest of the Giant's Reef fault, for a distance of about 6,000 ft.

Similar deposits occur in the South Alligator River area and at Sleisbeck (Sullivan, 1955). At the latter, saléeite-sklodowskite ores occur near the surface, and pyrite and sooty pitchblende appear at depths. In the former, the mineralized belt parallels a major fault zone close to a limestone reef breccia. At the El Sharana mine, pitchblende occurs with galena. The ores here are reportedly very rich (up to 9% UO_2) with 1 ton produced that assayed 80% UO_2. One ore body extends 350 ft, with an average width of 35 ft. In the Fergusson River prospect, uraninite ore occurs as disseminations and veinlets in muscovite gneiss. This deposit, which is representative of those closer to or in granite, contains pyrite, chalcopyrite, abundant cobaltite, loellingite, tennantite, covellite, and traces of enargite and native bismuth (Stillwell, 1952).

Secondary uranium minerals occur at the ABC prospect near Katherine, mainly in a felsic sill that intrudes altered mafic volcanic rocks close to a major fault. In the Edith River area, meta-autunite, torbernite, apatite, fluorite, hematite, and limonite occur in narrow quartz veins, in part brecciated and mylonitized, within a north-trending, greisenized shear zone in the Cullen granite.

In general in the area, uranium mineralization is associated with sheared anticlines and northeast-trending faults, especially where favorable host rocks (graphitic schist and slate) have been extensively shattered (Rade, 1956, 1957).

The deposits display many characteristics of typical replacement, epigenetic hydrothermal lodes—close structural control, both large and small scale; crosscutting relations to original host rock structures; close spatial relationships to abnormally radioactive granite; and regional zoning (Cu-rich and -poor, presence of Co). The mineralogical and geochemical association and the nature of the available structures suggest deposition under mesothermal conditions. It has been suggested, however, that all of the minerals, or all except chalcopyrite, were included in the sediments at the time of their deposition and were concentrated (*a*) during sedimentation, (*b*) during tectonic activities, or (*c*) during the period of granitic activity.

AFRICA

Witwatersrand, Union of South Africa

General

The gold ores of the Rand, one of the most famous and productive gold districts of the world for many years, occur in thin conglomerate beds ("reefs") within the Precambrian Witwatersrand system. Radioactive substances were first reported in the ores in 1915, and in 1923, Cooper (1923) identified the substance as uraninite. Diamonds, colored green by radiation, also had been found from time to time. Preliminary investigations by Bourret in 1944 led to field studies by Bain and Davidson in 1945 (Davidson, 1953), which not only indicated that uranium could be recovered as by-product to gold mining, but also that the Rand might become a major source of uranium. In October, 1949, a large pilot plant was installed at Blyvooruitzicht Gold Mining Company, Ltd., and in October, 1952, the West Rand Consolidated uranium mill began operations. By the end of 1956, 24 of 29 authorized mills were in production, with an annual output of 5,000 tons U_3O_8.

The district, the world's largest gold field, seems destined to become one of the world's largest uranium districts, if not the largest. By 1957, blocked-out ore totaled 65 million tons of grade 0.172 to 2.27 lb U_3O_8 per ton. The potential of the district is estimated at 1.1 billion tons of ore.

Geology

The Witwatersrand system is subdivided into a Lower (3 mi thick) and an Upper (2 mi thick):

B. Upper
   6. Kimberley-Elsburg series
   5. Main-Bird series
A. Lower
   4. Jeppestown series
   3. Government Reef series
   2. Hospital Hill series
   1. Dominion Reef series

The Lower consists of alternating quartzitic and argillaceous units, whereas the Upper is predominantly quartzite. Ore occurs in about a dozen thin conglomerate beds (bankets), mainly in the Upper subdivision, the chief ones being in the Main-Bird series with three payable members: Main Reef, Main Reef Leader, and South Reef, each 1 to 10 ft thick. In a particular area, usually only one or two beds are ore-bearing (Table 8.5). The beds are cut by dikes

TABLE 8.5. *Significance of the Witwatersrand reefs*

1. *Carbon Leader.* To be worked for uranium in Blyvooruitzicht and West Driefontein mines
2. *Main Reef series.* Although these reefs have accounted for over 95% of the Rand's gold production to date, no economic uranium occurrence has been reported in them
3. *Bird Reef series.* In the West Rand this includes several bands commonly poor in gold; one, the Monarch, is highly uraniferous. In the Klerksdorp and Orange Free State areas the Monarch Reef is equivalent to the Basal or Vaal Reef, above which lies the Leader Reef, of importance for both gold and uranium
4. *Kimberley Reef series.* Worked for gold in the East and West Rand. Significantly uraniferous in the East Rand (Daggafontein and Vogelstruisbult), but apparently not in the West
5. *Elsburg series.* Worked only south of Klerksdorp (Western Reefs). Important for both gold and uranium

of various types and ages and by numerous quartz veins both along and across the bedding. The beds have been folded into a broad syncline with low dips on the margins of the field and steep dips in the center. They also have been displaced by considerable faulting. The pebbles, averaging 70% of the conglomerate and just under an inch in size, are quartz, quartzite, jasper, quartz porphyry, tourmaline rock, and rare slate and schist. In the gold reefs of Southern Rhodesia, unlike those of the Witwatersrand to the south, only three minor uranium occurrences have been found (Davidson, 1956B).

Ore Deposits

The ore is mineralized conglomerate matrix, consisting mainly of pyrite (3 to 12%), gold, sericite, chlorite, chloritoid, secondary quartz, and pitchblende and thucolite. Other nonclastic minerals are minor calcite, dolomite, pyrrhotite, pentlandite, marcasite, chalcopyrite, sphalerite, galena, cobalt, and nickel arsenides including cobaltite and niccolite, rutile, tourmaline, and monazite. Regarded as detrital are chromite, corundum, zircon, platinum, iridosmine, and diamond. The quartz veins carry gold, talc, tourmaline, and sulfides.

The gold commonly is unevenly distributed, concentrated toward either the top or base of a conglomerate bed, usually associated with larger pebbles, well-graded pebbles, and oriented pebbles in elongated shoots that are as much as 1,000 ft wide and 5,000 ft long, with axes roughly parallel or braided. These features of the conglomerates are considered to result from flow in well-defined channels in which material was transported from the northwest and west, with the axes in a fan-shaped arrangement, open to the east and southeast in the Central and East Rand.

Gold and uraninite show similar distribution. Of the total tonnage treated, about 80% is mined chiefly for gold, with uranium as the by-product. The rest represents low-grade gold ore in which uranium is at least as valuable as the gold. Some important ore bodies to be mined for uranium would not have been worked for gold. Treatment of dump tailings for uranium presently is conducted at but a few mines.

Gold forms minute flakes closely associated with pyrite, as disseminations and replacements or as rare thin films on nodular pyrite. It occurs rarely as veinlets into peb-

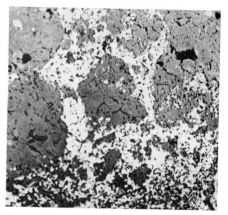

FIG. 8.18. Pitchblende (light) marginally replacing quartz pebbles (gray), West Rand Consolidated Mines, Union of South Africa. Reflected light (×50) (Davidson and Bowie, 1951, by permission of the Controller of Her Majesty's Stationery Office).

bles. Pyrite replaces matrix quartz and locally pebble quartz. Ramdohr (1955B) believes the pyrite is polygenetic. One type that forms rounded grains, which may be overgrown by a second euhedral generation, he regards as unweathered clastic pyrite. Another type he regards as of concretionary origin. In other pyrite grains or aggregates he finds relict features suggesting the mineral has replaced particles of ilmenite, titanomagnetite, and such iron-rich rocks as hematite quartzite, banded ironstone, and magnetite quartzite.

The uraninite occurs as rounded to subangular particles which are fractured and partly brecciated (Ramdohr, 1955B). Some are enclosed by pyrite, less usually by gold. Some are thinly veined by gold or galena and intergrown with subordinate galena, pyrite, skutterudite, and pyrrhotite. Ramdohr (1955B) recognizes cleavage in some particles but no typical botryoidal structure. Pitchblende also replaces conglomerate matrix, invading and partly replacing quartz pebbles (Davidson and Bowie, 1951).

Hydrocarbon

Uraniferous hydrocarbon, widespread in the Rand, was noted first in the Carbon Leader of the Far West Rand, a thin footwall seam of friable hydrocarbon-rich quartzite heavily impregnated by pyrite and pyrrhotite. The seam ranges from a parting plane with disseminated carbon spots to a thickness of 13 mm in which the hydrocarbon displays comb structure.

The hydrocarbon, which varies in optical properties, commonly forms small irregular nodules in conglomerate matrix. These include minute particles of pyrite, other sulfides, gold, quartz, and granules and angular pieces of pitchblende. A later generation of pitchblende fills cracks and cavities in the hydrocarbon. Hydrocarbon also forms annular rims on small pitchblende nodules. Some of the uranium, according to Ramdohr (1955B), is combined in hydrocarbon as a metallo-organic compound.

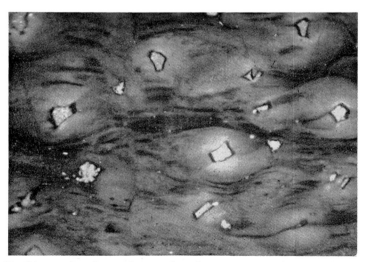

Fig. 8.19. Fibrous thucolite with particles of uraninite in halos of higher reflectivity, Basal Reef, Orange Free State. Reflected light, oil immersion (×250) (Ramdohr, 1955).

Origin

The origin of the Rand ores has been and still is very much in dispute (see Liebenberg, 1957). Three general theories have been advocated:

1. That the gold is of direct placer origin. An initial view, not supported by later information

2. That the gold, the uraninite, and most of the other metallic minerals were introduced by hydrothermal solutions under mesothermal conditions

3. That the gold was initially deposited with the gravels together with hydrocarbons, iron minerals, and detrital species; sulfur was introduced subsequently to form sulfides, and gold was recrystallized and somewhat redistributed

Miholić (1954) has suggested still another hypothesis, highly speculative: The destruction of an accumulation of uranium-concentrating microorganisms under anaerobic conditions gave rise to thucolite, uraninite, and pyrite. Gold was precipitated later by the organic material from "thermal waters."

Although volumes of arguments have been presented, it is certain that prior to the discovery of the abundant pitchblende some points were applicable to either side. Arguments advanced for the modified placer theory are:

1. The widespread occurrence of gold in gravels that also contain some unquestionable heavy detrital minerals.

2. The occurrence of gold in streaks that correspond to the distribution of stream gravels, and its close relation to sedimentary lithological features. There is little agreement on the environment of deposition of the gravels, however.

3. No matter how concentrated or dispersed the gold values are, the deposits show a consistently high variability, a feature characteristic of alluvial samples (McWhirter, 1956).

4. The ores are generally unrelated to fractures or faults, although a few faults are mineralized in ore beds. Gold-bearing veins are a subordinate feature; only one vein is known to contain pitchblende.

5. Ramdohr (1955B) has presented textural features that he believes indicate that uraninite and some pyrite, too, were originally of detrital origin.

6. A source for the hydrothermal solutions is not known.

7. The wide distribution of the gold is difficult to explain as the result of hydrothermal infiltration.

That the gold and the uraninite belong to the same period of mineralization is generally not disputed, and on this basis arguments for a hydrothermal origin are (Graton, 1930; Davidson and Bowie, 1951; Davidson, 1953, 1957; Turneaure, 1955):

1. Pyrite, gold, and uraninite may replace pebbles.

2. The suite of accompanying sulfide minerals (Zn, Pb, Ni, Co) and gangue minerals (sericite and chlorite) are typical also of numerous vein deposits in many places in the world.

3. The sedimentary lithological features associated with ore shoots afford favorable access to hydrothermal solutions.

4. The hydrocarbon is essentially identical with thucolites from hydrothermal veins and is younger than most of the uraninite.

5. The combination of sulfides and uranium as U^4 is not found in present-day placers or in other syngenetic deposits in coarsely clastic rocks (McKelvey et al., 1955). Uraninite, especially thorium-low uraninite, is an exceedingly rare placer mineral, hardly surviving even short distances of transportation (Davidson and Cosgrove, 1955). Likewise pyrite is unknown as a placer mineral. If both were to have persisted as detritals, they must first have been liberated by mechanical weathering and transported and deposited under non-oxidizing conditions.

6. The source rock for the assumed detrital uraninite must have been one of most widespread and uniform character, yet granite masses cannot qualify, since the lodes do not contain abundantly those heavy detritals that are not only characteristic granitic accessory minerals but which also would be more persistent under either oxidizing or reducing conditions of weathering and transportation. Indeed both chromite and zircon appear, indicating a mixed provenance.

7. The radiometric profiles in the sequence show greatest radioactivity in some conglomerate beds, other conglomerate beds being barren. In most sedimentary profiles the lowest radioactivity is registered from the coarsest beds.

8. The lodes worked for gold contain about 350 times as much sphalerite (about 0.1%), a relationship not approached in placers.

9. The uranium content of the ores is much greater than that known in any present placers.

The sequence of events under the hydrothermal theory is:

1. Deposition of gold, Pb, Zn, Cu, Co, and Ni sulfides, pitchblende, and gangue by replacement of the conglomerate matrix and in part the pebbles under mesothermal conditions

2. Introduction of gaseous hydrocarbon with polymerization around pitchblende grains; some solution of pitchblende

3. Consolidation of the hydrocarbon gel with flocculation of dispersed pitchblende to blebs

4. Syneresis and minor redistribution of pitchblende, gold, and sulfides along fractures

The apparent ages of the uraninite, based on Pb isotope/U ratios, are 1,328 to 1,352, 1,593 to 1,652, and 1,965 to 2,070 m.y. Horne and Davidson (1955) conclude that the minimum age of initial mineralization is approximately 2,000 m.y., with subsequent reworking of the reefs to give more than one generation of pitchblende and to yield free galena of abnormal isotopic composition.

SOUTH AMERICA

Serra de Jacobina, Bahia, Brazil

Uraniferous gold deposits that occur south of Jacobina in north-central Bahia, northeastern Brazil, resemble the Rand radioactive conglomerates (White, 1956). The area around the Canavieiras mine is underlain by a series of quartzite, itabirite, slate, and schist with a basal metaconglomerate (Jacobina series, Lower Algonkian). Mafic dikes cut the beds, which strike north and dip 45 to 65° E.

The gray, green, or brown metaconglomerate beds range in thickness from 2 cm to 2 m, consisting of gray to white quartz pebbles as much as 7½ cm long. One type, white and coarse grained, contains a little gold and shows very little radioactivity (<0.001% eU). The other type, gray, green, or brown, which in zones is heavily pyritized, is richer both in gold and uranium, locally having up to 0.2% eU and averaging 0.01% eU. Uranium, which increases with pyrite, occurs as pitchblende, some enclosed by pyrite. Other matrix constituents are quartz and chrome mica. Outcrops are strongly limonitic and have been leached of uranium.

THORIUM VEINS

LEMHI PASS DISTRICT, IDAHO AND MONTANA

The Lemhi Pass district lies across the Bitterroot Mountains along the Idaho-Montana line between Tendoy, Lemhi County, Idaho, and Brenner, Beaverhead County, Montana. The area is underlain chiefly by Beltian metasedimentary strata (argillite, quartzite, mica schist) that strike N. 30 to 76° W. and dip 16 to 60° NE. (Trites and Tooker, 1953). Copper veins that occupy fissures a few inches to 10 ft wide and as much as 500 ft long contain bornite, chalcopyrite, chalcocite, pyrite, quartz, hematite, silver minerals, gold, and thorite. Supergene products are limonite, manganese oxides, cuprite, azurite, and malachite. The associated quartz-hematite veins are 1 to 50 ft wide and 10 to 700 ft long, containing also chalcedony, goethite, barite, thorite, and traces of copper minerals. Thorogummite may be present in the iron oxides, and minor amounts of monazite and allanite have been found in some deposits. Goethite is pseudomorphous after siderite.

Some vein material is fractured, some is vuggy. In the Last Chance vein the sequence is quartz, barite, thorite, quartz, chalcedony, goethite, hematite, goethite. The thorite appears as very small, red-brown prisms that are markedly altered and associated with hematite, barite, and limonite. Analyses of samples from the 11 reported deposits indicate 0.1 to 1.2% ThO_2, 0.001 to 0.008% U, and the presence of rare-earth elements (Y, La, Nd) in at least one deposit.

Thorium veins, up to 5 ft across, also have been discovered near Porthill, Boundary County, Idaho. Assays of as much as 8% ThO_2 have been obtained, with values in Ti, Cu, and Ag.

STEENKAMPSKRAAL, UNION OF SOUTH AFRICA

In 1950, a unique monazite vein was discovered at Steenkampskraal, 50 mi north of Van Rhynsdorp, which is in the northwestern part of Cape Province, about 200 mi north of Capetown, Union of South Africa, in a semiarid region of low hills and broad flats (Nininger, 1954). The monazite vein, which cuts Precambrian granite, locally gneissic, is a few inches to nearly 6 ft thick and is exposed for about 600 ft. It has been formed along an east-west shear zone. Megascopically the dark brown to reddish vein material is very fine grained,

FIG. 8.20. Monazite vein rock, Steenkampskraal deposit, South Africa. Pyrite (opaque), monazite (high relief, dark gray), apatite (moderate relief, clear) in matrix of quartz and sericitized feldspar (×35).

stained by hematite and locally by supergene copper minerals. The hematitized wall rock contains smoky quartz and monazite disseminated as much as several inches from the vein.

Microscopic examination of vein material reveals a streaky subparallel texture with large corroded and sericitized feldspar grains, abundant fine-grained quartz and pyrite, hematite and subrounded grains of monazite and lesser apatite, magnetite, and leucoxene (Fig. 8.20). The monazite, which forms grains 0.1 to 0.6 mm in size, averaging near 0.3 mm, is locally marginally altered to hematite and another very fine grained secondary mineral. Three general stages of mineralization are indicated:

1. Feldspar, monazite, apatite, magnetite, ilmenite(?)
2. Quartz, pyrite, and chalcopyrite(?)
3. Sericite

Ore with as much as 75% monazite is reported, but along the hanging wall the content decreases to 20% (Davidson, 1956D). Analyses indicate up to 4 to 5% ThO_2 in the ore, with locally 5% Cu. An annual production of 8,000 tons of concentrates is projected, containing 55% combined thorium and rare-earth oxides. The predominating rare earths are Ce, La, and Nd.

Age determinations on the monazite by Tilton and Nicolaysen (1955) gave the following results:

$$U^{238}/Pb^{206} \ldots \ldots \quad 1{,}080 \text{ m.y.}$$

$$Th^{232}/Pb^{208} \ldots \ldots \quad 990 \text{ m.y.}$$

POÇOS DE CALDAS, BRAZIL

The Poços de Caldas region is partly in Minas Gerais, partly in São Paulo, about 130 mi north of the city of São Paulo, lying at an elevation of about 3,600 ft, with undulating relief of between 300 and 600 ft. Ridges rising sharply 600 to 1,200 ft above the plateau bound the area. Radioactive zirconium deposits lie within an area of about 460 sq km, or about half the area underlain by alkalic rocks (De Moraes, 1956). The zirconium ores (known variously as caldasite, zirkite, and brazilite) consist chiefly of baddeleyite-zircon mixtures together with variable amounts of other constituents (Fig. 8.21). The caldasite occurs as (1) veins and lenses in the alkalic rocks (Fig. 8.22), (2) eluvial deposits of broken vein material, and (3) alluvial deposits of rolled pebbles. The pebbles are ½ to 3 in. in diameter (favas), occurring in Recent and older stream bed deposits.

The vein caldasite shows a variety of textures, chiefly mammillary to botryoidal on surfaces, and fibrous, banded, or fine-grained massive internally. Zircon occurs as euhedra and microcrystalline aggregates. Many of the veins contain numerous vugs; some are banded with wall zones of fibrous fan-shaped baddeleyite aggregates, central globular baddeleyite masses also with a radial structure, and interstitial fillings of anhedral zircon (Fig. 2.40). Where bad-

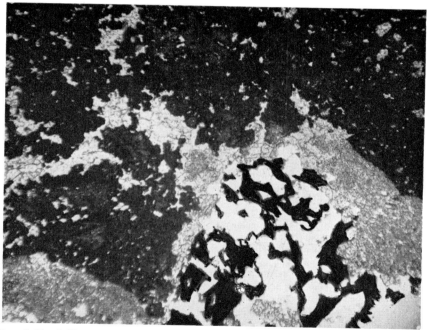

Fig. 8.21. Caldasite ore, Poços de Caldas, Brazil. Fine-grained zircon-baddeleyite intergrowth (dark gray), fine-grained quartz (clear), and magnetite(?) (black) (×35).

deleyite and zircon are intergrown, textures indicate that the baddeleyite crystallized first and that at least some of the zircon formed by replacement of baddeleyite (Franco and Loewenstein, 1948). The color of the ores varies from brick red to gray and blue black. Some types, rich in baddeleyite, contain 90 to 93% ZrO_2, whereas others with more zircon contain 73 to 85% ZrO_2. Radioactivity occurs in four types of material:

1. In the alkalic rocks themselves.

2. In residual clays resulting from weathering of the alkalic rocks. At the Morro Ferro such clay contains up to 14.34% rare-earth oxides, 2.33% ThO_2, and a negligible amount of uranium.

3. In the caldasite ores. High-grade material contains 1% U, rarely nearly 3% U. Most ore studied by Guimarães et al. (1953) contains up to 0.92% U_3O_8, with some having essentially no uranium, but with a range in $eU_3O_8 = 0.20$ to 1.1%.

4. In magnetite ore containing veins of bastnaesite and thorogummite.

The residual zirconiferous clays are lateroids containing fragments, pebbles, and boulders of caldasite, rounded pieces of fibroradial baddeleyite, bauxite concretions, and altered, rounded residual fragments of the alkalic rocks. The layers are 4 in. to 5 ft thick. Boulders of caldasite weighing as much as 30 tons have been reported (Miller and Singewald, 1919).

Most production has been obtained from eluvial and alluvial placers. Reserves are poorly defined, but may be of the order of 50,000 to 2,000,000 tons (De Oliveira, 1956).

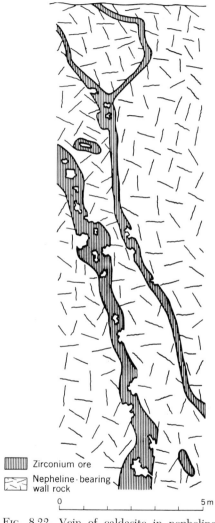

Zirconium ore

Nepheline-bearing wall rock

0   5 m

Fig. 8.22. Vein of caldasite in nepheline syenite, Serrote mine, Cascata, São Paulo, Brazil (Guimarães, 1948).

The alkalic rocks intrude or overlie an Archean gneissic complex and include nepheline syenite, nepheline-syenite porphyry, foyaite, microfoyaite, and nepheline and leucite phonolite. Because of the Cretaceous(?) sandstone over-lying the complex, its age is regarded as Upper Triassic (Rhaetic) to Jurassic (Guimarães, 1948). The most widespread rock is phonolite which underlies the over-all basinlike structure. The alkalic rocks are especially rich in Ti and Zr, with such accessory species as sphene, melanite, astrophyllite, eucolite, eudia-lyte, lavenite, pennaite, giannettite, and rosenbuschite. Even the sodic pyroxenes (acmite) contain Zr and Ti.

The alkalic rocks also have been extensively zeolitized and locally contain small fibrous aggregates of baddeleyite adjacent to zeolite clusters. The calda-site veins are believed to have been formed by alkaline hydrothermal solu-tions which circulated through the feldspathoidal rocks in postvolcanic time (Guimarães, 1948). Probably at least part of the zirconium in these solutions was obtained by destruction of the primary accessory zirconium silicates (Franco and Loewenstein, 1948).

The deposits are difficult to classify genetically, for they contain an essentially unique mineral assemblage and because they are incompletely known geo-logically. Frondel (1957A, p. 5) estimates that "The temperature of natural baddeleyite certainly is much below 1000° and in its main occurrence, at Poços de Caldas, Brazil, doubtless is much below 500°." The presence of crustifica-tion, numerous vugs, botryoidal structures, and the associated zeolites supports the suggestion of an environment at least within the mesothermal range. Host rocks are hypabyssal to volcanic.

• chapter nine

EPITHERMAL DEPOSITS

GENERAL

A well-defined group of uraniferous vein deposits includes those which are quartzose, fluoritic or both, and relatively poor in sulfides. The most widespread radioactive mineral is pitchblende, botryoidal to very fine grained.

Some of the veins are strongly quartzose containing usually fine-grained quartz, although rarely coarsely crystalline quartz also is present. The color of the quartz is white, red, gray, or black (smoky), rarely amethystine. Commonly much of it is chalcedonic. Quartz or chalcedony in two or more generations may be present, and usually the younger or youngest silica mineral is finer-grained and relatively dark-colored. Some of this late dark cherty quartz is relatively radioactive and may contain appreciable amounts of metallic elements (Wright and Emerson, 1957). Fracturing or brecciation may occur between periods of silicification. Some late silicification may be represented by opal.

Fluorite is widespread, ranging in amount from accessory to predominant. In fact, a complete series exists from siliceous to fluoritic types, and in some cases this gradation is present in a district or even a single deposit, e.g., Thomas Range, Utah, a deposit begins as a fluorite pipe and passes downward into chalcedonic replacement masses. The fluorite ranges from fine-grained and pulverulent to coarse-grained. Much is purple and even fetid, but green and white types also are represented, especially in fluoritic types, but are abundant in but few veins. Other gangue constituents are alunite, clay minerals, manganese oxides, iron oxides, calcite, and dolomite. Unlike the mesothermal veins, the epithermal types do not usually contain abundant hematite, and carbonates are absent or very subordinate.

Except for pyrite and marcasite, the metallic minerals are absent, rare, or minor. Few, if any, of the veins could serve as sulfide ores. Relatively widespread in small amounts are galena, sphalerite, and chalcopyrite; the last may be replaced by bornite, chalcocite, or covellite. The sphalerite is iron-poor,

330

normally. Molybdenum, present in some fluoritic types, occurs in jordisite, or ilsemannite, very rarely as molybdenite. Very rarely arsenopyrite, loellingite, bismuthinite, and tetrahedrite are present. Some extraordinary associates are the mercury sulfides-selenides at Marysvale and the As-Sb-Ni assemblage in Macedonia (page 353).

Uraninite is submicroscopic to relatively coarsely botryoidal. It is thorium- and rare-earth-low. Some is sooty ("parapitchblende"), but this type is generally near-surface and disappears with depth. Rarely uranothorite occurs (Jamestown, Colorado). Very fine grained coffinite also has been detected (La Baja, Colombia).

Wall rocks commonly are silicified. Argillization also is common, sericitization and hematitization less so. In a few cases, chlorite, alunite, or fluorite has been introduced (Kerr, 1956C). In some cases pitchblende is disseminated in walls.

Veins may be banded, showing crustification; others are streaked. Brecciation is common, and vugs may be prominent. The deposits follow shears, fractures, and breccia zones, forming veins, multiple veins, breccia fillings and pipes, and replacement masses. They occur in rocks ranging in age from Precambrian to Tertiary, but many are genetically associated with Hercynian granitic intrusives in Europe, or in the United States with Laramide granodioritic intrusives or Tertiary acid volcanics.

Few of the deposits are high grade. The fluoritic types rarely contain more than 0.1% U. Ore shoots, if definable, are related to cross fractures and abrupt changes in strike and dip.

The thorium counterparts contain thorite and thorogummite and very little uranium. Feldspar, smoky quartz, siderite, fluorite, barite, and hematite make up the characteristic assemblage. Reopening and erratic distribution of values are characteristic.

SILICEOUS PITCHBLENDE-SULFIDE VEINS

UNITED STATES

Boulder Batholith, Montana

General

Uranium minerals were discovered in veins early in 1949 near Boulder, Montana. In all, more than 100 occurrences and radioactive anomalies have been found, most of scientific interest only. Only a very few of the deposits have yielded any ore, but the district became notorious for the number of occurrences that were developed as radioactive "health mines." It is probable that the return on underground treatments has exceeded considerably profits from ore.

The general geology of the district and its uranium deposits has been summarized in reports by Reyner (1950), Thurlow and Jarrard (1954), Becraft and Pinckney (1954), Wright and Bieler (1953), Wright et al. (1954), Pinckney (1955), Becraft (1956A,B), Sahinen (1956), and Wright (1956).

Various parts of the district and various individual deposits have been described: Klepper (1950) and Roberts and Gude (1953A)—deposits west of Clancey; Thurlow and Reyner (1950), Cohen (1951), and Roberts and Gude (1953B)— Free Enterprise mine and adjacent area; Becraft (1953)—Comet area; Moen (1954)—Mooney claim; Emerson and Wright (1957)—W. Wilson mine; and Wright and Shulof (1957)—Lone Eagle mine.

Geology

The Boulder batholith, which underlies about 1,500 sq mi and extends from just south of Helena to about 20 mi north of Butte in western Montana, transects rocks of Precambrian to Cretaceous age (Knopf, 1957). It consists chiefly of granodiorite and quartz monzonite, and has been cut by (1) dikes, sheets, and irregular bodies of aplite, alaskite, and pegmatite; (2) rhyolite dikes and plugs; and (3) dacite dikes. Most of these intrusives are in a northeasterly zone parallel with the eastern contact of the batholith. Rhyolite flows and dacitic tuffs overlie batholithic rocks. Numerous faults, shear zones, and veins occur in two main sets—one east-west and one that trends N. 60° E.; both sets dip steeply. Nearly all shear zones, which are as much as 200 ft wide and locally occupied by Ag-Pb veins, strike east. Chalcedony veins ("siliceous reefs"), the second and younger type, trend either northeast (near Boulder and west of Clancey) or east (east of Clancey). The deposits are early Tertiary in age; the alaskite is 60 m.y. old by the zircon method (Chapman et al., 1955). An argon-potassium determination on orthoclase of the granodiorite gave a probable age of 87 m.y. (Knopf, 1956).

Deposits

The older Pb-Ag deposits, some of which also contain significant Zn, Au, and minor Cu (Gray Eagle, Comet mines), consist of veins and replacement lodes of galena, pyrite, tetrahedrite, and minor sphalerite, chalcopyrite, and arseno-pyrite. Gangue quartz is of two types: (1) coarse-grained, colorless, translucent; and (2) fine-grained, dark blue gray. Their quartz-monzonite wall rocks are silicified, sericitized, and argillized. The primary uranium mineral is pitch-blende, which at the Gray Eagle mine extensively replaces pyrite (Wright and Bieler, 1953). Sooty pitchblende and a mixture of yellow uranyl minerals occur in oxidized ore.

Numerous radioactive anomalies occur in or along chalcedony veins, but only the Free Enterprise and the W. Wilson mines have produced small amounts of ore. The vein zones, which are 1 to 10 ft thick, crop out conspicuously, and some are traceable over 1,000 ft. Along them, the quartz monzonite is altered in the sequence outward: silicification, sericitization, kaolinization. Four periods of silicification have been recognized in the veins (Fig. 9.1). Locally, at least one period of silicification has followed the intrusion of dacite porphyry. More than one period of silicification has been noted in similar uraniferous veins in France (pages 339–342).

The uranium minerals include scarce veinlets and nodules of pitchblende and relatively abundant uranophane, beta-uranophane, meta-autunite, metator-bernite, meta-uranocircite, metazeunerite, and phosphuranylite (Wright and Emerson, 1957). Some uranyl minerals also have been deposited from meteoric

solutions along fractures outside the ore bodies. The youngest of the chalce-
donies, usually black or dark gray, is usually the most radioactive (Wright et
al., 1954). Together with uranium, Ag, As, Co, Fe, Mo, Ni, Pb, Sb, and Zn
show a tendency to be concentrated in this dark chalcedony (Bieler and
Wright, 1956). A uraniferous chalcedony vein also occurs in prebatholithic
brecciated and altered volcanic rocks at the Red Rock mine, 1½ mi west of
Basin.

A few veins with the characteristics of both the Ag-Pb and the chalcedony
type also contain uranium (Lone Eagle mine). These have galena, silver
minerals, pyrite, and minor sphalerite and chalcopyrite in a predominantly
quartz-chalcedony gangue. Pitchblende replaces pyrite, chalcedony, and sphalerite, but is cut by veinlets of pyrite of another generation (Wright et al.,
1954). These veins may represent Ag-Pb veins reopened during the pitch-
blende-chalcedony period of mineralization.

The future of the district lies in the possibility of finding new uranium ore
bodies in some of the more continuous Ag-Pb veins.

Los Ochos Deposit, Saguache County, Colorado

Los Ochos deposit in the Cochetopa district, southeast of Gunnison, Colorado, has been localized along a northeast shear zone that follows the unconformable contact between Morrison sandstone and Precambrian granite containing schist xenoliths. The zone is 16 ft thick and at least 70 ft long (Derzay,
1956). Mineralization has permeated outward into the Morrison to thicken the
ore body to as much as 30 ft locally. The steeply dipping zone is displaced
by east-trending faults, including the major Los Ochos fault.

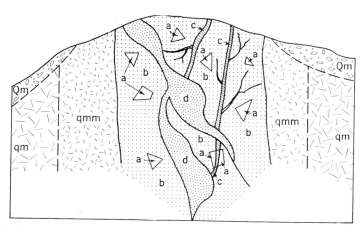

Fig. 9.1. Diagrammatic section showing four ages of quartz in siliceous uraniferous
veins of the Boulder batholith, Montana. Qm = mantle; qm = quartz monzonite;
qmm = silicified quartz monzonite; a = fragments of white or light brown to light
gray cherty quartz in light brown cherty quartz b, both cut by stringers of light
brownish-gray, brown to yellowish-brown cherty quartz c; d = veins of light
yellowish-brown opaline silica (Roberts and Gude, 1953A; *U.S. Geol. Survey*).

The wall rocks of mudstone, sandstone, and granite have been intensely silicified and kaolinized along the zone. Mineralization consists of sooty and granular pitchblende with marcasite and minor ilsemannite, bornite, chalcopyrite, and chalcocite in a gangue of clear to dark quartz, chalcedony, and some alunite and barite. Secondary minerals identified are uranophane, autunite, and sparse torbernite.

Other United States Occurrences

A silicified explosion breccia zone at the edge of a Tertiary volcanic vent at the Atlanta mine, Lincoln County, Nevada, consists of pieces of rhyolite porphyry and Paleozoic dolomite (Lovering, 1954). Minerals present are uranophane, hematite, clays, quartz, opal, calcite, and barite. Sharp (1956) reports mineralization of uranophane, autunite, and uraninite in silicified agglomerate, along numerous steep fractures.

Carnotite, copper sulfides, pyrite, and quartz fill north-trending, east-dipping shears in Precambrian schist and marble in the Van Horn district, Culberson County, Texas (Everhart, 1956B).

LA BAJA REGION, COLOMBIA

Uraniferous veins occur in the La Baja region, municipality of California, department of Santander, in northeastern Colombia. Three groups of deposits occur northeast of California in the La Baja River drainage; from west to east they are the San Celestino, the San Antonio–Pie de Gallo, and the Las Animas–San Cristobal. The fourth, the La Francia deposit, is east-southeast of the town in the Rio Vetas drainage (Bueno, 1955). The region has been known for its gold and silver deposits since Spanish colonial times.

The veins, which transect a hypabyssal, partly porphyritic leucogranite, are quartzose and contain hematite, pyrite, chalcopyrite, bornite, chalcocite, sphalerite, galena, and argentiferous tetrahedrite. Minor constituents are magnetite, ilmenite, feldspar, zircon, and alunite. Much of the uranium occurs in the quartz as minute black inclusions, which by x-ray methods were identified as uraninite and coffinite. Some radiobarite also is present, as are some secondary uranyl minerals. The mineralization, localized along fractures and breccia zones, was accompanied by hydrothermal alteration of the granite to sericite and alunite (Fig. 9.2). Bueno (1955) classifies the veins as transitional between mesothermal and epithermal.

In the San Celestino deposit, the average grade in accessible parts of the vein is 0.22% U_3O_8; the veins of San Cristobal–Las Animas deposit contain between 0.04 to 0.10% U_3O_8.

The most important vein in the San Celestino deposit strikes N. 75° W., dips 45° NE., and has been traced for 70 m. The Pie de Gallo vein trends northeast; the Las Animas and San Cristobal veins trend east and east-southeast; the La Francia trends north-northeast, dipping westward. In general the veins appear to be less than a meter thick.

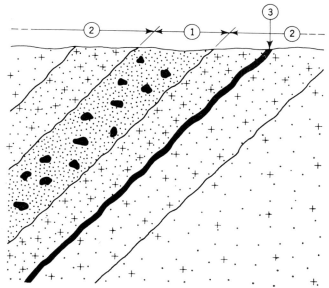

Fig. 9.2. Cross section of San Celestino vein, La Baja region, Colombia. 1, Central breccia zone mineralized with uraniferous quartz and sulfides. 2, Altered porphyry with little or no uranium; values chiefly in Au and Ag. 3, Fracture with filling of uraniferous quartz (Bueno, 1955; *Inst. Geol. Nac. Colombia*).

PRESIDENT PERÓN DEPOSIT, PROVINCE OF MENDOZA, ARGENTINA

The President Perón deposit (doubtless renamed) is 17 km west of Mendoza in the department of Las Heras. It consists of parallel veins with offshoots along multiple shear planes, all along a major north-trending fault of middle to upper Tertiary age. The fault places Triassic beds on the west against lower Tertiary clays, bentonite, and sandstone. The veins contain pitchblende in a gangue of quartz, calcite, pyrite, and magnetite. Fracturing and brecciation were followed by the introduction of opal (Belluco, 1956; Angelelli, 1956). Supergene minerals are Mn and Fe oxides, schroeckingerite, meta-autunite, phosphuranylite, gypsum, and copper carbonates.

PORTUGAL

Uranium deposits, discovered in Portugal in 1907, occur in three areas in the mountainous north-central part of the country, along the west side of the Spanish Meseta, the first area being the most important (Cavaca, 1956):

1. The Viseu-Nelas-Carregal do Sol region
2. The Guarda-Belmonte-Sabugal region
3. The Trancoso-Aguiarda Beira-Moimenta da Beira region

The veins are nearly entirely in Hercynian granite porphyry that intrudes Precambrian and Silurian schists and is itself intruded by diabase dikes. In the

Viseu region, the main controlling fractures are steep and strike north to N. 60° E. with an associated complex system of tension fractures that trend east-west and north-south. The veins, which fill breccia zones, consist of microcrystalline white quartz, reddish jasper, microbotryoidal pitchblende, pyrite, galena, sphalerite, and rarer arsenopyrite and chalcopyrite. The veins pinch and swell between 0.5 and 8 m. The granite wall rock, which has been hematitized, sericitized, and silicified near the vein and argillized more than 10 ft from the vein (Everhart and Wright, 1953), locally contains disseminated pitchblende in strongly sheared parts.

In the Guarda region the veins, which cut diabase and granite that contains secondary sericite and hematite, strike N. 40° E. to east and consist of white, fine-grained quartz, granular pitchblende, pyrite, and chalcopyrite. Vein breccias are cemented by cherty quartz and pyrite. The deposits of the Beira region, which trend N. 10 to 50° E., are vuggy fissure fillings and brecciated veins along tension fractures and consist of coarse white and black quartz with microbotryoidal pitchblende in veinlets, geodes, and as powdery crystal coatings.

Ore bodies are commonly near postmineralization cross fractures that follow ancestral faults, and/or along the straighter, more open parts of veins (Everhart and Wright, 1953). The veins are classed as epithermal of the siliceous type, comparable to those of the Boulder batholith, and their formation is believed to be correlatable with Alpine orogeny.

The veins have been deeply oxidized uranyl minerals persisting locally to 95 m. They include autunite, meta-autunite, sabugalite, saléeite, phosphuranylite, torbernite, uranophane, and uranyl sulfates and hydrous oxides.

The main mine, the Urgeirica, near Canas de Senhorim in the Viseu district, has accounted for 10,000 tons of the 18,000 tons of 1.0 to 1.8% U_3O_8 ore produced between 1911 and 1940. Some remarkable examples of the affinity of uranium for wood have been found at this mine, where mine timbers became so impregnated with secondary uranium and pine wood vats had absorbed so much uranium from leach liquors that their ash yielded over 6% U_3O_8 (Davidson and Ponsford, 1954). Other significant deposits are the Rosmaneira mine near Belmonte and the Reboleiro and Sebadelhe mines near Trancoso (Nininger, 1954).

FRANCE

General

Significant uraniferous vein deposits occur in France chiefly in the Brittany Massif, Massif Central, and in Vosges, all Hercynian tectonic units. Nearly all of the veins are of the epithermal type: some are rich in fine-grained, chalcedonic or cherty quartz with no fluorite; others contain appreciable fluorite together with chalcedony; still others have fluorite predominant over chalcedony; and a few contain fluorite as the principal gangue constituent. Many of the deposits are oxidized to considerable depths and contain mineable concentrations of such uranyl species as autunite, torbernite, and kasolite. Numerous other uranyl minerals occur in minor amounts.[1] These minerals may be supplanted by sooty pitchblende at depth or by pitchblende of botryoidal structure. The Lachaux veins have parsonite as the ore mineral (pages 536–538); no pitchblende has been found in them. Many of the veins are characterized by an accessory sulfide assemblage referred to by French geologists as B.G.P.C. assemblage, i.e., sphalerite (blende), galena, pyrite, and chalcopyrite. Both the pitchblende and the main uraniferous deposits have been described in detail in a monograph by Geffroy and Sarcia (1954). Roubault (1956) has presented a summary of the geology of the deposits.

Uranium mineralization in France has been known since 1800, when the newly discovered element uranium was identified in a bright yellow mineral, now known as autunite, from St. Symphorien de Marmagne, near Autun. Other scattered uranyl phosphate occurrences were found during the nineteenth century. Early in the twentieth century after the discovery of radium, several of the deposits were mined, and some additional ones were discovered at intervals until 1932. Prospecting was resumed in 1946, and in November, 1948, massive pitchblende was found at the La Crouzille deposit, Haute-Vienne. Other discoveries soon followed. Of the presently known deposits those of the Vendée district appear to be among the most promising, followed by Bois Noirs and La Crouzille.

Distribution

Uranium veins occur in France in three main areas: (1) In the southern part of the Brittany Massif in west-central France, the Vendée Division, where the deposits of Clisson (Ecarpière) occur, La Chapelle-Largeau, Mortagne, Les Herbiers, and Poitou. (2) In the Vosges in northeastern France: (*a*) in Haute-Saône, the deposits of Château-Lambert and Ronchamp; (*b*) in Haut-Rhin at Kruth and Schaentzel. (3) In the Massif Central of south-central France: (*a*) in the western part of the Massif in the Limousin region (Haute-Vienne) where there occur two main groups of deposits—the Bessines or northern group (Brugeaud, Champ Malauzat, Villard, Varnac), and the La Crouzille or southern group (La Crouzille, Les Sagnes, Fanay, Augeres, Tenelles, Fraisse-Jalinour, La Borderie, Ritord, Margnac I, II, III, Razès, l'Etang de Guillet); (*b*) in the northeastern part of the Massif (Saône-et-Loire) in the Autunois and Morvan—La Faye (Grury), Vernays, Bauzot, Oudots, Ruaux a St. Symphorien de Marmagne, and Outeloup; (*c*) Forez, in east-central part of the Massif (Puy-de-Dôme, Loire, and Allier) with deposits in three districts—Lachaux, Bois Noirs, and Saint-Rémy-sur-Durolle; (*d*) in the southern part of the Massif—Lozère, Hérault, and Aveyron.

---

[1] These have been described in detail and illustrated in four extraordinary color plates (24 figures, chiefly photomicrographs) in Chervet and Branche (1955). Two fine color plates of uranyl minerals (six photomicrographs) also are included in La prospection de l'uranium (by the Commisariat à l'Energie Atomique, 1955). Several of these are essentially identical with ones in Chervet and Branche (1955).

Types

The deposits have been classified by Geffroy and Sarcia (1954) into the following paragenetic types:

1. Limousin type, which varies between two subtypes
   - a. Massive pitchblende; quartz-poor; accessory microscopic sphalerite, galena, pyrite, and chalcopyrite; barite locally present; fluorite exceptional; commonly banded; sharp contacts, in some instances slightly argillized. Examples: La Crouzille and the Jean vein of Brugeaud
   - b. Pitchblende less coarsely developed; cryptocrystalline quartz very abundant; local fluorite; disseminated pyrite; brecciated texture; silicified contacts. Examples: Les Sagnes and Fanay
   - c. The Cyrille deposit of Brugeaud is transitional between these two subtypes
2. Forez type, with two subtypes
   - a. Pitchblende, gangue chiefly of chalcedonic quartz partly hematitized, and pyrite; a second mineralization of smoky, coarser quartz with sphalerite, galena, pyrite, chalcopyrite, and local fluorite. A period of fracturing may have occurred between the two periods of mineralization. Contacts sharp, somewhat silicified. Examples: Bigay, Saint-Rémy-sur-Durolle
   - b. Parsonite subtype (pages 536–538)
3. Type of the northeastern Massif Central
   - a. Thin veins with pitchblende in aggregates, with dominantly fluorite gangue, also red cryptocrystalline quartz, a little barite, microscopic grains of sphalerite, galena, pyrite, and chalcopyrite; hematite may be abundant. Examples: Bauzot, Vernay
   - b. Wide veins of red cryptocrystalline quartz and fluorite; Zn, Pb, Fe, Cu sulfides in some examples; disseminated pitchblende confined to the quartz. Example: La Faye

In Vendée the fluoritic type of the northeastern Massif Central is represented by the Ecarpière deposit and the quartz-pyrite type of Forez by the La Chapelle-Largeau.

These veins are all classed as epithermal by French geologists. Since the various subtypes occur close together, intergrade, and may even be represented at the same deposit, it is most practical to describe all of the French epithermal uranium mineralization as a unit. Not all French uranium veins are epithermal, however. The occurrences at Kruth, in the Vosges, contain Co and Ni minerals as well as fluorite and are believed to have been formed under mesothermal conditions.

Analyses of massive pitchblende from Bigay have yielded an age of a little more than 200 m.y., which is within the limits of Hercynian mineralization (Geffroy and Sarcia, 1954).

Vendée District, Brittany Massif

General

Uranium mineralization in the Vendée district is related to the Mortagne granite massif, most of the deposits occurring in the granite close to its margins, along granite-schist contacts, or rarely in the metamorphic rocks themselves, not far from the granite contact (Les Herbiers). Both fluoritic and siliceous types are present. Most of the fluoritic veins also contain fine-grained quartz.

Fluoritic Veins

The four deposits of the Clisson group are on the south side of the La Moine River, aligned east-west over 4 km. The main deposit, Ecarpière, about 7 km east of Clisson, consists of seven west-northwest trending, vertical to steeply south-dipping veins in granite near its contact with amphibolites. Mineralization has been found along 600 m and to a depth of 200 m. The veins, which vary in thickness from a few decimeters to 1 to 2 meters, consist of black fetid fluorite and chalcedony, with minute nodules and veinlets of pitchblende localized along contacts between fluorite and quartz bands. Pyrite increases in abundance with pitchblende. A sizable tonnage of ore averages 0.5 to 2% U.

Siliceous Veins

Epithermal veins of the siliceous type include those of the La Chapelle-Largeau group (about ten localities) and those in the Les Herbiers group. The former are brecciated quartzose veins striking north-northwest and dipping steeply northeast in granite. They contain pitchblende, pyrite, marcasite, galena, and uranyl minerals. The Belair deposit is in a silicified shatter zone mineralized to below 100 m with pitchblende, pyrite, galena, covellite, and a second generation of quartz.

Limousin Region, Haute-Vienne
Western Part of Massif Central

General

The Limousin deposits occur in granite north of Ambazac and west and southwest of the major fault known as the Argentat crushed zone. The coarse-grained granite encloses numerous pegmatites and is cut by a swarm of lamprophyres trending north-northeast and dipping 55 to 75° NW. The deposits are clustered in two groups—the Bessines (northern) group and the La Crouzille (southern) group. Many of the southern deposits occur along faults oriented at right angles to the lamprophyres.

Bessines Area

The Brugeaud deposits, on the Gartempe River, north of Bessines, occur in two north-south belts of mineralization along fractures and crush zones that trend northwest and dip southwest. Exploration to 65 m has revealed veins containing quartz, pyrite, marcasite, galena, chalcopyrite, covellite, and late fracture-filling calcite. The radioactive species are spherulitic and sooty pitch-blende, gummite, and autunite-group minerals. The enclosing granite has been argillized.

La Crouzille Area

La Crouzille. At the La Crouzille deposit three subparallel lamprophyres strike northeast and dip 70° NW. in coarse granite. The uraniferous veins cross the dikes at right angles. The Henriette vein is 15 to 20 m long, generally several centimeters thick, and has been explored to 170 m. Mineralization also occurs in the Cantiant vein and along the La Sapinère fault which lie successively to the northeast.

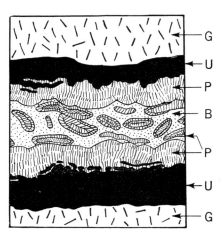

Fig. 9.3. Henriette vein, La Crouzille, Haute-Vienne, France. G = granite, U = uraninite, P = fibrous iron sulfides, B = barite (×1) (after Geffroy and Sarcia, 1954).

The Henriette is a vein of massive pitchblende with abundant later pyrite and marcasite and small local amounts of bismuthinite, sphalerite, galena, loellingite, chalcopyrite, bornite, chalcocite, and covellite. Quartz is a very minor mineral, but barite in two generations is abundant in some parts. Pitchblende invariably forms spherulites, some several centimeters across, usually in botryoidal aggregates. In parts of the deposit massive pitchblende is cut by iron sulfide veinlets. Elsewhere the deposit is banded: botryoidal pitchblende against the walls, overgrown by fibrous iron sulfide bands, and a central filling of fine-grained barite with iron sulfide nodules (Fig. 9.3).

Les Sagnes. Three vein groups at Les Sagnes strike east-west and dip 80° N., to the west of an 18-m microsyenite that strikes north-northeast and dips 65° NW. A central, brecciated quartz-fluorite vein is bordered by lensoid veinlets on the north, several centimeters thick, and on the south by veinlets only several millimeters thick. The northern veinlets contain pitchblende, pyrite, marcasite, covellite, and supergene gummite, autunite, and limonite. The minute southern veinlets consist of quartz, pitchblende, pyrite, marcasite, covellite, and purple fluorite. The central vein, commonly more than a meter thick, consists either of fragments of altered granite and minette cemented by quartz (locally chalcedonic) or of granite and siliceous breccia pieces cemented by purple fluorite. The siliceous breccia contains pyrite, marcasite, and fluorite.

Other deposits. The Augeres deposit consists of east-west veinlets near a minette dike. The gummite veinlets, in altered granite impregnated with autunite, passed with depth into a boxwork of altered pitchblende.

At the Razès deposit, uranium veins strike west-northwest and dip 75° SW. across a medium-grained granite near a northeast-trending minette dike. Veinlets 1 to 2 cm thick contain limonite, gummite, and relict pitchblende; autunite occurs in the surrounding granite. Other chalcedonic veinlets contain sooty pitchblende and pyrite.

Northeastern Part of Massif Central (Saône-et-Loire)

La Faye and Les Vernays

Various mineralogical assemblages characterize the low-temperature pitchblende vein of Autunois and Morvan. The La Faye and Les Vernays deposits, south of Grury, which follow fractures in granite along the western margin of the Luzy batholith, are chalcedony-fluorite veins with disseminated pitchblende. Some pyrite, marcasite, hematite, and traces of galena, sphalerite, covellite, and chalcopyrite occur in the La Faye deposit, which is the northern extension of the Crot-Blanc fluorite vein, exploited about 1930. The veins, which are 0.5 to 1 m thick and have been developed to 80 m, strike N. 10° W. and dip 40 to 75° NE. In the near-surface part, torbernite, autunite, and kasolite predominate, but sooty pitchblende, hard pitchblende, and sulfides appear at depth (Roubault, 1956).

The veins are mineralogically of three types: (1) siliceous—with sulfides, (2) siliceous (chalcedonic), and (3) fluoritic (Hélène vein).

The Vernays deposit, a north-south vein that dips east, contains quartz of two ages, fluorite, dolomite, barite, B.G.P.C. sulfides, and pitchblende.

Bauzot

The Bauzot deposit, 2 km southeast of Issy l'Evêque, was first exposed as a fluorite-pitchblende vein (La Borne Pilot), 20 cm thick, containing limonite, gummite, autunite, and uranophane. Pyrite, galena, and barite also are present. This vein strikes northwest and dips 80° SW. in coarse porphyritic granite. At a depth of 80 m, the parallel Alphonse vein was found; northeast of the La Borne Pilot and below 120 m, two northeast-dipping veins (Les Combes and Verchère) intersect the La Borne Pilot. The fluoritic ore contains 1% or less uranium as finely disseminated pitchblende. The banded vein contains the sequence inward: clear quartz, fluorite-pitchblende with ribbons of dark purple fetid fluorite, abundant ferruginous quartz, and minor dolomite with abundant calcite.

Forez, East-Central Part of Massif Central

Lachaux Area

In the Lachaux area, noteworthy for its parsonite veins (pages 536–538), chalcedonic pitchblende veins occur at Bigay and Gourniand. The Bigay vein, striking west-northwest in its eastern part, is deflected toward west-southwest in its western end and occurs in granite. It is nearly vertical and 20 to 50 cm thick. The pitchblende is spherulitic, crisscrossed by microveinlets of quartz or replaced zonally by quartz (Fig. 2.6). Sulfides of the B.G.P.C. group also are present, associated with smoky quartz. Other constituents are hematite, covellite, and opal.

Saint-Rémy-sur-Durolle

Pitchblende was found for the first time in France in 1927 in the deposits at Saint-Rémy-sur-Durolle, east-northeast of Thiers. It appears in small quartz-hematite veins near a large quartz vein locally mineralized with pyrite, galena, chalcopyrite, and covellite (Fig. 2.5). The spherulites are cut by pyrite veinlets and replaced by quartz.

Bois Noirs, Auvergne

The Bois Noirs region, east of the Lachaux district in Forez, contains uranium mineralization along the eastern edge of a granite massif bounded by major faults on both east and west (Forez fault). About six deposits of s.gnificance have been found (page 337). Limouzat, the most important, has been drilled to 200 m. It consists of a microgranite breccia lens 150 m long and up to 25 m thick, bounded by two faults. The silicified and pyritized breccia contains cementing spherulites and bands of pitchblende in hematitic cryptocrystalline quartz with minor galena, chalcopyrite, covellite, and marcasite. Some pitchblende is brecciated and veined by quartz. Near the surface, torbernite, autunite, ianthinite, and other uranyl species are abundant. The lens trends northwest and dips northeast adjacent to a hydrothermally altered diabase dike (Geffroy and Sarcia, 1954).

The Saint-Priest deposit, east of Limouzat, consists of a large uraniferous siliceous zone striking north-south along the Forez fault and an independent smaller quartz-carbonate vein with pitchblende which strikes N. 40° E. and dips 50° NW. The large deposit consists of a zone of brecciated, silicified, and sericitized granite cut by veinlets of quartz, pyrite, and pitchblende. In some veinlets the botryoidal pitchblende (Fig. 2.3) is localized against contacts. Second-generation veinlets contain amethystine quartz and a little galena, sphalerite, and covellite. Autunite and torbernite have been developed in abundance in the upper part.

The banded quartz-carbonate vein, up to 7 cm thick, contains spherulitic pitchblende, pyrite, marcasite, chalcopyrite, galena, and hematite. The carbonate is calcite rich in manganese and iron.

Southern Part of Massif Central

Uranium mineralization occurs in the departments of Lozère and Hérault. In the ravine of Pradel, east of St.-Léger-de-Peyre for a distance of about a kilometer, are about a score of small veins containing 1-mm threads of pitchblende, B.G.P.C. sulfides, and a variable gangue of quartz, barite, and carbonates.

At Colombières in Hérault, veinlets several millimeters across in muscovite schist contain quartz, pitchblende, and B.G.P.C. sulfides.

MACEDONIA, YUGOSLAVIA

In northeastern Macedonia, Pb-Zn veins cut propylitized andesitic and dacitic flows and tuffs of Oligocene to Pliocene age. The ores consist of pyrite, arsenopyrite, galena, sphalerite, copper sulfides, alabandite, lead and silver sulfosalts in a gangue of siderite, calcite, rhodochrosite, quartz, and barite (Ristic, 1956). The veins, which trend northwest and dip northeast, contain erratically distributed pitchblende mineralization associated with gray-black chalcedony. The pitchblende is postsulfide in age, deposited after reopening of the fissures. It is very fine grained (30 to 80 microns), in globular aggregates. Although the Pb-Zn deposits appear to be mesothermal-leptothermal, uranium deposition, which may be a late-stage manifestation of the same mineralization, appears to have taken place under the epithermal environment.

RADIOACTIVE FLUORITE DEPOSITS

General

Fluorite-rich hydrothermal deposits that are weakly to strongly radioactive occur widely in a variety of host rocks. The close geochemical association of fluorite with rare-earth, uranium, and thorium minerals in pegmatites has been emphasized by Heinrich (1948A). This association is also found in other igneous rocks—the fluorite-bearing, abnormally radioactive quartz bostonite of the Central City, Colorado (Phair, 1952) (pages 298–302), and the radioactive fluoritic granites of Conway, New Hampshire, and of Nigeria (pages 173–174). Another noteworthy occurrence of fluorite with uraninite is represented by the "vein-dikes" of Wilberforce, Ontario (pages 217–221). Fluorite also is a widespread accessory of uraniferous sulfide veins both of the pyrite-galena type and in the Ni-Co-Ag type. Some fluorite occurs in or with most of the major pitchblende vein deposits of the world; however, most commercial fluorite deposits do not contain any uranium. The close relationship of fluorite and uranium on the Colorado Plateau is demonstrated by the fluoritic uranium deposits in the Todilto limestone of the Grants district, New Mexico (pages 410–411).

Fluorite is a persistent mineral with a wide range of deposition; its presence alone is not diagnostic of a particular geologic environment. However, veins, pipes, and lodes rich in fluorite are formed most commonly under epithermal conditions.

According to Gabelman (1955), most of the commercial fluorite deposits of the Western United States are high-epithermal, with coarsely crystalline, blue to green, nonradioactive fluorite, whereas radioactive marginal or submarginal fluorite deposits are generally shallow, low-epithermal, with fine-grained purple fluorite. In some Colorado and New Mexico districts, younger and more shallow fluorite deposits characterize a zone outward from base or precious metal centers: the Mogollon front, the Rio Grande trench, and the Front Range mineral belt. Uranium deposits occurring on the margins of broad uplifted structures that contain high-epithermal fluorite deposits in their Precambrian cores are found in the Burro, Rincon, and Zuni Mountains of New Mexico and the Uncompahgre Range of Colorado.

Uraninite, thorianite, cerianite, and fluorite possess face-centered cubic unit cells with edges close to 5.50 A. Some of the very fine grained pitchblende disseminated in fluorite may originally have had its U^4 (ionic radius 1.05 A) in substitution for Ca (ionic radius 1.06 A), with later exsolution and combination with oxygen at lower temperatures. In some radioactive fluorite deposits, no discrete uranium minerals have been identified, and in these the bulk of the uranium may be in uranoan fluorite with U^4 isomorphous for Ca.

Uraniferous fluorite is usually purple and may be fetid (page 21). Goddard (1946) has correlated depth of color and strength of radioactivity for fluorite in Jamestown, Colorado, deposits. However, white, earthy, highly uraniferous fluorite occurs in some of the Thomas Range deposits. Thorium, probably mainly as uranothorite, may also be present in fluorite deposits: Jamestown, Colorado; Hardin County, Illinois; Rexspar, British Columbia; Sundance, Wyoming; Poison Lake lode, Beaverhead County, Montana.

On the basis of form and structure uraniferous fluorite deposits occur as (1) fissure veins (Wölsendorf); (2) pipes (Thomas Range, Utah); (3) bedded replacement deposits (Grants, New Mexico) and breccia zones (Jamestown, Colorado). On the basis of mineralogy three categories have been distinguished (Wilmarth et al., 1952):

1. Simple or massive fluorite deposits. With minor chalcedony, calcite, dolomite, barite, clay minerals, and manganese oxides. The fluorite is fine-grained pulverulent to coarse-grained, colorless to deep purple. Discrete primary radioactive minerals are very fine grained or have not been identified. Example: Thomas Range, Utah, deposits. Secondary uranium minerals include carnotite, autunite, and uranophane.

2. Fluorite-quartz-sulfide veins. Usually in or near igneous rocks. Massive, fine-grained quartz abundant, with green to purple fluorite in pods and veinlets and in some cases also veinlets and blebs of pyrite, galena, sphalerite, or chalcopyrite. Fine-grained pitchblende or a thorium mineral (uranothorite?) accounts for much of the radioactivity. Example: Marysvale, Utah (where Mo is relatively abundant); many deposits in France. Secondary uranium minerals include sklodowskite, uranocircite, soddyite, kasolite (identified from deposits in the St. Peters Dome area, Colorado), autunite, torbernite, uranophane, uranyl sulfates, and other phosphates.

3. Fluorite-sulfide deposits with quartz subordinate to absent. Either veins or breccia zones (Jamestown, Colorado) or replacement deposits (Grants, New Mexico). Other minerals are clay minerals, calcite, dolomite, barite, pyrite, and various combinations of galena, sphalerite, and chalcopyrite. Enargite and tennantite occur locally, as do quartz and chalcedony. The primary radioactive minerals are pitchblende, either very finely disseminated or in narrow veinlets (Black Dike claims, Pima County, Arizona), and uranothorite (with uraninite at Jamestown, Colorado). Autunite and torbernite are the main uranyl species.

Some deposits are insufficiently studied to be classified in detail. as, for example, the radioactive fluorite veins at Bayindir, Turkey. At Kavik, Yildizeli, Sivas Province, Turkey, uraninite occurs in a fluorite-carbonate breccia.

Massive Fluorite Deposits

Thomas Range, Juab County, Utah

Uraniferous fluorite veins and pipes occur in a 6- × 2-mi district in the western part of the Thomas Range, on Spors Mountain, about 50 mi northwest of Delta. They have yielded fluorite since 1943, but are of no present commercial significance as sources of uranium.

The deposits transect fine-grained Silurian and Ordovician(?) dolomite, terminating downward against underlying Middle Ordovician quartzite (Staatz and Bauer, 1951A, 1952; Thurston et al., 1955; Staatz and Osterwald, 1956; Peters, 1956). A few deposits are in rhyolite porphyry. The rocks also are cut by Tertiary(?) latite, quartz latite, rhyolite dikes and plugs, and breccia pipes. The sedimentary beds strike northeast and dip at a low angle northwest. Faults in five sets, three older and two younger than the Tertiary(?) volcanic rocks surrounding the Paleozoic sediments, occur closely spaced.

About 40 deposits have been found, about half have yielded fluorite; nearly all of these are pipes commonly associated with faults. Some pipes are vertical, but most plunge steeply northeast or southeast. In some the outlines are irregular (Fig. 9.4); others, which have yielded 95% of the fluorite, are circular to ellipsoidal in plan. Surface cross sections range in diameter from less than 1 to over 100 ft. Most deposits narrow downward, some pinch abruptly.

The veins range from a few inches in width and a few feet in length to a width of 14 ft and a length of 246 ft (Thurston et al., 1954). Only one has proved commercial. Most are along fractures in dolomite, a few along faults in rhyolite porphyry dikes. Disseminated fluorite deposits (up to 30%) occur in volcanic rocks along the south and west sides of Spors Mountain, in clayey layers in tuff, and in cavities and fractures in rhyolite and latite.

The ore consists of 65 to 95%, white to dark purple, fine-grained, soft, pulverulent fluorite. Other constituents are clay minerals, calcite, dolomite, quartz, opal, and uncommon carnotite. Carnotite occurs in fluorite at two deposits. An unknown uranyl silicate appears in dolomitic wall rock in two others. Generally no radioactive minerals can be seen, although the deposits are all abnormally radioactive, assaying from less than 0.003% to 0.33% U, but samples from only four deposits have more than 0.10% U. Ore from three pipes contains 2.5 to 6.5 times more vanadium than that necessary for carnotite on the basis of the uranium present (Staatz and Osterwald, 1956).

Near the surface, the uranium content of the deposits increases sharply, probably a supergene effect. Discrete uranium minerals also occur only in the upper parts of the deposits.

Fluorite with less than 0.10% U shows no concentrations on autoradiographs, and most of the uranium of the deposits is either in an unrecognizable mineral in colloidal-sized particles or in isomorphous substitution for Ca in the fluorite structure. Separate samples of yellow and purple fluorite from one deposit revealed more uranium in the yellow variety, which is the reverse of the usual fluorite-uranium relations (Peters, 1956).

In some deposits impurities increase with depth. Near-surface ore from the

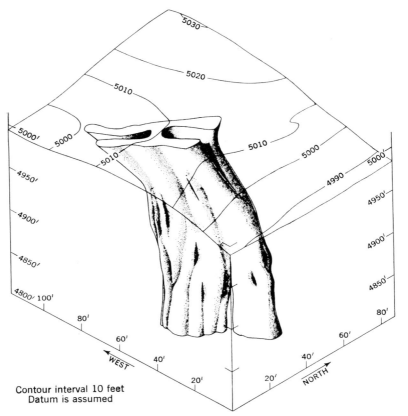

Fig. 9.4. Large fluorite pipe, Bell Hill property, Thomas Range, Utah (Staatz and Osterwald, 1956; *U.S. Geol. Survey*).

Blowout contained little gangue, but at 240 ft the deposit contained such large masses of montmorillonite and lesser quartz and carbonates that it no longer was ore. The Lucky Louie deposit changed from nearly pure fluorite near the surface to fluorite with chalcedony pieces at 90 ft to nearly entirely chalcedony at 120 ft.

The famous topaz-bearing rhyolites of the eastern part of the Thomas Range also contain uranyl minerals, and these rocks and the Spors Mountain volcanics are considered to be consanguineous. The fluorite deposits were formed by the replacement, chiefly of dolomite, by solutions that introduced F, U, V, Al, and H under epithermal conditions and probably were derived from the magma parent to the fluorine-rich rhyolites.

Narrow fluorite veins with pitchblende, pyrite, and oxidized Co, Cu, and Mn minerals occur in Tertiary granite in the Erickson district, Sheeprock Mountains, Juab County (Everhart, 1956B).

Stumbling Stud, Huerfano County, Colorado

The Stumbling Stud uranium prospect, near Badito Cone, 8 mi east of Gardner, Huerfano County, Colorado, is a replacement-type radioactive fluorite deposit in the Dakota formation near a monzonite plug. The gray sedimentary quartzite contains shaley beds and lenses, limonitic bands, as well as thin layers rich in carbonaceous plant debris. The clastic beds have been replaced wholly or in part by gray to deep purple, fine-grained radioactive fluorite (Fig. 9.5). Carnotite and green uranyl minerals appear locally along fractures.

Other United States Occurrences

The Monarch (Staats) fluorite deposits, which are about 35 mi by road northwest of Lund in the Wah Wah Mountains, Beaver County, Utah, occur along a fault contact between Cambrian limestone and Tertiary rhyolite porphyry, forming lenses in fault breccia. Autunite and uranophane occur locally as coatings on fluorite (Thurston et al., 1954).

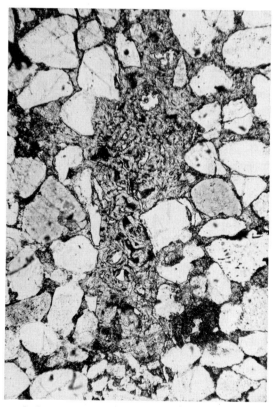

FIG. 9.5. Purple to dark purple radioactive fluorite replacing quartz grains in Dakota sandstone, Stumbling Stud deposit, Huerfano County, Colo. ($\times 66$).

Occurrences in the Honeycomb Hills, Juab County, Utah, consist of uranium minerals as coatings along minor fractures and as disseminations in white, rhyolitic tuff. A small, nearby vein of purple fluorite also is radioactive locally. Seven samples ranged from 0.009 to 0.053% eU (Staatz and Bauer, 1950). The uranium minerals are autunite and uranophane (Peters, 1956).

At the Daisy fluorite mine, about 5 mi east of Beatty, Nye County, Nevada, earthy, purple fluorite in veins and pipes cutting a silicified dolomitic limestone contains 0.002 to 0.015% eU (Lovering, 1954). The fluorite ore, which has been mined to 400 ft, contains clay seams and some limestone inclusions.

About 30 mi northeast of Tucson, Arizona, pitchblende and fluorite occur in a late Precambrian sericite schist (Pinal schist) (Wood, 1956A).

La Marquesa Mine, San Luis Province, Argentina

The La Marquesa deposit is on the western slope of the Sierra de Comechingones in the Rio Seco valley about 8 km northeast of Villa Larca, department of Chacabuco. Green and blue fluorite fills lenticular veins in granite and cements a granitic breccia; these deposits are of low radioactivity. They strike east-northeast and dip 70 to 75° SE. One vein on the southeast edge of the mineralized area consists of fetid, purple fluorite and some lighter fluorite with purple clay and granitic breccia. Uranophane coats fractures and granite fragments in thickness up to 50 cm. The grade is 0.30 to 0.50% U_3O_8 (Angelelli, 1956).

Fluorite-Sulfide Veins

Jamestown, Colorado

The Jamestown, Colorado, district has been a fluorite source since 1903, from veins and breccia zones in a northwest zone 2 mi long and ½ mi wide. The zone, which lies at the northern termination of the Front Range mineral belt, is in Precambrian schist and granite and in Tertiary granodiorite, near the southern and western margins of a sodic granite-quartz monzonite porphyry stock of Tertiary age (Lovering and Goddard, 1950; Goddard, 1946). Various types of dikes, including bostonites, occur in the district. The veins, several hundred to 1,000 ft long and several inches to 20 ft thick, consist of fluorite crystals and breccia pieces cemented by clay, carbonate, quartz, and more fluorite, with fragments of pyrite, galena, sphalerite, other sulfides, and quartz disseminated through the brecciated portions. Breccia zones or pipes are as much as 70 ft wide and 400 ft long and contain granite and fluorite fragments in a fine-grained clay-quartz-sericite-fluorite matrix. Pitchblende and uranothorite (Phair and Shimamoto, 1952) occur in purple fluorite breccia. Fluorite, which varies from white to deep violet, concomitantly ranges from 0.00029 to 0.0515% eU in radioactivity (Goddard, 1946).

The mineralizing solutions, which were genetically related to the Tertiary stock, first deposited fluorite, quartz, and sulfides, then dissolved some vein material, resulting in collapse and brecciation of ore bodies and their walls. A second fluorite cemented the breccia.

Uranium has been produced in the district from secondary concentrations of torbernite along fractures near a schist-granite contact. Finely brecciated fluorite occurs nearby (Peters, 1956). However, these fluorite ores are too low in uranium to be mined for it alone.

Other United States Occurrences

Fluorite, pitchblende, pyrite, and ilsemannite occur in veins transecting Jurassic igneous rocks in the Kern River, Canyon Area, Kern County, south-central California, at the Miracle mine and Kergon deposit, 35 mi northeast of Bakersfield. The first railroad shipment of uranium ore from California was made from the Miracle Mining Company on July 31, 1954. Autunite and torbernite are the most abundant radioactive species. The mineralization at the Miracle mine occurs along a vertical N. 33° W.–trending fracture zone in argillized Isabella granodiorite (granite to tonalite) and is 2 ft thick (Walker et al., 1956). Everhart (1956B) reports roscoelite in the ore.

At the Kergon deposit the 5-ft mineralized fracture zone strikes N. 50° W. and dips 75° NE. across biotite granite. Gouge material assayed as much as 1.1% fluorite, 1.08% U_3O_8, and 1.84% Mo. The molybdenum occurs as a soluble molybdate. Sooty pitchblende apparently increases with depth.

Similar mineralization occurs at the Sunrise No. 1 deposit, 7 mi northwest of McKittrich, Kern County, where yellow uranyl minerals with limonite and fluorite coat fractures and bedding planes in a fault zone that strikes N. 60° W. and dips 75° SW. across upper Miocene rocks (Walker et al., 1956). Pitchblende-fluorite veins also have been mined at the Knob Hill deposits at Castle Buttes, 10 mi northeast of Mojave, Kern County, California.

Rexspar Deposit, British Columbia

The Rexspar deposit is in the North Thompson River valley in south-central British Columbia, 80 mi north of Kamloops and 3 mi from the town of Birch Island (Wilson, 1929; Joubin, 1955A; Joubin and James, 1956B). The Precambrian metasediments and metavolcanics consist in sequence of

4. Sericite schist
3. Argillite
2. Trachyte flow and volcanic breccia
1. Greenstone

The layers strike northeast and dip 10 to 25° NW., and are cut by faults. The pyroclastic rock, which has a minimum thickness of 500 ft, has been replaced by pyrite-sericite-biotite–purple fluorite masses, up to 100,000 sq ft in outcrop area and as much as 50 ft thick. The ore contains 5 to 20% pyrite and contains very fine grained well-disseminated pitchblende and some uranothorite. Other minerals are celestite, albite, carbonate, and accessory zircon, monazite, and rutile. Minor sulfides are chalcopyrite, galena, sphalerite, and molybdenite. Oxidized surfaces locally are coated by secondary uranyl minerals. Two ore bodies, one 20 ft thick, the other 50 ft thick, contain 110,000 tons and 600,000 tons respectively, averaging a little less than 2 lb U_3O_8 per ton. Rare-earth elements (Ce, Y, La) and Th also are present. The radioactive fluorite deposits are associated with a larger deposit (1 million tons) of fluorite-celestite (each about 20%).

Harvey, New Brunswick

Near Harvey, New Brunswick, rhyolite flows and pyroclastics are radioactive. The highest-grade material is a brecciated rhyolite cemented by dark purple fluorite cut by pyritic fractures (Joubin and James, 1956A; Gross, 1957).

Fluorite-Quartz-Sulfide Veins

Marysvale, Utah

The Marysvale district occupies about 1 sq mi, 4 mi northeast of Marysvale, Piute County. It was the first new producing district discovered in the United States (June, 1949) as the result of post-World War II exploration (Nininger, 1954). It includes the most productive vein deposits in the United States, which lie in a zone along the west edge of a quartz monzonite. The early Tertiary Bullion Canyon volcanic series of alkalic latites and andesites (flows, tuffs, and agglomerates) was intruded by latite porphyry (oldest), quartz monzonite, and granite. Next followed an erosional interval that carved the volcanics and intrusives into a surface of considerable relief on which the later Tertiary Mount Belknap rhyolitic volcanics were deposited (Gruner et al., 1951; Kerr et al., 1951; Green and Kerr, 1951; Taylor et al., 1951; Wollard and Kerr, 1952; Kerr et al., 1952A,B, 1953, 1957; Kaiser, 1952; Peters, 1956; Sharp, 1956).

Most of the veins (Bullion-Monarch, Buddy, Freedom No. 1 and No. 2, and Prospector) are in quartz monzonite in vertical fault zones that strike N. 55 to 75° E. or along northwesterly zones that dip 40 to 60° SW. Each zone consists of one or more veins of chalcedony or coarse-grained quartz with considerable fluorite, adularia, and some hematite. Pitchblende, pyrite, marcasite, and jordisite also are present. The metacinnabar-onofrite-tiemannite series is found in its compositional entirety (Bethke, 1956). This association of mercury and uranium appears to be unique, but the presence of selenium as selenides recalls its occurrence in the Goldfields district, Canada (pages 307–308), its abundance at Shinkolobwe, Belgian Congo (pages 292–293), and its widespread distribution in Colorado Plateau deposits (pages 397–398). Fluorite increases with depth. Pitchblende and secondary uranium minerals are closely associated with dark purple fluorite and jordisite both in veins and hydrothermally altered wall rock, which also contains magnetite, pyrite, and ilsemannite. The pitchblende forms fine-grained veinlets, vein stockworks, irregular masses, and breccia cement, and in altered wall rocks also appears as grains, pods, fracture coatings, and vesicle fillings. In veins, pitchblende concentrations are restricted to a maximum width of a few inches in any zone.

Some faults are mineralized continuously over strike lengths of 800 ft and vertical distances of 700 ft. Some steeply plunging shoots occur along intersections of different fault sets or where faults change strike. Values as high as several per cent U_3O_8 have been obtained. Pitchblende is known to have a vertical range of at least 2,000 ft (Walker and Osterwald, 1956A).

Vein zones are separated by gouge from argillized wall rock in which biotite has been converted to chlorite and/or illite (Green and Kerr, 1953), feldspar to sericite, and magnetite to pyrite. Montmorillonite and kaolinite are other common argillic minerals developed in the altered rocks (Wollard and Kerr, 1951; Brophy and Kerr, 1951; Kerr et al., 1952B). Quartz and hematite also are local hydrothermal alteration products. The older alunite deposits of the district are generally not radioactive, although uranium mineralization may be nearby.

Some uranium mineralization occurs in the Bullion Canyon series accompanied by argillization, and altered Mount Belknap volcanics also contain some fluorite, pyrite, and pitchblende. The mineralization is believed to be Pliocene in age.

The assemblage of oxidized uranium minerals includes autunite, torbernite, metatorbernite, phosphuranylite, uranophane, beta-uranophane, schroeckingerite, johannite, uranopilite, zippeite, tyuyamunite, and rauvite (Walker and Osterwald, 1956A; Hamilton and Kerr, 1954A,B). Umohoite and sooty pitchblende probably also are secondary. Concentrations of these species occur in near-surface, oxidized extensions of fluorite-pitchblende veins. Factors controlling the assemblage are type and degree of wall-rock alteration, primary vein mineralogy, and depth beneath ground surface. The depth of oxidation extends from a few tens of feet to as much as 400 ft. Uranophane and beta-uranophane are most abundant and occur only in quartz monzonite, granite, and rhyolite as fracture coatings and veinlets. Other minerals of the oxidized zones include ilsemannite, goethite, manganese oxides, carbonates, and gypsum. Walker and Osterwald (1956A) conclude that some of the uranyl species were formed in place by supergene oxidation of primary pitchblende, but some have been precipitated directly from solutions similar to those that deposited pitchblende at depth under reducing conditions. The deposits are classified as shallow, epithermal (Gruner et al., 1951).

Several small deposits occur near Beaver, Utah, on the west slope of the Tushar Mountains (Sharp, 1956). The host rocks are the Mount Belknap and Bullion Canyon series. The mineralization, which occurs along dikes related to the vulcanism, consists of autunite, torbernite, uranophane, fluorite, pyrite, quartz, chlorite, sericite, and iron oxides along fractures, faults, and shear zones.

Pryor Mountains, Montana-Wyoming

Uranium mineralization in the Pryor Mountains, which lie across the Montana-Wyoming line west of the Big Horn Mountains, was discovered in September, 1955. It consists mainly of tyuyamunite disseminations in Upper Madison limestone (Mississippian), which on West Pryor Mountain are associated with silicified fractures or collapse breccia zones (Jarrard, 1957), and on East Pryor and Little Mountains are in intensely recrystallized zones. The deposits usually occur adjacent to and aligned with faults or anticlinal axes (Hart, 1956; Hauptman, 1956; Davis and Sharp, 1957). Some of these structures appear to be related to major rifts in the underlying Precambrian complex. The siliceous breccia deposits are cavern fillings in the Madison, some of which were open at the time of the overlying Amsden sedimentation.

West Pryor Mountain ores contain abundant fine-grained disseminated fluorite; those on Little Mountain have small amounts of sulfide minerals. Spectroscopic amounts of Mo, Ti, and Zr occur in the ores, and barite is locally abundant. The tyuyamunite fills pores, solution cavities, and breccia interstices, coats calcite crystals, and forms fracture coatings and seams, some of which have been traced for 50 ft. The ores are not in radiometric equilibrium, uranium being twice the radiometric equivalent.

Similar occurrences have been found along the western flank of the northern Big Horn Mountains, Big Horn County, Wyoming.

Other United States Occurrences

Uraninite and uranophane occur in fluorite and quartz veinlets cutting a Tertiary monzonite porphyry plug, in the Henry Mountains, Garfield County, Utah (Wood, 1956A), and have been cited as an example of a uraniferous vein deposit genetically related to the Colorado Plateau sandstone deposits.

At the Annie Laurie prospect, near Ruby, Santa Cruz County, Arizona, a breccia zone along a northeasterly fault(?) in a Tertiary porphyritic rhyolitic flow is cemented by carbonate veinlets also containing fluorite, pyrite, galena, sphalerite, chalcopyrite, metatorbernite, and uranophane. Pitchblende lenses several inches long occur in rhyolite, which has been silicified and hematitized (Wright, 1951; Anderson and Kurtz, 1955).

At the Moonlight mine in the Kings River area of north-central Humboldt County, Nevada, a north-trending fault breccia zone that dips 60° E. across Miocene rhyolite is mineralized with pitchblende, pyrite, smoky quartz, and fluorite. Autunite, torbernite, gummite, and limonite occur near the surface. The structure is mineralized to 270 ft (Sharp, 1956; Butler and Schnabel, 1956; Everhart, 1956B). The adjacent rhyolite has been silicified and sericitized.

Tertiary andesite with an included mass of brecciated chert of the Ordovician El Paso group is mineralized at the Pitchblende Strike prospect, Sierra County, New Mexico, by uraninite, uranophane, fluorite, and chalcedony (Everhart, 1956B). The Plainview prospect in the same county exposes a northeast-trending fracture zone in chloritized Precambrian granite, mineralized with uraninite, uranophane, galena, hematite, chlorite, and fluorite (Everhart, 1956B).

Germany

Fluorite veins in the Wölsendorf region of Bavaria, Germany, have been mined since 1850. The wall rocks are the Bunter granite, intrusive into Precambrian gneisses and paraschists, probably of Hercynian age (late Carboniferous-Permian). The veins, which are Lower Permian or uppermost Carboniferous in age, strike generally northwest and dip 70 to 80° SW. chiefly in granite; some are near granite-gneiss contacts extending downward into gneiss. The granite is argillized near the veins. The chief deposits north and east-southeast of Wölsendorf are the Erna, Eberhard, Roland, Johannes, and Marie mines.

The vein filling consists mainly of fluorite, green, yellow, yellow brown, and the dark purple, fetid type. Barite is locally abundant in some veins as central fillings. Some veins are symmetrically banded; in others the banding is asymmetric. Other constituents of variable abundance are quartz, chalcedony, and carbonates with minor hematite, pyrite, chalcopyrite, bornite, marcasite, and galena.

The paragenesis is complex; fluorite occurs in three generations, carbonates in two, quartz and barite in four (Riedel, 1954). Pseudomorphs of chalcedony after calcite, barite, and fluorite, of fluorite after calcite, and of hematite after siderite and calcite are local features (Strunz, 1952).

The sequence of mineralization (Kohl and Haller, 1934) is (1) carbonates (calcite, dolomite, siderite); (2) quartz and chalcedony; (3) fluorite, barite, quartz; (4) galena, chalcopyrite; (5) carbonates; (6) fracturing—barite, quartz, fluorite, hematite, pyrite, pitchblende. Some vein sections are vuggy with crystals of fluorite, barite, and quartz, as well as coatings of hematite, limonite, and marcasite. Pitchblende occurs as nodules in fluorite, as veinlets in fluorite, and as disseminations in granitic wall rocks. In the Marie vein the uraniferous section is 20 to 35 m long.

Sections of the veins are oxidized to assemblages of anglesite, cerusite, pyromorphite, wulfenite, limonite, goethite, psilomelane, covellite, azurite, malachite, chrysocolla, and cuprite. Secondary uranium minerals include torbernite, autunite, parsonite, uranocircite, phosphuranylite, uranophane, beta-uranophane, uranopilite, fourmarierite, becquerelite, ianthinite, schoepite, dewindtite, and kasolite.

The veins vary in thickness from a few centimeters to 4 m, and the largest mine has been developed over a length of 1,000 m and to a depth of 200 m. Only about 100 tons of by-product uranium ore has been obtained.

URANIFEROUS ANTIMONY VEINS

Macedonia, Yugoslavia

A unique geochemical association of U with Sb and As occurs in some stibnite deposits in part of Vardar zone in Macedonia (Ristic, 1956). This zone, which trends northwest, consists chiefly of serpentinized peridotites, intruded by masses of Miocene dacite-rhyolite and minor younger granite. The ores occur in the marginal parts of an older chromite zone in serpentinized peridotite at the contact of the dacite-rhyolite. The serpentinite has been transformed hydrothermally to ferruginous, siliceous carbonate masses, and the rhyolitic bodies have been altered to montmorillonite-nontronite-quartz-carbonate rocks. The paragenetic sequence is (1) chromite (relict); (2) spherulitic stibnite; (3) zoned spherulitic bravoite; (4) coarse- to fine-grained and needle-like stibnite; (5) fibrous stibnite; (6) unzoned bravoite; (7) realgar and orpiment; (8) stibnite needles in vugs in realgar; (9) minutely and uniformly dispersed radioactive mineral, unidentified.

THORITE VEINS AND BRECCIA PIPES

Wet Mountains, Colorado

In Precambrian rocks in the Wet Mountains, mainly in Custer County, Colorado, extending north into Fremont County, thorium deposits occur chiefly as veins in a northwest-trending area, at least 10×25 mi in size. The Precambrian complex consists of hornblende gneisses, garnetiferous biotite gneiss, sillimanite gneiss, quartzite, scapolite-pyroxene gneiss, and conformable granitoid lenses and layers (Christman et al., 1953; Singewald and Brock, 1956). Pegmatites are widespread. Toward the southern end of the area granite becomes increasingly abundant.

In general the foliation and layering of the metamorphics strike northeast, dipping usually steeply north but in places steeply south. Cutting the foliated rocks is an albite-syenite stock that displays about five times normal background radioactivity, chiefly due to thorium. Its age has been determined as 600 m.y. Dikes of syenite (many brick red in color) and mafic rocks also cut the complex. They trend N. 50° W. to S. 70° W.

Postmetamorphic faults and fracture zones are occupied by veins trending N. 30 to 80° W. and dipping steeply. Thorium mineralization occurs chiefly in veins and to a lesser extent in broad shatter zones and in altered breccia pipes. Hundreds of veins have been discovered, many of which are concentrated in sinuous belts that follow major discontinuous fault zones. Most veins are 10 ft or less wide, a few are as much as 50 ft wide. They can be traced for 100 to 5,000 ft. Some of the mineralization has followed fractures along which dikes previously had been emplaced, and some dikes have been partly or completely replaced by carbonate and other vein minerals.

Vein outcrops may be gossanized, yielding a strong fetid odor detectable for only a few seconds after the rock is broken. The veins contain chiefly quartz, pink feldspar, barite, limonite, and hematite with lesser amounts of purple, yellow, and white fluorite, siderite, magnetite, galena, chalcopyrite, bornite, and pyrite. Small amounts of silver and gold have been detected. Most quartz is white and massive; large smoky zoned crystals occur in vugs. The barite is red, cryptocrystalline to white, coarsely crystalline.

Nearly all of the radioactivity stems from finely disseminated veinlets and blebs of thorite and thorogummite. Xenotime is locally abundant. The paragenesis is (1) siderite; (2) fluorite, quartz, and copper sulfides; (3) galena and barite; and (4) thorite. Samples range from 0.02 to 12.5% ThO_2 with only trace amounts of uranium. Rare-earth elements also are present, chiefly Y, with Ce, La, Nd, Sm, Pr, Gd, Dy, and Yb also reported in a few samples. The thorium-rich concentrations are erratically distributed as pods and lenses.

Wall rocks are generally feldspathized; hornblende is converted to epidote. Near mafic dikes, the wall-rock alteration consists of carbonate and a sodic amphibole.

Some veins contain only feldspar, quartz, and iron oxide minerals, accompanying thorogummite. Others contain barite, smoky quartz, fluorite, and siderite locally, and still others have these minerals as relatively widespread constituents. In many cases the quartz-feldspar vein is spongy, with numerous cavities filled or lined with limonite representing leached and altered siderite. Locally this aggregate is weakly to intensely sheared with abundant limonite along shear planes. Similarly the baritic parts of the veins may be sheared or brecciated with limonite cementing the breccia (Fig. 9.6). In many veins, thorium minerals are nonuniformly distributed, the strongest radioactivity emanating from sheared or brecciated parts.

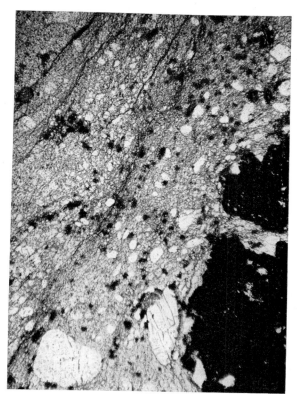

FIG. 9.6. Metamict thorite (dark) in mylonitized barite, stained by hematite, Tuttle Ranch deposit, Wet Mts., Colo. (×35).

Two of the largest ore shoots, with a cutoff grade of 0.3% ThO_2, measure (in feet):

Length	Thickness	Depth
200–300	6–26	400
100	2–10	140

Hicks Dome, Hardin County, Illinois

Hicks Dome, underlying 1½ sq mi, 13 mi south of Elizabethtown near Hicks Branch in northwestern Hardin County, Illinois, has been interpreted as a cryptovolcanic structure. It is represented by a breccia that begins at 1,600 ft (Brown et al., 1954). Associated are peridotite dikes. Structural doming also has been suggested as an explanation of its origin. The rocks are Devonian (New Albany) limestone and chert bordered by black shale (Bradbury et al., 1955). A drill hole into the structure found the breccia to be mineralized with fluorite, which ranges from about 5% in the upper part to about 2% near the bottom of the hole (2,944 ft). Diminishing downward with fluorite is radioactivity, which in the upper part is 0.029% eU and near the bottom is 0.001% eU. Most of the radioactivity is due to thorium and assays of 0.3 to 0.5% Th are reported, as are minor amounts of Nb and Zr. Very little uranium is present: 0.001% U in four analyses, and 0.024% U in one (Brown et al., 1954). Residual clays and breccias from within the Devonian–New Albany area of the dome are generally more radioactive than samples outside this area (Bradbury et al., 1955).

• chapter ten

EPIGENETIC STRATIFORM DEPOSITS
IN SEDIMENTARY ROCKS

GENERAL

The most widespread type of uranium deposit in the United States and that from which the bulk of United States uranium will be obtained at least during the next 10 years is one widely referred to as the "Colorado Plateau type." A concise descriptive designation of these deposits is difficult, for although they have many characteristics in common, they differ rather widely in form, nature of host rock, relations to structural and stratigraphic features, and mineralogy. Thus in the past, investigators have termed them, variously, "sandstone-type deposits," "arid concentration deposits," "disseminated deposits in continental sediments," "sedimentary deposits," "carnotite deposits," "uranium (-vanadium) sandstone deposits," and "uranium accumulations in sedimentary strata," illustrating the difficulties attendant to placing them in a precise category. This problem of classification has been markedly enhanced by the considerable controversy over their origin, which has made specific genetic terms unacceptable to all parties.

Most geologists today agree that the deposits are epigenetic. With some minor exceptions most are stratiform in general shape, granted contacts are locally and in detail, crosscutting. Most deposits occur in clastic sediments of terrestrial origin (noteworthy exception, deposits in the Todilto limestone in New Mexico). And last, the bulk of the uranium mineralization occurs as pore fillings and impregnations, with some replacement of organic material and of cement. Thus the majority of the deposits can be described adequately as *epigenetic stratiform disseminations in continental clastic sediments.*

Since the origin of these deposits remains in doubt, and indeed, since it is possible that not all of them have been formed in the same way, a completely genetic treatment is not presently possible. Deposits of this type, from their

357

various districts, therefore, are described together, and the different genetic theories are likewise considered jointly.

As has previously been noted (page 154), the Colorado Plateau deposits are similar in many of their general characteristics to those of Blind River, Ontario, and of the Witwatersrand, Union of South Africa (McKelvey et al., 1955). Yet the differences are numerous and sufficiently distinctive to warrant separate consideration of these latter two groups.

Most examples of deposits of the Plateau type occur in the Western United States and particularly in the environs of the Colorado Plateau itself, although they are being found increasingly outside of the Plateau, in Wyoming, South Dakota, Texas, Arizona, New Mexico, Nevada, and California. Minor occurrences are known in the Eastern United States. The type has been reported from but a few areas outside of the United States and from no other country in such abundance, concentrations, nor in representatives of such large size. Significant deposits are known in Argentina, in the U.S.S.R., and possibly in the Despeñaperros region, Spain (Alia, 1956A). Doubtless this unusual distribution of known deposits reflects to some degree the intensive nature of the search for uranium in the United States, but it is primarily the result of a combination of unusually favorable geologic factors: ample sources of uranium and other elements; hosts suitable structurally, stratigraphically, and petrologically; and geomorphological conditions permitting preservation.

COLORADO PLATEAU

INTRODUCTION

The Colorado Plateau, a relatively well defined physiographic and tectonic unit in the Cordillera of the United States, embraces about 150,000 sq mi within a roughly ellipsoidal area about 400×450 mi in plan. Included are the westernmost part of Colorado, northwestern New Mexico, northeastern Arizona, and eastern Utah (Fig. 10.1). The area of mineralization is bounded by lines from Craig, Colorado, westward to Vernal, Utah; thence southwestward to Castledale, Utah; thence south to Williams, Arizona; east to Albuquerque, New Mexico, northwestward to Placerville, Colorado; and north to Craig.

The area is not a single plateau but a region dominated by many plateaus, and yet more of it is in the form of plains, valleys, mesas, and mountains than plateaus. As stated by Kelley (1955A, p. 10), "It is difficult to find a single feature of physiography, climate, or structure that would characterize the areas as a whole for it is a province of considerable diversity." Nevertheless, it is distinctively separated from adjoining areas in its structure, stratigraphy, igneous rocks, and its mineral deposits. The tectonic unit of the Plateau does not coincide, in detail and particularly along its eastern margin, with the Plateau as a physiographic province (Kelley, 1955A).

The six major geomorphic subdivisions of the Plateau are (Hunt, 1956) (Fig. 10.1) (1) the Uinta Basin on the north, structurally the lowest part of the Plateau; (2) the High Plateau of Utah along the western margin, as high as 11,000 ft and with intervening, broad, north-trending valleys; (3) the

FIG. 10.1. Index map of the Colorado Plateau (Hunt, 1956; *U.S. Geol. Survey*).

359

Fig. 10.2. Canyon Lands section, Dead Horse Point, southwest of Moab, on the Colorado River, Utah, LaSal laccolithic mountains to east (J. Shappirio).

Canyon Lands south of the Uinta Basin, 5,000 to 7,000 ft high, with drainage deeply incised, hogbacks, and isolated laccolithic mountains (Fig. 10.2); (4) south of the Canyon Lands, the Navajo section, an area of broad valleys and mesas; (5) the lava-blanketed Datil section along the southeastern margin; and (6) the Grand Canyon section on the southwestern edge, structurally the highest of the Plateau.

The Colorado Plateau is a geological showcase exposing in great detail, over large areas and in thick sections, Precambrian to Tertiary strata, extrusive and intrusive igneous rocks, numerous small to major structural features of great variety, and a profusion of mineral deposits, not just of uranium and vanadium, but also of copper, silver, manganese, fluorite, salt, gypsum, sulfur, clay, coal, oil shale, petroleum, natural gas, and other substances.

HISTORY

The first users of uranium-vanadium ores were probably the Navajo and Ute Indians who decorated their bodies with brilliant yellow and red war and ceremonial paints. Although settlers knew of the existence of the yellow material in sandstone in the Paradox area before 1880, there has been considerable discussion as to who was the first to bring carnotite to the attention of mineralogists. Carnotite was first described by Friedel and Cumenge (1899) from Montrose County, Colorado. According to Bruÿn (1955), it was a Colorado photographer and "rock-hound" Thomas M. McKee who became interested in the bright yellow rock stains on the Tom Dullan claims at Roc Creek and in 1898 secured a sample for Charles Poulot, a mining engineer and former student of Friedel. Poulot, having identified the mineral as a vanadate, sent it to Friedel. Other reports claim that Gordon Kimball of Ouray was the first to obtain carnotite samples for Poulot (Coffin, 1921), and Kimball himself (1904) stated that he obtained samples of the "chrome copper ore" from Roc Creek in the spring of 1898 and sent them to Poulot. Kimball began developing the Roc Creek deposits in May, 1898, and in June of that year shipped 10 tons of 21% U_3O_8 ore to Denver where it was sold for $2,600.

With the disclosure that such ore contained both vanadium and uranium, thus being a source of radium discovered by the Curies in 1898, mining began in 1910,[1] and shipments to France continued until 1914, when World War I intervened. In 1913, the National Radium Institute and the U.S. Bureau of Mines began a cooperative operation in mining and concentration of carnotite. Between 1914 and 1917, 8½ g of radium were extracted in a Denver plant (Kithil and Davis, 1917). Vanadium and uranium also were recovered.

Mining continued actively until 1924, at which time production from the rich Congo deposits, first mined in 1921, brought a halt to the United States radium mining. Vanadium continued to be produced at Rifle, Colorado, until 1932, and production was resumed in 1936 to continue until 1945.

In 1939 the U.S. Geological Survey began a study of the deposits as part of its strategic minerals investigations program which continued through World War II.[2] Fischer (1956) estimates that in excess of 1,000 man-years of geological study has been devoted to the deposits since their discovery in 1898. In 1942 the Metals Reserve Company began a vanadium ore purchasing program. However, until 1944 mining was almost exclusively for vanadium, uranium being discharged in the tailings.

Early in World War II, mining companies in the Plateau redesigned their plants for uranium extraction under direction of the Manhattan Project of the U.S. Army Engineers, and during the war expansion of mining and milling facilities continued rapidly.

In 1946 the Atomic Energy Act created the U.S. Atomic Energy Commission, which in 1948 began its domestic uranium program designed to stimulate prospecting and mining of uranium. This was followed in 1951 by an increase in the base price of ore and the introduction of an initial production bonus. A tremendous expansion in prospecting followed, marked by intense public interest which reached its peak in 1954 to 1955. Numerous ore deposits were discovered, including some of significant size, and by 1955 about 2,000 individual deposits were known within the Plateau. Not all were newly found, of course, and at least 90% were of small size.

A distinct turning point in the history of Plateau mining resulted from the discovery of the now famous Mi Vida ore body in the Lisbon Valley area by Charles A. Steen in the summer of 1952, which demonstrated that large deposits of pitchblende-type ore existed in the Plateau. By 1954, about 24 major mining and oil companies were active, either in exploration or production, and

[1] In his summary of the early mining history of the Plateau, Coffin (1954) tells of Joe Dahl who directed initial exploratory operations of the Standard Chemical Company on Club Camp Flat (near Uravan) and who was promised a new Ford car if he found an ore body of at least 10,000 tons. The deposit he began mining eventually proved continuous for 2,500 ft, yielding 150,000 tons. Unfortunately, Dahl did not know how to drive his bonus.

[2] The initial published report of work in this period is that by Fischer (1942).

ore was shipped from approximately 1,000 properties. The most recent major development has been the discovery and development of the extraordinarily large deposits of the Grants–Ambrosia Lake area, New Mexico (pages 410–416).

The Atomic Energy Commission placed the reserves of uranium ore in the United States, as of November 1, 1955, at 60 million tons of which about 88% is in or adjacent to the Colorado Plateau area.

GEOLOGY

Regional

The Colorado Plateau represents a broad platform of relative structural stability surrounded by the more active tectonic units of the Rocky Mountain Cordillera. On the north the Plateau is bordered by the Uinta uplift and the axial fold belt; on the east the eastern Rockies orogenic belt forms the margin; on the south the northwest-trending part of the Arizona Basin and Range province is the boundary; and on the west it adjoins the Basin and Range province in Utah and Nevada.

Sedimentary strata ranging in age from Paleozoic to Tertiary crop out over much of the Plateau. Although over much of the area strata dip gently, along the flanks of numerous major structures they are moderately to steeply dipping. Igneous rocks of post-Laramide age occur as laccoliths (prominent as isolated mountain groups), minor intrusives, and flows.

Stratigraphy

The stratigraphy of three of the major parts of the Colorado Plateau is summarized in Tables 10.1, 10.2 and 10.3. Formations older than Pennsylvanian are rarely exposed.

Throughout much of the Plateau the Pennsylvanian is represented by the Hermosa formation, below whose upper limey beds lie the Paradox evaporites, considered by some geologists as a member (Picard, 1954) and by others as a separate formation. The Paradox has contributed material significant in the development of the piercement anticlines in the Paradox basin.

The Triassic-Jurassic formations are the most important in terms of the extent of mineralization, and much of the spectacular Plateau scenery results from their erosion (Cadigan, 1954; Harshbarger, 1957). The oldest Triassic, the Moenkopi, 0 to 2,000 ft thick, is red and buff sandstone, siltstone, greenish-gray to red shale (Fig. 10.3), and thin limestone beds, chiefly of fluvial origin. An unconformity separates it from the Cutler beneath, and an erosion surface of wide extent occurs between the Moenkopi and overlying formations, which is usually the Shinarump or the Chinle (McKee, 1954).

The Shinarump conglomerate, one of the most significant ore bearers, is 0 to 275 ft thick, commonly less than 100 ft. It is a fluvial deposit of cross-bedded, lenticular sandstone, conglomerate, and variegated shale. Its exact age is in dispute. Stokes (1954A) considers it a fossil pediment spread during a long period, possibly all of Middle Triassic time. Many geologists have considered it a basal conglomerate of the Chinle, and fossil plants indicate a late Triassic age (Daugherty, 1941). Strata previously called Shinarump in central and

TABLE 10.1. *Generalized upper Paleozoic to Cenozoic stratigraphy of eastern Utah–western Colorado (adapted from Finch, 1955)*

System	Series	Formation	
Tertiary			Uinta Bridger Green River Wasatch Tuscher
Cretaceous	Upper		Mesaverde grp. Mancos sh. Dakota ss.
	Lower		Burro Canyon
Jurassic	Upper	Morrison	Brushy Basin mem. Salt Wash mem.
		San Rafael group	Bluff ss. Summerville Curtis Entrada ss.
	Upper and Middle		Carmel
	Lower		Navajo
Jurassic(?)			Kayenta
Triassic	Upper	Chinle	Wingate ss.
			Moss Back ss. mem.
			Shinarump cgl.
	Middle and Lower		Moenkopi
Permian			Cutler
Permian(?) and Pennsylvanian			Rico
Pennsylvanian			Hermosa ls.

TABLE 10.2. *Generalized upper Paleozoic to Cenozoic stratigraphy of northeastern Arizona–northwestern New Mexico (adapted from Finch, 1955)*

System	Series	Formation	
Tertiary		Bidahochi Chuska ss.	
Cretaceous	Upper	Animas Ojo Alamo ss. Kirtland sh. Fruitland Pictured Cliffs ss. Lewis sh. Mesaverde grp. Mancos sh. Dakota ss.	
	Lower	Burro Canyon	
Jurassic	Upper	Morrison	Brushy Basin mem. Westwater Canyon mem. Recapture mem. Salt Wash mem.
		San Rafael group	Bluff ss. Summerville Todilto ls. Entrada ss.
	Upper and Middle	Carmel	
	Lower	Navajo ss.	
Jurassic(?)		Kayenta	
Triassic	Upper	Wingate ss. Chinle Shinarump cgl.	
	Middle and Lower	Moenkopi	
Permian		Cutler	
Permian(?) and Pennsylvanian		Rico	
Pennsylvanian		Hermosa ls.	

364

TABLE 10.3. *Generalized upper Paleozoic to Cenozoic stratigraphy of southwestern Utah–northwestern Arizona (adapted from Finch, 1955)*

System	Series	Formation
Tertiary		Wasatch
Cretaceous	Upper	Wahweap ss. Straight Cliffs ss. Tropic sh. Dakota(?) ss.
Jurassic	Upper	Winsor Curtis Entrada ss.
	Upper and Middle	Carmel
	Lower	Navajo ss.
Jurassic(?)		Kayenta
Triassic	Upper	Wingate ss. Chinle Shinarump cgl.
	Middle and Lower	Moenkopi
Permian		Kaibab ls. Toroweap Coconino ss. Hermit sh.
Pennsylvanian		Supai

east-central Utah are now believed to correlate with a prominent sandstone in the Chinle, 200 ft above its base in White Canyon, Utah (Stewart and Williams, 1954). Field relations indicate that the Shinarump extends northeastward from its type section in northwestern Arizona to pinch out along a northwest line 10 mi north of White Canyon in southeastern Utah. The Shinarump was deposited by streams flowing northwest, and channels cut in Moenkopi surfaces are of significance in some districts in the localization of ore.

The Chinle formation crops out widely on the Plateau and also contains important quantities of ore. It is the most complex Triassic unit, containing lenticular and intertonguing sandstone, conglomerate, shale, and limestone. Near its base it contains a prominent sandstone-conglomerate, widely referred to as the Moss Back member, confusable with the Shinarump (Groth, 1955).

Fig. 10.3. Ripple-marked red shale, Moenkopi formation; San Rafael Swell, Utah.

The Chinle is of fluvial and lacustrine origin and is 100 to 500 ft thick (Fig. 10.4).

In northwestern New Mexico and adjacent Arizona, the Todilto limestone unconformably overlies the Entrada and interfingers locally with the overlying Summerville. From southwest to northeast the formation changes from a 20-ft limestone (Fig. 10.5) to a 5- to 10-ft limestone overlain by 40 ft of gypsum secondary after anhydrite. The limestone is regarded as lacustrine (Gabelman, 1956A), although Smith (1951) believes both the carbonate and evaporite facies to be marine.

The most important uranium container is the Morrison formation. In eastern Utah, northeastern Arizona, northwestern New Mexico, and in part of western Colorado, it is divisible into a lower and upper part, each part with two members of distinctive lithology (Craig et al., 1955). The lower part consists of either the Salt Wash or Recapture member or both, which are age equivalents and intergrade. The Salt Wash, which is present throughout most of the Plateau, was formed as a large alluvial plain deposit by a system of braided streams fanning to the east and north from south-central Utah focus (Mullens and Freeman, 1957). Thus this member grades northeastward from mainly coarse clastics into fine clastics. Four facies are recognized (Fig. 10.6).

The Recapture member, which is centered around the Four Corners area, was formed similarly by streams originating from south of Gallup, New Mexico.

The upper part of the Morrison consists of the Brushy Basin and Westwater Canyon members. The latter is the lower portion of the upper unit around the Four Corners area, grading northward into the Brushy Basin. The Westwater is similar to the Recapture in distribution, lithology, and origin, but contains considerably coarser material.

The Brushy Basin, in contrast to the other three members, consists chiefly of variegated claystones with a few lenses of conglomeratic sandstone, formed as fluvial and lacustrine deposits. Some of the clay is bentonitic derived from volcanic ash.

Tertiary formations are important chiefly in the marginal parts of the Plateau and only locally in its interior. They are of continental origin exclusively, some containing appreciable amounts of pyroclastic debris, e.g., Browns Park and Bidahochi formations.

On the Colorado Plateau are exposed formations developed within nearly all of the major sedimentary environments: marine, lagoonal, paludal, lacustrine, fluvial, and eolian. However, with some conspicuous exceptions, most of the major units over much of the Plateau from Permian to Upper Cretaceous time (Dakota) are of continental origin.

Structure

The major rock masses involved in the deformation of the Colorado Plateau are (1) a strongly deformed and metamorphosed Precambrian complex, and (2) a relatively thin cover of Paleozoic-Mesozoic marine and continental sediments. The pre-Laramide thickness of this blanket wedges from about 4,000 ft along the southern and southeastern margin of the Plateau to nearly 20,000 ft in the northwestern part of the Uinta Basin (Kelley, 1955A). At no time since the beginning of the Paleozoic have geosynclinal troughs been present in the Plateau area to receive thick sedimentary deposits. The structural features

Fig. 10.4. Typical Chinle exposure northwest of Moab, Grand County, Utah. Bottom is Moenkopi, Chinle begins at base of prominent central bed; massive sandstone capping is Wingate.

FIG. 10.5. Thin-bedded Todilto limestone, mineralized with tyuyamunite (light gray coatings) films on bedding planes, Haystack Butte, N.Mex.

of the Plateau strata, significant to uranium mineralization, are mainly of Laramide origin. However, as Kelley (1955A,C,D, 1956) has pointed out, certain tectonic features developed in Pennsylvanian-Permian time (Ancestral Rocky Mountains) appear to have controlled the orientation of some of the Laramide structural trends.

Kelley (1955A) (Fig. 10.7) has defined the major structural elements of the Plateau as

1. Basins, covering about one-third of the area.

2. Uplifts (tectonic in contrast to igneous domes), one group trends northerly, a second northwest.

3. Intermediate elements: platforms, slopes, benches, saddles, arches, and sags, which constitute nearly 50% of the Plateau area.

4. Monoclines (Kelley, 1955B), many of which are boundaries between uplifts and adjacent basins.

5. Small folds, dominantly of northwesterly trend.

6. Salt structures, in the Paradox fold-fault belt (Fig. 10.8). These include such prominent structures as the northwest-trending Gypsum, Paradox, and Salt Valleys eroded along the crests of parallel anticlines that have been pierced by evaporites of the Paradox formation, with subsequent collapse into long irregular grabens. The structures are exceedingly complex in detail, and some differences of opinion exist as to the time at which they were initiated. Some geologists have concluded that piercement was Laramide in age, whereas others believe that salt intrusions began in Permian time (Kelley, 1955A, pp. 35–42).

7. Faults; chiefly vertical or steeply dipping, and of many orientations and diverse origins. The longest follow the margins of the High Plateau and have

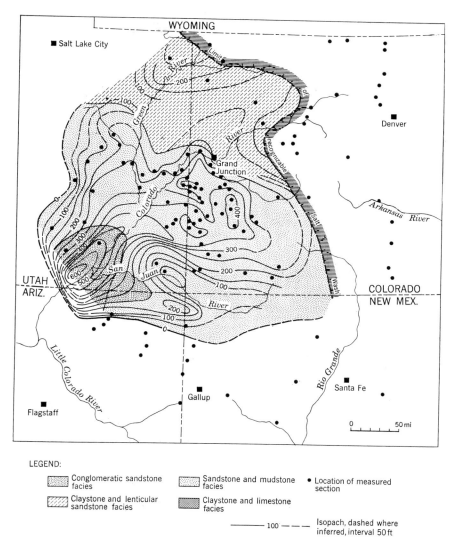

WYOMING

■ Salt Lake City

200

100

100

Green River

Uin...

River

Denver ■

Grand
Junction ■

un...recognizable

Arkansas River

Colorado

400

300

0

100

200

300

Salt ... Wash

200

UTAH
ARIZ.

San Juan

600
500

100

River

COLORADO
NEW MEX.

200

100

0

Little Colorado River

Rio Grande

Flagstaff ■

Gallup ■

Santa Fe ■

0   50 mi

LEGEND:

Conglomeratic sandstone
facies

Claystone and lenticular
sandstone facies

Sandstone and mudstone
facies

Claystone and limestone
facies

• Location of measured
section

———— 100 ——— Isopach, dashed where
inferred, interval 50 ft

FIG. 10.6. Isopachous and facies map of the Salt Wash member, Morrison formation (Craig and others, 1955; *U.S. Geol. Survey*).

369

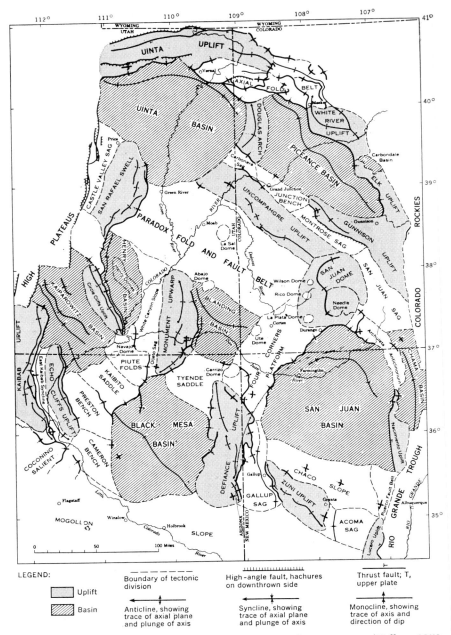

Fig. 10.7. Structural units of the Colorado Plateau and its environs (Kelley, 1956; U.S. Geol. Survey).

370

TABLE 10.4. *Major uplifts of the Colorado Plateau (Kelley, 1955A)*

Uplift	Area, sq mi	Relief,* ft
1. Defiance	3,450	3,000
2. Uncompahgre	3,500	2,500
3. San Rafael	2,600	4,000
4. Kaibab	2,600	3,000
5. Monument	2,500	3,000
6. Zuni	1,800	5,000
7. Echo Cliffs	1,300	500
8. Circle Cliffs	1,000	2,000

* Estimated on the top of the Chinle formation.

TABLE 10.5. *Major basins of the Colorado Plateau (Kelley, 1955A)*

Basin	Area, sq mi	Structural relief,* ft
1. Uinta	9,750	14,000
2. San Juan	10,600	6,000
3. Piceance	5,800	11,000
4. Black Mesa	7,000	800
5. Kaiparowits	4,200	1,000
6. Henry	2,100	4,000
7. Blanding	2,500	700

* Estimated on the top of the Chinle formation.

throws of as much as several thousand feet, whereas faults within the Plateau generally have throws of less than 100 ft (Fig. 10.9).

8. Joints; widespread in Permian and Mesozoic but also present in rocks of other age groups; particularly prominent in massive sandstones and limestones (Fig. 10.8).

9. Collapse chimneys. At Temple Mountain and in nine other places in the southern part of the San Rafael Swell, Utah. Chimneylike collapse structures of jumbled, down-dropped blocks occur within shallow structural depressions (Fig. 10.30). They are surrounded by rims of altered strata (Shoemaker, 1954; Kerr et al., 1955; Keys, 1956).

10. Lineaments. Kelley (1955A) has recognized three main tectonic lineaments across the Plateau in a northwesterly direction, defined ". . . as either

FIG. 10.8. Northeast limb of north end of Salt Valley anticline, Grand County, Utah. The prominently jointed white sandstone is the Moab member of the Summerville formation, overlain by the Salt Wash member of the Morrison.

FIG. 10.9. Fault with slickensides, in Navajo sandstone, northeast side Salt Valley anticline, Grand County, Utah.

372

a general alignment of structural features or a boundary between contrasting structural features" (Kelley, 1955A, p. 58). From north to south they are designated as the White River, the Uncompahgre, and the Zuni, and they divide the Plateau into three parallel northwest-trending strips or segments which have been called the Uinta, San Juan, and Mogollon (north to south).

Igneous Rocks and Structures

Intrusive Bodies

Although the Plateau is underlain predominantly by sedimentary rocks, igneous activity has been widespread within and around it (Fig. 10.10). The intrusive masses, which are Laramide or younger, include laccoliths, stocks, plugs, dikes, and sills, many of which are concentrated in "centers" of igneous activity. Numerous stocks and laccoliths of varying composition occur on the east side of the Plateau in the San Juan and West Elk Mountains. On the Plateau itself intrusive centers are of two main types (Kelley, 1955A): the porphyry laccolith-bysmalith-sill type and the plug-volcano type. Most of the laccolithic type are in the central or south-central part of the Plateau along three northwest trends. They probably range in age from Upper Cretaceous to Oligocene. Hunt et al. (1953) regard the laccolithic mountains as a series resulting from a single igneous process arrested at various stages of completion. The rocks range from diorite and monzonite porphyries to syenite porphyries. This progression in composition is accompanied by a change from hypabyssal to plutonic intrusive conditions, an increase in size and in intensity of the accompanying metamorphism, and probably a decrease in age (Hunt, 1956). The chief laccolithic mountain centers are Rico, La Plata, La Sal, Ute, Abajo, Carrizo, and Henry. Navajo Mountain on the Arizona-Utah border also is considered a center, although igneous rocks are not exposed.

In the Henry, La Sal, and Ute Mountains, the individual mountain domes are centered around a stock from which radiate tongue-shaped laccoliths. The Carrizos are built up mainly of sills, and the La Plata and Rico Mountains, each underlain by domes with central stocks, include numerous sills and laccoliths (Shoemaker, 1954). The laccolithic centers occur in or near basins, among salt structures, or on platforms, but not on tectonic uplifts.

The plug-volcano type of igneous center occurs as clusters of numerous individual punctures in several areas, especially in the southern part of the Plateau. The chief centers are the Taylor, Zuni, and San Francisco, in which the rocks are mainly basaltic with some andesites and rhyolites; and the Hopi and Navajo centers exposing alkalic mafic and ultramafic types (minette, monchiquite, and kimberlite) (Fig. 10.11).

Kelley (1955A) has pointed out that in the San Francisco field alone there are some 350 centers many of which are aligned along northeast- or northwest-trending master joints. In the Hopi field, about 250 diatremes associated with Pliocene alkalic basaltic flows and tuffs are exposed. The diatremes are funnel-shaped events, flaring to diameters of a mile or more at the level of the Pliocene surface out of which they burst (Shoemaker, 1954, 1956A). They have been eroded to varying depths, and their exposed diameters vary inversely

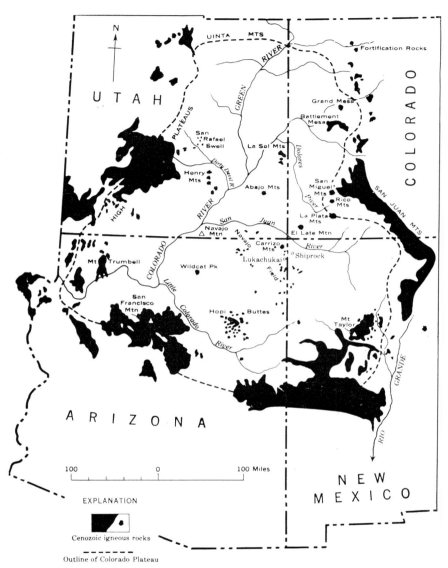

Fig. 10.10. Distribution of Cenozoic igneous rocks on and around the Colorado Plateau. Laccolith mountains are mainly in the central part of Plateau; plug-volcano centers are chiefly marginal (Hunt, 1956; *U.S. Geol. Survey*).

374

with depth of stripping. The filling material also changes with depth, beginning with tuff, limestone, and even layered clay, evaporite, and chert in the upper parts, grading downward into tuff, breccia, and masses of country rock, and still further into agglomerate and intrusive igneous rocks. Much of the well-bedded tuff is of fluvatile origin, with thicknesses up to 2,000 ft. With depth, beds steepen and are intensely sheared.

Uranium deposits occur in or adjacent to diatremes, particularly those of the Hopi Buttes area (Shoemaker, 1956A). Concentrations of uranium are in the fillings of limestones, and especially in claystones and in siltstones. Highest concentrations are in laminated siltstones that overlie unconformably coarse pyroclastic beds.

In the Carrizo Mountains a plug (Navajo alkalic type?) intrudes the laccoliths (Kelley, 1955A). In the Hopi field, extrusives from the centers are interlayered with the middle Pliocene Bidahochi formation. The normal basaltic rocks of the Taylor and San Francisco centers are late Pliocene in the main, but some Taylor occurrences may be Miocene and others Quaternary, and many of those in the Zuni center are probably Quaternary (Kelley, 1955A).

Dikes are widely scattered throughout the Plateau and are abundant in some areas. Many are basaltic or lamprophyric (Fig. 10.12); more silicic types occur along the eastern margin. At the southwest end of the San Rafael Swell, thin but extensive sills are accompanied by a large dike swarm. Most of the sills are composites of alkalic diabase injected by syenite (Gilluly, 1927). Short dikes also are numerous between the San Juan Basin and the southern end of the Monument upwarp (Kelley, 1955A).

Fig. 10.11. Shiprock, N.Mex., an erosional remnant of a tuff-filled diatreme, Navajo field.

Fɪɢ. 10.12. Diabase dike cutting mineralized Morrison formation, Jack Pile mine, Grants district, N.Mex.

Cryptovolcanic Structures

Structures that partly resemble some of the diatremes but do not expose igneous rock are widespread over the Plateau (Shoemaker, 1954). The Upheaval Dome, 3 mi across, shattered centrally and surrounded by a ring syncline, occurs just east of the Green River about 25 mi southwest of Moab, Utah. Its central part has been interpreted as highly deformed Moenkopi beds cut by sandstone dikes (Shoemaker, 1954).

The Woodrow deposit near the Jack Pile mine in the Grants district, New Mexico, is a mineralized, nearly vertical pipelike structure, roughly circular in plan and about 25 ft across punched through Morrison beds. The pipe is filled with breccia and gangue (Cook and Wylie, 1956), and has been mineralized with uranium minerals and sulfides through fracture fillings and fracture-controlled replacement.

Volcanic Rocks

In addition to the flows and pyroclastic materials associated with plug-volcano centers and diatremes, extensive areas underlain by volcanic rocks lie marginal to the Plateau, infringing upon it (Fig. 10.10). Among these are the thick pile of Tertiary volcanic rocks of the San Juan Mountains on the east-central edge; the volcanic area of the High Plateaus of Utah on the northwestern side; the Tertiary volcanics of the Mogollon province extending northward from the Gallo and Datil Mountains along the eastern part of the southern boundary of the Plateau in New Mexico; and the volcanic rocks of the Jemez Caldera near the southeastern corner of the Plateau.

Geochemistry

The igneous rocks of the Plateau as a petrographic province are high in alkalies and aluminum. Hunt (1956) distinguishes four subprovinces: (1) in the interior, in laccolithic intrusives, soda greatly exceeds potash; (2) in the High Plateaus soda and potash are about equal; (3) potash exceeds soda in the Navajo field; and (4) along the southern margin of the Plateau soda exceeds potash.

Extrinsic elements of the uranium deposits that are present in amounts spectrographically detectable in igneous rocks of the Plateau are V, Cu, Pb, Ni, and Co. These elements are known to vary in abundance systematically with the differentiation sequence (Shoemaker, 1955). In the lavas of the San Francisco field the relations are Ni follows Mg, substituting in early silicates; Cu and Co follow Fe^2; V follows Fe^3, probably controlled by crystallization of magnetite; and Pb follows K, chiefly in feldspars.

In the Henry Mountains, one series of minor-element trends is similar to that above, another is represented by enrichments of Cu and V in the most acid rocks. Anomalous concentrations of Cu and V also have been found in the most acid differentiates of the intrusive groups in the La Sal and La Plata Mountains.

GEOLOGIC HISTORY

Precambrian orogenies in the Plateau area probably were numerous. Archeozoic rocks are intensely deformed and metamorphosed and were intruded by batholiths at several times. The dominant structural trends are northeast. Probably in Algonkian time much of the Plateau was downwarped geosynclinally to receive sediments, which were eroded subsequently from highlands produced during later Algonkian deformations. With the development of the major late Precambrian erosion surface, Algonkian rocks were preserved only locally in troughs (Kelley, 1955A).

The Cambrian seas moved across a surface having at least 800 ft of relief. In early and middle Paleozoic times the area alternated between a coastal plain, with oceans to the west, and a partly submerged shelf. In Pennsylvanian-Permian time, three northwest-trending positive areas of the Ancestral Rockies were developed on and adjacent to the Plateau (Front Range, Uncompahgre, and Zuni). Deformation continued intermittently into Triassic time, but in most places seas had been drained from the land by the end of Pennsylvanian time. The Paradox basin, which was developed southeast of the Uncompahgre highland, was filled, first with evaporites, then with limestone, and last with clastic continental sediments. Salt anticlines and piercements may have been initiated in late Pennsylvanian time.

In Triassic and Jurassic times the Plateau appeared as a broad, west-sloping plain onto which alluvial debris was extensively deposited. Western margins were at or near sea level, and brief invasions from this direction are indicated by the marine tongues of the Carmel and Curtis formations. Volcanic activity is represented in Chinle and Shinarump strata by pyroclastic debris now altered to clay minerals.

In late Jurassic time playa and lacustrine conditions appeared in the southern parts of the Plateau. Sharp marginal uplifts accompanied by vulcanism are recorded by Morrison conglomeratic beds interbedded with coarse, tuffaceous sandstones. The chief source areas for Morrison sediments were in west-central Arizona, southeastern California, and west-central New Mexico.

Throughout most of the Cretaceous, much of the Plateau remained stable. With the rise of the Cordilleran geanticline during late Cretaceous time the Plateau area began to sink, receiving sediments to a thickness of 5,000 to 6,000 ft. The axis of this late Cretaceous geosyncline was east of the Plateau, but ocean waters extended to its western edge. At the close of the Cenozoic, the area had become a coastal plain with mountains to the west and southwest and the sea withdrawing eastward.

The principal folds began to form in early Paleocene time. The San Juan volcanic highlands, initiated in latest Cretaceous, continued to grow. Most of the present structural features of the Plateau were developed in Laramide time, although minor faulting also occurred in the Pliocene. A large lake initiated in late Paleocene time (Hunt, 1956) had degenerated to playas by Oligocene time. During Oligocene time, sedimentation continued from the east (Rockies), north (Uintas), and from the west and southwest.

During early Miocene time, the Plateau was raised above the level of valleys in the adjoining Basin and Range province, and degradation supplanted aggradation. Hunt (1956, p. 77) states that "The superposition of the main streams across the large upwarps is presumed to have occurred at about this stage." Laccolithic intrusions in the central Plateau and the beginnings of vulcanism in the southern Plateau occurred in middle Miocene time. Considerable cutting had already defined the site of the Grand Canyon.

Uplift continued into middle Pliocene, with displacement continuing along border faults. Northeastward tilting resulted in ponding of the drainage and deposition of such formations as the Bidahochi and Browns Park. Eruptions of basalt and alkalic basalt were extensive. In the final stage, late Pliocene to Recent), streams reoccupied and deepened the canyons. Extensive sheets of basaltic and andesitic lava were erupted onto the southern and western edges of the Plateau.

ORE DEPOSITS

Geographic Distribution

The major sources of uranium ore in the United States are the deposits of the Colorado Plateau. By 1954, about 1,000 mines had shipped ore, and the number of occurrences must be reckoned as many thousands. To a considerable extent the distribution of the known significant deposits is controlled by the pattern of the outcrop areas of the four most productive formations, but even these units are irregularly mineralized, with notable concentrations of deposits in recognizable districts. The belts or districts have been variously defined (Finch, 1955; Fischer, 1956); the major ones are:

A. In the northeastern corner of the Plateau, in Colorado
1. Meeker district, Rio Blanco County
2. Rifle district, Garfield County. Primarily vanadium
B. On the west side of the San Juan Mountains, in southwestern Colorado. Primarily vanadium. From north to south:
3. Placerville district, San Miguel County
4. Rico district, Dolores and San Juan Counties
5. Lightner Creek district, west of Durango, La Plata County
C. The Uravan mineral belt, chiefly in central-westernmost Colorado, with local extensions into easternmost Utah. In a general way from north to south:
6. Gateway district, Mesa County, Colo., and Grand County, Utah
7. Uravan district, Montrose County, Colo.
8. Paradox district, Montrose County, Colo., and San Juan County, Utah
9. Bull Canyon district, Montrose and San Miguel Counties, Colo.
10. Gypsum Valley district, San Miguel County, Colo.
11. Slick Rock district, San Miguel County, Colo.
D. In northwestern New Mexico
12. Grants district (including Ambrosia Lake area), McKinley and Valencia Counties
E. In northeastern Arizona, extending for short distances into northwesternmost New Mexico
13. Carrizo Mountains–Lukachukai Mountains district (Shiprock district), Apache County, Ariz., and San Juan County, N.Mex.
F. Near Cameron, Ariz.
14. Little Colorado district, Coconino County
G. In eastern Utah. From north to south:
15. Green River district (poorly defined), including Thompsons area, in Grand, Emery, and Wayne Counties
16. Moab district, including Big Indian Wash–Lisbon Valley area, in Grand and San Juan Counties
17. Monticello-Blanding district, San Juan County
H. In east-central Utah. Generally north to south extending into northern Arizona
18. San Rafael district, Emery County, Utah
19. Capitol Reef district, Wayne County, Utah
20. Circle Cliffs district, Garfield County, Utah
21. Henry Mountains district, Garfield County, Utah
22. White Canyon district, San Juan County, Utah
23. Monument Valley district, San Juan County, Utah, and Navajo and Apache Counties, Ariz.
I. In southwestern Utah and adjacent Arizona
24. Silver Reef district, Washington County, Utah, and Coconino County, Ariz., with scattered deposits (e.g., Bulloch group) to the east in Kane County, Utah

Stratigraphic Distribution

Although about 90% of the United States uranium production has been achieved from fluvial strata of Triassic and Jurassic ages on the Colorado Plateau (Table 10.6), uranium mineralization has been found in 33 sedimentary

TABLE 10.6. *Uranium production from sedimentary units of the Colorado Plateau (modified from Wood, 1956A)*

Unit	Per cent of U.S. production
Salt Wash	40.9 (some from Black Hills)
Chinle and Shinarump	38.7
Brushy Basin	9.2
Todilto	7.4
Dakota	0.4 (some from Black Hills and Wyoming)
Recapture (including Westwater)	0.2
Entrada	0.1
Cutler	0.1
Others	Trace

units on the Plateau, ranging in age from Pennsylvanian to Tertiary (Table 10.7), and ore has been produced from 22 of these (Isachsen et al., 1955; Mitcham, 1955; Wood, 1956A).

The wide stratigraphic distribution in rocks of nearly all depositional environments shows that age and general type of host rock are not significant in localization of ore. It is also the first major argument for the epigenetic nature of the mineralization. Although the stratigraphic distribution is extreme, within individual areas deposits of economic significance are usually restricted to a single zone within a sedimentary unit.

Number, Size, and Grade

Although traditionally the uranium deposits of the Plateau have been regarded as small, intensive and systematic exploration has rapidly changed ideas on the scale of mineralization, not only regionally but also locally. In size, the deposits vary tremendously, ranging from occurrences a few inches thick and a few feet across to bodies that range from 6 to 8 ft thick and several hundred feet in breadth. A few deposits are locally over 100 ft thick.

In 1948, only two mines were known to have ore bodies in excess of 100,000 tons. Of the 1,000 or so deposits that yielded some production in 1954, some 950 were estimated to contain between 100 and 10,000 tons of ore. At that time, 15 ore bodies were known to contain more than 100,000 tons of ore, and perhaps 3 or 4 were considered to be multimillion-ton deposits (Eardley et al., 1955). In two years the picture has changed significantly. Late in 1956, 33 deposits capable of producing more than 100,000 tons of ore and 8 deposits capable of yielding in excess of 500,000 tons were known. Nevertheless, the number of small deposits discovered will doubtless continue to exceed very greatly those of even moderate size. Of the 1,750 deposits found by mid-1955, 1,625 were small, yielding a few tons to several hundred tons.

TABLE 10.7. *Uraniferous sedimentary units of the Colorado Plateau (modified from Isachsen et al.,* 1955; *Wood,* 1956*A*)

Period	Unit	Production	Mineralization type	Example
Tertiary	Browns Park fm	m *	U-PO_4	0.5 mi N Juniper Sprs., Moffat Co., Colo.
	Bidahochi fm	p †	U-V	40 mi N Holbrook, Navajo Co., Ariz.
	Uinta fm	p	Cu-U-PO_4	Between Myton and Ouray, Utah
	Wasatch fm	p	U-V	6 mi N Thompson, Emery Co., Utah
Cretaceous	Fruitland fm	m	?	Boyd claims, 10 mi NW Farmington, N.Mex.
	Mesaverde group (Toreva ss)	p	U-V	Black Mesa, 12 mi NW Black Mtn. Trading Post, Apache Co., Ariz.
	Dakota ss	MP ‡	U-V	Silver Spur No. 5 mine, 12 mi N Prewitt, N.Mex.
	sh	p	U-C	Hogback monocline, E of Gallup, N.Mex.
	Cedar Mountain fm	m	?	Cedar Mtn., 10 mi E Huntington, Emery Co., Utah
	Burro Canyon fm	m	U-V	Berties Beauty No. 1 claim, Baboon Basin, 7 mi NW Naturita, Colo.
Jurassic	Morrison fm: Brushy Basin	MP	U-V	Jackpile mine, 6 mi W Laguna, N.Mex.
	Morrison fm: Recapture sh and Westwater ss	MP	U-V	Enos Johnson claim, 8 mi W Sanastee, San Juan Co., N.Mex.
	Morrison fm: Salt Wash ss	MP	U-V	Uravan Belt, Colo.
	Bluff ss	m	U-V	2 mi NW Carrizo Mtns., Apache Co., Ariz.
	Summerville fm	p	U-V	Bulloch claims, Kane Co., Utah
	Curtis fm	p	Cu-U-V	2 mi NW Skull Cr., Moffat Co., Colo.
	Todilto ls	MP	U-V	Grants dist., N.Mex.
	Entrada ss	MP	U-V	Joker mine, 21 mi W Naturita, Colo.
	Carmel fm	m	Cu-U	N of Saucer Basin, 30 mi S Green River, Utah
	Navajo ss	m	Cu-U	2 mi W Red Mesa Trading Post, Utah
			Cu-U-V	Garnet Ridge, 10 mi N Dinnehotso Trading Post, Apache Co., Ariz.

(*Continued on page* 382.)

Period	Unit	Production	Mineralization type	Example
Jurassic(?)	Kayenta fm	p	U-V	Big Chief claim, Roc Cr., 11 mi NW Naturita, Colo.
Triassic	Wingate	p	U-V-C	Temple Mtn. collapse, San Rafael Swell, Utah
	Chinle fm (incl. Moss Back ss)	MP	U-V	Big Indian Wash and Temple Mtn., Utah; numerous deposits in Utah
	Shinarump cgl	MP	U-V, Cu-U	Numerous deposits SE Utah, NE Ariz.
	Moenkopi fm	P §	U-Cu-C	Elk Ridge, 34 mi W Blanding, Utah
Permian	Cutler (Big Buck) fm	MP	U-V	Big Buck claims, Big Indian Wash, San Juan Co., Utah
	DeChelly ss (Cutler fm)	P	U-V	Monument No. 2 mine, Apache Co., Ariz.
	Kaibab ls	m	Cu-U	Willaha siding, N of Williams, Ariz.; Temple Mtn. collapse, San Rafael Swell, Utah
	Coconino ss	m	Cu-U-Pb	Orphan Lode, 1½ mi from Bright Angel Lodge, Grand Canyon, Ariz.
	Hermit sh	P	Cu-U-PO$_4$	Hacks Canyon, 39 mi SW Fredonia, Ariz.
	Supai fm	m	Cu-U-V	Ridenour mine, 30 mi N Peach Springs, Ariz.
	Rico fm	m	U-V	Cane Springs Canyon, 10 mi SW Moab, Utah
Pennsylvanian	Hermosa fm	P	U-V	Bald Eagle mine, NE flank Gypsum Valley anticline, 13 mi SW Naturita, Colo.
	Weber qtzite	m	U-V	6 mi NE Skull Cr., Moffat Co., Colo.

* m = mineralized.
† p = minor producer, <1,000 tons.
‡ MP = major producer (measurable fraction of total U.S. production, see Preface.
§ P = producer, >1,000 tons.

Many newly discovered deposits have been quickly exhausted. In 1953, 500 deposits shipped ore, and since altogether through 1953 1,250 deposits had shipped ore, 750 deposits were worked out or became inactive for other reasons. In 1954, 1,000 deposits shipped ore, of which at least 500 represented new discoveries. Thus from 1942 to 1954, about 1,750 deposits shipped ore. Estimates indicate that 1 property out of every 9 has yielded ore (Eardley et al., 1955).

The grade of the deposits is likewise highly variable, and ranges from 0.1 to 1% U_3O_8, and locally much higher. The grade of many mined falls in the range of 0.2 to 0.4% U_3O_8. During the mining period before and after World War I, much relatively high-grade material was selectively mined or hand-sorted. In the Maggie C deposit, Long Park, Colorado, the largest of three mineralized fossil logs contained 360 lb of ore reported to contain 20% U_3O_8, as well as other 8 to 10% U_3O_8 ore, making the log worth $5,000 at $5/lb of U_3O_8 (1920). At the Cracker Jack claim, Calamity Gulch, Colorado, a log 80 ft long and about 2 ft across, a smaller 18-in. log 30 ft distant, and the intervening sandstone yielded 180 tons averaging 5.65% U_3O_8, 8% V_2O_5, and containing 2.6 g Ra. The gross value was $350,000. Two logs on the Dolores claims were worth $232,900 in U, Ra, and V, all in 1920 prices (Hess, 1933A).

Shape

Most of the deposits are tabular to lensoid bodies, others are irregular (Fig. 10.13). In some cases contacts are smooth, in others irregular, but both are usually well defined. Some deposits thin laterally to knife-edge seams, others bulge centrally or irregularly. Still others are saucer-shaped in section. Dactylic marginal extensions may be present. The tabular bodies usually have their long direction parallel with the bedding and with the long axis of the host sandstone or conglomerate lens. In detail the surfaces of ore bodies are undulant and crosscutting. The ratio of length to width ranges from nearly 1:1 to 10:1 or more (McKelvey et al., 1955). Thus in plan, deposits are circular to elliptical; some are semicircular.

Contacts may cut across bedding, particularly as rolls. Roll deposits are ore bodies that transect bedding in smooth, markedly curving forms (Shawe, 1956A). Cross sections of rolls are C-, S-, or socket-shaped. In plan, roll bodies are linear (Fig. 10.14) with sharply plunging noses. Their long axes may continue for many hundreds of feet. Some roll surfaces are fractures separating mineralized rock from barren host and are best developed along ore bodies of the carnotite or roscoelite type but also occur as contacts of unoxidized uranium ore bodies.

Along or across their axes, roll bodies may grade into tabular masses. In some cases sinuous axes double back on themselves so that the double roll body consists of mirror-image pairs. In general, axes coincide with trends of current lineation, channels, and other syngenetic sedimentary structures, probably reflecting the orientation of the most permeable paths in the layers. Not uncommonly rolls lie against mineralized logs or are indented by logs across their axes. Concentric layering parallel with roll surfaces characterizes many

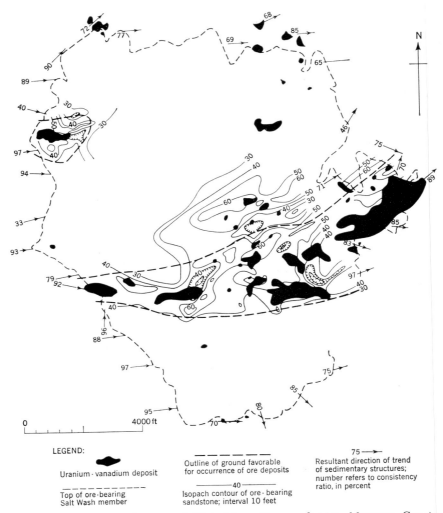

FIG. 10.13. Uranium deposits of Club Mesa, Uravan district, Montrose County, Colo., showing shapes in plan and relation to sedimentary structures (Boardman et al., 1956; *U.S. Geol. Survey*).

384

Fig. 10.14. Roll ore body in Salt Wash sandstone, Morrison formation, Cougar Mine, Slick Rock district, San Miguel County, Colo. (N. L. Archbold).

rolls, and minor elements may be asymmetrically distributed across rolls (Fig. 10.15).

Roll ore bodies are most commonly developed in the Salt Wash sandstone, especially near the base of thick sandstone units with sharply defined mudstone partings, against which they wedge out tangentially, or by which they may be split. They also occur in older formations. Even in the Salt Wash they are less common than tabular deposits.

At the Monument No. 2 deposit many of the major ore bodies form flattened cylinders, or rods, which usually show mineralogical zoning and in some cases have a core of silicified wood (Fig. 10.41) (Witkind, 1956B).

Relation to Tectonic Structural Features

Kelley (1955A, p. 89), on the basis of his analysis of the regional tectonics of the Plateau, has concluded that "There is little obvious or direct relationship between the regional structure and the distribution of uranium and related deposits in the Plateau. However, the tectonics, probably as far back as Permian time, have had a most important bearing, indirectly, on the distribution through other geologic factors that may have contributed more directly to the distribution of ore." Similarly McKelvey et al. (1955, p. 494) state, "By and large most of the uranium deposits on the Plateau show no obvious relation to local structures other than those of sedimentary origin." Nevertheless, they recognize a close spatial relationship between concentration of deposits and such tectonic features as laccolithic intrusives and salt anticlines.

The fact that a very large number of significant deposits is concentrated in recognizable districts which, in many cases, are centered around one or

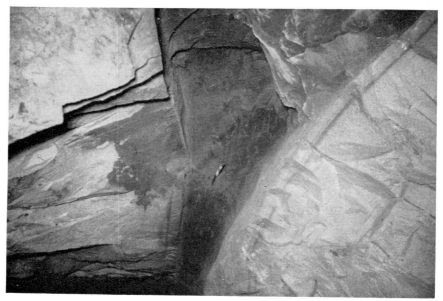

FIG. 10.15. Junction of two rolls showing concentric layering parallel with roll surfaces, Little Pittsburg No. 5 Mine, Grand County, Utah (N. L. Archbold).

more major structural features suggests, in itself, a degree of direct or indirect structural control of mineralization.

Kelley's tectonic map (1955A, Fig. 2) and the map compiled by Finch (1955) clearly emphasize the concentration of deposits within and adjacent to such structural features as salt anticlines, in the Uravan belt and in parts of the Moab and Green River districts; laccolithic domes, in the Carrizo, Abajo, and southern Henry Mountains; uplifts, San Rafael Swell and Circle Cliffs; monoclines, Gateway district and Lukachukai Mountains; synclinal axes, northern Henry Mountains; basin-upwarp contacts, Blanding area; and diatremes, Hopi centers. Isachsen (1956B) also has pointed to the peripheral distribution of most Plateau deposits about laccolithic mountains, and Fischer (1956, p. 613) likewise states, "Many uranium deposits in the region are within a few miles of the major structural features."

In some districts a much more intimate order of structural control of ore bodies can be recognized (Shoemaker, 1956B). This is well demonstrated by the deposits of the Todilto limestone in the Grants district, and by those in the Big Indian Wash–Lisbon Valley area. In the Grants district, deposits in the Todilto occur in two belts, an eastern, localized along a fault zone and coincident with a synclinal axis, and a western, along the flank of a large syncline. Within the belts, individual ore bodies are elongated along anticlinal axes. Gabelman (1956A, p. 343) says, ". . . the obvious clustering of ore bodies near fault zones cutting the Thoreau monocline indicates that the faults may have been vertical feeders." A casual relationship between ore and fractures also has been suggested by the studies of Bucher and Gilkey (1953), and in the Long Mountain, South Dakota, area by those of Braddock (1957).

Anticlinal control of mineralization in the Lisbon Valley area is indicated by the restriction of all but one of the ore deposits to the interval 6,200 to 6,700 ft above sea level (Steen et al., 1953; Isachsen, 1956A). In the San Rafael Swell, tectonic structural features which in part have controlled the distribution of ore are (1) collapses, (2) grabens, (3) faults, and (4) secondary flexures on anticlinal flanks (Wood, 1956B).

At the Atomic King deposit, Cane Creek, San Juan County, Utah, uranium mineralization of ore grade occurs along a steep east-trending fault in Rico, Moenkopi, and Chinle strata (Wright, 1955A). Fischer (1956) notes the localization of mineralization along fracture zones in the Richardson Basin in east-central Utah and along Roc Creek in southwestern Colorado. A genetic relation between uranium deposits and faults is known at six deposits in the central Plateau (Shoemaker, 1956B).

The very obvious relationship between ore deposits and syngenetic sedimentary features in many parts of the Plateau and the formerly widely held hypothesis of a syngenetic origin for the deposits have no doubt restricted consideration of the relationship of mineralization to tectonic structures until recently. Reinhardt (1954) has suggested that structural controls of four magnitudes have been operative in ore deposition: first-order structures—the structural dome of the Plateau itself; second-order structures—the uplifts and laccolithic mountains; third-order structural—piercement anticlines; and fourth-order structures—faults and joints. An analogous idea has been advanced by Isachsen (1956B), who relates mineralization to (1) regional, (2) areal, and (3) local tectonic features. Both Kelley (1955A) and Isachsen (1956B) have pointed out that the preponderant concentration of significant deposits occurs within a single major northwest-trending tectonic element (called the San Juan segment by Kelley) to which all of the laccolithic centers also are confined.

Whether the spatial relation of ore bodies to tectonic features in fact represents a direct genetic relation has been debated. Kelley (1955A) believes that the tectonics have influenced the provenances and environments of sedimentation, the paleohydrology, the igneous activity, and the geomorphology, and that these factors may have contributed more directly toward the control of ore distribution. The spatial relation also has been interpreted by some geologists simply as a reflection of better exposure of deposits along tectonic structures.

Relation to Stratigraphic and Sedimentary Structures

Craig (1955) has pointed out that uranium deposits of the Shinarump and Chinle tend to be in the lower parts of these units along their unconformable contacts with the Moenkopi. Along a northeast section across the Plateau, as the Upper Triassic units successively onlap the Moenkopi, uranium deposits occur first in the Shinarump, next in the Monitor Butte member of the Chinle, and finally in the Moss Back member of the Chinle. Craig (1955, p. 14) states, "Vertically moving mineral-bearing solutions may have been dammed by the relatively impermeable claystone or mudstones of the Moenkopi or

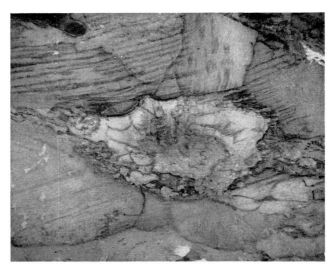

Fig. 10.16. Mudstone gall, Morrison formation, Jack Pile mine, Grants district, N.Mex.

Chinle formations and the solutions may have migrated laterally along the relatively permeable sandstones."

In host rocks consisting of siltstone, sandstone, and conglomerate (e.g., the Morrison, Chinle, and Shinarump), the deposits are closely related to a variety of syngenetic sedimentary structures or features (Fig. 10.13). These include:

1. Ratio of mudstone to sandstone
2. Thickness of sandstone unit
3. Channels and details of their configuration
4. Fossil logs and other fossil plant debris
5. Pinch outs

The most common type of host rock is a sandstone deposited in a stream-flood-plain environment. Most of these are lenticular. Eolian and marine sandstones are, in contrast, mineralized to a much lesser extent or not at all.

Over large areas deposition has generally favored units varying from relatively pure sandstones to those containing up to nearly equal amounts of mudstone in the form of interbedded layers, partings, lenses, and galls (Fig. 10.16). For example, deposits on Holiday Mesa in the Monument Valley district tend to favor Shinarump sandstone units with as much as 25% mudstone (Isachsen, 1956A). In some cases well-developed bedding planes separating sandstone and mudstone have been mineralized. At the Happy Jack mine, White Canyon district, high-grade ore occurs in a carbonaceous sandstone that wedges out into mudstone (Miller, 1955). The mudstones normally are red, but mudstones within and directly below ore-bearing sandstones have been altered to gray (pages 393–394) (Weir, 1952; McKay, 1955).

In many districts the size of ore bodies is proportional to the thickness of the sandstone lenses. Beds 15 to 35 ft thick usually contain only small ore deposits, whereas both small and large deposits occur in the thicker sandstones (McKay, 1955). In southwestern Colorado no large deposit has been found in sandstone with an original thickness of less than 40 ft (Weir, 1952). In the Poison Canyon area, Grants district, the sandstone unit favorable for mineralization is more than 150 ft thick (Hilpert and Freeman, 1956) (Fig. 10.17).

Deposits in many districts, particularly Shinarump deposits, are localized in channels, which are paleostream scours into underlying beds (Miller, 1952; Finch, 1953; Witkind, 1954; Stokes, 1955) (Fig. 10.18). Symmetrically or asymmetrically trough-shaped in section, the channels are straight to sinuous in plan, showing meander bends, deeps or intrachannel scours, splits or branches, and smaller-scale features such as cross-stratification, current lineation, ripple marks, and oriented fossil logs. In the Monument Valley area, individual channels range in width from 15 to 2,300 ft, with most about 350 ft across (Witkind, 1956A,B). Some have been scoured as much as 150 ft into underlying strata, most of them about 75 ft. Some do not exceed 2 mi in length; others have been traced for many miles. Morrison channels in the Thompson area are 2 to 20 ft wide, 5 to 50 ft long, and 0.5 to 5 ft deep (Stokes, 1952B).

Within a sedimentary unit, channels may occur chiefly along one horizon, as do Shinarump channels, or they may be present as a complex of many smaller channels both adjacent and superimposed ("stacked"), as for example, in the Morrison formation in the Northern Chuska Mountains area of Arizona (Lowell, 1955). Similar *en echelon* ore body and channel patterns have been observed in the Uravan district in the Morrison, reflecting the shifting of braided streams (McKay, 1955; Boardman et al., 1956).

Fig. 10.17. Open cut in thick mineralized sandstone in Brushy Basin member, Morrison formation, Poison Canyon deposit, Grants district, N.Mex.

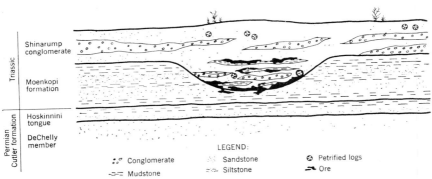

FIG. 10.18. Schematic cross section of uranium deposits in Shinarump paleochannel, Monument Valley, Ariz. (Mitcham and Evensen, 1955; *Econ. Geol.*).

In the Monument Valley area some channels occupy the center of and are colinear with broad, shallow swales, which range in width from 1 to 3 mi and have a relief of about 40 ft (Witkind, 1956A,B). These swales may be traced beyond the extent of their channels.

Features that may be used to indicate the axis or orientation of channels include (1) current lineation—a linear aggregation of sand grains (Fig. 10.19), (2) symmetrical ripple marks, (3) elongation of conglomerate lenses, and (4) positions of fossil logs, all of which are bidirectional features. The flow direction may be determined by means of asymmetrical ripple marks and cross-stratification, either of the trough (festoon-bedding) or planar type (Stokes, 1952B; Poole and Williams, 1956). Plotting of flow directions may define paleostream intersections, a favorable loci for ore deposition. Axes of ore bodies also have been found to be aligned at small angles to the average cross-stratification direction (Lowell, 1955).

Ore bodies in channels tend to occur at the base, low along the flanks, and at the top (Fig. 10.18). They also show a tendency to favor meander bends, branches, and scours below the general level of the channel floor (Stokes, 1952B). In the Monument Valley district, large ore bodies favor channels floored by sandstone and having widths between 300 and 1,000 ft (Mitcham and Evensen, 1955). In the Shinarump, irregular channels and especially sharp scours incised along the axes of channels of medium width appear to have exercised close control of mineralization (Wood and Grundy, 1956).

Pinch outs or the wedging out of favorable units may have restricted uranium-bearing fluids and resulted in concentration of deposits on a regional scale (Trites et al., 1956). In southeastern Utah the northeast regional pinch out of the Shinarump occurs a short distance beyond a clustering of deposits (Craig, 1955).

Relation to Sedimentary Petrology

The distribution of uranium deposits also can be correlated in varying degrees with a variety of sedimentary petrological characteristics, including (1) lithofacies, (2) color, (3) calcite, (4) kaolinite, and (5) carbonaceous fossil plant material or asphaltite. Sandstones of ore-bearing units contain chiefly detrital quartz but commonly are arkosic or micaceous (chiefly muscovite). Cementing materials include quartz, clay minerals (kaolinite or illite), and calcite. Organic material is locally abundant. Volcanic debris, altered to montmorillonite, has been recognized in the Salt Wash, Brushy Basin, Chinle, and Shinarump (Waters and Granger, 1953; Griffiths et al., 1954).

The Salt Wash member of the Morrison formation was formed as a large alluvial plain deposit by an aggrading, braided stream system fanning to the north and east from a south-central Utah apex. Thus its sediments grade from coarse to fine from the apex to its margins. Four arbitrary lithofacies have been recognized: conglomerate sandstone (south-central Utah), alternating sandstone-mudstone (southeastern Utah and southwestern Colorado), claystone-lenticular sandstone (northeastern Utah and northwestern Colorado), and claystone-limestone (central Colorado) (Craig et al., 1955; Craig, 1955; McKay, 1955). Nearly all uranium deposits of the Salt Wash occur in sediments of the alternating sandstone-mudstone facies, particularly in areas in which the sandstone lenses are relatively uniform and well sorted (Jones, 1954). The lithofacies control also operates on a more localized scale, as in the Lukachakai Mountains where the ore belt conforms to the belt of the lenticular sandstone-mudstone facies (Masters, 1955).

Many Plateau ore bodies are in sandstones marked chiefly by a light yellow-brown color and by minute limonitic spots. In other cases the host sandstones are white, yellow gray, gray buff, tan, or lavender. In some cases this color forms a halo that may extend for several hundred feet beyond the edges of the deposits. Sandstone with a pronounced reddish hue generally is not mineralized or contains but small or few deposits (Weir, 1952; McKay, 1955). In most

Fig. 10.19. Current lineation in sandstone, Salt Wash member, Morrison formation, Colorado Plateau (N. L. Archbold).

places the nonred colors apparently are syngenetic (or at least diagenetic), resulting from reducing conditions during sedimentation. In some deposits, however, the color-halo contacts transgress bedding, and the colors are epigenetic, related to mineralization (Wright, 1955A).

Changes, believed to be diagenetic or at least pre ore, noted in some post-sandstones in the Uravan district, include dolomitization, weak chloritization, alteration of clay minerals, deposition of pyrite and barite, and leaching of ferric iron (Weeks et al., 1957). Intergranular argillic alteration has been demonstrated by Kelley and Kerr (1957) in the Temple Mountain ores.

Sandstones adjacent to ore deposits in the Salt Wash member contain low to moderate concentrations of $CaCO_3$ except along contacts with mudstone where concentrations are high (Archbold, 1955). In the northwest Carrizo Mountains, Arizona, abundant pink calcite usually occurs in bands a few inches thick above and below ore (Chenoweth, 1955). In unoxidized ores, calcite cement is replaced by uraninite or montroesite and has apparently served as a precipitant of uranium. This is confirmed, in part, by the decrease in calcite in mineralized sandstone in some districts. Griffiths et al. (1954) report that in Salt Wash deposits silica cement appears to be associated with ore whereas carbonate cement is associated with barren sandstone. However, on Mesa 4½, Lukachukai Mountains, zones of carbonate-impregnated sandstone are associated with ore, the carbonate forming flat, tabular bodies a few inches to 6 ft thick and as much as 160 ft long (Dodd, 1956). Some masses are discordant, and the carbonate, unlike its usual appearance as interstitial cement, is in 1- to 10-in. poikiloblastic masses, colorless to red and black (owing to Fe, Mn, and V oxides), and some may be siderite or ankerite as well as calcite.

Thus it appears that syngenetic or diagenetic calcite in the host sandstones may have been dissolved or redistributed during mineralization, or that less commonly, calcite may have been introduced during mineralization.

Cadigan (1955) has pointed out that Shinarump and Moss Back sandstones not associated with ore contain a mean of 10% kaolinite, whereas those sandstones associated with ore contain a mean of 22% kaolinite. Thus in detail there is repeated the association of ore with sandstone and interbedded mudstone.

Fossil plant material is widespread and locally abundant in host sandstones, forming one of their most striking similarities. The material varies greatly in size, from logs to branches, twigs, ferns, and leaves, to macerated debris (carbon "trash"), and down to microscopic shreds. Minor amounts of low-rank coal are present locally. Numerous logs and branches have been silicified, and these generally are not associated with uranium mineralization (Fig. 10.20), although in some districts these too have been replaced to some extent. Much of the woody debris is carbonized, and such material is either intimately associated with uranium mineralization or is itself replaced by uranium minerals (Fig. 10.21). Some exceedingly rich logs replaced by carnotite were mined in the early periods of activity (page 383), and recent mining has uncovered countless examples of fossil logs and wood replaced to varying degrees by uraninite, in some cases together with sulfides, especially those of copper. At the Happy Jack mine, for example, wood cell walls are replaced by uraninite, and chalco-

FIG. 10.20. Silicified fossil log, not mineralized, Chinle formation, Temple Mt., San Rafael Swell, Utah.

pyrite fills the cell centers. Bornite and pyrite also replace wood cells (Miller, 1955). Calcite may fill cells in carbonized wood.

One additional reason for localization of uranium deposits in channel bends lies in the presence of large amounts of plant debris that accumulated in areas of pronounced bends and confluence (Stokes, 1954B).

Altered Mudstone

Mudstone interbedded with host sandstones usually is red, but near or directly below ore deposits the mudstone is bleached to gray, white, or pink colors (Fischer, 1950; Weir, 1952). The bleached zone beneath the ore may be as much as several feet thick, extending and thinning laterally a few hundred feet away from the deposits. In larger deposits in some districts, mudstone overlying the ore-bearing sandstone also is gray. Bleached mudstone crops out as areas that are usually several times as large as the ore body and thus serve as an effective guide to ore. In the Carrizo Mountains, Arizona, ore deposits are underlain, overlain, or both by gray mudstone which may become markedly thicker near deposits and pinch out into reddish-brown mudstone away from deposits (Chenoweth, 1955).

The red mudstone contains more total iron and more ferric iron than the

FIG. 10.21. Carbonized log largely replaced by carnotite (outer light gray) and montroesite and uraninite (inner black). Rattlesnake No. 6 deposit, north and Lisbon Valley, San Juan County, Utah (J. Shappirio).

gray (Weeks, 1951). In some cases iron has been almost completely removed (Evensen, 1955). No differences in gross clay mineralogy have been found to distinguish the red from the gray mudstones. Both types have illite, and both types may also contain kaolinite or chlorite, depending on the stratigraphic zone (Keller, 1955). Thus the chief change involved appears to be leaching of hematite. Although the change is most conspicuous in mudstone, bleached halos also occur in sandstone (Wright, 1955A).

Huff (1955) has found that near the Oyler mine, Capitol Reef district, Utah, a bleached zone at the base of the Chinle formation contains abnormal amounts of Zn and Cu and also differs from the rest of the Chinle in acidity, oxidation potential, and iron content. It is suggested that bleaching and other changes were produced by the same solutions that deposited ore in Shinarump nearby.

Shawe (1956A,B) has grouped postdepositional changes in Plateau strata into three main types:

1. Diagenetic
   a. Oxidation of magnetite, ilmenite, and other iron-bearing heavy detritals to form hematite, which was redistributed as coatings on quartz and other grains. This results in a red sediment.
   b. Reduction of iron from allogenic species in the vicinity of carbonaceous

material, redistribution to form pyrite. This produces gray to greenish-gray colors.

2. Epigenetic

Removal of iron-bearing minerals (including diagenetic hematite), formation of anatase, recrystallization of barite. This takes place in presence or absence of carbon, but close to ore bodies and results in gray to white colors.

At Temple Mountain dolomitization accompanied by collapse preceded uranium mineralization to form replacement masses in Wingate sandstone as much as hundreds of feet across. The rising solutions probably dissolved calcite and dolomite from the Kaibab and Moenkopi below and also produced argillic alteration (Bodine and Kerr, 1956).

Relation to Transmissivity

The capacity of a sedimentary rock as a whole to transmit fluids is called its transmissivity, whose coefficient equals the thickness of a bed multiplied by its mean permeability. The generally transmissive rocks of the Plateau ore strata are conglomerate, sandstones, arkoses, and siltstones, whereas the mudstones and limestones are generally nontransmissive. Plateau rocks with appreciable transmissivity can be grouped into two main types (Jobin, 1956): (1) eolian and marine sandstones and siltstones whose thickness and permeability are relatively uniform over wide areas, and (2) fluvial conglomerates and sandstones of lenticular character and variable transmissivity. Most of the uranium deposits are in strata that have a moderate to low regional transmissivity, vary greatly in local transmissivity, and are overlain by a thick nontransmissive unit. Phoenix (1956, p. 325) has aptly described the Salt Wash sandstone strata that are favorable to ore as a "complex, nearly horizontal 'plumbing system,' " in which ore deposits are localized in largest parts of the conduits, where conduits change in size, at connections between conduits, and where "baffles" are numerous. Internal baffles of the conduits are represented by bedding planes, mudstone lenses, local disconformities, and other sedimentary structures, all of which affect rate and direction of flow.

Mineralogy

General

Although the mineralogy of Plateau ores is, in the aggregate, exceedingly complex, the relatively recent discovery of the more simple unoxidized ores and the decipherment of the relation between oxidized and unoxidized ores have resulted in the recognition of the several natural mineralogical ore types, based on their geochemical associations and genesis (Weeks et al., 1953, 1955, 1956; Weeks and Thompson, 1954; Fischer, 1956; Botinelly and Weeks, 1957):

I. Primary (unoxidized) ores
    A. Vanadiferous
        1. V:U = 15:1
        2. V:U = 15:1–1:1

Fig. 10.22. Roscoelite as overgrowths on quartz grains replacing clayey cement in sandstone, Morrison formation, Lumpsen Group, Gateway, Colo. ($\times$110).

    B. Nonvanadiferous
        1. Sulfide-poor
        2. Sulfide-rich, including the U-Cu type
II. Secondary (oxidized) ores
    A. Vanadiferous
        1. Corvusite ore (partly oxidized)
        2. Carnotite ore (fully oxidized)
    B. Nonvanadiferous
        1. Sulfatic
        2. Others

Primary Ores

Vanadiferous. These primary ores characteristically are black and contain U^4 as uraninite and coffinite together with low-valence vanadium minerals, especially micaceous vanadium minerals (Fig. 10.22) and montroesite (Fig. 10.23).

Minor amounts of Fe, Cu, Pb, and Zn sulfides, selenides, and arsenides also may be present (Table 10.8). Sulfides in the Morrison and Entrada consistently contain abnormal amounts of selenium, whereas those from Chinle and Shinarump deposits are selenium-low except for ones in the Temple Mountain district, which may contain up to 0.5% Se (Coleman, 1956). Early (diagenetic) pyrite is poor in Co and Ni relative to the pyrite formed during mineralization. The highly vanadiferous ores generally lack fossil wood, but those with V:U ratios between 15:1 to 1:1 have abundant associated carbonized wood and plant debris, which is widely replaced by uraninite and may have cell fillings of coffinite or montroesite.

Nonvanadiferous. Some ores are poor in sulfides; many contain sulfides in abundance. In the latter, copper sulfides are dominant in some deposits (Fig. 10.24), Fe, Pb, and Zn sulfides dominate in others. Fossil wood again is abundantly associated with uraninite. The Temple Mountain asphaltic ore belongs in this category.

Secondary Ores and Oxidation Processes

The primary ores were deposited in a reducing environment and remained stable until exposed to oxidizing conditions. A complete series of deposits is available to demonstrate the transitional mineralogical assemblages that represent stages from unoxidized to fully oxidized ores. In some cases much of the sequence can be traced within a single deposit (Heyl, 1957). The results of

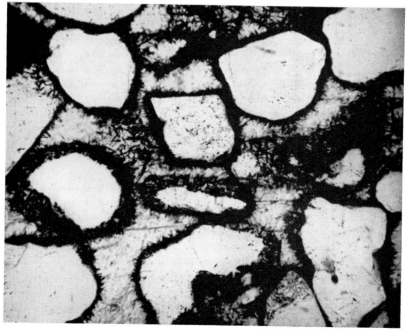

Fig. 10.23. Montroesite (black) replacing calcite cement and corroding quartz grains in sandstone of Morrison formation, Martin mine, Carrizo Mts., Ariz. (×210).

TABLE 10.8. *Mineralogy of primary ores*

Type	Uranium minerals	Vanadium minerals	Metallic minerals	Other minerals	Examples
V:U = > 15:1 (up to 40:1)	Subordinate coffinite, uraninite	Silicates dominate over oxides. Roscoelite, mixed-layer V clay minerals (Hathaway, 1956), montroesite	Galena, chalcopyrite, rare pyrite, and mareasite	Calcite, dolomite, Cr mica at Placerville	Rifle and Placerville districts, Colo., in Entrada along eastern margin of Plateau
V:U = 15:1–1:1	Uraninite, coffinite, uraniferous asphaltite	Montroesite, paramontroesite (Weeks et al., 1953; Evans and Mrose, 1955)	Pyrite and mareasite in two generations, one diagenetic, the other with ore. Galena, minor chalcopyrite, sphalerite, greenockite, clausthalite, eucairite, arsenic	Calcite, dolomite, kaolinite, barite, fluorite, pre ore gypsum in some districts	Widespread in Salt Wash sandstone, Colo., Utah; to a lesser extent in Chinle and Shinarump
Nonvanadiferous	Uraninite; coffinite rare	Absent or very rare	Two generations of pyrite. Ni and Co minerals incl. gersdorffite. Chalcopyrite, bornite, chalcocite, covellite, galena, sphalerite, smaltite, greenockite. Traces of Mo and Hg	Calcite, kaolinite uncommon, barite	Chiefly in Shinarump and basal Chinle sandstones, White Canyon district, Happy Jack mine

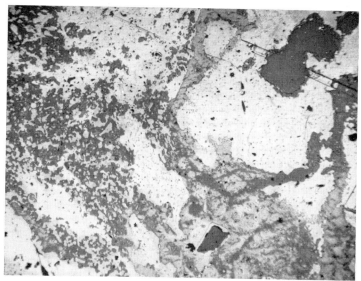

FIG. 10.24. Bornite (white) and minor pyrite intergrown with pitchblende (light gray) and quartzose gangue (black), Maybe mine, Utah. Reflected light (×44).

oxidation are much simpler in the nonvanadiferous ores than in the vanadiferous ones.

Nonvanadiferous. The first main change involves oxidation of U in pitchblende to U^6 (as the uranyl ion). Hydrated uranyl oxide minerals, e.g., becquerelite, may be formed locally in small amounts, but rarely persist owing to the usual abundant availability of SO_4^{2-}, CO_3^{2-}, or other anions. Where the primary ore was sulfide-rich, uranyl sulfates may be abundantly represented in the oxidized equivalent (Table 10.9). Sulfates of elements other than uranium may also be conspicuous, for example, at the Dexter No. 7 mine, San Rafael Swell, Rosenzweig and Gross (1955) have identified goldichite and other iron sulfates. Uranyl carbonates (Table 10.9) are developed, if the primary ore was sulfide-poor and the host sandstone contains ample calcite cement. Uranyl phosphates are uncommon except where PO_4 ions were available from fossil bone. Uranyl arsenates and silicates are rare.

Because the uranyl oxides, sulfates, and especially carbonates are relatively soluble, they tend to be dissipated rapidly, and thus ore bodies of this type are uncommon and usually small.

Vanadiferous. Ores with vanadium have a built-in oxidation indicator. Vanadium appears in numerous minerals, which are exceedingly responsive to changes in pH and in oxidation. In primary ores, vanadium is as V^3—montroesite, $VO(OH)$, which alters quickly to V^4—paramontroesite, VO_2, and several other newly recognized V^4 minerals. Next follows the corvusite stage in which vanadium exists as both V^4 and V^5. Accompanying these changes in vanadium is oxidation of U^4, which apparently is dispersed into an unknown, possibly colloidal phase (Weeks, 1956).

TABLE 10.9. *Mineralogy of secondary ores*

Type	Uranium minerals	Vanadium minerals	Other minerals	Examples
Nonvana-diferous	*Oxides:* becquerelite, schoepite, fourmarierite *Sulfates:* zippeite, johannite, uranopilite *Carbonates:* liebigite, rutherfordine, schroeckingerite, bayleyite, andersonite, rabbittite *Phosphates:* autunite, torbernite, phosphuranylite, bassetite *Arsenates:* abernathyite, metazeunerite, novacekite *Silicates:* uranophane, sklodowskite, cuprosklodowskite, U-opal, U-allophane	Nil (Volborthite)	(Cu) Malachite, azurite, chalcanthite, brochantite, antlerite, chrysocolla, conichalcite, chalcoalumite, boothite (Co) Erythrite, bieberite-cobaltocalcite, Co-pickingerite, lithiophorite (Mo) Ilsemannite, ferrimolybdite Wad, limonite, kaolinite, alunite, jarosite, gibbsite, pyrolusite and other Mn oxides	*Sulfates:* Happy Jack mine, White Canyon, Utah *Carbonates:* Shinarump No. 1, Grand County, Utah
Vanadiferous. Incompletely oxidized	U-V minerals Rauvite (Hess, 1925B) Uvanite(?)	Other V minerals Paramontroesite, corvusite, melanovanadite, duttonite (Evans and Mrose, 1956; Thompson et al., 1957); simplotite (Thompson et al., 1956), sherwoodite, doloresite (Stern et al., 1957)	Native Se (Thompson et al., 1956), gypsum, limonite, realgar, sulfur	Abundant in Uravan Belt deposits; Temple Mt.; Monument Valley No. 2 mine, Monument Valley district
Fully oxidized	Carnotite, tyuyamunite. Uranophane, torbernite, autunite, zippeite, schroeckingerite, andersonite, becquerelite, schoepite	Navajoite (Weeks et al., 1955); hewettite, pascoite, rossite, metarossite, Na-hewettite, hummerite, steigerite, fervanite, volborthite, calciovolborthite, Pintadoite reported. Santafeite (Sun and Weber, 1957)	Calcite, gypsum, limonite, thenardite, jarosite, halotrichite, barite, fluorite (Grants district), wulfenite, variscite, mansfieldite	Uravan Belt deposits and eastern Utah (carnotite), Grants district (tyuyamunite)

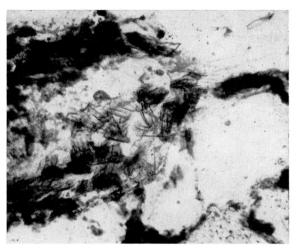

FIG. 10.25. Carnotite crystals, iron oxide minerals in clay interstitial to quartz grains, Shinarump conglomerate, Monument No. 1, Ariz. ($\times$210).

With further oxidation all vanadium is transformed to V^5 and combines with the uranyl ion and the metallic ions K and Ca to form rauvite and finally carnotite (Fig. 10.25) and tyuyamunite (Fig. 10.26). Thus in ores with an excess of vanadium, uranium eventually becomes completely fixed in vanadates that are relatively insoluble. The excess oxidized vanadium combines with Cu, Ca, Fe^2, Mg, K, Na, and Al to form a complex assemblage of nonuraniferous vanadates (Table 10.9).

Paragenesis

In highly vanadiferous ore, roscoelite in fine micaceous aggregates is interstitial to detrital quartz; montroesite may be interleaved. In roscoelite-rich stringers, quartz grains are markedly corroded (Fig. 10.27). Carbonates appear to be contemporaneous with the vanadiferous mica. The replacement of cell walls of woody tissue by uraninite and copper sulfides (Rosenzweig et al., 1954), and the filling of cell cavities by coffinite and montroesite are widespread microtextural features of many Plateau ores. The replacement of wood by montroesite tends to destroy ·the structure. Pyrite of diagenetic origin also replaces wood or forms nodules. Galena may be present in two generations, one represented by cubic euhedra included in uraninite and by veinlets cutting uraninite.

Uraninite also occurs as fine-grained cement of quartz grains and may replace secondary quartz overgrowths of the grains, and clay and calcite cements. The cementing uraninite forms blebs 0.01 to 0.02 mm across and local pods up to several centimeters across (Gross, 1956). Montroesite needles also penetrate the quartz overgrowths and the grains themselves. Some montroesite is precalcite in origin. Locally uraninite with or without coffinite follows minute fractures across the sandstone fabric (Fig. 10.28). Chalcopyrite also fills fractures in grains and across grain aggregates (Miller, 1955). Where chalcopyrite

FIG. 10.26. Radial clusters of tyuyamunite fibers in cavity in fossil wood, Morrison formation, Jack Pile mine, Grants district, N.Mex. (×66).

and bornite occur together, the latter forms a grating-type exsolution intergrowth with chalcopyrite as the host (Miller, 1955).

Miller (1955, p. 164) concludes (1) that ore minerals are younger than quartz cement, and (2) that some uraninite is younger than copper sulfides, but that "the lack of a clear time sequence of mineral growth suggests a simultaneous deposition of the ore minerals." In the Mi Vida deposit some of the montroesite followed other primary U-V minerals (Gross, 1956; Laverty and Gross, 1956).

Detailed paragenetic studies of a number of Plateau deposits indicate that in general minerals have been formed in the following sequences of groups:

1. *Detrital constituents:* quartz, feldspars, clays, and clastic carbonate.
2. *Authigenic quartz.*
3. *Diagenetic and cementing minerals:* pyrite, marcasite, illite, calcite, dolomite, barite, and fluorite. In some deposits barite may be post ore minerals.

4. *Primary ore minerals:* uraninite, coffinite, roscoelite, vanadium clays, doloresite, montroesite, sulfides, and calcite. In some cases uraninite continued to be deposited after precipitation of iron and copper sulfides ceased, and in other cases some montroesite (or paramontroesite?) was developed after uraninite. Some galena is preuraninite, but much of it together with greenockite appears to be younger than uraninite and chalcopyrite. Some bornite developed by exsolution from chalcopyrite.

5. *Early oxidized minerals:* paramontroesite, rauvite, corvusite, selenium, hydrated uranium oxides, gypsum, hematite; solution of calcite.

6. *Late oxidized minerals:* carnotite, tyuyamunite; other vanadates; uranyl sulfates, carbonates, phosphates, arsenates, and silicates; copper carbonates; hematite, and manganese oxides.

Summary

Thus the complex mineralogy of Plateau ores is the result of two main variations: (1) original variations of the proportions of their main elements (U, V, Cu, Fe, and S), and (2) variations in the degree of oxidation (Garrels, 1953, 1955A,B). The oxidized ores are derived from the primary ores, and their development is related to the lowering of the water table and the specific water retentivity of different host rock types (Weeks, 1955, 1956). Lowering of the water table followed the beginning of canyon cutting in the present

F<small>IG</small>. 10.27. Roscoelite corroding quartz grains in Morrison sandstone, San Miguel County, Colo. ($\times 66$).

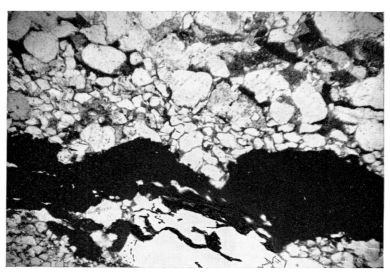

Fig. 10.28. Coffinite-uraninite veinlet across quartz grain aggregate, Vanura Claims, Emery County, Utah (×35).

erosion cycle. However, where host rocks retained water in abundance owing to structural features and high porosity, access of air to ores was impeded or prevented, and oxidation was retarded. Thus some partly oxidized ores remain perched above the regional water table, e.g., at the Corvusite mine, Beaver Mesa, Utah, and at the Peanut mine, Montrose County, Colorado (Thompson and Roach, 1955). At the J.J. mine of the Jo Dandy group in Paradox Valley, oxidized ore above the water table grades into unoxidized ore below the water table.

Weeks (1955, 1956) points out that the oxidized ores are of three types: (1) those formed in situ by "moist-air" oxidation with no significant migration of material; (2) those modified during the corvusite oxidation stage, with down-dip vanadium migration; and (3) near-surface deposits leached of some uranium and vanadium by surface and ground water.

In the northern Black Hills the close association between the uranyl deposits and the reddish sandstone contacts suggests that the uranyl minerals were deposited concomitantly with the formation of hydrous ferrous oxide minerals in the sandstone. If this is the case, the secondary species were probably deposited from ground water moving down dip where mildly reducing conditions supplanted oxidizing conditions as the result of structural features, decrease in permeability, or increase in carbonaceous material (Vickers, 1955). The black ores are certainly older than the carnotite ores (Bell and Bales, 1955). Oxidation also took place in situ, but some uranium and vanadium have been moved recently by ground water, with carnotite and tyuyamunite migrating as much as 20 ft down dip from corvusite-rauvite aggregates. Oxidized ores occur in a slightly carbonaceous to a noncarbonaceous environment. A carnotite-impregnated musk ox bone gave a C^{14} age determination of 9,700 yr (Bell et al., 1956). Some deposits are not in radioactive equilibrium, being radium-deficient, and radiobarite has been found in one deposit as a joint coating.

Regional Zoning

Associated with the introduction of uranium into Plateau host rocks are the following main, accessory, extrinsic elements (Miesch, 1955): Cu, Pb, Zn, Ag, Co, Ni, Mo, Se, and As; Cd, Cr, Ba, and F are locally significant. As has been pointed out by Fischer (1956) and Weeks (1956), a regional variation in the U/V ratio of ores is well defined. High vanadium ores (V:U = 15:1) occur along the eastern margin of the Plateau (Fischer, 1942), where the vanadium deposits of the Rico, Placerville, and Lightner Creek areas of Colorado contain by-product uranium (Bush, 1956). Deposits with lower V/U ratios occur in the Morrison in a broad area oriented roughly north-south on both sides of the Utah–Colorado and Arizona–New Mexico lines. The greater number of the nonvanadiferous or low-vanadium ores lie west and southwest of this area, with Cu-U deposits, in which copper may be several times as abundant as uranium, occurring chiefly in the White Canyon district of southeastern Utah. The copper-uranium deposits closely resemble, in their occurrence, that of the "Red Bed-type" copper deposit (Finch, 1933; Fischer, 1937, 1956; Soulé, 1956), which occurs chiefly throughout New Mexico and in north-central Texas and Oklahoma in Permian and Triassic strata. Some of these also contain uranium in minor amounts (pages 417–418). Cu-Ag veins occur in several places in the Uravan district (Fischer, 1936).

According to Miesch (1955) the variations of Cu, Pb, Zn, and Ag differ in detail but are similar in general in showing well-defined "highs," roughly coincident with the salt anticline area of western Colorado and eastern Utah. Likewise he finds the various patterns of Ni, Co, Mo, and Se basically similar, with a broad "high" in the northwestern part of the central Colorado Plateau. Arsenic appears to be randomly distributed, although arsenic minerals (native arsenic, realgar, abernathyite) have been noted in deposits in the southern part of the San Rafael Swell. Coleman (1956) has demonstrated that selenium variation is related to host rocks, with Morrison and Entrada (and Wind River) strata having high-selenium sulfides, whereas Chinle and Shinarump beds contain sulfides low in selenium, except at Temple Mountain (Coleman and Delevaux, 1957).

Silver has been mined from Plateau-type deposits, chiefly in the Silver Reef district of southwestern Utah and on Brush Creek, near Eagle, Eagle County, Colorado, both occurrences lying marginal to the Plateau (Hess, 1933A; Fischer, 1937). Several Silver Reef deposits (Cu-V-Ag-U type), which are in the Chinle, contain uranium as carnotite, together with cerargyrite, copper carbonates, and volborthite. Silver sulfides, chalcocite, and pyrite occur below the water table. Plant remains are replaced by silver minerals (Stugard, 1952; Proctor, 1953).

Chromium (as a chromian micaceous mineral) occurs in concentration closely associated with the Placerville vanadium ores (Hess, 1917, 1933A; Fischer, 1937), finely disseminated in a light green sandstone 5 to 10 ft below the vanadium horizon in the Entrada. Vein deposits containing an assemblage of Cu, Pb, Mo, Co, U, Au, Ag, and V occur near Placerville.

Molybdenum is conspicuous in a deposit at Ouray, Utah, in the Eocene Bridger formation (Hess, 1925B, 1933A), which contains ilsemannite and pyrite disseminated in dark streaks and bands in a thin lenticular sandstone. Rhenium occurs in the Sun Valley deposit, northern Arizona, with U and Mo (Petersen et al., 1957).

Fluorite is relatively abundant in the uranium ores of the Todilto limestone in the Grants district, New Mexico, which appear to be related to fluorite veins of the Zuni Mountains just to the south.

Age

Lead-uranium age determinations on primary Plateau ores have yielded data indicating an average calculated age of approximately 70 m.y. (Stieff and Stern, 1952, 1955; Stieff et al., 1953), with a range of 55 to 80 m.y. (late Cretaceous to early Tertiary). Uranium ore from deposits in Jurassic strata (130 m.y.) yield calculated ages that are essentially the same as those in Triassic beds (150 m.y.). Determinations of the isotopic composition of lead from Plateau lead minerals indicate an average Pb^{207}/Pb^{206} ratio equivalent to 425 m.y. (Stieff and Stern, 1953; Stieff et al., 1953), with the Pb^{206} content of uranium-free minerals ranging from about 24 to 60%. This has been explained by suggesting the addition of small amounts of old radiogenic lead that is approximately a billion years old. The isotopic compositions of lead minerals from deposits of Tertiary age in areas adjacent to the Plateau show marked similarities and point to a common or similar source for the original as well as the added radiogenic lead. These similarities offer independent support for the late Cretaceous–early Tertiary age of the deposits.

DESCRIPTIONS OF SELECTED DISTRICTS

Uravan Region, Colorado and Utah

The Uravan region, chiefly in southwestern Colorado, has six districts (pages 378–379) extending south from Gateway to the southern San Miguel County line. Along the eastern margin of the region, Fischer and Hilpert (1952) have defined the "Uravan mineral belt," an area 1 to 10 mi wide extending in a long north-south arc, concave westward. Within the belt, carnotite deposits in the Salt Wash member of the Morrison have closer spacing, larger size, and higher grade than those in adjacent parts of the districts. Deposits in the belt tend to be clustered in areas 1,000 ft or more wide and usually a mile or more long, with axes normal to the trend of the belt. The belt crosses the northwest salt anticlines, and deposits may be grouped on the flanks of these structures.

The ores are chiefly carnotitic, averaging 0.25% U_3O_8 and 2% V_2O_5. They occur as irregular tabular bodies in sandstone 2 to 4 ft thick, parallel with the bedding of the Morrison formation. Fossil logs are common, and roll deposits are well represented, with parallelism of roll axes and logs.

Big Indian Wash—Lisbon Valley Area, Utah

Relatively large uranium deposits occur chiefly in the Moss Back member of the Chinle formation on the southern flank of the northwest-trending Lisbon Valley anticline (Moab district) (Steen et al., 1953; Dix, 1954; Isachsen, 1955). Representative deposits include the Mi Vida (Utex), La Sal, Rattlesnake (one of the few open-pit Plateau operations), Radon, Big Buck (in Cutler formation and initial producer in 1948), Cal Uranium, and Homestake. All but one occur between 6,200 and 6,700 ft above sea level. The single exception is localized along a major normal fault along the anticlinal axis. Maximum ore thickness is 30 ft, averaging 8 ft (Isachsen, 1956A), with an average grade of about 0.45% U_3O_8. Nearly all the bodies are tabular with long axes following the strike of host beds.

The dominant ore mineral is uraninite with minute coffinite inclusions. Vanadium hydromica and montroesite with finely intergrown doloresite are the main vanadium minerals (Laverty and Gross, 1956; Gross, 1956). In the Mi Vida deposit, vanadium is more abundant in the up-dip part of the ore body, and vanadium-uranium becomes nearly equal down dip (Salo and Lekas, 1956).

White Canyon District, Utah

In the White Canyon area, copper-uranium deposits, the most famous of which is the Happy Jack mine, are localized chiefly in Shinarump channels cut

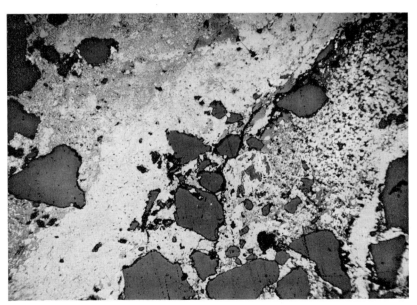

Fig. 10.29. Fine-grained intergrowth of uraninite (medium gray) with chalcopyrite (light) and bornite (light gray) partly replaced by chalcocite, corroding quartz grains, Shinarump conglomerate, Happy Jack mine, White Canyon district, Utah. Reflected light (×44).

Fig. 10.30. North Temple Mountain and "collapse area," *right of center*. Wingate *top*, Chinle *below*, Moenkopi *bottom right* (dark beds). San Rafael Swell, Utah.

in the Moenkopi formation, which beneath the deposits shows bleaching. Some 64 channels have been mapped, of which 24 are known to be mineralized. The host conglomerates and sandstones typically are interbedded with siltstone and claystone and contain abundant carbonized wood (Dodd, 1950; Benson et al., 1952; Trites, 1955; Trites and Chew, 1955; Miller, 1955; Trites et al., 1956; Isachsen, 1956A). The primary deposits consist mainly of pyrite, uraninite, and copper sulfides (Fig. 10.29); sphalerite and galena also are present. Minor As, Ba, Co, Mo, Ni, and Mg also are in the ore. Uraninite and copper minerals form cement, replacing secondary quartz overgrowths and also replace fossil wood. Oxidation along the Shinarump rim has produced an ore body of uranyl sulfates, arsenates, oxides, and some phosphates, together with copper sulfates and carbonates. The gangue includes limonite, hematite, jarosite, alunite, gibbsite, gypsum, barite, chalcedony, and clay minerals (Weeks, 1952).

San Rafael Swell, Utah

At Temple Mountain, near the southeastern margin of the San Rafael Swell, uranium deposits are closely related to structural depressions ("collapse areas") —pipelike masses of down-dropped strata (Fig. 10.30). The Swell is an asymmetric anticline whose axis trends northeast and whose eastern flank dips up to 85° SE. Near Temple Mountain the dip has flattened to 5 to 10°, and the collapse areas lie in synclinal warps. Surrounding each is a narrow zone of strata altered to white and pale green colors.

Within the collapse structures Moenkopi, Chinle, and Wingate blocks have slumped. Moss Back blocks are included, although the Moss Back block has been removed by erosion—slumping occurred prior to the present erosion cycle (Kerr et al., 1955; Keys, 1956). Dolomite and ankerite masses have been formed near the top of the Chinle and in the Wingate as replacements of sandstone (Bodine and Kerr, 1956), in one place hundreds of feet across. The dolomitization preceded uranium mineralization and is believed to have been affected by rising epithermal solutions that removed considerable carbonate at depth from the Kaibab limestone and the Moenkopi. This removal led to the formation of the collapse features (Kerr et al., 1957; Johnson, 1957).

Uranium ores in small amounts are in the pipes and along their margins. Larger deposits around Temple Mountain include those in the Calyx mine area to the south which are representative of the uraniferous asphaltite type of deposit (Isachsen, 1956A) (Fig. 10.31). These form ellipsoidal tabular bodies ($300 \times 20 \times 4$ ft in size) with dactylic extensions 50 ft long, occurring in the Moss Back sandstone. The essentially unoxidized ores consist of coffinite and pitchblende minutely dispersed in a brittle, subvitreous, asphaltic hydrocarbon. In addition, nonradioactive liquid and solid hydrocarbons also are present, and ore also is associated with carbonized woody debris and logs. The chief vanadium minerals are montroesite and corvusite. Uranyl vanadates, arsenates, carbonates, sulfates, and phosphates are minor, as are nonuraniferous vanadates. The origin of the asphaltite (pages 527–528) has been much debated (Breger, 1955; Gruner, 1955A, 1956B; Davidson, 1955; Hausen, 1956). Kerr and Kelley (1956) have concluded that the introduction of the uranium into the petroliferous material was accompanied by induration of the latter and that (p. 389) "The most likely hypothesis is that the induration of the hydrocarbon is caused

F$_{\text{IG}}$. 10.31. Chinle formation prospected for uranium. Calyx mine area to left. Southeast-dipping flank of Temple Mt., San Rafael Swell, Utah.

by polymerization and oxidation of the oil by mineralizing solutions accompanied by more than normal heat."

The Delta mine, which illustrates the nonasphaltic type, is on the edge of a structural terrace in a monocline forming the southern margin of the Swell. Dikes of diabase and syenite and faults that are nearby trend northwest. Copper-uranium-vanadium ore occurs in a semicircular body in the lower third of a sandstone lens, 33 ft above the base of the Chinle (Isachsen, 1956A) and below the Moss Back. The ore has a maximum thickness of 20 ft, but the thickness is highly variable. Beneath ore is a green mudstone containing illite and kaolinite.

Carnotite and zippeite are the chief ore minerals; uraninite locally replaces logs. Pyrite, galena, copper sulfides, secondary copper minerals, wulfenite, volborthite, and cobalto-calcite also are present.

Grants District, New Mexico

Deposits in Todilto Limestone

In the Grants district (also Gallup-Laguna area), McKinley and Valencia Counties, New Mexico, uranium deposits replace Todilto limestone (Upper Jurassic), localized along anticlinal crests. The primary assemblage is pitchblende, pyrite, barite, calcite, and fluorite, with secondary carnotite, tyuyamunite, metatyuyamunite, beta-uranophane, uranophane, sklodowskite, gummite, hematite, limonite, and manganese oxides. Cuprosklodowskite and a new hydrous silicate of Mn, Al, and V, ardennite, also have been identified (Sun and Weber, 1955). Microscopic pitchblende(?) inclusions have been observed in highly radioactive fluorite (Kerr and Dahl, 1953). Some of the ores consist in large part of fine-grained fluorite; others are relatively free of fluorite. The dark purple uraniferous fluorite forms grains and clusters in recrystallized limestone and may replace calcite (Gruner et al., 1951).

Many of the fluorite veins in the Zuni Mountains have the same northeasterly trend as the uranium fluorite ore bodies. A genetic relation is suggested by Peters (1956). Radioactivity is associated with joint and fracture coatings and fillings of fluorite, calcite, malachite, azurite, and chrysocolla in Permian arkosic sandstones and conglomerates and in altered Precambrian granite in T. 11 N., R. 12 W., Zuni Mountains. Samples contain 0.009% U, 0.02% V_2O_5, and 4.5% Cu (Lovering, 1956).

The Todilto formation, up to 20 ft thick, in the southwestern part of the area, is here a relatively pure limestone, locally interfingering with overlying silty Summerville beds. The limestone crops out as a broad bench as wide as 2,000 ft in places, trending northwest along the northeast flank of the Zuni Mountains (Fig. 10.32). In the northeastern part of the area, the 5- to 10-ft petroliferous limestone bed is overlain by 40 ft of gypsum. Uranium deposits are more numerous in the pure limestone than in the silty or evaporite facies (Lovering, 1956).

Mineralization is generally confined to the basal platy Todilto limestone except where secondary minerals have been deposited along joints throughout the formation. In the Gray Eagle area, mineralization is in the upper massive unit and locally extends a few feet into limey lenses of the overlying Summerville formation, which has been bleached in halos over the ore bodies. In some banded ore, original bedding has been preserved. Replacement has been markedly selective along some thin beds, and may end sharply against fractures (Gabelman, 1956A).

The district, discovered in 1950 (Anderson, 1957), is on the southeast end of the Thoreau monocline which forms the northeast flank of the Zunis. Broad folds trend northeast across the monocline, with major faults roughly coincident with fold axes. Shorter *en echelon* faults of lesser displacement trend east-northeast, north-south, and north-northwest.

The eastern, Poison Canyon, uranium belt is localized along a fault zone and coincides with an anticlinal axis. The western, Haystack Butte, zone lies along the southeast flank of a syncline. The zones extend northeast into Morrison formation rocks which, however, contain no fluorite. Some ore bodies are lenses, some more than 200 ft long; others are elongated sinuous masses 5,000 ft long and 5 to 30 ft wide.

The controlling structures are Tertiary, and the solutions are regarded as hydrothermal because of the intimate fluorite-pitchblende(?) intergrowth, the structural control, the selective replacement, the bleached Summerville halos, and the upward limitation by Summerville shaly siltstone. Termination against underlying Entrada suggests lateral solution migration either from the faults or from fluorite vein conduits in the Zuni Mountains (Gabelman, 1956A).

Fig. 10.32. Uranium mining in Todilto limestone, Haystack Butte, Grants district, N.Mex.

Deposits in Morrison Formation

Jack Pile–Poison Canyon area. In addition to fluoritic-type deposits in the Todilto, the district also contains the largest sandstone-type deposits of the Plateau, with New Mexico reserves estimated at 41 million tons of 0.24% U_3O_8 ore. This is 68.4% of the domestic ore reserves. The large deposits are in the Brushy Basin member of the Morrison, but small sandstone-type deposits also have been found in the Summerville and in the Dakota (Gabelman, 1956A). The deposits are localized in areas of more intense fracturing and faulting along the northeast flank of the Zuni uplift (Konigsmark, 1955; Carlson, 1955).

Prior to the discovery of the Ambrosia Lake deposits, the Jack Pile ore body, 6 mi north of Laguna, was one of the largest that had been found on the Plateau (Fig. 10.33). It consists chiefly of black ores, apparently mainly coffinite, and subordinate yellow ores of tyuyamunite, uranophane, autunite, and schoepite disseminated through a thick sandstone (Jackpile sandstone—Schlee, 1957) in the upper part of the Brushy Basin member overlain unconformably by the Dakota. The sandstone ranges in thickness from 60 to 175 ft and near ore deposits changes in color from yellowish orange to yellowish gray (Hilpert and Freeman, 1956).

The two main ore bodies, the Jack Pile and North Jack Pile, are being mined in an open-cut operation designed to connect the two pits. The vanadium-poor ore is covered by 100 to 130 ft of overburden. The massive sandstone contains clay galls, carbonaceous trash, and mineralized fossil logs (Fig. 10.34). The Jack Pile ore body is cut by a diabase dike (Fig. 10.12); uranyl minerals occur

Fɪɢ. 10.33. Open-cut mining operation, Jack Pile deposit, Brushy Basin sandstone, Morrison formation, Grants district, N.Mex.; 100 to 130 ft of overburden covers the ore body, *lower right.*

Fɪɢ. 10.34. Fossil log replaced by coffinite, in part altered to tyuyamunite. Note halo of secondary uranyl minerals in sandstone of Morrison formation. Jack Pile deposit, Grants district, N.Mex.

along fractures in the dike margins. The tabular ore bodies, which follow the bedding, are up to several tens of feet thick and up to hundreds of feet wide and long. The deposit is estimated to contain 15 million tons of 0.16% U_3O_8 ore.

Smaller nearby ore bodies include the Wind Whip and Woodrow. The latter is a breccia pipe, 20 to 30 ft in diameter and steeply dipping to vertical, which has been dropped 25 to 40 ft relative to surrounding Morrison rocks. The high-grade mineralization, which consists mainly of coffinite, abundant pyrite, and minor amounts of other minerals in gouge and breccia, filling fractures and replacing sandstone along fractures, has been found to extend below 100 feet (Fig. 10.35). The mineralization is believed to be of hydrothermal origin (Cook and Wylie, 1956).

The Poison Canyon mine, 10 mi north of Grants, is also in the Brushy Basin member of the Morrison, in a 45-ft thick sandstone near the base of the member, underlain by 20 ft of mudstone. The main ore body trends east-west for about 550 ft and is as much as 50 ft across. Along the trend of its axis, about 1,500 ft to the east, is the Mesa Top mine with an irregular ore body 1,200 ft long and 20 to 100 ft across. Minor faults with 2 to 12 ft of displacement strike north-northwest and dip 65 to 75° NE. or SW. across the flat-lying Poison Canyon body (Dodd, 1956). Grade and thickness of ore reportedly increase adjacent to faults, which are coated by secondary minerals.

The ore, which has an average V:U ratio of 0.5:1, contains coffinite, pyrite, galena, metatyuyamunite, autunite, gypsum, kaolinite, calcite, and asphaltite. The asphaltite coats sand grains and also forms small lensoid pods, both of which contain coffinite (Fig. 10.36).

Ambrosia Lake area. Uranium mineralization was discovered near Ambrosia Lake [1] in drill cores in April, 1955, by Lewis Lothman, and within 1½ yr the area has become foremost in the United States in reserves. It is in the south-

[1] Ambrosia Lake is a grass-covered flat which has water only for a few days after cloudbursts. Originally named Ambrosio, now popularized as Ambrosia.

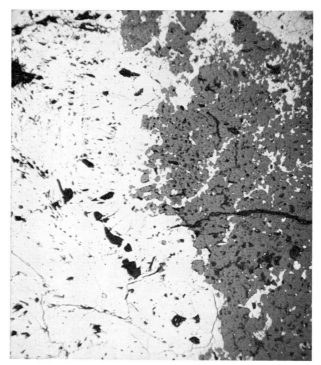

Fɪɢ. 10.35. Pyrite-marcasite veinlet (light) in brecciated sandstone (dark), Woodrow pipe, Grants district, N.Mex. Reflected light (×44).

eastern part of McKinley County, west of San Mateo and 20 mi north of Grants and includes all of T. 14 N., R. 10 W. and parts of adjoining townships. Much of the area is a valley, directly underlain by the Mancos shale, bounded on the northeast by a cuesta capped by the Hosta sandstone of the upper Mesaverde group and on the southwest by a cuesta of the Dakota sandstone and Jurassic formations (Gabelman et al., 1956).

The deposits, which occur in the Westwater Canyon member of the Morrison formation, are localized by structures developed on the Thoreau homocline, which dips gently northwestward away from the Zuni uplift. In the Haystack Butte block to the southwest, the homocline is segmented by northeasterly faults flanking synclinal structures to which uranium mineralization in the Todilto is related (pages 410–411). The Ambrosia deposits may be considered as the down-dip counterparts of those in the Haystack Butte area. The Haystack synclines pass northeastward into anticlines, of which five principal ones have been defined around Ambrosia Lake (Young and Ealy, 1956). Two anticlines have domal features, but only the Ambrosia Lake dome is of significance in ore control. This dome, on the southern end of the South Ambrosia Lake anticline, is localized where the north-south fold axis turns abruptly southeast. It has an indicated closure of over 500 ft on the top of the Dakota. There is some thinning of Jurassic sediments over the dome.

Three systems of nearly vertical normal faults, N. 10 to 30° E., N. 50 to 70° E., and N. 10 to 20° W., with the first two as major sets, are generally restricted to anticlinal crests. Sediments on both sides of faults are downwarped; apparently the faults were separated sufficiently to permit slumping.

The initial L-shaped ore body, about 2,500 ft long, was found in sec. 11, T. 14 N., R. 10 W. at about 300 ft. Other significant mineralization occurs at various depths to about 1,000 ft, in the same township in secs. 10, 12, 13, 15, 22–26, and 36. Large ore bodies, several of multimillion tons, have been developed in secs. 22 and 36, T. 14 N., R. 10 W., and in secs. 21, 23, 32, and 34, T. 14 N., R. 9 W. (Fig. 10.37). Ore thicknesses range from one to over 100 ft; the Ike No. 1 mine has 50 to 150 ft of ore at 950 ft of depth. In one drill hole, three ore zones, 30, 15, and 7 ft thick were cut within about 100 ft.

Fɪɢ. 10.36. Blebs and grain coatings of uraniferous asphaltite (black) in arkosic sandstone, Brushy Basin member, Morrison formation, Grants district, N.Mex. (×35).

FIG. 10.37. Mining operation, Rio de Oro deposit, Ambrosia Lake, Grants district, N.Mex. (Alice Corey).

"Stacked" ore bodies are common. Reserves (early 1957) approach 30 million tons with average grade probably about 0.25% U_3O_8.

The ores are out of equilibrium, with radiometric values up to twice chemical values. They occur throughout the Westwater Canyon sandstone, which is 110 to 250 ft thick, all the way from the lower contact with the Recapture shale member up to the upper contact with the Brushy Basin claystone-sandstone member. The host rock ranges from a poorly sorted pebble conglomerate to a coarse- to medium-grained sandstone, usually with clay cement. Calcite cement is absent, minor, or predominates, and in some, ore forms poikiloblastic grains up to 6 in. across. Sandstones that are mineralized have been bleached from reddish to gray.

The ore consists of pyrite and asphaltite in which coffinite is minutely dispersed. The asphaltite replaces clay cement and detrital grains, especially feldspar, fills minute cracks, and coats quartz grains (Fig. 10.38). It is a petroliferous derivative and has served as a precipitant for uranium. Calcite, which may have also been introduced with uranium, appears to be later than asphaltite. It replaces clay cement and forms pseudomorphs after detrital grains of feldspar(?) and quartz that have rims of uraniferous asphaltite. Tyuyamunite has been found in one ore body very close to a fault.

According to Young and Ealy (1956) the sequence of events in the formation of the deposits has been:

1. Rise of the Zuni uplift; growth of the Ambrosia dome during Westwater and Brushy Basin time (late Jurassic)
2. Migration of oil into the dome (late Jurassic to late Cretaceous)
3. Tilting to northeast, slight erosion, preceding Dakota deposition
4. Tilting to north, slight erosion of Dakota (early in late Cretaceous)

5. Compressional folding, further tilting, some faulting, with flushing of oil and entry of the uraniferous solutions (late Cretaceous to early Tertiary)

6. Tension faulting (late Tertiary)

Coyote District, New Mexico

Uraniferous copper deposits that occur in steeply dipping Sangre de Christo formation strata (Permian) south of Coyote, Mora County, New Mexico, consist of copper sulfide nodules scattered in lenticular carbonaceous zones in shales and arkosic sandstones. The nodules are chiefly of chalcocite, with some bornite, covellite, pyrite, carbonaceous material, and intimately intergrown uraninite. They average about 2 in. long and are superficially altered to malachite and azurite. Samples from the carbonaceous zones, which contain as much as 0.067% U and average 3% Cu, may be several inches to 5 ft thick and several feet to over 100 ft long (Gott and Erickson, 1952; Zeller and Baltz, 1954; Soulé, 1956). Metatyuyamunite occurs disseminated in associated arkosic beds.

Some of the lower limestone beds in the formation are undoubtedly marine, and all the copper deposits occur within the lower half of the formation. Zeller and Baltz (1954) have suggested that the deposits are of sedimentary origin, with copper and uranium in small amounts deposited with clastic materials and concentrated in the carbonaceous zones during diagenesis. The

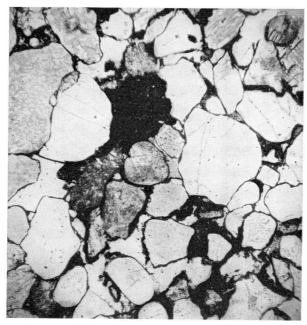

FIG. 10.38. Uraniferous asphaltite (black) replacing clay cement and feldspar grains and coating quartz grains in Morrison sandstone, Rio de Oro deposit, Ambrosia Lake, Grants district, N.Mex. (×35).

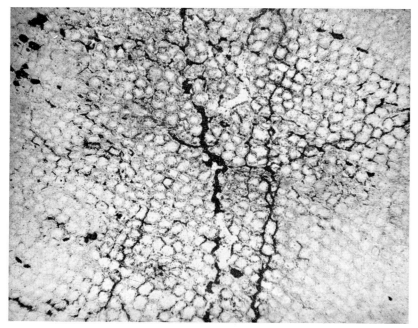

Fɪɢ. 10.39. Carnotite replacing fossil wood, Shinarump formation, Monument No. 2 mine, Monument Valley district, Ariz. (×66).

deposits are of little economic significance, but illustrate an aberrant type of Plateau deposit.

There are numerous other deposits of generally similar nature ("Red bed" copper deposits) throughout New Mexico and southeastern Colorado (Soulé, 1956), but radioactivity is reported in only a few. A deposit similar to the Coyote occurrence is in the Sangre de Christo formation at Cuchara Camp, Huerfano County, Colorado (Finch, 1956).

Monument Valley District, Arizona and Utah

The district, which lies at the southern end of the Monument upwarp, a broad asymmetrical anticline, contains deposits chiefly in Shinarump-filled channels incised into the Moenkopi (Fig. 10.18), with considerable ore locally extending down into the Moenkopi and into the De Chelly member of the Cutler. The channels are from 15 to 2,300 ft wide and 10 to 70 ft deep (Witkind 1954), and some are known to lie in the center of broad, shallow swales (Witkind, 1956A,B). Channels less than 2 mi long are more likely to have ore than those of the longer type. Pliocene volcanic necks and dikes of minette tuff-breccias are common. The dikes follow joint sets oriented from north to N. 45° W.

The channel sediments contain considerable fossil wood, silicified, carbonized, and replaced by uranium and copper minerals (Fig. 10.39). Ore consists chiefly of tyuyamunite and carnotite, but unoxidized uraninite-roscoelite ore also is present. Other oxidized species include hewettite, malachite, azurite, chrysocolla, jarosite, alunite, barite, limonite, and gypsum. Other unoxidized constituents are chalcopyrite and chalcocite.

In the Monument No. 2 mine (Fig. 10.40), the most important in the district, many of the major high-grade ore bodies are crudely ovate, flattened, elongate cylinders termed rods by Witkind (1956B) (Fig. 10.41). Many complex rods contain colinear silicified wood. The rods are outlined by a circular fracture pattern, in which fractures across grains are filled by U-V minerals. Some rods proxy for buried logs subsequently replaced by sand, silt, and clay and then mineralized; others appear to have resulted from deposition within aureoles of humic colloids and organic resins around coalified logs (Witkind, 1956B).

Lukachukai Mountains, Arizona

The Lukachukai Mountains are in the northern end of the Defiance uplift in northeastern Arizona. The larger uranium deposits are in Salt Wash sandstone in a zone of interbedded sandstone-mudstone trending north to northeast across the mountains (Masters, 1955; Dodd, 1956). The mineralization consists of carnotite, vanadium oxide minerals, and lesser amounts of uraninite(?) and calcium vanadates. The largest ore bodies measure 350×90 ft and are rarely more than 4 ft thick, with larger dimensions parallel with bedding, although contacts locally cut bedding sharply, as rolls.

The Rattlesnake deposits occur on an anticline, but in general neither the positions nor trends of ore deposits show any apparent control by structural features. Deposits tend to occur as clusters along the flanks of channels in gray or brown sandstone adjacent to red sandstone.

Fig. 10.40. Mined-out ore body, Shinarump formation, Monument No. 2 mine, Monument Valley district, Ariz.

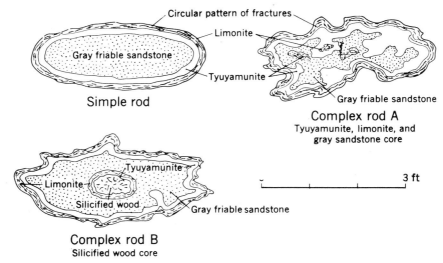

Fig. 10.41. Cross sections of rod ore bodies, Monument No. 2 mine, Monument Valley district, Ariz. (Witkind, 1956B; *U.S. Geol. Survey*).

WYOMING

GENERAL

Bedded deposits of uranium minerals in Wyoming outside of the Black Hills area are widely distributed, occurring mainly in clastic terrestrial sediments of Tertiary age (Vine, 1956B). Schroeckingerite (first called dakeite) was discovered in the Red Desert area in 1936 (Larsen and Gonyer, 1937), and in 1951 carnotite was found at Pumpkin Buttes. The discovery of radioactive sandstone in the Gas Hills area on September 9, 1953, by Neil McNeice subsequently led to the development of the Lucky Mc and other mines in that district.

Deposits occur in intermontane basins between generally isolated mountain ranges whose Precambrian crystalline cores are flanked by dipping Paleozoic to Mesozoic, Cambrian to Cretaceous strata, with Silurian generally absent. The basin fills, of Paleocene to Pleocene fluvial strata, derived from adjoining highlands, consist mainly of fine- to coarse-grained arkosic sandstones, conglomerates, siltstones, and shales (Table 10.10). Coal beds are found in Paleocene and Eocene formations, and volcanic ash [1] and pyroclastic contaminants are widespread in Oligocene or younger beds. In general the beds are flat-lying except where locally folded and faulted.

The deposits occur chiefly in permeable arkosic sandstones especially of the Wind River, Wasatch, and Browns Park formations, but shale, mudstone, and limestone also are host rocks locally. Structural features appear to have been

[1] Including seleniferous tuff (Everett and Bauerle, 1957) near Lysite in Fremont County.

TABLE 10.10. *Generalized stratigraphy of the Tertiary of Wyoming (after Grutt, 1956)*

Epoch	Formation	Character
Pliocene	North Park	Tuff, sandstone, bentonitic claystone
Miocene	Browns Park	Tuffaceous sandstone, conglomerate, marl
Oligocene	White River	Tuffaceous claystone, arkosic conglomerate
Eocene	Green River	Shale, marlstone, claystone
	Wasatch	Sandstone, shale, claystone
	Wind River	Sandstone, shale, conglomerate
Paleocene	Fort Union	Sandstone, shale, coal

of secondary importance in localizing the deposits, although in the Lost Creek area it appears that the schroeckingerite deposits are associated with the Cyclone Rim fault (Page, 1950B), and some deposits in other areas are on anticlinal structures. The chief ore controls appear to be stratigraphic and lithologic.

Deposits are generally close to the surface and can be stripped, but in the Gas Hills and Green Mountain areas some ore has been found at depths of 300 to 400 ft. The Gas Hills area has been the most active and by June, 1956, had produced over 100,000 tons of ore (Mencher, 1956).

Unlike the deposits of the Colorado Plateau, uranyl vanadates are not among the principal ore minerals except in one area. Grutt (1956) has delineated five mineralogical provinces, each with a characteristic mineral association (Fig. 10.42). Although most ores are oxidized (yellow ores), discoveries of unoxidized (black) ores of pitchblende and/or coffinite have been made in the Wind River, Poison, and Powder River Basins (Grutt, 1956; Stieff et al., 1956). The primary, unoxidized ore bodies occur mainly as ellipsoidal masses generally conformable with the bedding. Deposits of uranyl minerals are more irregular, surrounding the black ores as halos, forming irregular disseminations, lenses, concretionary masses, and bands, which may transect the stratification. Carbonaceous material is locally abundantly associated with the ores. In some districts halos of soft white, "bleached" sandstone with limonitic stains and spots surround the oxidized ores, or the uranyl species occur concentrated along contacts between normal pink sandstone with bleached gray on buff sandstone.

Finch (1956) recognizes three types of deposits: (1) deposits in carbonaceous sandstone associated with uraniferous lignites; (2) small concretionary deposits in sandstone; and (3) poorly defined stratiform disseminations in sandstone, arkose, or mudstone.

PUMPKIN BUTTES

More than 250 occurrences of uranium minerals are known in the Pumpkin Buttes area in the south-central part of the Powder River Basin, in south-

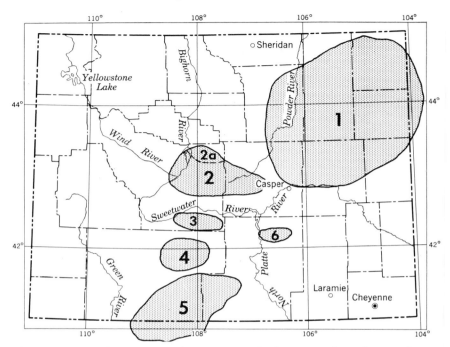

Fɪɢ. 10.42. Uraniferous areas of Wyoming and their mineralogy (principal type first). 1, Powder River Basin and Black Hills: vanadates, silicates, oxides. 2, Wind River Basin: phosphate, arsenate, fluorphosphate, carbonate. 2a. Owl Creek Mts.: silicate, phosphate, sulfate. 3, Green Mts.: silicate, phosphate, oxide. 4, Great Divide Basin: sulfate-carbonate. 5, Washakii Basin and environs: silicate, phosphate, sulfate, oxide. 6, Shirley Mts.: vanadate (Grutt, 1956; *U.S. Geol. Survey*).

western Campbell and southeastern Johnson Counties. The Buttes are capped by erosional remnants of Oligocene White River siliceous clastic beds, less than 100 ft thick, unconformably overlying fluvial clastics of the Wasatch formation. The basin is a broad asymmetrical anticline whose northwest-trending axis passes just east of the Buttes. Dips are of the order of 30 to 100 ft/mi (Love, 1952; Troyer et al., 1954; Sharp et al., 1956).

Uranium occurrences are of three main types: (1) disseminations of uranyl minerals in porous sandstone or near calcite-impregnated sandstone; (2) uranyl minerals disseminated as halos marginal to manganese oxide concretions, or in sandstone zones, 2 in. to 10 ft across, rich in these concretions with associated coaly plant debris; and (3) uraninite-pyrite concretions with thick shells of uranyl minerals. The deposits occur in sandstone lenses in the lower half (500 ft) of Wasatch formation exposures. The quartzose sandstone contains about 15% feldspar and minor clay, mica, and heavy accessories. Calcite is a major cement locally.

The disseminations consist of metatyuyamunite, carnotite, uranophane, and rare hewettite, usually replacing calcite (Fig. 10.43). The manganese concretions contain manganite, pyrolusite, manganosite, and psilomelane cementing quartz and feldspar, with uranophane, metatyuyamunite, and carnotite filling pores. The uraninite nodules, up to several cubic feet in size, contain pyrite either as a core or as disseminated blebs. Fossil plant material is closely associated with the uraninite that cements sand grains. Paramontroesite also forms black irregular masses as much as a foot across. Liebigite has been found as an efflorescence.

BAGGS–POISON BASIN AREA

The Poison Basin, 6 mi west of Baggs, Carbon County, has been eroded in the Miocene Browns Park formation, 300 ft of the conglomerate, soft, white, cross-bedded sandstone, tuffaceous sandstone, and sedimentary quartzite (Vine and Prichard, 1954; Wilson, 1955). Scattered deposits of uranophane, meta-autunite, phosphuranylite, and minor schroeckingerite occur disseminated in red-brown or green-gray sandstone, medium- to coarse-grained and highly cross-bedded. The unoxidized ores contain uraninite, coffinite, and pyrite. Select samples contain as much as 3.2% U, but most deposits appear to be of limited dimensions. Some deposits also contain selenium in concentrations up to 0.69% Se (hence the name Poison). Fracture zones are mineralized in some places; elsewhere faults have served as barriers to mineralizing solutions (Grutt, 1957).

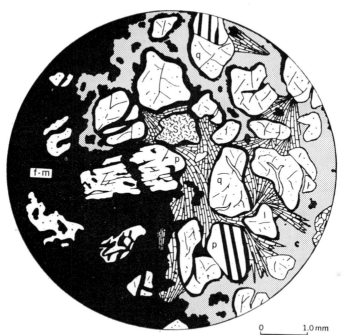

Fig. 10.43. Grains of quartz (q), plagioclase (p), and shale pieces (s) in calcite cement in arkosic sandstone of Wasatch formation. Bladed aggregates of uranophane, *center,* replace calcite. Iron and manganese oxides (f-m) replace calcite and clastic grains. Pumpkin Buttes, Wyo. (Troyer et al., 1954; *U.S. Geol. Survey*).

MILLER HILL AREA

The Miller Hill area, 35 mi northeast of Poison Basin, is underlain by similar rocks correlated by Love (1953A) with the Browns Park formation but possibly somewhat younger (Vine and Prichard, 1954). The formation, more than 1,000 ft thick, consists of basal conglomerate, tuffs, tuffaceous calcareous sandstone, and a thin, persistent, radioactive algal limestone 335 to 400 ft above the base. The last contains up to 0.15% U and is as much as 10 ft thick. Unusually high radioactivity occurs where the limestone is fractured and brecciated and contains secondary chalcedony and opal (Vine and Prichard, 1953). Calcareous sandstone beds also are mineralized locally. The chief radioactive mineral is uranophane.

LOST CREEK AREA

Near Lost Creek near the center of the Great Divide Basin (Red Desert), in Sweetwater County, 40 mi north of Wamsutter, Wyoming, are unusual uranium deposits consisting of schroeckingerite as rounded masses in green, brown, or purply clay and as tiny disseminated flakes in arkosic sand or sandy clay (Wyant et al., 1956). The host materials are probably of Wasatch or younger age. The masses, as much as 1 in. across, are somewhat concentrated in beds 2 to 24 in. thick, which strike northwest and dip 14 to 27° NE. Mineralized beds are commonly in contact with an iron oxide band (Wyant, 1952). The deposits, which lie north of the Red Desert radioactive lignites (pages 542–543), are associated with the Cyclone Rim fault, a major structural feature that trends northwest to west, dips steeply southwest, and has been traced for 25 mi. The main deposit measures 1,100 × 10,000 ft in plan; a second, subparallel and to the north, is 600 × 8,200 ft in size. Ore extends to depths of at least 7 ft. The average of 28 samples of ore was nearly 0.08% U_3O_8.

GAS HILLS AREA

In the Gas Hills area of Fremont and Natrona Counties, uranium mineralization occurs chiefly in lenticular arkosic sandstones and conglomerates of the Wind River formation that dip 3 to 6° S. and rest unconformably on eroded Mesozoic strata. The flanks of the Gas Hills anticline expose Triassic (Chugwater) to Cretaceous (Cody) strata. Overlying the Wind River formation are younger Eocene, Miocene, and Oligocene beds, many of volcanic or tuffaceous character (Love, 1954A; Grutt, 1956). Uranium also occurs to a lesser extent in middle Eocene rocks and in the early Cretaceous Thermopolis shale. The host Wind River beds show torrential cross-bedding, contain disseminated carbonaceous plant fossils, and have calcareous, ferruginous, or argillaceous cements.

The ore bodies are lensoid, tabular, or irregular, generally conforming to sedimentary structures but locally following fractures across them. Some 200 occurrences are known (Grutt, 1957). Many ore bodies are underlain by impervious mudstones or shales.

At the Lucky Mc mine, primary black ores form pinch- and swell-lenses up to several feet thick and 1 to 15 ft wide (Fig. 10.44). The mineralization ap-

Fig. 10.44. Open-cut operations at Lucky Mc mine, Gas Hills area, Wyo. Ore, *lower right and center,* is in irregular lenses generally parallel with bedding in sandstone of Wind River formation.

pears to be most strongly concentrated in permeable coarse-grained sandstone lenses and in strongly fractured rock. Prominent fractures that strike from N. 70° W. to N. 35° E. appear to have been significant in localization of ore (Grutt, 1956). The secondary mineralization surrounds black ore as halos or is distributed through oxidized sandstone as disseminations, bands, or irregular masses (Fig. 10.45). The deposit is surrounded by an envelope of soft white sandstone containing limonite or jarosite blotches. Some carbonaceous shales also are radioactive with up to 0.062% U. The unoxidized sooty ores commonly have chemically determined uranium in excess of radiometrically determined uranium, whereas in the oxidized ores the equivalent uranium is usually in excess.

The black ores consist of fine-grained uraninite and coffinite with abundant pyrite and gray-green uraniferous carbonate-fluorapatite. Secondary ores contain liebigite, meta-autunite, phosphuranylite, rutherfordine, metazeunerite, metatorbernite, and possible uranospinite. Meta-autunite appears to be the most abundant. Native selenium is locally abundant, some samples containing as high as 6%; molybdenum and arsenic also are present.

In addition to control by permeability and fracturing, other factors localizing ore probably include above-average amounts of calcite cement, proximity to the underlying unconformity, bends or the borders of channels (Grant, 1955), the presence of impervious intercalated shale beds, and local carbonaceous material. Because fossil plant material is not abundant and because of nearby gas seeps, Grutt (1957) has suggested H_2S from natural gas as the chief reductant of uranium carried in ground water.

Fɪɢ. 10.45. Lensoid mass of oxidized uranium minerals with abundant limonite in coarse-grained sandstone, Wind River formation, Lucky Mc mine, Gas Hills area, Wyo.

CROOKS GAP AREA

The Crooks Gap area lies in the Green Mountains, 65 mi north of Rawlins in Fremont County. The northwest-trending Green Mountains consist mainly of Eocene beds bounded on the north by a north-dipping thrust and on the south by the Great Divide Basin. Folded Wasatch strata uncomformably overlie strongly folded beds of the Fort Union and older units (Grutt, 1956). Most uranium deposits are in the Wasatch, which consists of alternating lensoid conglomerates, arkosic sandstones, and carbonaceous shales. Ore zones with uraninite and pyrite occur over a stratigraphic distance of over 400 ft (Grutt, 1957).

At the Sno-Ball mine the ore zone, up to several feet thick, pinches and swells along the dip and is irregular along the strike. Most production has come from near the top of a persistent mudstone bed dipping 15° E. The oxidized ore consists of uranophane, meta-autunite, and phosphuranylite as cement and grain coatings, in lenses of coarse-grained arkosic sandstone, and in upper parts of underlying and interbedded carbonaceous mudstone. Abundant carbonaceous plant fossil fragments or carbonaceous shales are associated with the highest-grade ore.

A few faults and fractures are mineralized; metazeunerite occurs along a fault at the northeast end of Crooks Gap (Wilson, 1955). A conspicuous white, "bleached" sandstone envelope apparently is the result of alteration accompanying mineralization. Limonite is abundant in the mineralized zone. Some high-grade specimens assayed as much as 3% U_3O_8, but ores average 0.20 to 0.25%.

BLACK HILLS AREA, SOUTH DAKOTA AND WYOMING

GENERAL

In 1951, carnotite ores were discovered in Craven Canyon near Edgemont, Fall River County, southwestern South Dakota, on the southwest edge of the Black Hills. By 1954, carnotite had been found at numerous places along the western flank over 100 mi to Aladdin, Wyoming, and ore was being mined from several dozen deposits near Edgemont. The Carlisle deposit, the largest producer from the northern Black Hills up to 1955, lies at the westernmost extension of the Black Hills, northwest of the Belle Fourche River; two other large ore bodies are near the Little Missouri River; and some production has come from Barlow Canyon near Devils Tower, all in Wyoming (Page and Redden, 1952; Baker et al., 1952; Bell and Bales, 1955; King, 1956A; Bell et al., 1956; Jones et al., 1956).

The Black Hills area is thus noteworthy not only for the first commercial United States carnotite deposits found outside of the Colorado Plateau but also for the variety of radioactive deposits occurring in it:

1. Radioactive minerals in pegmatites in the Precambian core. Uraninite and its alteration products in the Bob Ingersoll No. 2 pegmatite (page 194).

2. Pitchblende and autunite with chalcopyrite, auriferous pyrite, and quartz in vein deposits in Precambrian paraschists and gneisses—Bald Mountain District, Lawrence County, South Dakota. Autunite with fluorite also coats fractures in the Deadwood (Cambrian) formation in the same area.

3. Colorado Plateau-type—carnotite and pitchblende—coffinite lodes in Cretaceous sandstone. Edgemont area, South Dakota and Carlisle area, Wyoming.

4. Uraniferous lignite in various members of the Fort Union formation (Paleocene), Cave Hills, Slim Buttes, and other localities (pages 541–542).

5. Carnotite-bearing sandstone of the Chadron formation (Oligocene), Slim Buttes area, and uranocircite in sandstone in the same formation in the White River Badlands, Pennington County, South Dakota (page 551).

6. Weakly radioactive black shales in the Minnelusa (Pennsylvanian) formation.

7. Consolidated monazite-bearing placers in the basal Deadwood conglomerate in the Bear Lodge Mountain area (page 518), and radioactive consolidated placers in the same formation near Rochford, south of Lead.

GEOLOGY

The Black Hills, which are 25 mi long and 60 mi wide, forming an isolated dome with an axis trending from north to west of north, have a Precambrian core flanked by quaquaversally dipping sediments of Cambrian to Upper Cretaceous age. The dome is complicated by numerous satellitic structures, including several major, generally north-trending anticlines or monoclines with intervening or adjacent structural "flats" or terraces: along the southern end of the Black Hills—the Cascade and Chilson anticlines; along the western side of the Hartville uplift near New Castle and the Moorcraft anticline east of Carlisle, Wyoming; and along the northern-edge anticlines that plunge northwestward from the Bear Lodge Mountains and from near Sturgis, South Dakota. Numerous laccolithic-type domes (Bear Lodge Mountain) and plugs and stocks (Devils Tower) occur in the northern Black Hills. The rocks of these early Tertiary intrusives are monzonitic-syenitic in composition.

DEPOSITS

The uranium deposits occur as bedded bodies in sandstones of the nonmarine formations of the Inyan Kara group (early Cretaceous), which is 500 to 600 ft thick. From bottom to top the group includes the Lakota sandstone, the Fuson formation, and the Fall River sandstone. Locally the thin Minnewuste limestone separates the Lakota from the Fuson. The Fall River is the approximate equivalent of the Dakota of nearby regions. The formations consist of sandstone, siltstone, and mudstone, alternating and lenticular in shape. Black shales, arkosic pebble conglomerates, and lenses and pockets of carbonaceous debris are common.

The ore bodies are tabular masses and irregular pods that conform to the stratification in gross structure but in detail transgress individual beds. Unlike deposits of the Colorado Plateau, rolls are absent, depositional control by channels is not recognized, and fossil logs, branches, and twigs are rare to absent. The ore minerals coat sand grains, fill pores, and coat fractures and joint surfaces, locally forming thin irregular concentric bands. The bodies range in size from small, unmineable pods to masses containing 50,000 tons. Thicknesses range from less than 1 ft to nearly 20 ft.

A purplish-pink ferruginous sandstone characteristically envelops the deposits as a halo (Fig. 10.46). Carnotite deposits in the Fall River sandstone

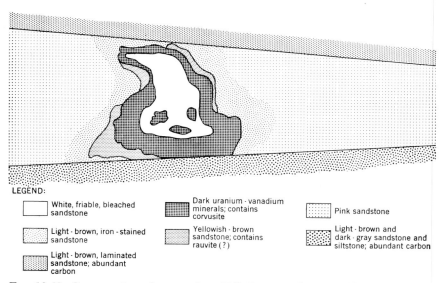

LEGEND:

White, friable, bleached sandstone	Dark uranium - vanadium minerals; contains corvusite
Light - brown, iron - stained sandstone	Yellowish - brown sandstone; contains rauvite (?)
Light - brown, laminated sandstone; abundant carbon	
	Pink sandstone
	Light - brown and dark - gray sandstone and siltstone; abundant carbon

Fig. 10.46. Cross section of ore pod in Fall River sandstone, Fall River County, S.Dak., with halo of iron-stained sandstone (Bell and Bales, 1955; *U.S. Geol. Survey*).

in the northern Black Hills occur where the sandstone changes from normal yellowish gray or buff down dip to reddish up dip. Field radioactivity measurements indicate uranium is concentrated continuously along the sinuous color line for at least 5 mi (Vickers, 1955, 1957). Bell et al. (1956) recognize three types of host sandstones in the southern Black Hills, each dominant in a particular part of the area (Table 10.11). Most of the deposits are in sandstones

TABLE 10.11. *Types of sandstones in the Inyan Kara group host to uranium deposits, southern Black Hills, South Dakota (after Bell et al., 1956)*

Sandstone type	Shape and dimensions	Ore deposits and minerals
Markedly heterogeneous, fine- to coarse-grained, noncarbonaceous, cross-bedded; locally contains sedimentary breccia in scours	Lenses 100 ft thick, 1 mi wide, 3 mi long. May truncate older beds	Irregular to tabular bodies locally discordant. Predominantly carnotite and tyuyamunite; corvusite and hewettite uncommon. Largest single deposit occurs in this sandstone type
Fine- to medium-grained, homogeneous in texture and structure, carbonaceous	Units 250 ft thick, several miles wide, length unknown. Composed of series of sandstone lenses overlapping and truncating underlying lenses	Small but numerous deposits. Associated carbonaceous material. Some localized near fractures. Carnotite and tyuyamunite are chief ore minerals; minor vanadium. Black ores occur locally
Well-sorted, fine-grained with alternating laminated carbonaceous siltstones. Carbonaceous debris and pyrite abundant	Sandstone-siltstone sequences 25 ft thick	Deposits of 5,000 tons or less, in sandstone beds usually less than 5 ft thick. All contain black ore with high percentage rauvite and corvusite; least oxidized

of the Fall River and Lakota formations; the Fuson is mineralized scantily and in only a few places.

Carnotite and tyuyamunite are the most important ore minerals (yellow ores) but in some deposits corvusite and rauvite are important or even predominate (black ores). Minor are pitchblende, coffinite, becquerelite, autunite, hummerite, doloresite, hewettite, and metahewettite. In the yellow ores the V:U ratio is less than 1:5, whereas in the black ores it exceeds 1:5. Native selenium is present in some deposits in the Edgemont area.

Calcite-poor sandstones that occur marginal to larger, carbonate-cemented sandstones are favorable loci for uranium concentration, either in detail, as in sandstone adjacent to carbonate nodules or carbonate-filled fractures, or on a larger scale. A close relationship of uranium to calcite cements also is suggested by the pattern of thermoluminescence in the carbonate cements, which show banded or concretionary forms near ore deposits. On the basis of these relations, drilling in calcite-poor sandstone between areas of calcite-rich sandstone resulted in the discovery of an extensive ore deposit containing a significant amount of mineralized rock with as much as 3% eU_3O_8 (Gott, 1956).

Carbonaceous material with abundant pyrite is irregularly distributed but locally abundant, especially in association with black ores. Thin, lensoid coal beds occur in some places. Limonitic and carbonate concretions are also abundant locally.

The deposits also differ from some of those of the Colorado Plateau in the essential absence of Cu; uraniferous asphaltite likewise is unknown.

Ore produced from the Fall River and Lakota formations in 1952 contained about 0.2% U_3O_8 and 0.6% V_2O_5, with that from the Fall River containing higher percentages of vanadium (Bell and Bales, 1955).

COLORADO

MIDDLE PARK, GRAND COUNTY

Uranium mineralization occurs in the Troublesome formation (Oligocene-Miocene) in Middle Park, Colorado, a Laramide structural basin between the Front and Park Ranges. The formation, which consists of conglomerates, sandstones, and clays, contains disseminated carnotite, autunite, schroeckingerite, green and brown vanadium minerals, marcasite, and jarosite. The deposits form lensoid masses in the lower 160 ft, chiefly within a 40-sq mi area north of Troublesome. Carbonaceous plant debris is abundant and radioactive; some uranium minerals coat vertical fractures. The lenses are 10 to 20 ft long and up to 4 ft thick (Schlottmann and Smith, 1954). The upper 800 ft of the formation consists of beds of volcanic ash, as much as 30 ft thick, intercalated clays, and fluvial sands.

GARO, PARK COUNTY

Uranium-vanadium-copper mineralization occurs at the Shirley May deposit in South Park, near Garo, Park County, Colorado, in three sandstone beds of the Maroon formation of Permian age. The deposits, which are on the northeast flank of the Garo anticline, are related in part to several faults trending north to northeast. One type of ore, consisting of tyuyamunite in sandstone, which is found only along faults, is rich in calcium and contains 0.001 to 0.5% U. The principal type, obtained from all three sandstone beds, contains tyuyamunite, carnotite, volborthite, calciovolborthite, vanadium oxide minerals, chalcocite, covellite, azurite, and malachite which occur disseminated, as cement, and as fracture coatings together with calcite, manganite, and hematite. In this type the outer sandstone zone is calcite-rich, well-cemented, and rich in uranyl vanadates, whereas the core is friable, calcite-poor, and rich in hematite, manganite, and green to dark brown vanadium minerals. The grade ranges from 0.002 to 0.3% U with as much as 4.34% V_2O_5 and 1.34% Cu (Wilmarth, 1953B).

Most of the 272 tons of ore produced came from the No. 1 bed, 50 to 150 ft above the others. The ore averages 0.16% U and 0.72% V_2O_5. The mineralization has been controlled by faults and permeability of adjacent sandstone.

OTHER OCCURRENCES

Mineralization similar to that of the Poison Basin, Wyoming, has been found in the Browns Park formation near Maybell in Moffat County (Grutt, 1956, 1957), where deposits occur at several horizons near faults.

The Mike Doyle prospect, 10 mi south of Colorado Springs in El Paso County, exposes carnotite along fractures and replacing fossil wood in Morrison strata. Associated are limonite and secondary quartz (Beroni and King, 1952).

Along Tallahassee Creek in Fremont County autunite is disseminated in Tertiary conglomerates and sandstones (Heinrich and Bever, 1957). Uranium mineralization also occurs in Tertiary sandstones near Gardner in Huerfano County (Simon, 1956), and in Florissant Lake beds (Miocene) in Teller County.

BASIN AND RANGE PROVINCE

GENERAL

In the Basin and Range province of Nevada and parts of Utah, Arizona, and California, subparallel, north-trending mountain ranges are separated by broad troughs (graben) with interior drainage, filled by thick accumulations of Tertiary fanglomerates, siltstones, water-deposited pyroclastics, and continental evaporites, and developed in post-Laramide time.

Uranium mineralization is widely distributed in the terrestrial clastics of the troughs, usually as bedded deposits. High-grade ore is most common along weak to strong shear zones, faults, and small fractures (Davis and Hetland, 1956; Finch, 1956). Host rocks include waterlain tuffs, ash beds, and sandstones. Deposits are generally small, ranging from a few tons to a few hundred tons. The radioactive minerals include carnotite and uranyl phosphates (although vanadium is not abundant), and uraniferous apatite and opal.

TONOPAH, NEVADA

Uranium occurs 3 mi west of Tonopah in lake-bed tuffs of the Siebert series (late Miocene or early Pliocene). Uraniferous opal and collophane occur as lenses, some coated by yellow uranyl minerals. No vanadium is reported. The mineralization extends over an area of 1×8 mi and to a depth of 40 ft along a north-south trend which may represent concentration along a limonitized zone (Davis and Hetland, 1956).

Other occurrences in Nevada are summarized in Table 10.12. Some of these deposits, at least their oxidized parts, very likely have resulted from ground-water redistribution (pages 550–551).

TABLE 10.12. *Radioactive occurrences in Tertiary formations in Nevada*

Locality	Host rock	Mineralization	Reference
Dacie Creek, NW Lander County	Rhyolite and underlying water-lain tuff	Thin opal layers in tuff. No uranium minerals identified. Both tuff and rhyolite are radioactive. Highest anomalies along minor fractures in tuff	Davis and Hetland, 1956
Garfield Hills, 10 mi SE of Hawthorne, Mineral County	Fine-grained tuffaceous sandstone in Tertiary Esmeralda fm. Northwest of deposit rhyolite plug is faulted against uraniferous sandstone	Carnotite along closely spaced fractures in sandstone. Recent alluvium has pebbles and boulders coated by yellow uranyl minerals	Davis and Hetland, 1956
Panaca, Lincoln County	Water-lain tuff in Pliocene(?) Panaca fm. with interbedded silt and sand	Carnotite(?), minor carbonaceous material, lenses of opal in higher beds. Mineralized tuff 6 in.–2 ft thick, exposed for 200 ft	Davis and Hetland, 1956
Atlanta district, 50 mi north of Pioche, Lincoln County	Coarse silicified rhyolite agglomerate	Uraninite, uranophane, autunite, concentrated near steep fractures that trend N 35° W	Sharp, 1956
Antelope Range, Washoe County, Nev., and Lassen County, Calif.	Tertiary rhyolite and rhyolite tuff overlying Jurassic granite	Gummite and uranophane along narrow, silicified, northeast fractures in volcanics	Sharp, 1956
South end Silver Peak Mts., 4 mi S Coaldale, Esmeralda County	Tertiary welded rhyolitic tuff, closely jointed	Autunite and phosphuranylite coat fractures and joints; also gray to black radioactive siliceous veinlets	Duncan, 1953
	Breccia pipe 10 ft across of silica-cemented welded tuff fragments	Uraniferous silica	Duncan, 1953

CALIFORNIA

Mojave Desert Area

Deposits of secondary uranium minerals occur at several localities in the Mojave Desert, Kern and San Bernardino Counties. At the Rosamond prospect, which is 10 mi south of Mojave, Kern County, uranium occurs as autunite and gummite in tuffaceous rocks of the Miocene Rosamond formation. The autunite mainly coats joints and fractures and to a lesser extent is disseminated in dacitic dikes, flows, and tuffs as far as 10 ft from faults. Gummite occurs on fault surface along with autunite, limonite, and chlorite(?) (Walker, 1953; Walker et al., 1956). Uranium mineralization is irregularly distributed over about 15 acres, with assays averaging slightly less than 0.08% U.

Numerous other deposits of a similar nature occur in the area, chiefly in Kern County. Some examples include (1) the Verdi deposit where meta-autunite coats fractures in granitic rock separated from tuff and sandstone of the Rosamond formation by a fault; (2) the Jumpin claim, 5.5 mi west-northwest of Rosamond, where autunite, gummite, and limonite line fractures in rhyolite-intruding Cretaceous(?) quartz monzonite; (3) the Stillwell deposit, 5 mi northwest of Rosamond, containing autunite in Rosamond tuffs as joint and fracture coatings and as disseminations; and (4) the Chilson deposit with torbernite and autunite as joint coatings and vug crystals in intrusive dacite and quartz latite, 6 mi north of Randsburg in the Summit Range.

In adjacent San Bernardino County, examples include (1) Kramer Hills deposits containing carnotite in marly clay of the Miocene Barstow formation; (2) autunite and carnotite(?) in cherty and carbonate beds of the Barstow formation coating bedding and fracture surfaces at the Harvard Hills, 9 mi east of Yermo.

Olancha, Inyo County

Autunite and uraniferous opal occur in bentonitic clay and fine-grained sandstone of the Coso formation (late Pliocene or early Pleistocene) at Olancha near the southern end of Owens Valley. Three persistent radioactive layers, lying about 30 to 40 ft below the lowest of three caliche zones, range from 8 to 24 in. thick and crop out for 2,000 ft. All three are enclosed by or adjacent to 1-in. to 4-ft limonitic bands. Some strongly radioactive bands display no discrete uranium minerals. A fault zone is exposed east of the deposit (Davis and Hetland, 1956).

Secondary uranium minerals have been discovered in the Coyote Creek area, 7 mi west of Ojai, Ventura County, along or near the contact between the Coldwater formation of Eocene age and the Sespe formation of Oligocene age. Numerous other examples of similar deposits occur elsewhere in Inyo and Mono Counties (Walker et al., 1956).

ARIZONA

In southwestern Yavapai County, carnotite accompanied by silicification occurs in carbonaceous layers of a mudstone-limestone unit of Tertiary lake sediments (Reyner and Ashwill, 1956; Davis and Sharp, 1957). Mineralization, exposed at intervals for 3 mi, is higher grade on the flat south limbs of minor synclinal structures, and is confined to a horst bounded by strong normal faults.

TEXAS

Uranium minerals have been found widespread in various parts of Texas in sedimentary and volcanic rocks ranging in age from Permian to Pleistocene.

In the King Mountain area, 2 mi north of McCamey, southwestern Upton County, carnotite, tyuyamunite, and metatyuyamunite form coatings on joint planes and tabular cavities 1 to 2 in. across also partly filled with limonite. The host rock is the Edwards marine limestone of early Cretaceous age, and uranyl vanadates have been observed from 2 to 7½ ft beneath the ground surface (Eargle, 1956). One channel sample contained 0.002% U.

In the Hueco Mountains area of El Paso and Hudspeth Counties, uranium mineralization occurs in Hueco Gap, on Sabina Mountain, and at several other localities in calichified colluvium as carnotite and minor tyuyamunite coating boulders and fractures. To a lesser extent, the vanadates also coat joint surfaces in the Hueco limestone (Permian). In the colluvium, coatings have been found as deep as 20 ft below the surface; in the Hueco, they extend to 12 to 15 ft below the surface. Selected samples from the former contain up to 0.023% U. In both areas the chemical uranium exceeds equivalent uranium indicating the relatively recent age of the mineralization.

In Brewster County, uranium deposits are in the Tertiary Pruett tuff in basal conglomerate filling small irregularities in an unconformity. In the same area, Tertiary rhyolites contain uranophane in amygdules and as coatings (Thurlow, 1956B), and uranophane clusters have been found in Tertiary welded tuff in Quinn Canyon in the northwest corner of Presidio County.

Uranium mineralization is known in carbonaceous siltstone of the Triassic Dockum group in San Saba and Lubbock Counties (Finch, 1956).

In southeastern Texas relatively large uranium deposits with minor vanadium and copper occur in the flat-lying Jackson formation (late Eocene) and probably in the overlying early Oligocene beds. The strata consist of marine and terrestrial tuffs, sands, and sandy clays. Uranyl phosphates and silicates occur as disseminations and fracture and bedding plane coatings. Associated are concentrations of As and Mo (Finch, 1956). Strongest mineralization occurs with limonite and bentonite and in sands of irregular bedding. Carbonaceous material is rare. The deposits range in size from a few to several hundred feet across, the latter with many thousands of tons of ore. For example the Harper No. 1 deposit in the Harmony Hills area, Karnes County, is reported to contain about 50,000 tons of ore averaging 0.13% U_3O_8. At Tordilla Hill, Karnes County, mineralization consists of carnotite, tyuyamunite, autunite, and uranophane (Eargle and Snider, 1957).

Pitchblende has been reported in deposits in Atasco County. Carnotite occurs in poorly sorted Miocene sandstones of the Catahoula formation, near Sample in Gonzales County, and of the Gueydan formation near Freer, Duval County.

TABLE 10.13. *Other examples of stratiform deposits in sedimentary rocks, western United States*

Location	Host rock	Mineralization	Reference
Tillman, Cotton, and Jefferson Counties, Okla.	Garber sandstone (Permian). On south, gently dipping flank of Wichita uplift	Copper and uranium minerals in fine-grained sandstone and siltstone or uranium minerals in asphaltic, arkosic sandstone. Torbernite, autunite, uranophane, malachite, azurite, Fe and Mn oxides; wood replacements common	Finch, 1956
Datil area, eastern Catron and western Socorro Counties, N.Mex.	In sandstone of upper part of Mesaverde fm. (Upper Cretaceous). Traces of U in Datil fm. (Late Tertiary) in welded tuffs	Locally for 15 mi, with zones up to 3 in., containing as much as 0.56% U. Carnotite, organic material, and limonite; also black U mineral in calcite seams. Mineralized zones lie above shale beds	Griggs, 1954
Quay County, N.Mex.	Sandstone and limey sandstone, late Jurassic age	Carnotite or tyuyamunite	Finch, 1956
Santa Cruz County, Ariz.	Arkosic sandstone beds near base of Cretaceous	Disseminated kasolite	Finch, 1956
Near Lakeview, Lake County, Ore.	Tertiary tuffaceous lake sediments	Ba-uranyl arsenate	
Northwest prop., Spokane Indian Reservation, Wash.	Tertiary arkosic sandstone and conglomerate; "carbonaceous" lake deposits	Autunite and uranophane, interstitial to grains and grain coatings	Davis and Sharp, 1957

TABLE 10.14. *Examples of stratiform deposits in sedimentary rocks in the eastern United States*

Location	Geology	Host rock	Mineralogy	Geochemical association	Reference
Bucks County, Pa.; Hunterdon County, N.J.	Lenticular masses of disseminated minerals in limonitic sandstone, 15–25 ft long, 6 in.–3 ft thick	Stockton formation, Newark group (Triassic)	Torbernite, uranophane, limonite, clay, pyrite, gypsum	U-Cu-P	Finch, 1956
Jim Thorpe (Mauch Chunk), Carbon County, Pa.	Disseminations and fracture coatings in lenticular masses a few feet to several hundred feet long. On flanks of Panther Valley syncline	Coarse graywacke conglomerate of Pottsville fm. (Pennsylvanian) (Fig. 10.47) and graywacke of Catskill fm. (Devonian)	Pottsville—carnotite, tyuyamunite, uranophane. Catskill—autunite, kasolite, uranophane	U-V U-Pb, some carbon trash	Wherry, 1912, 1915; Klemic and Baker, 1954; Montgomery, 1954; Dyson, 1955; Walthier, 1955; Finch, 1956
Near Pulaski, southwest Virginia	Widespread anomalous radioactivity in a limonitic horizon in sandstone, below a coal bed and within a few hundred feet of a fault	Price sandstone (Mississippian)	(?)	(?)	Stow, 1955

Fig. 10.47. Coarse graywacke conglomerate of the Pottsville formation with carnotite as fracture coatings, Mauch Chunk, Pa.

ARGENTINA

Uranium mineralization similar to that of the Colorado Plateau has been found in two areas in Argentina. In Catamarca Province, about 20 km southwest of Tinogasta, U-V-Cu ores occur along bedding planes of moderately dipping, yellowish clayey sediments of Triassic or lower Tertiary age (Angelelli, 1956). Carnotite and other uranyl and secondary copper minerals form thin films and local, irregularly distributed concentrations. Veinlets of chalcopyrite and chalcocite also have been found.

In the Andes foothills in Mendoza Province, radioactive ores have been found at several deposits over a large area about 40 km southwest of Malargüe (Angelelli, 1956; Linares, 1956). The host rocks are continental conglomerates and arkosic sandstones of Upper Cretaceous age (Diamantian) which near the surface contain carnotite, tyuyamunite, uranophane, and lesser autunite. Sulfides at depth include pyrite, pyrrhotite, sphalerite, galena, chalcopyrite, bornite, and chalcocite, which have been altered to copper carbonates and sulfates and limonite. Associated with the sulfides are uraninite and thucolite.

The ore bodies are lenticular disseminations chiefly in gently dipping, dark asphaltic sandstones and conglomerates lying between two clayey beds. Permeable zones in the clastic rocks are especially mineralized, but ores also fill

Fig. 10.48. The limestone hill of Tyuya Muyun and the gorge of the Aravan River, Russian Turkestan. Uranium mine on low hill to the right (after Chirvinsky, 1925; *Mineral. Mag.*).

fractures and coat fault surfaces. Significant deposits include the Cerro Huemul (Eva Perón), Agua Botada, Cerro Mirano, and Pampa Amarilla.

The asphaltic material may have been derived from bituminous shales of Lower Cretaceous age, migrating into Upper Cretaceous rocks, there to serve as a precipitant for uranium from hydrothermal solutions of Paleocene age (Chiletitic magmatic period) (Linares, 1956).

FERGHANA BASIN, U.S.S.R.

Uranium deposits were first studied in the Ferghana Basin (40 to 41° N., 70 to 73° E.) on the north side of the Alai Mountains, in Uzbekistan, in 1900 to 1903, where scattered deposits have been found over about 1,000 sq mi in the semiarid mountainous region (Fig. 10.48). Mining began at Tyuya Muyun [1] in 1908, and by 1913 about 700 tons of ore averaging 0.97% U_3O_8 had yielded 2.39 g of radium. Geological studies have been made by Fersman, Kirikov, Pavlenko, and Butoo and Zaitsev (see Shimkin, 1949, and Chirvinsky, 1925, for references to the original articles in Russia).

The Tyuya Muyun deposits are in Carboniferous limestone, which is coarse-grained and reddish or brownish violet in color, locally brecciated and veined by calcite. The limestones, which are bordered by carbonaceous Silurian shales, strike N. 70° E., are nearly vertical, and have been intruded by dikes of keratophyre and sills of diabase. Volcanic breccias and tuffs are interlayered. Extensive karst topography, solution channels, and caves were developed in Tertiary times. Vugs partly filled with radial masses, stalagmites, and crusts of calcite also are present.

---

[1] Tyuya Muyun is the name given a hill in the northern part of the Alai Range, 37 mi south of Andijan. It is bisected by the north-flowing Aravan River which has cut a gorge 350 to 400 m deep, thus presenting in profile two knobs or "camel's humps." Tyuyamunite takes its name from this locality, but fortunately in naming the mineral one syllable was omitted, or it would have been tyuyamuyunite.

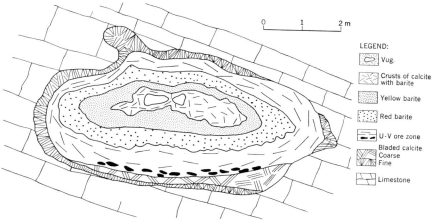

LEGEND:

- Vug.
- Crusts of calcite with barite
- Yellow barite
- Red barite
- U-V ore zone
- Bladed calcite Coarse Fine
- Limestone

FIG. 10.49. Schematic cross section of an ore pipe, Tyuya Muyun, Russian Turkestan (adapted from Fersman).

By 1933, 5 uraniferous veins and 30 barren, barite veins were reported. The radioactive veins occur near the center of the field along a line paralleling their strike, N. 70° E. Barite veins extend as much as 1,500 m from this center. Ore occurs both in fissure veins and in karst caverns. Around the veins the limestone has been dolomitized, and the sinkholes contain pipes of stalagmitic onyx which also coats their walls. The onyx is banded with layers of calcite, barite, and uranium minerals (Fig. 10.49).

The ore bodies vary in thickness and in length from a few centimeters to 1.5 m. Ore is fine-grained and massive, banded, brecciated, or vuggy. It consists of tyuyamunite along fractures as 1 to 3 mm layers and 5 mm lenses and as disseminations with copper vanadates [1] (calciovolborthite, var. tangeite; turanite; and volborthite, var. uzbekite), calcite, malachite, chrysocolla, barite, goethite, quartz, and the dubious species ferghanite (page 106). Older red barite is overgrown by reddish quartz; younger barite is yellow. Some of the barite is radian, $(Ba,Ra)SO_4$, but uranium-free. Uranium-free radian calcite also is reported. Some vugs contain radial crusts of calciovolborthite and less-common turanite with very complex calcite crystals, goethite needles, and barite crystals of flat habit.

Some of the ore contained

Tyuyamunite	2.3%
Calciovolborthite and turanite	9.0
Limonite and goethite	6.0
Barite	2.7
Calcite	80.0

[1] Copper reportedly was mined in primitive fashion from these deposits, possibly as early as the Bronze Age (Savage, 1954).

TABLE 10.15. *Composition of ores from the Tyuya Muyun deposit, U.S.S.R.*

	Range, per cent	Average, per cent
U_3O_8	0.6–4	1.6
V_2O_5	1.5–7	3.8
CuO	1.5–7	3.0
$(Al,Fe)_2O_3$	1.5–5	3.6
$BaSO_4$	0–20	2.7
SiO_2	0.5–5	2.5
CaO	37–49	46.6
CO_2	28–39	35.7
H_2O	0.3–1	0.5

Ores ranged from 0.6 to 4.0% U_3O_8 (Table 10.15), higher values occurring in lower parts of deposits. However, some karst ores locally were exceptionally rich with up to 26 to 50% U_3O_8. In 1925 to 1926, 534 metric tons of hand-sorted ores was produced from the Tyuya Muyun deposit. In 1922, proved reserves were only 5,000 tons, owing to the irregular nature of the deposits. Production has continued and exploration has discovered additional deposits.

Near the Tyuya Muyun mine and extending with some breaks for 200 km along the Alai and Turkestan Ranges is a belt of quartzose schists containing the doubtful species kolovratite, a slightly radioactive nickel vanadate.

It has generally been stated that the uranium (and other elements) in these deposits has been leached by a combination of weak hydrothermal and supergene solutions from a thick series of black shales (Silurian) that crop out in the Alai Range and contain as much as 0.05% U_3O_8. Fersman distinguishes a complete series between a primary residuum of the karst process to material completely transformed by ore solutions (ascending) (Jost, 1932). At Potekhina and the Julia mine it has been suggested that the source was an overlying gray Devonian shale or a red Devonian sandstone that contains sparsely disseminated carnotite (Bain, 1950). Shimkin (1949), however, believes the history of the ores to be more complex:

1. Deposition by low-temperature hydrothermal solutions, related to the Variscan revolution (upper Paleozoic)
2. Faulting during Alpine(?) orogeny
3. Post-Eocene karst formation, with partial destruction of veins, redistribution, and reconcentration of the ores

Chirvinsky (1925) also states that the deposit was formed by postvolcanic hydrothermal solutions. The uranyl minerals are secondary, presumably still being formed at the present time, for tyuyamunite was found on human bones that remained in the mine for three years during the revolution. It seems unlikely that the barite veins with their dolomitized wall rocks are anything but hydrothermal. No compelling evidence that the source of uranium must have been the black shales is cited. Thus the karst deposits may represent supergene reworking of material derived from the oxidized baritic veins.

The Yuigur Sai (Uigar-Sai) deposit in the Papsk region of northern Ferghana resembles closely deposits of the Colorado Plateau. Carnotite forms disseminations, lenses, cavity linings, and coatings along minor faults in a continental Miocene sandstone. Concentrations occur near fossil logs and carbon trash associated with mudstone lenses. Ore lenses may have cores of higher-grade material.

About 6 km from Tyuya Muyun at Almalyk, a vein in Carboniferous limestone contains Cu, Ni, Fe, Mn, and radioactive minerals in a barite-calcite gangue. Another vein contains sphalerite, galena, cerrusite, wulfenite, crocoite, turanite, and volborthite in barite gangue (Kohl, 1954).

Carnotite deposits were discovered in 1934 on the right shore of the Maili-Su (41°18′ N., 72°27′ E.), 50 km north of Andishan. They occur as impregnations in Tertiary sandstone. The bed has a thickness of 0.8 m and occurrences have been found along a distance of 150 km.

The Kara-Tau deposit, 90 km northeast of Chiili, in the western part of the Ferghana district, consists of carnotite-roscoelite disseminations in Cambrian shale with interbedded dolomite. The ore bed is 8 to 14 m thick, underlying 40 to 50 sq km. At nearby Suleytan Say a uraniferous vanadinite occurs (Bain, 1950). The Kara-Tau deposits are regarded as resulting from the supergene enrichment of uranium in bituminous shales. A peculiar uranium deposit at the southwest end of the Kara-Tau Mountains (44°30′ N., 67°30′ E.) reportedly represents thin, siliceous sedimentary layers containing V-U minerals that were later metamorphosed (Kohl, 1954).

At Chodshent, 100 km northeast of Ferghana, ores said to average 3% U_3O_8 were reportedly found in 1934. Small amounts of a uraniferous vanadium (0.36% U_3O_8) mineral in allophane concretions were found in 1925 on the right bank of the Erba River, east of the Ferghana region, south of Potekhina in the Minussinsk district.

ORIGIN

GENERAL

To state that the origin of the Colorado Plateau ores has been and continues to be strongly disputed is perhaps the only point touching on their genesis to which all parties would subscribe. The controversy is comparable to that which has marked consideration of the origin of the Rand gold-uranium ores and that which is rapidly developing over the origin of the Blind River, Ontario, pitchblende-brannerite deposits. The three groups of deposits have many general points of similarity: occurrence in clastic rocks, generally tabular and conformable ore bodies, conspicuous relation to sedimentary structural and lithological features, poorly defined relations to tectonic structural features and fractures, uncommon relationships to intrusive igneous rocks, inconspicuous wall-rock alteration, and largely nondiagnostic mineralogical assemblages and textural features.

PROBLEMS

Extrinsic Elements

The chief elements that have been introduced along with uranium are vanadium, iron, magnesium, sulfur, and lesser copper, lead, zinc, silver, nickel, cobalt, molybdenum, arsenic, and selenium. Of minor or local importance are barium, fluorine, strontium, chromium, beryllium, boron, yttrium, and ytterbium (Finch, 1954; Miesch, 1955; McKelvey et al., 1955; Shoemaker et al., 1956). Major elements vary regionally, and both major and minor elements show areal variations within sections of the Plateau (Miesch, 1955). Selenium appears to vary stratigraphically (Coleman, 1956). In some deposits both major and minor elements increase proportionately with uranium (E. S. Davidson, 1956). Studies of a deposit in the Jo Dandy group, Montrose County, Colorado, reveal a sharp megascopic ore boundary, an abrupt increase in all extrinsic elements, and the absence of negative anomalies in trace elements, which might suggest leaching during mineralization (Garrels and Pommer, 1955).

The presence of abundant potassium in some of the ores (incorporated in carnotite upon oxidation) has been correlated by McKay (1955) with the presence of potassium chloride and high-potash shales in piercement salt bodies.

Shoemaker (1955) has found anomalous concentrations of copper and vanadium in the most acid differentiates of the Henry, La Sal, and La Plata Mountains. According to Shoemaker (McKelvey et al., 1955), around the east side of the La Sal Mountains a partly overlapping zonal arrangement of Cu-Au, Cu-Ag, and U-V deposits can be defined. Chester reports that some intrusive dike rocks of the Monument Valley district are abnormally rich in uranium (Mitcham and Evensen, 1955).

The geochemical similarity of the various extrinsic element suites to those characteristic of vein pitchblende deposits is marked. In the past there has been considerable emphasis on the supposed anomalous association of vanadium with uranium, vanadium not being associated abundantly with acid differentiates or their hydrothermal fractions (Fischer, 1955). However, as examples of various such vanadium occurrences may be cited (1) the discovery of the iron vanadate, nolanite, in several uranium deposits in the Goldfields district, Canada (Robinson, 1955A); (2) the presence of roscoelite and vanadiferous muscovites in various hydrothermal ore deposits of Au, Te, and F, of Fe, of Mn, and of B and Ti (summarized in Heinrich et al., 1953); (3) vanadium in aegirine and other alkali pyroxenes; (4) vanadinite and other vanadates in the oxidized parts of hydrothermal lead deposits; (5) a maximum content of 500 g/ton V in uraninites of the U-Ni-Co type of vein (Leutwein, 1941); (6) vanadium in trace amounts in cassiterite of tin deposits; (7) vanadium in uraniferous fluorite deposits (pages 345–346) (Staatz and Osterwald, 1956); and (8) vanadium in uranium veins at Placerville (page 406) (Hess, 1917).

Selenium, too, occurs in abundance as cobalt and nickel selenides in the

Shinkolobwe deposit (pages 292–295) and in local concentrations in some deposits of the Goldfields district, Canada (pages 307–308).

The Todilto fluorite-rich deposits (pages 410–411), although mineralogically unusual, are no more atypical of Plateau deposits than some other aberrant types, e.g., the Silver Reef silver deposits. The Todilto deposits are related closely through distribution, structural control, and mineralogy (Gabelman, 1955) to the Zuni Mountains fluorite veins, some of which also are radioactive (page 410). Fluorite-quartz veinlets containing uranophane and uraninite also transect a Tertiary monzonite porphyry plug in the Henry Mountains, 30 mi east of Hanksville, Utah.

On the other hand, the geochemical assemblage also shows some marked similarities to that characteristically accumulated in sediments of the "redbed" environment. As outlined by Krauskopf (1955) this is represented by a region of semiarid plains furnished with fine to coarse clastic debris from adjacent humid highlands. Concentration is effected by some evaporation. The assemblage includes Cu, Ag, less Pb and Zn, and V, Cr, Mo, and Se. The suite also is closely similar to the assemblage of accessory elements contained in petroleum. Shoemaker et al. (1956) suggest six possible sources for the extrinsic components: (1) sandstones of the uranium deposits themselves; (2) the marine Mancos shale (Cretaceous); (3) bentonitic shales of Jurassic and Triassic age; (4) petroliferous Pennsylvanian rocks; (5) Precambrian crystalline basement rocks; and (6) Cretaceous or Tertiary magmatic reservoirs. They consider the Precambrian rocks as the most likely major source.

Stieff and Stern (1955) have pointed out that isotopic composition of the lead minerals of Plateau ores shows marked similarities to that from lead minerals in Tertiary vein deposits of adjacent areas, suggesting that the two groups of deposits have shared, at least in part, a common geological history and environment.

Nature of Solutions

McKelvey et al. (1955) have summarized evidence for the nature of the transporting medium and conclude that it had a density about that of pore water and (p. 505) "would either be a liquid or a dense gas with the general properties of a liquid." Garrels and Richter (1955) have discussed the possibility of deposition from a separate CO_2 gas phase. The work of Pommer (1957) has shown that at low temperature in the presence of a small amount of carbonate in aqueous solution, a field of high joint solubility of uranium and vanadium is defined by a relatively high pH (>8) and a moderately low Eh (-300 to 400 mv). This is in general accord with conditions that appear to have characterized host rocks, through which the uraniferous solutions probably moved for long distances in equilibrium before precipitation took place.

In carbonate solutions at low temperatures, uranium is held as the stable uranium-tricarbonate ion, $[UO_2(CO_3)_3]^4$ (Blake et al., 1955). Gruner (1956C) has found that the concentration of uranium in this form is markedly reduced by the copresence of vanadium, but that the two elements may be jointly transported in calcium bicarbonate solutions at pH from about 6 to over 7.

Solutions capable of maintaining both uranium as U^{4+} and vanadium as V^{3+}

would have to be of considerable acidity. Yet as McKelvey et al. (1955) have pointed out, geologic considerations make it unlikely that vanadium was transported in the higher oxidized states, for its reduction from V^{5+} to V^{3+} would require an enormous amount of reducing material, and large vanadiferous ore bodies occur in sandstones essentially free of carbonaceous matter. They believe that the strongly reduced solutions may have contained in equilibrium the ions V^{3+}, Fe^{2+}, and $(UO_2)^{2+}$ leading to the direct precipitation of montroesite and pyrite but requiring a reduction step for the precipitation of uraninite and coffinite.

Movement of Solutions

For most of the deposits, movement of the solutions, at least in their immediate vicinity, has been lateral. Large-scale mineralization along major fracture systems is not important except for deposits in the Todilto limestone and in a few scattered localities. However, the absence of such mineralization does not prove that these and other tectonic features have not served as vertical conduits, no more than the absence of mineralization or alteration in permeable parts of strata proves that these channelways did not serve as lateral conduits. Garrels (1957, p. 3) has pointed out that for most deposits in the several major regions "Feeding fissures are no more in evidence for reduced ores than for oxidized ones," and ". . . ore emplacement evidently took place prior to regional fracturing." Possibly a study of the distribution of thermoluminescent minerals or of variations in oxygen/isotope ratios in carbonate minerals in fractured rocks might lead to tracing the paths solutions followed prior to precipitation.

On a regional scale the distribution of ore deposits is related either directly or indirectly, in many cases, to tectonic features; and on a local scale the distribution is controlled primarily by sedimentary structural features, one of the most important of which is transmissivity. For the regional distribution Kelley (1955A) believes that the relationship is indirect and that the tectonic features have controlled directly the Tertiary paleohydrodynamics which have influenced both the behavior and nature of added hydrothermal solutions.

McKelvey et al. (1956) point out that fracture systems in impermeable limestone (Todilto) may be mineralized because of the inability of solutions to escape into their walls, some passing upward into permeable and otherwise favorable sandstones (e.g., Morrison) where they were free to migrate away from their conduits. Brecciated zones in sandstone deposits may be difficult to recognize if strongly mineralized. This appears to be the case at the Monument No. 2 mine where movements along bedding planes brecciated channel-filling sediments. According to Finnell (1957, p. 25), "Resistance of the thicker channel sediments to the bedding plane slippage set up stresses that formed a zone of enechelon strike-slip vertical faults . . . ," which may have served as conduits to lead solutions into brecciated sandstone. A clayey siltstone prevented further rise of the solutions.

In the Black Hills area the localization of deposits at edges of sandstone lenses or near intercalated mudstone possibly indicates that their parent solutions were moving laterally or attempting to move vertically and were impounded beneath relatively impermeable layers. At the Gould mine the ore deposit is in sandstone beneath an irregular contact with an overlying impermeable silt-boulder conglomerate that acted as a seal (Bright, 1955). Other structural features that have controlled deposition in the Black Hills deposits include structural flats or terraces on margins of anticlines or between anticlines and monoclines, anticlinal noses, and joints.

Precipitation

Garrels (1953, 1955A,B) has investigated the stability fields and thermodynamic relations of the major minerals in Plateau deposits, and his conclusions (Fig. 10.50) are consistent with the precipitation of a mineral assemblage of uraninite, montroesite, pyrite, galena, sphalerite, and copper sulfides in a reducing environment. Since the solutions apparently traveled considerable distances in sediments, the two must have been in equilibrium, and precipitation was effected where materials were available to cause reduction of the uranyl ion to relatively insoluble pitchblende.

A number of substances have been suggested as precipitants for pitchblende and its associated minerals in Plateau rocks. Carbonaceous fossil plant material is widespread, and many deposits contain this material partly or wholly replaced by uraninite and sulfides. In several districts, detailed studies have indicated a direct correlation between the presence of ore and carbon. Yet it is not universally present, even in some of the larger deposits. Asphaltite, which is abundant at Temple Mountain and in the large Ambrosia Lake deposits, also served as a reducing and thus precipitating agent. However, considerable difference of opinion remains on the time relation of the asphaltite to the uranium (pages 527–528).

Experiments by Gruner (1956B) and others have demonstrated that an excellent reductant for uranyl solutions is H_2S or the S^{2-} ion, which commonly is associated with decaying plant material. Grutt (1957) suggests the H_2S from natural gas has been the precipitating agent in several of the Wyoming districts. The host rocks also commonly contain premineralization or diagenetic pyrite, which has been suggested as a reductant (Thompson and Krauskopf, 1956).

Kaolinite also has been suggested as a possible precipitant. In some districts, kaolinite is appreciably more abundant in ore-bearing Shinarump or Moss Back sandstones than in their unmineralized phases (Cadigan, 1955). The host formations may also contain montmorillonite derived from volcanic debris (Waters and Granger, 1953). Both H-montmorillonite and H-kaolinite absorb UO_2^{2+} ions as a function of their exchange capacity (Goldsztaub and Wey, 1955). For montmorillonite the amount of uranyl ion fixed increases with the pH. The presence of uraniferous allophane has been noted in some Plateau deposits (Weeks, 1956), but it is probably secondary.

Phosphate as bone collophane also has precipitated uranium but has been of only very local significance (pages 547–550).

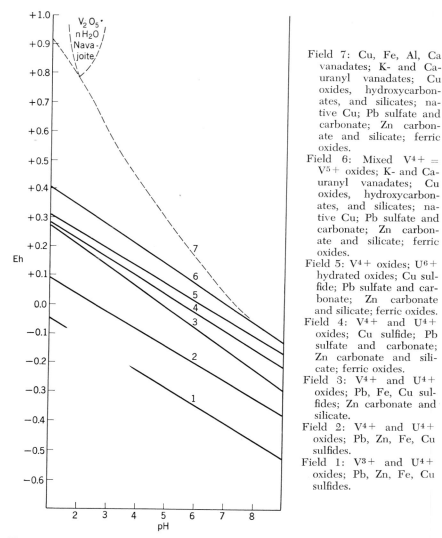

Field 7: Cu, Fe, Al, Ca vanadates; K- and Ca-uranyl vanadates; Cu oxides, hydroxycarbonates, and silicates; native Cu; Pb sulfate and carbonate; Zn carbonate and silicate; ferric oxides.

Field 6: Mixed $V^{4+} = V^{5+}$ oxides; K- and Ca-uranyl vanadates; Cu oxides, hydroxycarbonates, and silicates; native Cu; Pb sulfate and carbonate; Zn carbonate and silicate; ferric oxides.

Field 5: V^{4+} oxides; U^{6+} hydrated oxides; Cu sulfide; Pb sulfate and carbonate; Zn carbonate and silicate; ferric oxides.

Field 4: V^{4+} and U^{4+} oxides; Cu sulfide; Pb sulfate and carbonate; Zn carbonate and silicate; ferric oxides.

Field 3: V^{4+} and U^{4+} oxides; Pb, Fe, Cu sulfides; Zn carbonate and silicate.

Field 2: V^{4+} and U^{4+} oxides; Pb, Zn, Fe, Cu sulfides.

Field 1: V^{3+} and U^{4+} oxides; Pb, Zn, Fe, Cu sulfides.

FIG. 10.50. Summary of data on stability relations of some major minerals of Colorado Plateau uranium deposits (Garrels, 1955A; *Am. Mineralogist*).

446

Temperature of Formation

Mineralogical evidence for temperatures of deposition of the Plateau minerals has been summarized by Coleman (1957). Using the size of the unit cell edge of sphalerite as a function of the amount of iron it retains in a system with excess iron (i.e., in the presence of pyrite), Coleman finds that the temperatures of formation of sphalerites from the Happy Jack and Hidden Splendor deposits are 138°C, and calculates that with an overburden of 10,000 ft of sediment the temperature would have been about 110°C and the pressure near 800 atm. He concludes (p. 2) that ". . . it would seem that the temperature during the period of ore deposition was not vastly different from the 'normal' temperature of the enclosing host rock."

Uraninite has been experimentally precipitated from acid uranyl solutions by H_2S or pyrite even at room temperatures (Gruner, 1956B,C); coffinite has been synthesized at 250°C under alkaline conditions by Hoekstra and Fuchs (1956). The fact that Plateau pitchblende is essentially free of thorium or rare-earth elements and that its unit cell is relatively small ($a_0 = 5.40$ to 5.415 A) (Berman, 1955), probably because of the considerable U^{6+} present, is further support for a low-temperature origin. The U^6/U^4 ratio in fresh pitchblende increases, apparently with decreasing temperature of formation.

Interrelations of various copper sulfides have been used to suggest temperatures of formation (Coleman, 1957). The presence of grating exsolution texture of bornite in chalcopyrite has been noted by Miller (1955), but Gruner (1955B) points out that this texture has resulted experimentally at 90 to 100°C. Attempts to use the O^{16}/O^{18} ratios of pitchblendes as criteria for their depositional environment (Hoekstra and Katz, 1956) have not proved successful.

McKelvey et al. (1955) conclude that, if a Cretaceous cover was present, temperatures of formation were of the order of 100 to 120°C and pressures in the range of 200 atm (hydrostatic load) to 800 atm (lithostatic load).

THEORIES

Theories of origin that have been advanced or are currently in contention include:

I. Syngenetic
  A. Crystallization from materials introduced at the time of deposition of the sediments with or without some redistribution: multigeneration sedimentary deposits in the strict sense
II. Penecontemporaneous
  A. Crystallization from materials introduced shortly after deposition of the sediments by ground water: multigeneration supergene deposits
III. Epigenetic
  A. Deposited from ground water that derived its metal content from:
    1. Granitic rocks, pegmatites, and hydrothermal veins in surrounding mountainous areas
    2. Overlying and interbedded abnormally radioactive volcanic ash

       3. Material originally contained in the sedimentary strata or associated strata (arkoses) at their time of deposition

    B. Deposited from ground water that obtained its metals from granitic rocks and volcanic ash, with concentration through several stages of oxidation-solution-migration-accretion ("recycling")

    C. Derived from petroleum

    D. Deposited from hypogene (hydrothermal) solutions

        1. Which were derived and also obtained the metals through crystallization of igneous rocks

        2. Which obtained their metals from sedimentary rocks in which the metals were syngenetic

        3. Which were modified by mingling with ground water

    E. Deposited from ". . . solutions that were mildly hydrothermal but not hypogene" (Bain, 1957), with some or most(?) of the uranium secured by leaching from uraniferous red jasperoid pebbles

Early ideas on the origin of the ores were centered around the syngenetic or penecontemporaneous theories and are now primarily of historical interest. These ideas and theories were advocated mainly by Hess (1914, 1933A) and Coffin (1921) and modified by Fischer (1937) who stated (p. 943, his italics), ". . . these ores are . . . *syngenetic in the sense that the concentration of the metals occurred at the time of deposition of the beds in which they are found.* The present *minerals* in all cases are believed to be epigenetic." Subsequently, Fischer's ideas were stated as (1942, p. 389): "The primary ore minerals are thought to have been introduced into their present position not long after the sands were deposited. If this is true, the metals were probably transported and deposited by ground water. . . . This hypothesis probably requires at least three separate periods of ore deposition." These hypotheses have been ruled out by newly available information: (1) the occurrence of ores in some 30 formations of different ages (Pennsylvanian to Tertiary); (2) the ages of the ores by the Pb-U method are the same regardless of their host rocks and are Tertiary; (3) the occurrence of ores in both marine and nonmarine rocks and in the latter in types formed within nearly all depositional environments—eolian, fluvial, littoral, paludal, and lacustrine; and (4) ore bodies may be crosscutting in detail.

Lindgren (1933) recognized the epigenetic character of the deposits and summarized his ideas on their origin thus (p. 414): "it [uranium] has been concentrated with vanadium, by meteoric waters, which derived the metals from terrigenous sediments resulting from the disintegration of pre-Cambrian igneous rocks and pegmatites" (Theory III-3).

Butler (Butler et al., 1920) held somewhat similar views (p. 158):

The deposits are regarded as having been formed by circulating waters that collected the metals disseminated through the sedimentary rocks and deposited them on contact with carbonaceous material. The circulation in some places is believed to have been of artesian character and to have been controlled to a large extent by structural features. Most of the minerals at present exposed are the products of alteration of the original minerals by surface solutions. The formation of the deposits probably began in Tertiary time. . . .

Thus Butler et al. incorporate in their theory many of the genetic features of the ores emphasized in current ideas:

1. Their epigenetic nature
2. Carbonaceous material as one of the major precipitants
3. The indirect influence of tectonic structural features on their distribution
4. Their oxidation
5. Their Tertiary age

A sedimentary source for the metals carried by ground water continues to be advocated, as for example, by Boardman et al. (1956) in their discussion of the origin of the deposits in the Uravan district (p. 334), "The deposits are more easily explained, perhaps, if it is assumed that the ore elements were originally contained in some part of the sediments at the time of deposition and were subsequently concentrated by solution and precipitation in approximately the present positions of the ore bodies."

Similarly Sharp et al. (1956, p. 406) in discussing the origin of the Powder River Basin deposits, Wyoming, state that "Concentrations of uranium, vanadium, iron, and manganese minerals and calcite may best be explained by the redistribution and concentration of these original components of the sandstone lenses."

Koeberlin (1938) suggested that pyroclastic rocks might serve as sources from which disseminated metals could be leached by ground water to be redeposited in underlying sedimentary strata in more concentrated form. Denson et al. (1950) originated the theory that uranium in South Dakota lignites was deposited from ground water that dissolved it and other elements from overlying Tertiary pyroclastic formations that show abnormal radioactivity (pages 180–182). Love (1952) applied this theory to the origin of the uranium deposits of the Pumpkin Buttes area, Wyoming, and subsequently to deposits in Wyoming in the Miller Hill area (Love, 1953A), in the Gas Hills area (Love, 1954A), and in the Mayoworth area (Love, 1954B).

Proctor (1953), from his study of the Ag-Cu-U-V deposits of the Silver Reef district, Utah, concluded that these metals were primary constituents of Triassic volcanic tuffs, were dissolved, and were transported by streams to be deposited as syngenetic constituents of the Silver Reef sandstone member of the Chinle formation. Further concentration was effected by ground-water and secondary enrichment by meteoric waters. A bentonitic shale bed 300 ft above the sandstone contains cupriferous concretions and minor silver and gold.

Waters and Granger (1953) recognized argillized volcanic debris in the Salt Wash and Brushy Basin members of the Morrison as well as in the Chinle and Shinarump formations. They believe that the vanadiferous micaceous minerals of the Plateau uranium-vanadium deposits have been derived from montmorillonite, itself the result of devitrification. Alkalies, uranium, vanadium, silicon, and other elements were released to ground water whose circulation was reactivated through Tertiary deformation or through mingling with Tertiary metalliferous hypogene solutions. They believe that, although leaching of volcanic ash has been a contributing source, some (or most?) of the metal content is of hypogene derivation.

Arguments generally cited in support of the volcanic ash–leach hypothesis include (Vine and Prichard, 1954):

1. Absence of nearby intrusive rocks
2. The lack of alteration in wall rocks adjacent to ore deposits
3. The wide areal distribution of deposits
4. The presence or probable former presence of overlying Tertiary pyroclastics of anomalous radioactivity, or the presence of pyroclastic debris in the host beds themselves
5. The presence of uranium in relatively high concentrations in spring and stream waters in regions in which uranium deposits occur (Murphy, 1956; Walton, 1956)

Thompson and Krauskopf (1956) believe that uranium precipitation from ground water requires concentration of 10 ppb or more and that such concentrations may be attained by leaching of volcanic ash and probably some arkoses.

Grutt has presented evidence for the origin of the Wyoming deposits by deposition from ground water. His arguments include:

1. Many deposits lie above impervious siltstones or shales
2. Many are localized where ground water is abundant and flow is strong
3. Radioactive equilibrium has not been established in most of the unoxidized black ores
4. The unconformity between Tertiary strata and older rocks has served to determine the lower limits of mineralization
5. Faults and gentle folds have been structures assisting in localizing deposits by controlling ground-water flow

He believes that the uranium may have been derived either from Tertiary tuffaceous rocks or from Tertiary arkoses resulting from the erosion of Precambrian granite. Natural gas containing H_2S is suggested as the main agent of precipitation of the uranium. Sulfur isotope ratios in sulfides from the uranium deposits are regarded as suggesting that the sulfur was derived from H_2S formed by anaerobic bacteria (Jensen, 1957).

The theory of deposition from ground waters has been actively supported by Gruner (1951, 1954A, 1956C), who has developed the idea of concentration by "multiple migration-accretion." As sources of uranium he points to the many thousands of cubic miles of Precambrian granitic rocks calculated to have been weathered and eroded on and around the Plateau since Pennsylvanian time. From this mass of rock plus smaller amounts of volcanic tuff at least 400 million tons of uranium were made available. Under arid or semiarid conditions with continental sedimentation he postulates long-distance transport of uranium, as the stable uranyl tricarbonate ion, through neutral rocks of favorable permeability to reducing environments in which precipitation took place. According to Gruner (1956C, p. 496), "Concentration of large deposits could proceed by several stages of oxidation-solution-migration-accretion, a kind of 'recycling' action. . . . Orogenic movements with resulting new unconformities and new gradients would make more uranium available and, of course, add to the large number of depositional variations encountered in space and time." Unless one believes that uranium also was deposited syngenetically, all of such "recycling" must have occurred in Tertiary time. Gruner believes (1956C, p. 513) that the span of 40 m.y. of Tertiary time (based on the range in age of the deposits of 50 to 90 m.y.) ". . . is more than adequate to produce large individual ore concentrations by ordinary groundwater leaching." However, subsequently, in comparing the Wyoming deposits in Tertiary rocks with those of Plateau proper in older rocks, he notes the former's smaller size and inquires (p. 516), "Could the reasons be that because they are younger they have gone through fewer cycles of erosion and precipitation . . . ?"

Gott and Erikson (1952) have advanced the idea that the uranium of asphaltic-type deposits, such as those around Temple Mountain in the San Rafael Swell, was transported by fluid hydrocarbons from which it was concentrated as the result of natural fractionation brought about by differences in pressure, temperature, and porosity, with flushing out of lighter fractions after exposure of the reservoir by erosion. If the Temple Mountain uraniferous asphaltites have indeed originated in this manner, they would be unique among Plateau deposits for most do not have asphaltite, and in the Ambrosia Lake area it appears that the introduction of petroleum preceded uranium mineralization, which sequence also has been deduced by Kerr and Kelley (1956) for the Temple Mountain ores.

The theory of deposition from hydrothermal solutions has recently received considerable support on the basis of new detailed information on the geology of the deposits and through critical evaluation of such data by several geologists (e.g., Stieff et al., 1953; Cater, 1954; McKay, 1955; Rasor, 1956; McKelvey et al., 1955; McKelvey, 1956). Various modifications have been discussed, such as the intermingling of ground waters and juvenile waters (Kelley, 1955A) or the transfer of syngenetic metals from original sedimentary hosts by hydrothermal solutions (Wright, 1955B).

For deposits of the Colorado Plateau itself, arguments for a hydrothermal origin are strongest and, to many geologists, convincing. As Garrels (1957) has pointed out, the age determination data indicate that for many of these occurrences deposition took place beneath thousands of feet of sediments and that they have remained unaffected, even during tectonic activity, since early Tertiary time. The discoveries of widespread "Colorado Plateau-type" deposits in other areas, such as in Wyoming, the Basin and Range province, and even Texas, where relations to structural features are, in the main, not defined and to intrusive bodies unknown, materially weaken the idea that *all* deposits of this general nature have originated from a magmatic source. Garrels (1957, p. 5) concludes that ". . . the original case for a deep source has progressively weakened as more and more deposits have been found in roughly similar sedimentary environments but with wide geographic and stratigraphic distribution."

SUMMARY

It cannot be doubted that the stratiform uranium deposits in clastic sedimentary rocks of the Colorado Plateau and of other areas display many geological and mineralogical features that are unequivocally characteristic of either a hydrothermal or a ground-water origin. The very existence of such ambiguous features gives some support to the idea that neither type solution has been operative solely in all areas. Many of the deposits were formed in highly permeable rocks in which abundant ground water most certainly was present. Hydrothermal solutions entering such an environment to supply the bulk of the mineral material would have been influenced in their composition, concentration, temperature, and movement.

It may well be asked whether the evidence is such that it compels the adoption of a *single* theory of origin for all deposits of this general nature. Can all deposits of this category be crammed, legitimately, in a single genetic pigeonhole? The final chapter on the genesis of these deposits has not yet been written. Doubtless theories will continue to be modified. The writer believes that on the basis of presently available evidence the uranium deposits of the Colorado Plateau itself are of magmatic descent formed in Laramide time under low-intensity conditions in rocks already inhabited by ground water and subsequently modified by oxidation, largely in situ. Similar deposits outside of the Plateau, especially those in Tertiary rocks, are apparently more closely related in genesis to supergene processes.

Below the thunders of the upper deep;
Far, far beneath in the abysmal sea

The Kraken
Alfred Tennyson

• chapter eleven

URANIFEROUS PHOSPHORITES

GENERAL

Uranium in minor amounts occurs in many sedimentary phosphatic formations originally deposited in marine waters. These formations are of many different geological ages (lower Paleozoic to Tertiary) and are widespread throughout the world (McKelvey and Nelson, 1950; McKelvey, 1956). The uranium within them is believed to be in the main syngenetic in origin, although it may be affected by some local supergene redistribution. None of the phosphorites contain sufficient uranium so that they may be exploited for that element alone; in all cases such uranium will be by-product to the production of calcium phosphate. Only very rarely are independent uranium minerals found in phosphorites, and then only in trifling amounts. In general, beds richest in phosphate also are likely to contain the highest amounts of uranium. However, the distribution of uranium may also be modified by leaching by means of surface and ground waters, resulting in some cases in a diminished phosphate content and a somewhat increased uranium content. Phosphorites not of marine origin, formed by weathering of phosphatic limestones or by the alteration of guano, normally do not contain appreciable amounts of uranium. For example, the brown-rock Tennessee phosphorites, which are residual accumulations from leached phosphatic limestones, generally have less than 0.005% U. The low uranium content results from the inhibiting effect of the CO_3 ion on the initial adsorption of uranium and some differential leaching of uranium during weathering.

Marine phosphorites occur throughout the geological column, but are most abundant in the Cambrian, Permian, Upper Jurassic, Cretaceous, and Tertiary periods. They have been deposited in both geosynclinal and platform environments, in the former associated with siliceous carbonate rocks, in the latter with clays and sands (Gimmelfarb, 1956; Schatsky, 1956).

The chief phosphate mineral is carbonate-fluorapatite, generally occurring

453

as a cryptocrystalline to isotropic variety known as collophane (or collopha-nite) and as a microcrystalline to fibrous equivalent called francolite. The abnormal radioactivity of phosphorites was first noted in 1908 by the British physicist Strutt (1908), who found that samples of phosphorite were many times more radioactive than the average rocks of the crust of the earth.

The abnormal radioactivity of phosphorites is due almost exclusively to uranium; thorium and its derivatives are hardly ever present in amounts above 0.001% (Davidson and Atkin, 1953). If the phosphorite is subjected to acid leaching, the amount of uranium dissolved is directly proportional to the amount of phosphate dissolved. However, those beds of phosphorite that are rich in calcite are generally low in uranium. The antipathetic relationship between carbonate and uranium is further demonstrated by the fact that phosphatic nodules from limestone or calcareous shales are generally free of radioactivity, whereas similar nodules from clay shales usually are uranifer-ous. Small amounts of uranium may also occur in organic material in phos-phorites. The bulk of the radioactivity of some black shales from Oklahoma (Cherokee and Woodford shales) and from California (Playa del Rey nodular shale) is associated with phosphatic material (Ross, 1952). The uranium con-tent of phosphorites is generally very low, usually not exceeding about 0.03% U_3O_8.

It has generally been assumed that the uranium ion proxies for the cal-cium ion in the apatite structure (U^4 for Ca^2). If this is the case, it is diffi-cult to explain why only small amounts of uranium occur, since the apatite structure is capable of numerous other and extensive isomorphous replace-ments. Other rare metals also are concentrated significantly in phosphorites (Table 11.1). Some of these (Ag, As, Mo, Ni, Pb, V, Zn, Cr) owe their con-centration to the presence of organic matter in phosphorites. Sr, Pb, As, and rare earths may be concentrated directly in the phosphate phase (Krauskopf, 1955).

Not all uraniferous phosphorite deposits have carbonate-fluorapatite as the chief phosphate mineral. In another type the phosphate appears chiefly as aluminum or calcium-aluminum phosphates such as wavellite or crandallite. This type is exemplified by the leached zone of the central Florida deposits, the phosphate deposits of Abeokuta province in Nigeria, and those of Thiès in Senegal. The Florida leached zone deposits and those of Senegal are notable in having higher concentrations of uranium than those characterized solely by the presence of carbonate-fluorapatite. The crystallochemistry of uranium in aluminous phosphate rocks is not well understood. Although it has been dem-onstrated that even in these zones the concentration of uranium correlates well with PO_4, F, and Ca and not at all well with Al, it is known that aluminous phosphates (wavellite and turquois) can be uraniferous (Davidson and Atkin, 1953). In turquois, U^{4+} might proxy for Cu and in crandallite it might replace Ca. In wavellite, however, neither element is available. Altschuler et al. (1956) have shown that the U is preferentially associated with the Ca-Al or alkali-Al phosphate and to a lesser extent with wavellite. Moreover, it seems likely that in the formation of supergene wavellite from uraniferous apatite, U^4 was oxidized to U^6. In a few places minute amounts of secondary uranium (U^6)

TABLE 11.1. *Concentrations and enrichment factors of rare metals in phosphorite (Krauskopf, 1955)*

Metal	Conc. in phosphorite, ppm		Enrichment factors	
	Average	Maximum	Average	Maximum
Ag	7(?)	300	70(?)	3,000
As	5–35	150	1–7	30
Ba	30–300	1,000	0.1–1.2	4
Be	<5–10	100(?)	<2–5	50(?)
Co	2–50	300	0.1–2	13
Cr	30–400	10,000	0.15–2	50
Cu	4–40	3,000	0.06–0.6	43
Ga	<10(?)	100	<0.7(?)	7
Ge		<50		<7
Li		1.1(?)		0.02(?)
Mo	1–100	3,000	1–100	3,000
Nb	40–90(?)	3,000(?)	2–4(?)	125(?)
Ni	4–200	3,000	0.05–3	38
Pb	20–200	3,000	1–13	190
Rb		7.7(?)		0.03(?)
R.E.	100–1,000	1,500	0.7–7	10
Sn	1–20(?)		0.02–0.5(?)	
Sr	50–1,000	3,000	0.2–3	10
V	30–200	30,000	0.2–1.3	200
Zn	4–200	10,000	0.03–1.5	77
Zr	10–1,000(?)		0.05–5(?)	

minerals have been detected in altered phosphorites: autunite in the Florida leached zone; carnotite in some of the French North African deposits (Chervet and Branche, 1955); and tyuyamunite in weathered Phosphoria formation of the Crawford Mountains, Rich County, Utah.

By late 1954, recovery of by-product uranium from Florida phosphorite had been begun at four plants, following initial uranium production from phosphate rock in 1952 by the Blockson Chemical Company of Joliet, Illinois.

PHOSPHORIA FORMATION

Distribution

One of the major groups of phosphorite deposits of the world is contained in the Permian Phosphoria formation of the Western United States, which underlies parts of the states of Montana, Idaho, Utah, Wyoming, and the northeastern corner of Nevada (McKelvey and Carswell, 1956). Deposits of comparable age but in much thinner units also occur in Canada near Banff and

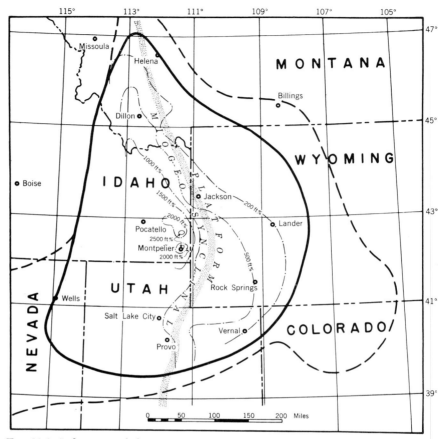

FIG. 11.1. Index map of the Western United States phosphorite field, with limits of the Phosphoria formation and its correlatives, *dash line,* and phosphate deposits, *solid line.* Contours, *dash-dot line,* indicate total phosphate, in feet P$_2$O$_5$. *Stippled line* is boundary of platform environment to east with miogeosynclinal zone to west (Swanson, 1953; McKelvey et al., 1953; *U.S. Geol. Survey*).

Calgary, in the Rocky Mountain quartzite. The formation has received the vigorous attention of numerous geologists for many years (Harris et al., 1954). The Phosphoria formation, which was originally deposited over an area of about 135,000 sq mi in the United States (Fig. 11.1), participated in Laramide and Tertiary orogenies during which it was faulted, thrust, and folded. Later erosion removed much of the originally deposited material. The formation crops out in southwestern Montana south of Helena, Butte, and near Dillon. It also occurs in southeastern Idaho on the Fort Hall Indian reservation and in the vicinities of Georgetown and Montpelier. In northeastern Utah it is exposed in the Crawford Mountains near Ogden and on both flanks of the Uinta Mountains. In Wyoming it is exposed in the Teton basin and its flanking ranges, in the Wind River Mountains, and in the Owl Creek Mountains.

Stratigraphy

The formation, whose type section is in Phosphoria Gulch, a small canyon near Georgetown, Idaho, correlates at least in part with the Park City formation of the Park City district in Utah and to the east with the Embar formation. In the Black Hills area it is the approximate equivalent of the Opeche and Minnekahta formations. Generally the Dinwoody formation (Triassic) overlies the Phosphoria, separated from it by a slight unconformity, and beneath it is the Tensleep sandstone. Although the exact age limits of the Phosphoria are not yet completely established, it very likely encompasses most, if not all, of Permian time.

The formation as a whole varies in thickness from about 18 in. near Banff to a maximum of about 1,500 ft, in general thickening westward and to the south. In southeastern Idaho at the type locality, the formation consists of a phosphatic shale member approximately 175 ft thick overlain by the Rex chert member, about 240 ft thick.

On the whole, individual units of the formation persist without change in lithology for considerable distances, particularly in a north-south direction. However, within the entire depositional area the formation shows marked facies changes. McKelvey et al. (1953) have recognized two facies, a miogeosynclinal and a platform facies. The former is represented by the occurrences in south-central Idaho, where the formation is approximately 700 ft thick and consists of about 3% carbonate-fluorapatite, 59% chert, and 38% carbonaceous mudstone (McKelvey et al., 1953); calcareous rocks and sandy layers are entirely absent. Westward in eastern Nevada, the formation consists of approximately 1,000 ft of cherty carbonate rock which overlies 160 ft of mudstone, chert, and a very minor amount of low-grade phosphorite and a thin redbed. Eastward from south-central Idaho the formation thins to about 300 ft, and in the vicinity of the Wyoming-Idaho border it passes into the platform facies. As this boundary is approached, the phosphorite, which reaches a maximum thickness of about 73 ft in southeastern Idaho, diminishes markedly within a few miles and gradually dwindles eastward, disappearing altogether in central Wyoming. In general from west to east, the formation decreases in phosphate, bedded chert, carbonaceous shale, and increases in nodular chert, carbonate rock, and sandstone. This lateral sequence, which is partly or wholly reproduced or reversed in vertical sections, is the result of deposition on a shelving bottom; the vertical sequence from mudstone to evaporite resulted from deposition on a rising bottom and vice versa (McKelvey and Carswell, 1956).

The Bear River region of southeastern Idaho contains the greatest total of phosphorite and the thickest beds of high-grade phosphorite.

Petrology

Texturally the phosphorites are of several types. Some are oolitic to pisolitic (Fig. 2.41); some contain ovules (pellets similar to oolites but lacking the concentric layering); others consist of shell fragments; and still others of combinations of oolites, ovules, and shell fragments cemented by phosphatic matrix material. Some beds consist chiefly of fragments of phosphatic brachiopods, of fish scales, or of phosphatic casts of small gastropods. The thickest phosphate beds usually are made up of fine-grained ovules; thinner phosphorites of the marginal areas of deposition more commonly are coarse-grained oolitic to pisolitic or bioclastic.

The following minerals are present: calcite, dolomite, chalcedony, fluorite, pyrite, glauconite, anhydrite, gypsum; detrital muscovite, quartz, and clay minerals; and carbonate-fluorapatite in the form of francolite and collophane. In hand specimen the phosphorites are black or dark colored, but in transmitted light in thin section they range in color from nearly white to dark brown or black. Many outcrops show a thin coating of secondary grayish-purple fluorite, known to the miners as phosphate bloom.

Ovules appear to be much more common than oolites in many areas. These massive pellets, a few of which may be as much as several inches long, have cores of mineral grains, particularly quartz, fish teeth, and foraminiferal fragments, and also may contain some irregularly distributed quartz and mica particles. Commonly they are well sorted. Some show slight abrasion; some are fractured and crushed. Oolites, distinguished by concentric banding (Fig. 11.2), commonly of darker cores and lighter outer zones, also may show alternating bands of collophane and francolite, or of collophane and cal-

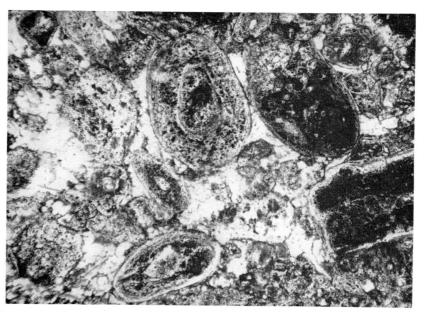

Fɪɢ. 11.2. Oolitic phosphorite, Phosphoria formation, lower phosphatic unit, Cream Puff Mt., Teton County, Wyo. Organic material zonally distributed in oolites, matrix of collophane and quartz.

cite. Commonly francolite fibers are normal to the bands. The matrix consists of cryptocrystalline to isotropic collophane of carbonate, detritals, and organic material, the last commonly forming minute, curly, hairlike, and branching fragments apparently representing plant material (fungi?).

Originally the phosphate was in the form of collophane, which recrystallized in part to francolite. Locally some calcite has replaced oolites, probably diagenetically. Some chalcedony also has replaced central parts of oolites and calcite. Thus the paragenetic sequence is (1) collophane, anhydrite, pyrite, calcite, with detrital quartz, muscovite, clay and organic material; (2) francolite; (3) calcite; (4) chalcedony; (5) fluorite, probably supergene.

Uranium

Only the phosphatic beds of the Phosphoria are appreciably uraniferous. The uranium is dispersed, acid soluble, and concentrated in the phosphate mineral where it probably substitutes as U^4 for Ca^2. In general, uranium increases with increasing P_2O_5; however, exceptions are numerous. These exceptions are probably due, in part, to variations in the length of time that the phosphate was exposed to uraniferous waters. Thompson (1954) has determined that the $U-PO_4$ correlation is better in phosphorite with high-average eU than in that with low-average eU, and also that with decreasing average eU content the correlation between eU content and organic material shifts from strongly negative to positive. In one group of samples with a positive U–organic matter correlation, the correlation between uranium and the product of organic matter and P_2O_5 is better than that for U with either alone. These relations indicate that minor uranium may occur in organic material, but larger amounts only in apatite. Uranium also varies inversely with CO_2. Bioclastic phosphorite generally is less uraniferous than ovulitic phosphorite of the same P_2O_5 content (McKelvey and Carswell, 1956). Some of the uranium variation is the result of weathering. In semiarid climates carbonate-fluorapatite resists decomposition, and in some sections of the formation, upper beds are somewhat richer in P_2O_5. However, uranium is selectively leached from higher beds, and these become slightly depleted in uranium (Table 11.2). Waters from phosphorite mines contain as much as 0.022 ppm U, whereas surface and ground waters have but 0.001 ppm or less (McKelvey and Carswell, 1956).

TABLE 11.2. *Effect of weathering on P and U contents of successively lower phosphorite beds, Phosphoria formation, Sublette Ridge, Lincoln Co., Wyo.* (*McKelvey and Carswell,* 1956)

Locality	Elevation, ft	Thickness, ft	P_2O_5	eU, per cent	U
Layland Canyon	7,000	6.8	30.5	0.016	0.010
Coal Canyon	6,850	6.7	29.2	0.020	0.018
Raymond Canyon	6,400	6.4	22.8	0.022	

Areally uranium varies much as total phosphate, the maximum increasing westward. However, the uranium content of beds of the same P_2O_5 content also increases as the total phosphate content of the phosphatic units increases (Table 11.3). Original differences in sea water, textural variations in phos-

TABLE 11.3. *Increase in U in beds of same P_2O_5 content (20–25%) with increase in total phosphate content; fields listed east to west (McKelvey and Carswell, 1956)*

Locality	Feet × per cent P_2O_5 in Phosphoria formation or equivalents	eU content (per cent) of beds containing 20–25 per cent P_2O_5	
		Average eU	Range in eU
Lander, Wyoming............	260	0.0035	0.001–0.007
Wyoming Range, Wyoming.....	500–700	0.0065	0.004–0.010
Sublette Ridge, Wyoming......	1,400	0.0075	0.004–0.017
Aspen Range, Idaho..........	2,000–2,600	0.0080	0.002–0.018
Fort Hall, Idaho.............	1,100–1,200	0.007	0.004–0.009
Mud Springs, Idaho..........	800	0.005	0.004–0.006

phorite affecting adsorption, thickening or thinning caused either by sedimentation or deformation might affect the uranium content.

In addition to uranium, the Phosphoria formation is enriched in other rare elements, particularly in Ag, V, Pb, Cr, Ni, and Mo, in which it is enriched on the average of 2×, and in Se (Davidson and Gulbrandsen, 1957).

Other rare elements detected in significant concentrations include B, Ba, Be, Cd, Co, Cu, Ga, Ge, Mn, Nb, Sr, Ti, Zn, Zr, and rare earths (Y, La, Dy, Er, Gd, and Nd). Vanadium is particularly abundant, and locally ranges of 0.5 to 2.0% V_2O_5 are reported by Rubey (1943), who estimated reserves of many millions of tons of rock containing 0.75% or more V_2O_5.

Origin

McKelvey et al. (1953) have in general accepted Kazakov's (1937) ideas on the origin of marine phosphorites, modifying them for the Phosphoria formation in some details (p. 62):

The Phosphoria formation accumulated in a large shelving embayment bordered by lands of low relief that contributed little detritus to the sea. Cold, phosphate-rich waters upwelled into this basin from the ocean reservoir to the south or southwest. Phosphorite was deposited from these ascending waters, probably in depths of 1,000 to 200 meters, as their pH increased along with increase in temperature and decrease in partial pressure of CO_2. Carbonates were precipitated from these waters when they reached more shallow depths, at a somewhat higher pH. The phosphate-rich waters nurtured a luxuriant growth of phytoplankton, as well as higher forms of plant and animal life, some remains of which were concentrated with fine-grained materials in deeper waters away from shore. Part of the phosphate and probably some of the fine-grained silica in the formation were concentrated by these organisms. Finally, these conditions persisted over much of Permian time.

The Phosphoria sea in which normal marine facies were deposited covered about 225,000 sq mi with marginal seas occupying an additional 25,000 to 75,000 sq mi. The basin shelved to the west, north, and east, with deepest parts in central Idaho and western Utah. The phosphate, fluorine, and rare metals, including uranium, were derived from sea water. McKelvey et al. (1953) estimate the Phosphoria contains about 1.7×10^{12} tons of P_2O_5, which is more than five times the P_2O_5 content of the oceans today but less than half of the volume of P_2O_5 brought to the seas during the time of Phosphoria deposition. Fluorine, once suggested as being of volcanic derivation (Mansfield, 1940), actually is much more abundant in sea water than is phosphate.

The rare metals appear to be the result of two major types of processes: (1) concentration by organisms, chiefly phytoplankton, and (2) adsorption by isomorphous replacement by phosphatic colloids; uranium belongs mainly to the latter type. The phosphatic pellets and nodules are now generally regarded as chemical precipitates similar to phosphatic nodules recently deposited from marine water (Dietz et al., 1942). They apparently accumulated initially as colloidal collophane, and adsorbed uranium during their (variable?) periods of exposure to ocean waters or from sea water percolating through the materials prior to complete consolidation.

McKelvey et al. (1953) have also pointed to the importance of a negative factor in the accumulation of phosphatic material—the absence of large amounts of clastics as a diluent—and they state (p. 57) that had ". . . the 5,000 feet of Permian sedimentary rocks in Texas contained about 0.15 percent P_2O_5 (the average in sedimentary rocks) the section would contain about 750 feet-percent P_2O_5—an amount similar to that in the Phosphoria formation."

FLORIDA

General

Florida, one of the major phosphate-producing areas of the world, contains deposits of four different types: (1) land-pebble phosphates in west-central peninsular Florida, (2) rock phosphates in the northern part of the state, (3) river-pebble deposits in the northern part of the state, and (4) aluminum phosphate deposits (leached zone). Approximately 95% of the total production has been obtained from the land-pebble deposits, and it is these deposits and particularly their overlying leached zones that contain small concentrations of uranium recoverable as by-product to phosphate mining.

Rock phosphate accumulations rest in depressions on the surface of the

Vicksburg limestone (lower Oligocene), as part of the Pliocene Alachua formation. They are residual accumulations formed by leaching and successive deposition of phosphate material dissolved from the overlying phosphatic Alum Bluff formation. Deposition has been both by open-space filling and by replacement resulting in a mass of subangular to rounded phosphatic nodules and concretions ("rocks" or "pebbles"). In some places these deposits are 100 ft thick; the average thickness is 30 ft. Locally they are rudely sorted into layers of coarse and fine nodules in a matrix of clay, sand, and soft phosphate. The nodules, which range in size from a few inches to as much as 10 ft, are light gray, fine-grained, and in some places contain cavities crusted with secondary phosphate that shows mammillary texture. Scattered bone fragments and shark's teeth occur.

Pleistocene river-pebble deposits, which occur as bars and banks in stream channels, consist of hard phosphate pieces gathered by alluvial action from upstream phosphatic outcrops. These are the least important of the Florida phosphate deposits.

Land-pebble Deposits

The land-pebble deposits, which occur chiefly in Manitee, Hardy, Hillsboro, and Polk Counties, are in the Bone Valley formation, generally considered to be Pliocene in age, overlying the Hawthorn formation (Miocene). In the northernmost part of the district, where the Hawthorn has been eroded away, the underlying formation is probably the Tampa limestone (lower Miocene) (Cathcart, 1956), which also contains some phosphatic nodules. The Hawthorn formation ("bedrock") as a unit probably averages less than 5% P_2O_5 and about 0.001% U_3O_8, and its phosphatic nodules probably average less than 20% P_2O_5 with less than 0.005% U_3O_8. A thin, plastic sandy clay ("bed clay") that intervenes locally between the top of the Hawthorn and the base of the Bone Valley was apparently formed from the dolomitic Hawthorn by leaching of carbonate. It ranges in U content from 0.002 to 0.015% U_3O_8. Above the Bone Valley lie unconsolidated Pleistocene sands 3 to 20 ft thick.

The economic land-pebble deposits ("matrix") vary in thickness from knife-edge to nearly 50 ft (Fig. 11.3). In the center of the area underlain by the Bone Valley formation, phosphate particles are mainly coarse, whereas in peripheral parts they are fine. Coarse pebble deposits, which contain from 30 to 34% P_2O_5, are found mainly on basement highs. Fine pebble deposits containing 32 to 36% P_2O_5 occur in basement lows (Cathcart et al., 1953). In the northern part of the field the deposits generally contain more phosphate particles and the P_2O_5 content is higher than in the southern part of the field. In the northern part of the district the Bone Valley is divided into an upper unit consisting chiefly of quartz and montmorillonite with only traces of phosphate and a lower unit, averaging 20 ft thick, of crudely bedded pebbly, clayey phosphatic sand with a persistent basal phosphatic conglomerate.

The phosphorite consists of phosphate pellets and nodules (commonly referred to as pebbles and sand), quartz grains and montmorillonite clay in approximately equal amounts. The phosphate nodules, which consist in the main of carbonate fluorapatite (collophane and francolite), range in diameter from less than 0.1 mm to about 60 cm. The nodules are rounded to irregular.

(a)

(b)   (c)

Fig. 11.3. (a) Stripping operation, land-pebble phosphorite deposits, Bone Valley formation, Bonny Lake, near Plant City, Fla. (b) Nodular phosphate, Bone Valley formation, Bonny Lake, near Plant City, Fla. (c) Sandy phosphate, Bone Valley formation, Bonny Lake, near Plant City, Fla.

463

TABLE 11.4. *Stratigraphy and composition of rock units, land-pebble phosphate district, Florida (modified from Cathcart, 1956)*

Age			Composition	Mining terminology	
Pleistocene		Terrace deposits	Unconsolidated quartz sand	Overburden	
Pliocene	Middle	Bone Valley fm.	*Upper Unit* — Gradational contact, local channeling into underlying beds. Unweathered: Clayey sand, trace of phosphate. Francolite-collophane, quartz, kaolinite. U = 0.003%. Weathered: Clayey, phosphatic sand, vesicular. Quartz, crandallite, wavellite, millisite, francolite-collophane, kaolinite, gibbsite, attapulgite, Mn-oxides. U = 0.012%	Unweathered Overburden	Weathered / Leached zone
			Gradational contact. *Lower Unit* — Clayey, quartzose, phosphoritic. Francolite-collophane, montmorillonite, quartz, chert, calcite (at base). U = 0.008%	Matrix	
			~~Unconformity~~		
Miocene	Lower and Middle	Hawthorn fm.	Clayey, sandy, phosphatic dolomite. U = 0.0016% + Sandy, phosphatic, calcareous clay. U = 0.005%		Bed clay
Miocene	Lower	Tampa limestone	Clayey, sandy, phosphatic limestone	Bedrock	
			Sandy, clayey limestone to calcareous sandstone		

464

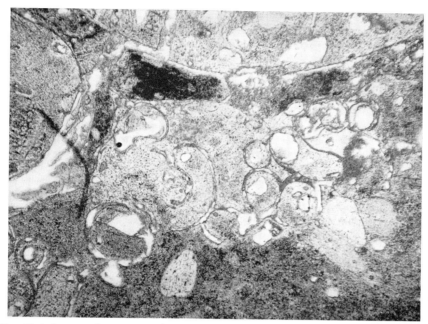

Fig. 11.4. Section of composite phosphate nodule, Bone Valley formation, Achan mine, Mulberry, Fla. ($\times$35).

concretionary in structure, and vary in color—black, blue gray, brown, blue white, and chalky (Fig. 11.4).

The depositional hypothesis has generally been accepted to explain the origin of the Bone Valley formation. This hypothesis states that erosion of the Hawthorn limestone took place at the end of Miocene time, and that in Pliocene time the lower unit of the Bone Valley formation was deposited in a shallow marine near-shore environment. The upper unit of the Bone Valley formation was deposited in a marine offshore environment. Petersen (1955), largely on the presence of attapulgite in the Bone Valley and the association of attapulgite and fresh-water fossils in the Tampa limestone, states that the land-pebble deposits were formed in part, if not entirely, by reworking of Hawthorn phosphate in a fresh-water environment.

Cathcart et al. (1953) conclude that the depositional hypothesis is applicable to the deposits in the north-central part of the district, whereas in the peripheral parts of the district the residual hypothesis is more likely to be correct. This latter theory attempts to explain the entire sequence of unconsolidated material above the Hawthorn limestone as the relatively insoluble residue concentrated by weathering in situ. The presence of distinct bedding in the Bone Valley formation argues strongly against the application of this hypothesis in most places. Likewise conglomerates and irregular contacts at the base of the Bone Valley formation indicate unconformities. Differences in size distribution and in the heavy mineral suites indicate the Bone Valley was not derived from the Hawthorn by simple leaching of Ca.

With regard to the origin of the uranium, Cathcart (1956, p. 519) states:

The inverse relation between grain size of the apatite nodules and their uranium content is constant throughout the district. This relation precludes downward percolation of ground waters as a source for the uranium, because the relation holds even in deposits that contain more than 95% of fine-grained apatite nodules. Any downward movement of uranium-bearing solutions through this type of deposit would almost certainly enrich the finer grained nodules. In addition, the nodules in the Hawthorn formation contain less uranium than do those in the Bone Valley formation. These relations can best be explained by assuming that the uranium in these deposits is syngenetic, and was absorbed by the phosphate particles as they formed on the sea floor. The period of weathering that followed the deposition of the Hawthorn formation resulted in the development of a residuum, and this material was available for reworking into the Bone Valley. Thus, phosphate particles originally formed in the Hawthorn sea were exposed a second time to the action of sea water, and are consequently higher in uranium content. In addition, the explanation for the higher uranium content of the coarser particles may be that the coarser particles were exposed for a longer time to the action of sea water by virtue of their size and consequent slower burial.

Aluminous Phosphate Deposits

The Bone Valley formation (either unit or both) has been altered by downward percolating acid waters into a vesicular leached zone, a clayey sand consisting chiefly of quartz, aluminum phosphate minerals, and kaolinite. It averages about 6 to 7 ft thick and ranges from knife-edge to as much as 50 ft. Phosphate and uranium content vary widely, depending on which Bone Valley unit was leached. Altschuler et al. (1956) report crandallite and millisite concentrates contain 0.03 to 0.04% U, whereas pure wavellite contains only 0.002 to 0.004% U. The aluminum phosphate zone in the Peace River area is thickest, most continuous, and highest in both P_2O_5 and U in the flatwoods part; thin, discontinuous to absent on the ridge tops; and absent in the Peace River flood plain. There are extreme variations in thickness and composition in short distances. High P_2O_5 and high U generally correspond, these highs also generally corresponding with thicker sections.

Variable amounts of aggregated aluminum phosphate minerals are present, chiefly wavellite and crandallite (pseudowavellite) and some millisite. Crandallite and wavellite replace clay minerals and apatite. Locally wavellite forms spherulites 1 to 11 mm in diameter showing both radial and concentric structures (Bergendahl, 1955). In this zone, calcium has been leached from francolite-collophane and remaining phosphate has been combined with aluminum from clay minerals to form the aluminum or calcium-aluminum phosphates. At the base of the zone, collophane of the unweathered pebble phosphate is incipiently altered. Uranium has been somewhat increased in the leached zone, averaging 0.012%, but still shows good correlation with PO_4, F, and Ca and not particularly with Al (Cathcart, 1956). The leached zone is believed to have been formed in the interval between Bone Valley and Pleistocene glacial time, when the phosphates were exposed to weathering.

SOUTH CAROLINA

Phosphorites occur in South Carolina near Charleston, chiefly in Berkeley, Charleston, Dorchester, Colleton, and Beaufort Counties (Rogers, 1915). They begin near the Broad River at the south, extending northeasterly for about 75 mi in a seacoast belt generally less than 30 mi wide. The tan to dark gray deposits occur in the Edisto marl (Miocene), an irregular bed 1 to 2.5 ft thick honeycombed with cavities up to 4 in. in diameter, partly filled by black sandy calcareous and phosphatic clay, locally containing cetacean bones, sharks' teeth and vertebrae, coprolites, bones of Miocene, Pliocene, and Quaternary land vertebrates, and a few Eocene shells. In some cases the cellular marl has disintegrated to a mass of rough to smooth broken fragments ("nodules"), and the clay acts as cement.

Phosphorite also occurs as irregular, loose river-bed deposits consisting of rounded pebbles and cobbles, usually of darker color and of higher specific gravity than the Edisto rock. Some nodules are well rounded with an enameloid coating; others are siliceous, enclosing numerous quartz grains.

Measurements by Davidson and Atkin (1953) gave 0.038 to 0.054% eU_3O_8, and measurements in the Mineralogical Laboratory, University of Michigan, gave 0.025 to 0.030% eU_3O_8.

SOUTHWESTERN STATES

Ordovician phosphate-bearing strata (Cason shale) occur in Independence, Stone, Izard, and Search Counties in north-central Arkansas, but all samples tested had 0.002 to 0.003% eU (Ryan, 1956).

Uraniferous phosphate occurs as nodules in black shales in Oklahoma and Kansas. In Kansas, such nodules are found in the top of Bourbon formation and in the Stark and Hushpuckney shales, all of Pennsylvanian age (Runnels, 1949; Runnels et al., 1953). In Oklahoma they are at the top of Checkerboard limestone member of the Coffeyville formation and near the top of the Fort Scott limestone (both Pennsylvanian). Some shales contain uranium even where no phosphatic nodules are present, but wherever nodules appear they usually contain more uranium (McKelvey and Nelson, 1950). The average composition of nodules in eastern Kansas is 0.017% U_3O_8, 30.2% P_2O_5, 3.2% F. Samples of phosphatic nodules in southeastern Kansas averaged 0.015% eU (Ryan, 1956). Samples of phosphatic shale from eastern Oklahoma localities averaged 0.002% eU (Ryan, 1956).

In the Woodford shale of Oklahoma, bands and grains of carbonate and phosphate have three times the radioactivity of the organic material (Ross, 1952). The radioactivity of the Cherokee shale of Oklahoma also is largely related to phosphate nodules, with organic material only very weakly radioactive (Ross, 1952).

Phosphorite of lower Pennsylvanian age occur south of Marble Falls, in the eastern Llano uplift of central Texas (Barnes, 1954). The 11-ft bed is composed of oolites, ovules, and fossil remains. A basal reddish-brown conglomerate, 3 in. thick, consists of pisolites. Three thin limestone layers are interbedded. Analyses indicate $P_2O_5 = 13.92$ to 15.36%; $eU_3O_8 = 0.017\%$. Only small tonnages are available.

ALASKA

Uraniferous phosphorite occurs in Alaska on the north flank of the central Brooks Range in the upper part of the Lisburne group (Mississippian) (Matzko, 1955B; Patton, 1955). The zone, which is nearly 40 ft thick, consists of phosphorite, phosphatic limestone, and phosphatic mudstone. The dark brown to black phosphorite contains generally 20 to 30% P_2O_5, but two beds have as much as 34% P_2O_5 with 0.024% U and 0.49% V_2O_5. The phosphorite consists of ovules and less commonly oolites of collophane usually 0.1 to 2 mm in size, with varying amounts of calcite, dolomite, quartz, feldspar, fluorite, carbonaceous material, and phosphatized fish remains.

MEXICO

Phosphorites occur in Mexico as compact and earthy concretionary masses in Upper Jurassic marly limestones and argillaceous marls of Mazapil and Concepción del Oro, state of Zacatecas (Rogers et al., 1953, 1956); in Cretaceous limestones of Cerro Topo Chico near Monterrey in Nuevo León; in the Sierras de Minas Viejas, Nuevo León; and at Rincón de Arizmendi and Ayancual, Nuevo León. The Zacatecas material (La Caja formation) ranges in grade from 15 to 58% BPL,[1] with a maximum of 70% in a zone 1.5 to 3 m thick. For Topo Chico material the range is 27 to 43.4%; for Minas Viejas rock 22.88 to 37.90%; and for Rincón de Arizmendi rock 7.13 to 33.92% (Flores, 1953).

The nodules are variable in structure, some are compact, others oolitic or even banded, set in a fine-grained matrix. The color is white to grayish yellow. In addition to collophane, relics of calcite and some fluorite may be present. Some pellets contain microfossils and miniature gastropods and pelecypods (Van Vloten, 1956). Fluorapatite also occurs in the matrix. Macrofossils are rare, although some fragments of fossil bone and wood have been found. A V_2O_5 content of 0.018% for the upper zone of the Concepción del Oro material has been reported (Rogers et al., 1953).

BRAZIL

Phosphorites occur in Brazil at Ipanema and Jacupiranga (in limestone) in the state of São Paulo; at Salinas, northeastern Minas Gerais; at Arapiráca, state of Alagôas; at Camisão, Bahia; and at Forno da Cal, near Olinda, state of Pernambuco (Upper Cretaceous). Most of Brazil's production has come from the deposits at Ipanema, São Paulo, where the rock is beneficiated to a

---

[1] BPL = bone phosphate of lime = %$P_2O_5 \times 2.185$.

high-grade concentrate, chiefly by magnetic separation of iron oxide. Total Brazilian reserves are estimated at 572 million metric tons (Jacob, 1953). Samples from the three most important mines at Ipanema gave 17.9 to 21.7% P_2O_5.

Newly discovered deposits at Forno da Cal, Pernambuco, occur in the coastwise Maria Farinha formation, consisting of limestone, marl, shale, and sandstone which vary considerably in their proportions (Fine and Frommer, 1954; Leonardos, 1955).

The phosphatic marl contains collophane; minor calcite, dolomite, and iron oxide; and detrital quartz, feldspar, ilmenite, tourmaline, and glauconite with a clay binder (illite). The collophane replaces fossils principally but also occurs in the clayey matrix fraction. Where it is underlain by the friable sandstone, it also is friable and yellowish (the predominant type). Where the phosphatic marl overlies compact sandstone, it too is hard and greenish. Preliminary exploration indicates a reserve of 92 million tons of 24% P_2O_5-grade in a bed averaging 8.5 ft thick. Analyses of a composite sample revealed 21.4% P_2O_5 and 0.013% U_3O_8.

WESTERN EUROPE

Marine phosphorites have been exploited in England, Ireland, France, Spain, Belgium, and Germany. Minor operations or occurrences are in Austria, Switzerland, and on the island of Malta.

Great Britain and Ireland

Except for those rich in calcite, British phosphorites are uraniferous with 0.01 to 0.10% U_3O_8. Most of the deposits are of small extent or low grade, consisting of phosphatic nodules or of localized "coprolite" gravels. Some of the occurrences are apparently similar to those of Kansas and Oklahoma: in Devon, phosphatic nodules occur in shaly limestones; in the Midlands, they occur in black shale.

Ordovician phosphorites occur in north Wales between the mountains north and west of Dinas Mowddwy and the town of Llanfyllen. The beds, which are steeply dipping to vertical, consist of rather closely packed, black to yellow, pyritiferous phosphatic concretions in black clay shale. The concretions range in size from 2 to 8 in., containing 60 to 69% BPL; the bed as a whole contains 46% BPL. In some places the phosphatic bed is separated into two or even three units by interlayered limestone. Davidson and Atkin (1953) report 0.003% eU_3O_8.

A Carboniferous phosphate from the Alton marine band has been found to be exceptionally high in U (Davidson and Atkin, 1953): $U_3O_8 = 0.10\%$. Other determinations by Ponsford (1955) show 0.002 to 0.020% eU_3O_8.

The most productive deposits have been those in the upper Green Sand (Cretaceous) of Cambridge, where beds, 8 to 12 in. thick, consist of dark brown to black nodules, and in Suffolk where a similar bed is 12 to 18 in. thick. Similar deposits occur in Bedfordshire. In some places three phosphatic zones may be present, the lower of which usually is cemented by calcareous material, whereas the two upper are sandy and friable. Elsewhere (at Sandy) only one zone occurs. The thicknesses range from 6 to 24 in. The beds are conglomerates of phosphatic nodules and pebbles (¼ to 2 in.) cemented by ferruginous sand. The nodules have light brown exterior, covering a black or dark brown interior. All gradations exist between massive phosphorite and phosphatic sandstone. Detrital pieces of fossils, especially ammonites, are present, and the older fossils in their original beds are not phosphatized, indicating the Cretaceous age of the phosphatization. The beds represent the basal conglomerate of the transgressing Cretaceous sea. At Ely two types of phosphate have been distinguished: (1) a soft red-brown variety; (2) a dark brown, hard heavy type containing organic material, which occurs primarily in the upper part of the horizon and which appears to have been once in plastic colloidal masses. Shrinkage cracks and leathery surfaces characterize some nodules. Measurements by Davidson and Atkin (1953) indicated 0.007 to 0.008% eU_3O_8.

Tertiary phosphorites occur in England in Norfolk, Essex, and especially in Suffolk. These are the "coprolites," first used for fertilizer in 1790, consisting of a 2 to 18 in. conglomerate bed of phosphate nodules, shells, bone, and teeth fragments, and rock and mineral pebbles. Davidson (1956A, p. 206) believes ". . . the uranium content of the phosphates is due to adsorption from acid meteoric waters."

The Irish deposits, of Millstone Grit age (upper Carboniferous), consist of lenses and thin discontinuous layers in as many as five horizons with interbedded dark shale resting on an erosion surface of limestone. They occur in County Clare. Each younger bed lies further south than its predecessor, i.e., a constant distance from a retreating shoreline (O'Brien, 1953). The gray to black phosphorites are compact and hard, consisting of 0.2 mm rounded to subangular collophane grains coated by cryptocrystalline silica in a carbonate matrix. Some detrital quartz is present. The surfaces of the beds may be covered by a thin mat of elongated vermiform pellets (not coprolites) apparently formed through rolling and accretion on the sea floor. Some collophane grains show contraction cracks; in others francolite has formed by recrystallization of collophane. In three horizons the average content ranged between 45 to 55% BPL. Two radiometric analyses by Davidson and Atkin (1953) showed 0.021 to 0.022% eU_3O_8; by Delayney et al. (1953) 0.018 to 0.024% eU_3O_8.

Belgium

Belgian phosphate deposits occur chiefly (1) at Ciply and Mesuin in the vicinity of Mons, and (2) near Liège, both of Cretaceous age. Those near Liège occur in two contiguous zones, a rich upper and a poorer lower. In the upper, as much as 30% rounded phosphatic grains and nodules occur in a clayey matrix with chert in a zone up to 0.5 m thick. In the associated chalk are foraminiferal shells filled by phosphate. The clayey irregular lower zone is 0.4 to 0.5 m thick and displays gray or white banding. These deposits have resulted from the residual concentration of phosphate through solution of carbonate from the phosphatic chalk. Davidson and Atkin (1953) have assayed two samples radiometrically: 0.002 to 0.004% eU_3O_8.

The deposits near Mons are similar, being either residual concretions or phosphatic chalks. The cherty phosphatic chalk consists of carbonate fossils (foraminifera, clams, etc.), fragments of bones and teeth, phosphate grains, and minor quartz and feldspar grains. Transitions occur to massive chert of replacement origin. A fossil log surrounded by a 20- to 30-cm richer phosphate zone has been reported (Cornet, 1913). At Cuesmas the phosphatic chalk is underlain by a phosphate conglomerate consisting of limestone nodules and phosphatized fossils.

In numerous localities in Belgium phosphatic nodules occur in Eocene strata (upper Ypresian)—sands and clays.

France

French phosphorites are chiefly of Cretaceous age, to a lesser extent of Jurassic and Devonian age, occurring mainly:

1. In northern France, in the departments of Nord, Oise, Pas de Calais, and Somme
2. In northeastern France in the departments of Ardennes, Marne, and Meuse
3. In north-central and northeast-central France in the departments of Côte-d'Or, Yonne, Haute-Saône, Cher, and Indre
4. In the department of Sarthe in northwest-central France
5. In the departments of Drôme and Isère, in southeastern France
6. In the Pyrenees

In addition to these bedded deposits, unusual phosphate veins occur in the departments of Lot, Tarn-et-Garonne, Lot-et-Garonne, Gard, and Ardèche ("phosphorites of Quercy"). These irregular veins, cutting chiefly Jurassic limestones, range from several centimeters to 60 m in thickness and consist of gray to red, rarely blue, concretionary calcium phosphate containing I, F, and S. Accessory constituents include ferruginous clay, limonitic pisolites, marl, calcite in vugs, and numerous fossil bones of Eocene and Miocene age. The deposits are regarded as originally sedimentary, formed by descending solutions (Stutzer and Wetzel, 1932). They are low in uranium (Davidson and Atkin, 1953), with but 0.002% eU_3O_8.

The phosphorites of the northern departments are Cretaceous in age, occurring in three horizons: Gaultian (20% P_2O_5), Cenomanian (25% P_2O_5), and upper Senonian; the last is economically the most important. The Gaultian deposits consist of phosphatic nodules or fossil pieces in a clay layer 0 to 15 cm thick. The Cenomanian deposits are in a porous and friable layer 15 cm to 1 m thick, overlain by glauconitic sand and underlain by marl. Deposits in the Senonian consist of phosphatic chalk and sand containing 0.2 to 0.3 mm collophane grains, isotropic to cryptocrystalline interiorly, and radial-fibrous marginally (francolite).

Like most of the Continental European phosphorites, the radioactivity is low, 0.004 to 0.007% eU_3O_8, but this in part may be due to the low phosphate content of the samples (Davidson and Atkin, 1953).

Deposits of the Ardennes area are in Cretaceous greensands, where beds 5 to 25 cm thick contain nodules and fist-sized masses of greenish-brown, compact phosphate. In north-central France phosphate nodules, locally with oolitic iron ore, in beds 5 to 60 cm thick, occur in the Jurassic (Lias) beds as residual concentrations from limestone. Several zones may be present. In Cher and Yonne, Cretaceous phosphorites occur as nodules in sands.

The Pyrenees deposits in Upper Devonian black shales consist of nodules within which occur fossils or pyrite crystals.

Other radiometric measurements by Davidson and Atkin (1953) are: Bordeaux phosphate—0.003% eU_3O_8, and Bourbonnais coprolites—0.004% eU_3O_8.

Germany

In Germany phosphate deposits are widely distributed:

Region	Age	Description
Vogtland (East Germany along Czechoslovakian border)	Upper Silurian	Black, round, ellipsoidal, or flattened nodules 2–10 cm in diameter in alum shale. Microstructure is festoonlike and radial-fibrous. Some have detrital quartz with calcite envelopes as nuclei. Accessory pyrite and chlorite. Silica fills microvugs
Lahn-Dill region, Hessia-Nassau (central Germany)	Devonian	Residual accumulations from altered shell limestone, in hollows in massive limestone. Massive, cellular, brecciated, or earthy. In thin plates or in reniform-botryoidal masses. Fragments of limestone, dolomite, quartz, iron and manganese oxides included. Microscopically brecciated with phosphatic or cherty cement
Brunswick (north-central Germany)	Cretaceous. Near Helmstadt—lower Oligocene	Four beds, 15–50 cm; at Zilly a bed up to 3 m thick. Phosphatic nodules ("coprolites") in glauconitic sand
Leipzig, Saxony	Middle Oligocene	Nodules of sand grains in sandstone cemented by yellow-brown collophane

The radioactivity of these, like other European phosphorites, is low (Davidson and Atkin, 1953): Nassau—0.001 to 0.004% eU_3O_8; Zilly, Magdeburg—0.005 to 0.007% eU_3O_8.

Spain

Phosphate deposits occur in Spain chiefly in Cáceres Province on the Portuguese border, as phosphatic veins with quartz and calcite in Devonian limestone, Cambrian shale, and Precambrian granite, and as phosphatic nodules and fragments in Devonian limestone. Torbernite occurs in the phosphate beds of the Albalá area, Cáceres (Hernández-Pacheco, 1945). A single determination by Davidson and Atkin (1953) shows 0.002% eU_3O_8. Some Cretaceous glauconitic marls and marly limestones in Murcia Province also are phosphatic, with 0.25% V (Stutzer and Wetzel, 1932).

U.S.S.R.

Uranium-bearing phosphorites are reported at a great number of localities in the U.S.S.R. (Nininger, 1954). They include beds of many different ages— Silurian, Devonian, Upper Jurassic, Cretaceous, and Lower Tertiary. They are especially widespread in European Russia (Stutzer and Wetzel, 1932); mining reportedly began in 1885. Many European Russian deposits are sandy phosphorites consisting of quartz grains cemented by colloform, radial-fibrous francolite or cryptocrystalline to isotropic collophane (Tschirwinsky, 1911). Data on the Th and Ra content of Russian phosphorites have been presented by Rusakov (1933).

Southern U.S.S.R.

The deposits of south Russia, in the regions of Kursk and Orel, extend for approximately 500 km northwest-southeast. Deposits referred to as being near Kursk, Voronezh, and Kiev are in this region. They are Cretaceous and Tertiary in age, the main ones being Cenomanian.

The top of the zone consists of small brownish-black disseminated phosphatic nodules in sandy glauconitic chalk (Sourka layer). This is underlain by glauconitic sand in which occurs the main phosphorite band, 2 to 3 m thick, with a lustrous brown crust. The phosphate content of the unit is 180 to 750 kg/m^2, and P$_2$O$_5$ = 13 to 16%. In addition to fibrous francolite-cemented quartz grains the deposits contain glauconite, iron oxides, calcite, siderite, organic debris, sponge spicules, foraminiferal remains, detrital minerals, and some francolite oolites. The layer of massive phosphorite ("Poliwa") contains 30 to 38% P$_2$O$_5$, and consists chiefly of colloformly banded francolite with microvugs filled with quartz. Some phosphatized wood has been found. Deposits near Voronezh are of Cretaceous age (Kokscharow, 1855) and consist of beds up to 1½ ft thick, gray, brownish gray, brown, and black brown in color. Some phosphatic bone material is present.

Central and Northeast Soviet Russia

The phosphorites of central and northeastern Soviet Russia occur in the Upper Jurassic (Volga beds) and Lower Cretaceous rocks, marked by marine transgression and regression. Near Moscow the lower part of the Volga stage contains a lowermost zone of shiny, black phosphate nodules; a middle 25-cm zone of compact, black phosphatic concretions and breccia fragments; and an upper layer (0.1 to 0.3 m) of sandy phosphatic concretions. These are separated by gray clays, glauconitic sand, and bituminous shale.

Deposits of Upper Jurassic age have been exploited near Vozhkressiensk and Yegorevsk, where three phosphatic horizons occur. Grade has been determined as 23% P$_2$O$_5$.

Cretaceous phosphorite beds, well developed in the Ryazan region, consist of glauconitic sands and a 30- to 50-cm phosphatic, ammonitic sandstone ("Soukhar") containing 26% P$_2$O$_5$. Large deposits occur in the Vyatka-Kama-Syssola watershed. The Lower Cretaceous phosphorites, which average 400 kg phosphate/sq m with 27% P$_2$O$_5$, consist of loosely bonded phosphatic nodules in a zone 0.6 to 0.7 m thick.

The widespread Kostroma deposits of Lower Cretaceous age are phosphatic nodules in gray marly clays; some contain barite. The clay-carbonate matrix contains nodules averaging 20 to 28% P_2O_5 in a unit 28 m thick.

Southeast Soviet Russia

Phosphorites occur in the regions of Tambov, Penza, Ulyanovsk (Simbirsk), Saratov, and Stalingrad. Cretaceous beds, which overlie the Jurassic unconformably, contain phosphate in a basal conglomerate which encloses some phosphatic nodules with Jurassic ammonites. The main type of nodule, which contains belemnites, consists of pebbles of dark argillaceous phosphate cemented by sandy phosphate; P_2O_5 = 22%. Phosphatic zones also occur higher in the Cretaceous, in the Albian (concretions in sandstone, in clays, and phosphate conglomerate), in the Cenomanian (nodules in coarse sandstone), in the Turonian, and in the lower and upper Senonian. Significant radioactivity was detected by Rusakov (1933) in Tertiary phosphorites near Volsk, in the Saratov region.

Podolia, West Ukraine

Podolian phosphorite nodules occur at the base of Lower Cretaceous (Cenomanian) glauconitic sandstone, and are at least in part derived from primary phosphorites in the underlying Silurian rocks. The Cretaceous bed 5 cm thick contains phosphatic nodules 1 to 15 cm in diameter, averaging 1 kg in weight; rarely, some weigh as much as 20 kg. The matrix phosphate is carbonate apatite, that of the nodules is fluorapatite. Generally the grade is 640 to 700 kg phosphate/sq m; but some of the richer beds contain 1,000 to 1,800 kg phosphate/sq m, especially where depressions occur in the unconformity on top of the Silurian. Smooth, waterworn cobbles of phosphorite from Podwoloczyska, Podolia, in the University of Michigan collections show <0.01% eU_3O_8.

Region of the Chkalov-Tashkent Railroad

Exploited deposits of Cretaceous age occur along both sides of the Chkalov (Orenburg)-Tashkent railroad near Tamdi and Kandagach. As many as three phosphorite zones are present; in some places there is only one. The two lower are nodular, weakly cemented; the upper is massive, strongly coherent. Some noncommercial phosphate also occurs in the underlying Upper Jurassic and in the overlying early Tertiary rocks.

Other Deposits

1. In the Jurassic and Cretaceous rocks of the region of the Soura, Mokcha, and Volga Rivers.

2. In the upper Eocene sediments in the eastern part of the Kiev region.

3. In the Lower (Aptian) and Upper (Senonian) Cretaceous rocks of the Caucasus at Akoucha and Kassoum-Kent.

4. In Turkestan, in the Mangyshlak region in Middle Cretaceous.

5. Gray (1943) also reports two discoveries in 1937 of deposits in the Ishimbayevo district, Ural region, and near Kara-Tau in Kazakhstan. The former consists of two beds, the upper 1.5 m thick and the lower 2.5 to 3.5 m thick, extending about 5 km. The Kara-Tau deposit, extending over 70 to 80

km, varies in thickness from 0.6 to 6.0 m and ranges in grade from 28 to 32% P_2O_5.

6. Deposits are reported 160 mi southwest of Balkhash on Golodnaya steppe near the west end of Lake Balkhash.

7. There are occurrences in or adjacent to Poland, in Volhynia and at Jaroslaw.

8. In Estonia, 30 km from Reval, occur Upper Cambrian or Lower Ordovician phosphorites in a sandstone 5 to 20 m thick which contains coquinas of the brachiopod, *Obolus* (40 to 60%), shells of which contain 39% P_2O_5

Still other deposits are listed by Noyes (1944).

Much of the U.S.S.R.'s phosphate is obtained from the apatite deposits of the Kola peninsula at Kukisvumchorr, where a great lens of apatite-nepheline rock, 4 km long and 150 to 200 m thick, lies along the contact of underlying ijolite-urtites and overlying nepheline syenite (Hurlbut, 1938). This deposit is of magmatic ancestry and is very low in U (<0.001 to 0.001% eU_3O_8 and 0.003% U_3O_8) (Davidson and Atkin, 1953).

NORTH AFRICA

Morocco

Phosphate deposits occur in North Africa in Morocco, Algeria, and Tunisia. The deposits in Morocco are in eroded sediments, generally horizontal, between the Atlas Mountains to the east and the Atlantic coast to the west, in a northeast-southwest belt approximately 30 km long. The main groups of deposits are (from northeast to southwest) (1) Oulad Abdoun, (2) Ganntour, and (3) Meskala. In the Haut Atlas to the south are (4) deposits of Oued Erguita, and east-northeast of these are (5) deposits of Khelaa d'Ouarzazate (Salvan, 1952). The largest producing mine is at Kourigha, in the Oulad Abdoun, and the second most important is at Louis Gentil, in the Ganntour.

The deposits in the Oulad Abdoun occupy the major part of the structural element known as the "plateau of phosphates." They are very extensive, underlying an area about 125 km long in a generally east-west direction and are divided into three zones:

1. Zone of Khouribga-Oued Zem, the only one mined
2. Zone of El Borouj
3. Zone of Kasba Tadla and of the Atlas border

In the Ypresian (Wasatch) a lower exploited horizon (Bed I) consisting of sandy phosphate, 1.5 to 1.8 m thick, is separated by chert, limestone, and marl from an upper sandy phosphate (Bed O) about 0.5 m thick. Above Bed O is a complex of marl, chert, and limestone in which occur two individual thin beds of sandy phosphate (Streaks *a* and *b*) (Fig. 11.5).

The stratigraphy of the deposits worked near Louis Gentil, Ganntour, is similar (Fig. 11.6), with sandy phosphate beds (Beds III and II) in the Maestrichtian and in the lowermost Montian (Bed I).

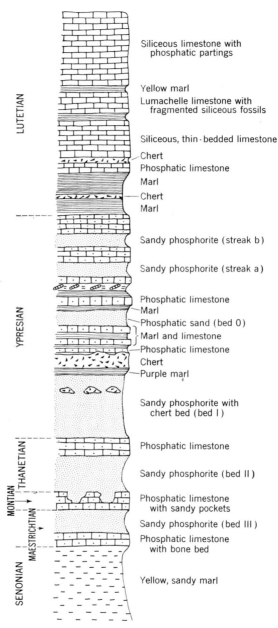

Fig. 11.5. Stratigraphic column of phosphatic beds, Oulad Abdoun, Morocco (Salvan, 1952).

476

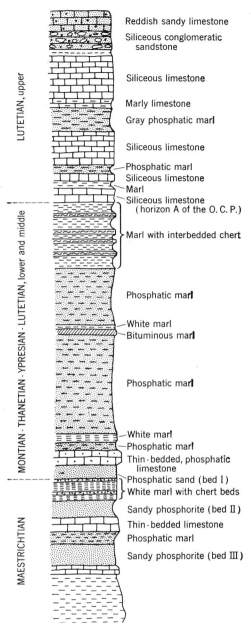

FIG. 11.6. Stratigraphic column of phosphatic beds near Louis Gentil, Ganntour, Morocco (Salvan, 1952).

477

The Moroccan phosphatic deposits occur in three different rock types: (1) sandy phosphorite, (2) phosphatic limestone, and (3) phosphatic chert. The last two are too low in phosphate to be of economic significance. The sandy mass consists of (1) very small ovules ("pseudo-oolites") of carbonate-fluorapatite (collophane and francolite), (2) phosphatic coprolites, (3) phosphatic bone debris, (4) detrital minerals, and (5) cement. The percentage of ovules and the collophane content also vary greatly with the stratigraphic unit, with the deposit, and even with location in the same deposit. In general the lower strata also are lower in phosphate.

Phosphate cement has not been found in the Moroccan phosphorites. In general, detrital minerals are not abundant. Carnotite occurs locally in some calcareous and siliceous beds of the phosphatic formations of Louis Gentil and El Borouj (Chervet and Branche, 1955).

Reserves of phosphate rock in Morocco are estimated at 21,000 million metric tons (Jacob, 1953).

Algeria-Tunisia

Phosphate deposits occur along both sides of the Algerian-Tunisian border, extending from about 75 mi south of the Mediterranean southward to Metlaoui, a distance of 125 mi. The deposits are in general similar to those of Morocco, occurring in extensive, folded, and truncated lower Eocene strata of limestone, marl, and conglomerate with one to three beds of pseudo-oolitic phosphorite, up to 4.5 m thick (Fig. 11.7). The ovule fraction contains 58 to 70% BPL, and the cement, which is commonly phosphatic in contrast to the Moroccan deposits, may contain 25% BPL.

In Algeria important mines are at Djebel Kouif, 25 mi north of Tebessa, and at Djebel Onk, 60 mi south of Tebessa. In Tunisia the largest mines are at Metlaoui and Redeyef. Algerian-Tunisian reserves are estimated at 3,000 million metric tons.

Uranium

Uranium is widespread in North African phosphate deposits. Hébert (1947) reports values in the range 0.009 to 0.034% eU, whereas Guntz (1952) and Guntz and Arene (1953) give an average grade of 20 to 30 g/ton, with a range of 10 to 50 g/ton. Davidson and Atkin (1953), who state that Hébert's values are uniformly too high and that those of Guntz are uniformly low, report the following values:

	U_3O_8, per cent	eU_3O_8, per cent
Morocco (10)	0.012–0.014	0.016
Algeria (3)	0.011–0.014	0.011–0.012
Tunisia (7)	0.0047–0.009	0.004–0.005

Lenoble et al. (1952, 1954), who give for Moroccan deposits the range 0.01 to 0.06% U, have shown that uranium is widely distributed and occurs in phosphate rock in most of the Moroccan areas. In most cases no discrete uranium minerals have been found, but traces of a uranium vanadate, believed to be either tyuyamunite or ferghanite, have been reported (Arambourg and Orcel,

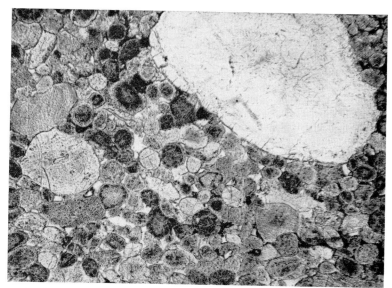

Fig. 11.7. Phosphatic ovules and oolites in phosphatic cement, Constantine, Algeria (×35).

1951). The bulk of the uranium occurs within the structure of the collophane or francolite. Small amounts of uranium may also be contained in clay minerals, and some uranium mineral coatings are related to marly veinlets in some phosphate beds in the Ganntour Basin (Visse, 1954).

Visse (1954) has noted several relationships between phosphate content, uranium content, and geology:

1. The U/P ratios (U% × 10^3/P%) are both higher and more irregular in phosphorites of the geosynclinical zone than in rocks of the platform zone (1.1 for Morocco versus 0.5 or less for Algeria)

2. The U/P value locally is higher in the initially deposited beds of a sequence, independent of the phosphate content; the relative increase in the U/P ratio appears to be related to either the beginning of a cycle of phosphatic deposition (transgression) or its close (regression)

3. The U/P values show no relation to the thickness of the strata. High values occur in thicker, mineable beds or in thin, nonexploitable strata, or are variable in beds of the same thickness

4. The U/P ratios are independent of the variation in proportion of ovules versus coprolites. The proportion of U in coprolites and ovules from the same phosphorite is comparable

5. In North Africa the U content is uniformly lower in those phosphorites rich in organic material (Tunisia), but this does not seem to be the case in Togo, where the U/P values of phosphate beds with a notable content of organic material are identical if not higher than those of beds free of organic material

The North African phosphate deposits taken together with those of Rio de Oro, Senegal, Togo, and Nigeria and those of the Middle East—Egypt, Israel, and Jordan—form the greatest phosphate rock province in the world, containing estimated reserves of at least 5×10^{10} tons with more than 58% BPL (Davidson and Atkin, 1953). Many of the deposits contain concentrations of U comparable to those of the Florida phosphates from which uranium is being recovered as a by-product, and in all likelihood in these and in other African countries recovery of uranium by-product to the extraction of super-phosphate can and will become a significant source of uranium in the future.

MIDDLE EAST

In the Middle East, phosphate deposits occur in Egypt, Israel, and Jordan. The Egyptian deposits, which are similar to those of Algeria-Tunisia, are about 20 mi inland from the Red Sea (Noyes, 1944). Mining is carried on at Safaga and at Kosseir to the south. The deposits occur in Cretaceous marls, limestones, and cherts containing thin phosphorite beds, that have between 63 and 70% BPL. Uranium values determined by Davidson and Atkin (1953) are:

$$eU_3O_8,$$
per cent

Kosseir (4 samples) 0.007–0.010
Safaga (4 samples) 0.009–0.012

Other Egyptian occurrences are east of the Nile at Sebaia, Qurn, and Hamazu and in the Libyan desert at the Kharga and Dakhla Oases. Egyptian reserves are estimated at 179 million metric tons (Jacob, 1953).

In Israel in the Neguev region, phosphorite deposits occur in folded strata of upper Campanian age (Upper Cretaceous), reaching thicknesses of 2 to 8 m (Bentor, 1953). A series of generally parallel, asymmetric anticlines that trend northeast or east-northeast is constructed of beds of chalk, chert, gypsiferous marl, and phosphorite. The Campanian chert-phosphorite series lies on Santonian chalk and is overlain by the gypsiferous marl of Maestrichtian age. The phosphatic beds, which occur at several horizons, range in thickness from 0.5 to 10 m and in P_2O_5 content between 30 and 34%. The phosphorites are soft, friable, granular, and prevailingly gray or brown. In depth the color is gray to black, due to organic material. Locally the rocks have an oolitic structure. Material from 'Ein Yahav is white to gray with white pisolites. Fish remains are abundant. A characteristic feature is the presence of small, angular chert pebbles with a green crust. In the desert of Judea, lower-grade phosphates occur in the Santonian chalk series. Israel is reportedly producing by-product uranium from phosphorite.

In Jordan, Upper Cretaceous deposits occur at Er Ruseifa, east of Amman, in a cherty limestone formation that has undergone minor folding. It contains two to four beds of phosphorite with a total of 4.4 to 5.9 m of rock averaging over 70% calcium phosphate. Pulverulent phosphorite also occurs between Zarqa and Naqb Ishtar in four beds of 5 m total thickness, averaging 50% calcium phosphate (Quennell, 1951).

SENEGAL

Phosphorites occur in Senegal at Thiès, and in the districts of Pallo, Lam Lam, and Baraglou, as well as south of Thiès (Capdecomme, 1952, 1953). The phosphorites consist of aluminous phosphate cappings formed by supergene alterations of apatitic marine marls, clays, and limestones. They occur as pulverulent types, as layered types, or as hard and coherent breccias and are separated from the underlying marine formations by a screen of impermeable clay. The secondary phosphorites consist of crandallite, augelite, minor turquois, wavellite, and an unidentified Ca-Fe-Al phosphate. A section through them has:

4. A gray, earthy, pulverulent zone
3. Nodular rock in which the nodules, in some places compact and opaline, elsewhere disintegrated, lie in a porous cement
2. Breccia with fragments of the above nodules becoming finer downward, cemented by a porous paste
1. The impervious barrier, always clayey, in some places limonitic, containing concretions of calcium phosphate commonly strongly corroded

The deposits are similar to those of the leached zone of Florida and are lateroidal in origin. They are relatively rich in Ti (0.15 to 3.5% TiO_2) and contain fluorine, a little vanadium, and chromium. The uranium content is high, in the order of 400 g/ton (Guntz and Arene, 1953).

NIGERIA

Eocene prosphorites occur in the Abeokuta Province of Nigeria. The phosphatic mineral in much of the field is not collophane, but wavellite. Davidson and Atkin (1953) found:

	eU_3O_8, per cent
Collophane type (2)	0.004, 0.007
Wavellite type (4)	0.006–0.011

No F was detected.

The deposits (Russ and Andrews, 1924) occur along both sides of the railroad between Lagos and Abeokuta, approximately midway between the two, in lagoonal clays containing gypsum and aragonite. The original phosphorites (collophane type) are of marine origin, fine-grained to nodular. The fine-grained type is composed of 1-mm phosphatic grains and minor fossil remains and coprolites. The nodular rocks are coarser-grained types containing some wavellite with collophane. The vesicular secondary phosphorites consisting chiefly of wavellite overlie the collophane types and were derived by leaching of the marine phosphorites. Estimated reserves are 60 thousand tons of 60% BPL grade.

SOUTHERN AFRICA

In northern Natal, phosphate rock occurs in the upper Ecca shales (Permian) as hard gray nodules, lenses, and discontinuous layer. Some fish scales are included as well as fragments of phosphatized wood. In the Union of South Africa, near the base of the upper Dwyka shales (Lower Permian and directly beneath the Ecca series), collophane nodules occur near Laingsburg (Strydom, 1950). These phosphatic bodies range from spherical masses, about a foot across, to lenses up to 30 ft long and rarely more than 15 in. thick. In addition to collophane and secondary francolite, they contain carbonaceous material, quartz and mica fragments, local traces of pyrite and chalcopyrite, limonite, and radiolarian, fish, and tree stem remains. Specimens of compact black phosphorite from Laingsburg show very low radioactivity, $<0.01\%$ eU_3O_8.

Carbonaceous phosphorite in Karoo sediments at Livingstonia in Nyasaland contain 0.73% U_3O_8 (Davidson, 1956C).

INDIA

Phosphatic nodules occur near Trichinopoly in Madras in Cretaceous (Trichinopoly) clayey strata and contain up to 0.01% U_3O_8. Reserves are estimated at 8 million tons.

CHINA

Marine phosphorites occur (1) in the Fengtai district, North Anhwei, immediately east of the city of Fengtai and on the opposite side of the Huai River, and (2) within 15 to 60 km of Kunming in central Yunnan (eight deposits) (Hsieh and Chao, 1948). The Fengtai deposits consist of an upper phosphatic limestone and a lower phosphatic sandstone, the two forming a unit 0.5 to 1 m thick lying directly on a Cambrian basal limestone conglomerate. The phosphatic cement of the sandstone is believed to have been obtained by leaching of the overlying phosphatic limestone (5 to 10% P_2O_5). Probable reserves are 2,500,000 tons.

The Yunnan deposits consist of lenticular oolitic and ripple-marked collophane beds (20 to 40% P_2O_5) in limestone, 10 m above the Sinian-Cambrian contact. A bed of phosphatic quartzite underlies the contact. Probable reserves are estimated at 43 million tons.

• chapter twelve

URANIFEROUS MARINE BLACK SHALES

GENERAL

Uranium and such metals as Mo, Ag, V, Ni, Cu, Ge, P, Zn, As, and others (Krauskopf, 1955) are characteristically concentrated in environments in which carbonaceous marine shales are deposited concomitantly. However, not all black marine shales are notably radioactive; those of the sapropelic type more commonly are uraniferous, in contrast to those of the humic type. The uranium content generally falls between 0.001 to 0.03% U. Such shales are widespread in many parts of the United States (Fig. 12.1), Europe, and Asia, and doubtless occur abundantly on other continents where they have remained unrecognized because of their low radioactivity. Only in Sweden do black shales constitute uranium ore.

Petrology

Most uraniferous black shales contain in abundance sulfides, especially pyrite, minutely dispersed carbonaceous material, and disseminated distillable hydrocarbon compounds. They are usually low in calcite, but relatively rich in collophane (0.5 to 3% P_2O_5), either finely disseminated or in nodules as much as a foot across. Other identifiable minerals are clay species (commonly illite), silty quartz, feldspar, sericite, and chlorite. Pyrite occurs as minute crystals or as nodules and lenses. Fossils are uncommon. Although many uraniferous shales have been recognized previously as oil shales and in some formations there is a crude correlation between increasing oil content and increasing uranium, yet some oil shales are not especially uraniferous (Swanson, 1956). Usually shales that yield 10% or more distillable oil have appreciable uranium (Bain, 1950).

No discrete primary uranium mineral has been identified. Most of the uranium is in acid-soluble form. It generally increases with:

Fɪɢ. 12.1. Distribution of significantly uraniferous black shales in the United States (Swanson, 1956; *U.S. Geol. Survey*).

1. Collophane (or phosphorus) content (Whitehead, 1954)
2. Amount of colloidal matter
3. Carbon content or "blackness" (Burton and Sullivan, 1951)
4. Content of distillable hydrocarbons
5. Pyrite or total sulfur content

And it decreases with quartz, feldspar, clay minerals, and Fe_2O_3 content (Bates et al., 1954).

Autoradiographic studies show that the uranium is associated with both organic and mineral fractions. In the Chattanooga shale it is localized about concentrations of organic material and pyrite, but does not appear in resolvable particles. This uranium probably is either adsorbed by carbonaceous material or is chemically bonded as a urano-organic compound. However, in some occurrences uranium, although acid-soluble, is not removed by organic solvents and apparently is fixed in the argillaceous rather than in the organic fraction (Brown and Keller, 1952). Ross (1952) and Whitehead (1954) found that the radioactivity of shales from several Oklahoma, Texas, and California localities was concentrated to a greater extent in the inorganic matter (probably mainly collophane) by a factor of 2.5. Thus uranium may occur in black shales in at least three ways: (1) as an element isomorphous in collophane (pages 128–129); (2) as ions adsorbed on the surface of colloidal clay particles; (3) in carbonaceous material as a urano-organic compound.

The demonstrated ability of carbonaceous material to absorb uranium (in coal, petroleum, asphaltite, and in fossil carbonaceous trash and wood in sandstones) (Moore, 1954), the close association of uranium and organic material in many shales, and the essential absence of uranium in noncarbonaceous shales and clays, indicate that the uranium in black shales usually is contained in the organic material, probably as a compound.

Although no uranyl species have been detected in unweathered black shales, occurrences of various secondary uranium minerals have been found in rocks associated with black shales. These minerals have been formed by leaching of uranium from black shales by supergene solutions and deposition along fractures and bedding planes in nearby rocks or in lower shale strata. For example, torbernite coats cracks in a Pennsylvanian fire clay near Martinsburg in north-central Missouri, and metatorbernite occurs in clay in east-central Missouri (Keller, 1952). The uranium was probably leached from overlying Pennsylvanian black shales as they were eroded away. Carnotite also has been found in Ste. Genevieve County, Missouri, along joints in the Spergen (Mississippian) limestone and along bedding planes of the overlying black shale (Muilenberg and Keller, 1950).

When uraniferous black shales undergo low-grade regional metamorphism to slates, with resulting transformation of carbonaceous material to graphitic carbon, it is possible that the uranium may be reconstituted to fine-grained pitchblende. Black slates of the Precambrian Uncompahgre formation in the Upper Uncompahgre district, Ouray County, Colorado, commonly show radioactivity of 1.5 to 2 times background and are moderately radioactive throughout their exposures. At Bear Creek near U.S. Highway 550, sheared and crenulated zones in the slate, several to 10 ft wide, contain up to 0.5% U or eU. The higher grade bands are not over several inches to a foot wide. The zones contain pyrite and other metallic minerals. Spectroscopic analyses indicate a little Pb, Cu, Zn, and V. Burbank and Pierson (1953, p. 3) state, "The widespread radioactivity of the slates and the structural environment of local uranium concentrations are suggestive of an initial pre-Cambrian low-grade concentration, which has been enriched locally by early Tertiary processes of mineralization"; or locally obtained and concentrated by solutions active during the period of fracturing? Uraniferous carbonaceous Westphalian schists are known in the Schaentzel, Haut-Rhin, France (Roubault, 1956). The uranium mineral has not been identified, but an important total tonnage is represented.

Origin

Very slow accumulation of fine-grained sedimentary material, chiefly colloidal clay particles, with simultaneous and continued coverage of partly decomposed, finely comminuted carbonaceous material, or similar slow deposition with poor circulation, toxic conditions, and little oxygen, are combinations of environmental factors under which marine black shales are deposited.

As the carbonaceous mud accumulated, it adsorbed uranium and other metallic ions selectively from sea water and doubtless continued to receive some uranium from water expelled during diagenesis and lithification; in any event the uranium is syngenetic or penesyngenetic. The chief agent of absorption was carbonaceous matter, but if phosphatic colloids were available, uranium was differentially attracted to them, as is evidenced by these features: (1) in shales containing phosphatic lenses more radioactivity is associated with these lenses than with the organic portions; (2) where the black shales occur in a thick phosphorite sequence, the shales are usually not appreciably radioactive and the bulk of the uranium is concentrated in the phosphorites; and (3) experiments by Moore (1954) show that ground phosphate rock extracts 63% uranium from solutions whereas oil shale removes but 28%.

This latter relationship also may indicate that the uranium was obtained from sea water chiefly locally, with relative impoverishment during periods of phosphate deposition. However, in restricted embayments uranium doubtless is replenished by circulation, with new uranium obtained chiefly from granitic terrains under the attack of chemical weathering (Strøm, 1948; McKelvey et al., 1955).

Normally where phosphatic colloids were subordinate, uranium ions were adsorbed mainly by carbonaceous material, or to a lesser extent by colloidal clay particles, over a long period of time. McKelvey et al. (1955) suggest that uranium precipitation takes place only when the pH and Eh lie within narrow limits.

CHATTANOOGA SHALE

The Chattanooga shale (late Devonian) occurs chiefly across central Tennessee extending into Alabama and Kentucky, underlying 40,000 sq mi (Conant, 1956) (Fig. 12.2). Of the radioactive shales in the United States, it is the most favorable possible future low-grade uranium source, because it is relatively radioactive, widespread, relatively thick, and is generally not deeply buried (Swanson, 1956). Slightly radioactive correlatives of the Chattanooga are (in Michigan) Antrim, (in Indiana, Illinois, and Kentucky) New Albany, (in Ohio and Kentucky) Sudbury and Kentucky, (in New York) Dunkirk member of the Perrysbury, (in Kansas, northern Arkansas, and Oklahoma) Chattanooga, and (in Texas and Oklahoma) Woodford.

In Tennessee, the Chattanooga is generally less than 35 ft thick (knife-edge to several hundred feet), consisting of black siliceous shale and gray clay shale, minor thin sandstone and chert layers, limestone lenses, and phosphatic nodules. Bentonite is present locally (Conrad et al., 1954), and a 0.1-ft bentonite bed near the top of the upper unit of the Dowelltown member underlies at least 4,000 sq mi in east-central Tennessee (Hass, 1956). Plant remains are abundant, as are conodonts, fish bones, and linguloid brachiopods. The shales yield 3 to 15 gal oil/short ton.

The upper radioactive units contain 25% silty quartz, 35% clay, feldspar, and mica, 20% carbonaceous material, 15% pyrite, and accessory calcite, collophane, chlorite, and heavy detrital minerals. The uranium content (0.001 to 0.035%) is uniform over large areas, correlating positively with "blackness," total carbon, pyrite, and sulfur, and negatively with iron and clastic minerals (Bates et al., 1954). Uranium, however, is independent of pyrite (Bates and Strahl, 1956, 1957). The uranium is localized chiefly around concentrations of organic material and pyrite and exists chiefly as a colloidal phase dispersed through the organic material (Deul, 1955), probably a urano-organic compound (Swanson, 1953). Certain "bitumen" layers are richest in uranium and a particular time-stratigraphic unit has its highest uranium content where it is thinnest, other

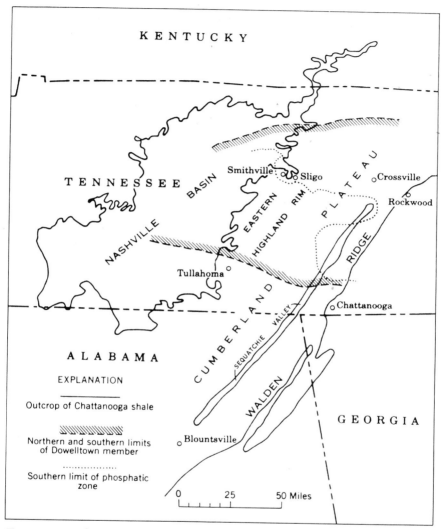

Fig. 12.2. Distribution of the most uraniferous part of the Chattanooga shale (Brown, 1956; *U.S. Geol. Survey*).

487

factors equal. In central Tennessee the upper member (Gassaway), 15 ft thick, averages 0.007% U. In eastern Tennessee the vertical variation in uranium content is (Brown, 1956):

U, *per cent*

Gassaway member:
    Phosphatic zone............ 0.0016–0.0036
    Top black unit............ 0.0060–0.0086
    Upper siltstone............ 0.0028–0.0058
    Middle black unit......... 0.0039–0.0066
Dowelltown member:
    Middle gray unit.......... 0.0011–0.0020
    Lower black unit.......... 0.0024–0.0052

Trace amounts of Be, Zr, Ga, B, Ag, Sc, Y, Yb, La, Pb, Cr, Cu, Co, Ni, V, Sn, Sr, and Ba cannot be correlated with uranium content.

The Chattanooga shale was deposited in a comparatively shallow sea, largely landlocked and lacking circulation. The source lands of crystalline rocks to the east may have provided uranium beyond that normally present in sea water, or abnormal amounts may have been derived from volcanic ash (Brown, 1956).

OTHER UNITED STATES OCCURRENCES

Illinois

Black shales in Illinois in strata of Pennsylvanian, Mississippian, and Devonian ages contain up to 0.017% eU, with 0.001 to 0.014% U_3O_8 (Ostrom et al., 1955). Phosphatic bands and nodules are more uraniferous than their host shales, containing as much as 0.075% U_3O_8. For the black marine shales in Pennsylvanian cyclothems of the western part of the Illinois basin, both geological data and statistical analysis indicate no strong regional gradient in radioactivity, supporting the idea that the uranium was deposited syngenetically rather than introduced diagenetically (Krumbein and Slack, 1956).

Midcontinental Area

Some 20 abnormally radioactive black shale beds, 0.5 to 2 ft thick, occur within Pennsylvanian sequences in eastern Kansas and adjoining parts of Missouri and Oklahoma. As much as 0.017% U has been found (Swanson, 1956); the associated coals are essentially nonradioactive. Many of these shales contain small phosphatic nodules that are more radioactive than their shaly matrix (Ross, 1952, page 467).

Northern Rocky Mountains and Great Plains

The Hartville formation (Pennsylvanian) in eastern Wyoming and western Nebraska includes several thin beds of black marine shale containing up to 0.019% U. The most radioactive beds, several thousand feet below the surface, which are less than 1 ft thick, usually contain more than 0.01% U, whereas beds up to 10 ft thick have only 0.005% U or less.

TABLE 12.1. *Other radioactive black shales in the United States*

Locality	Stratigraphic unit	Petrology	Uranium content	Reference
Michigan	Antrim (late Devonian)	Black shale	20 ppm U	Burton and Sullivan, 1951
Nebraska, South Dakota, northern Kansas, northeastern Colorado	Sharon Springs member of Pierre shale (Cretaceous)	Hard, pyritic black shale, a few feet to 500 ft thick	Up to 0.01% U in thin beds; usually less than 0.003% U	Swanson, 1956
Western Colorado	Hermosa fm. inc. Paradox member (Pennsylvanian)	Thin black shale	0.003–0.004% U	Swanson, 1956
Mississippi	Upper Cretaceous	Shale, sandstone, and chalk	6.5–12 ppm U	Burton and Sullivan, 1951
Central Texas	Barnett fm. (middle Mississippian)	Phosphatic black shale	0.015–0.033% U	Swanson, 1956
East Texas	Upper Cretaceous	Shale, sandstone, and chalk	3.3–6.7 ppm U	Burton and Sullivan, 1951
Playa del Rey, California	Miocene nodular shale	Phosphatic black shale	Some uranium in organic material, more in phosphate; avg. 16 ppm U	Ross, 1952 Burton and Sullivan, 1951
East-central Alaska, Nation River region	Calico Bluff fm. (Upper Mississippian)	Black shale	Traces of U	Nininger, 1954

489

Mapel (1956) has examined 22 formations containing black shale in North Dakota, Montana, Utah, Idaho, and Oregon. Most have less than 0.003% U, but several are higher, for example, thin black shales at the base of the Mississippian have 0.005 to 0.007% U in Montana, and an 8-ft phosphatic black shale bed at the base of the Brazer limestone (middle-late Mississippian) contains up to 0.009% U. On the basis of gamma-ray logs the Heath shale (late Mississippian) of Montana and the Dakotas contains as much as 0.01% eU. Swanson (1956) reports up to 0.009% U in the Heath shale and a 4-ft bed in Fergus County, Montana, with 0.006% U.

MANSFELD KUPFERSCHIEFER

The Kupferschiefer, a black bituminous Upper Permian shale, is widely distributed in central Germany and has been mined since 1150.[1] The formation, a bed about 2 to 3 ft thick underlying the Zechstein limestone, is regarded as having been formed in a long arm ($1{,}500 \times 200$ mi) of a sea extending from Russia across Poland and Germany to England (Trask, 1925). Locally the formation contains as much as 2 to 3% Cu, but larger areas are underlain by shale containing concentrations of Pb and Zn (Table 12.2). The metallic min-

TABLE 12.2. *Areas of the Kupferschiefer containing more than 5 kg/m^2 of metals (Deans, 1948)*

Metal	Area, sq mi
Cu...............	100
Pb...............	560
Zn...............	2,200

erals, bornite, chalcocite, chalcopyrite, galena, sphalerite, and tetrahedrite, occur as minute disseminated grains, as lenses, or small rounded masses, rarely over 0.1 mm long and generally parallel with the bedding. The ore also contains small amounts of Ni, Co, Se. V, Mo (Cissarz, 1930), Ag (0.015%), and U (2×10^{-7}%) (Kohl, 1954). The shale consists of clay minerals, quartz, sericite, and bituminous material.

Strong radioactivity is concentrated in a 1–2-cm pitchy horizon ("Erdpechhieke"), which is 20–50 mm above the base along the contact between fine- and coarser-grained shale and which is believed to consist of polymerized petroleum that has adsorbed uranium from the surrounding shale (Kohl, 1954).

Where the shale is undisturbed sulfide particles do not replace shale. In faulted and folded zones migration of copper sulfides appears to have occurred, with consequent replacement textures. The distribution of the ore, however, is generally independent of faults, except that barite-quartz veins

---

[1] Upper Zechstein rocks are evaporites; thus in the Mansfeld region, copper and potash have been produced from the same mine, but from different levels.

with the Ag-Co-Ni-Bi-U assemblage of minerals occupy some faults ("Rücken") (page 288).

Syngenetic deposition of the metals is favored by many geologists who have studied the deposits, with some diagenetic or supergene alterations. Under this theory, copper, lead, and zinc were contributed to the black shale environment of the shallow Zechstein sea by meteoric ground waters, with the traces of vanadium, nickel, molybdenum, etc., representing biogene concentrations either of aquatic organisms or humus soils. Krauskopf (1955) suggests that the prevailing climate before and during deposition may have been arid, permitting some previous concentration of heavy metals in a redbed environment. The source of the unusual amounts of the metals may well have been the veins of the Harz and Erzgebirge (Deans, 1948; Kautzsch, 1956).

The Kupferschiefer deposits compare in many respects with the Nonesuch cupriferous shale deposits of northern Michigan, which are regarded as syngenetic (White, W. S., 1953), but which are not uraniferous.

ALUM SHALE, SWEDEN AND NORWAY

Strata of uraniferous alum shales (Cambrian, Ordovician) occur widely in six areas of southern Sweden, especially in the Billingen-Falbygden district of Västergötland Province and in the Kvarntorp district, Närke Province, and also in Norway in the Oslo district (Svenke, 1956; Siggerud, 1956). In Sweden, beds richest in uranium begin the *Peltura scaraboides* zone, which contains a carbonaceous substance, kolm, megascopically not unlike boghead coal, in layers and lenses. The shale itself contains 200 to more than 400 g U/ton, whereas the kolm contains about 3,000 g U/ton. The inorganic constituents of the kolm, with which the radioactivity is chiefly associated (Ross, 1952) are fine-grained pyrite, carbonate, and phosphate.

In Västergötland, uraniferous shale underlies about 500 sq km, averages 3 m thick, and 300 g U/ton. The ore reserves here are estimated to be about one million tons. In the Kvarntorp district the 5- to 6-m bed contains 200 g U/ton with reserves of 100,000 tons. It overlies an oil shale which is also mineable for its 5% kerogen content. The possibility of the recovery of by-product sulfur and vanadium also has been investigated. Kolm was mined at Stora Stolan in 1909 for radium. About 200 tons of kolm with 0.5% U_3O_8 was obtained from 8,000 tons of shale.

In the Oslo district, Norway, the formation consists of alum shales with calcite concretions, interbedded with limestone, flat-lying in the south, folded in the north. The highest uranium content (170 ppm) is in the *Eurycare* and *Peltura* zones (Upper Cambrian). The beds are 10 to 15 m thick, contain 50% carbonate, and average 100 ppm U. Uranium and bituminous material increase together, except in the northern folded strata, but kolm is absent. Some of the very fine grained, pyritiferous shale contains as much as 0.15% V_2O_5. Discrete radioactive particles are absent. Although the volume of rock available is large, the Norwegian material is uneconomic. The shales are regarded as having been deposited as sapropelic muds, the uranium being syngenetic.

In northern Norway at Holandsfjord in Nordland, a mica schist of the

Caledonian mountain chain contains uraniferous graphitic layers. The bands contain:

Quartz	35%
Feldspar	15
Mica	35
Graphite	7
Metallic minerals	8

Pitchblende forms discrete grains; pyrrhotite is the chief metallic constituent. It is estimated that the reserves are 350,000 tons averaging 140 ppm U and 2 million tons averaging 35 ppm U. It has been suggested that the graphitic schist represents the metamorphosed equivalent of the alum shales, with uranium reconstituted as pitchblende during orogeny (Siggerud, 1956).

U.S.S.R.

The Cambro-Ordovician *Dictyonema* shales of the Leningrad district, U.S.S.R., contain 0.008 to 0.03% U_3O_8, with up to 0.21% eU_3O_8 reported in material from the Popovka River region. Bain (1950) estimates that the reserves of the district are about 100,000 tons U_3O_8, but that 5,000 to 10,000 tons of rock would have to be treated to yield 1 ton of U_3O_8. The equivalent of the Swedish alum shale also occurs in Estonia and is uraniferous.

Along the north flank of the Alai Range south of the Ferghana basin, thick black shales and slates (Silurian) contain up to 0.05% U_3O_8, but supergene enrichment under desert conditions probably has increased the grade near surface.

According to Bain (1950), the Kara-Tau carnotite deposit (page 441) represents a surface enrichment in bituminous shale.

According to Althausen (1956) both the platform facies (Baltic region, Sweden, and the Siberian platform) as well as the geosynclinal facies (Kara-Tau, Tian-Shan, Ulutau, and Timan) of the Cambro-Ordovician black shales contain relatively high concentrations of Mo, V, P, Ba, and Sr (and presumably U).

RADIOACTIVE NODULES IN NONCARBONACEOUS SHALES

Radioactive vanadiferous nodules occur sparsely in Permian-Triassic marls in many localities in England, especially in Permian beds west of Budleigh, Salterton, in Devon (Carter, 1931; Perutz, 1939; Davidson, 1956A), where they occur in red marls and are surrounded by bleached halos. The concentrically banded masses range from 0.5 mm to 30 cm in diameter. Most show a dark hard core, an intermediate lighter shell, and an outer black zone with stellate ribs extending to the edge of the nodule. Much of the radioactivity is concentrated as a film along the boundary between light and dark shells, the latter containing up to 13.96% V_2O_5 (probably as black vanadium oxide minerals), the former containing only 1.91% V_2O_5. Niccolite also is present at the contacts, along with two unidentified metallic minerals. Uranium ranges from 0.3 to 0.5%. The thickness of the bleached halos varies unsystematically with the diameter of the nodules. The halos are lower in Fe^3 than the unbleached clay.

Similar vanadiferous nodules are reported from coal mines in the Rotliegende (Permian) at Ölsnitz and other localities in Saxony (Schreiter, 1925A,B). Here in red shale occur ovoid to subspherical masses of dark greenish-black material, 1 mm to 4 cm across, containing about 15% V_2O_5, enclosed in a pale green halo with but 0.1 to 2.4% V_2O_5. The color of the green halo is ascribed to reduction of Fe^3 of the red clay to Fe^2 in the presence of vanadium.

On Sibley peninsula on the north shore of Lake Superior near Nipigon, Ontario, nodules similar to those of Devon occur in the Sibley series (Proterozoic?), a sequence of flat-lying sediments about 500 ft thick. Two members of red mudstones and shale, aggregating 400 ft in thickness, contain locally abundant nodules at intervals over 50 mi (Tanton, 1948). Individual nodules range from a fraction of an inch to several inches in diameter. Bleached halos surround the nodules, which are concentrically shelled in black, grayish or reddish buff, and white. Some nodules are composites of two or more; some are dotted by bleached spots. The radioactivity is concentrated in the black shells.

The vanadiferous nodules of England are suggested to be biogenetic in origin (Perutz, 1939), but this is not likely for those in the unfossiliferous Sibley formation, if it is of Proterozoic age. Tanton (1948, p. 74) suggests they are ". . . due to inorganic agencies operating in sediments derived from the erosion of amygdaloidal lavas and tuffs lower in the Kaministikwan group." Actually the nodules have not been studied sufficiently to formulate any theory of genesis.

And many a luminous jewel lone
—Crystals clear or a-cloud with mist,
Ruby, garnet, and amethyst—
Made lures with the lights of streaming stone
In the clefts of the hills of Habersham

Song of the Chattahoochee
Sidney Lanier

• chapter thirteen

PLACER DEPOSITS

OF RADIOACTIVE MINERALS

GENERAL

Introduction

Placer deposits, either alluvial or littoral, of radioactive resistate minerals are among the most widespread of radioactive mineral deposits. By far the largest fraction of thorium and uranium in clastic sedimentary rocks is contained in detrital grains of a relatively few species of radioactive resistates. The grade and size of these deposits vary greatly, but until recently they have served as sources of most of the world's thorium and cerium rare-earth elements, largely from monazite, which commonly has been secured as a by-product to the production of ilmenite, cassiterite, gold, or zircon. However, a few placers have been operated chiefly for monazite. The quantity and variety of resistates in placers are functions of (1) the nature of the source rocks underlying the parent terrains, (2) the nature and intensity of weathering in source area, (3) the distance and duration of transportation, (4) the extent of reworking at the site of deposition, and (5) in some cases, particularly for consolidated placers, the extent of authigenic changes, including intrastratal solution.

Stability of Radioactive Minerals

Many of the discrete uranium minerals of igneous rocks, pegmatites, and hydrothermal ore bodies are readily altered upon weathering or destroyed by abrasion and solution during transportation. This is due to

1. The ease with which U^4 is oxidized to U^6 and the extensive solubility of the uranyl ion

2. The metamict character of many multiple oxides and some silicates that contain uranium and thorium

494

3. The fine grain, micaceous character, softness, and general solubility of most of the uranyl carbonates, sulfates, phosphates, arsenates, vanadates, and silicates

Neither uraninite (in crystals) nor pitchblende normally survives even mild weathering or transportation. The ease of surficial alteration of uraninite to gummite and to an extensive assemblage of secondary uranyl minerals is notorious. Even where unaltered pitchblende may be available, it disappears quickly with transportation. Davidson (1953) has pointed to the absence of pitchblende in the placers around Placer de Guadalupe, Chihuahua, Mexico (pages 315–316), where gold veins contain pitchblende. At Carbis Bay on the north coast of Cornwall, an old mine dump feeds pitchblende into a small pebble beach (Davidson and Cosgrove, 1955). Rounded pitchblende fragments appear among the gravel, but upon comminution to sand size the pitchblende is destroyed, chemically and physically, within a few hundred yards along the shore line.

Although uraninite has been rather widely reported in placers, examination has in most cases proved the mineral to be thorianite. The addition of thorium to uraninite markedly increases its resistance to weathering and transportation. Authenticated placer pitchblende has been reported by Steacy (1953) from British Columbia. Some thorium minerals, especially thorite and thorianite, are somewhat more resistant and survive considerable weathering and transportation. Metamict thorium minerals are destroyed readily.

The bulk of uranium and thorium in placers is in mildly radioactive species that are widespread as accessory minerals in most igneous and many metamorphic rocks. These are chiefly zircon, monazite, xenotime, apatite, and sphene. Zircon and monazite are relatively stable heavy detritals (Table 13.1).

TABLE 13.1. *Stabilities of some heavy minerals (Dryden and Dryden, 1946), with garnet as 1.0*

Mineral	Stability index
Zircon	100
Tourmaline	80(?)
Sillimanite	40
Monazite	40
Kyanite	7

Types

Radioactive placers, on the basis of their geological history, are of three types:

1. Alluvial placers
2. Littoral placers
3. Consolidated placers

On the basis of the mineral or minerals chiefly responsible for the radioactivity, placers can be grouped into three intergradational categories:

1. Monazite placers
2. Zircon placers
3. Placers of "radioactive blacks"—euxenite, samarskite, thorite, thorianite, and betafite

Monazite placers may be formed in stream channels or along beaches, and most consolidated ("fossil") placers are of the monazite type. Zircon-rich placers are principally of the beach type but may also be consolidated. "Radioactive black" concentrations occur almost always in river placers that have been transported but short distances, although thorite may persist to the ocean shore, if the distance is not great. Although in many cases the "blacks" are derived from pegmatites, it now appears that euxenite, thorite, and probably other radioactive complex oxides may occur widely but erratically distributed as primary accessory minerals in such igneous rocks as granite and syenite.

Origin

Concentration of heavy minerals in stream placers requires (1) a large outcrop area of suitable host rock which contains radioactive accessory minerals; (2) disintegration and decomposition of the host to free these relatively resistant accessories; (3) residual concentration of the heavies through subtraction of much of the light fraction of chemically susceptible species by weathering and erosion; (4) relatively rapid movement of this somewhat concentrated mantle to streams; and (5) trapping and concentration of heavy fractions, e.g., within meanders, behind bars, and at the mouths of canyons emptying onto flood plains.

In some cases special geological conditions, as for example glacial disturbance of drainage, permitted the accumulation of valley fill. Compared to gold, monazite is much more mobile in stream sands and thus tends to be dissipated downstream and to avoid concentrations along bedrock surfaces. Many gold placers contain some monazite, and it is present in nearly all of the cassiterite placers of the world.

Steps common to the geological history of titaniferous littoral placers, which usually contain zircon and/or monazite, are (Gillson, 1949):

1. The existence of a large source area of "crystalline" rocks—granitic rocks, gneisses, and schists, containing the heavy minerals as accessories
2. A period in which a deep, extensive regolith was formed, from which magnetite and all soluble silicates were leached, leaving quartz, titanium minerals, and the accessory resistate silicates and phosphates
3. Uplift and rapid erosion of the soil zone and dumping of the sands into the ocean
4. Formation of a coastal plain sedimentary series, later elevated and eroded
5. Subsidence of the coast and attack of the sediments. Building of offshore bars. Concentration of heavies by wave action

Deposits of this type are characterized by the absence of magnetite, which was destroyed during weathering of the parent rock, and by the alteration of the ilmenite in varying degrees to leucoxene, which commonly is finely crystalline rutile, rarely brookite. This alteration is accompanied by progressive textural, optical, and x-ray changes and by progressive decrease in magnetic susceptibility (Lynd et al., 1954; Bailey et al., 1956). The altered titanium mineral is not "arizonite."

Significant beach placers tend to lie along coasts of considerable stability or those that are slowly emergent. Deposits on Recent beaches may show considerable seasonal variation, with much stronger concentrations developed during monsoon weather or the spring tide period. Deposits occur on (1) Recent beaches, (2) offshore bars or spits, especially at the mouths of estuaries, (3) elevated beaches or bars, and (4) dune sands formed inland from beaches in regions of prevalent onshore winds. The last type is usually of lower grade than the others.

UNITED STATES

THE CAROLINAS AND GEORGIA

Distribution

Monazite occurs in North and South Carolina and Georgia in two crystalline rock belts of the Piedmont (Mertie, 1953), in residual saprolite derived from these rocks, in colluvial sheet wash accumulations, in alluvial placers, in Cretaceous to Recent sediments of the Coastal Plain, and in coastal placers (Overstreet et al., 1956). Alluvial placers were first worked for monazite about 1886 to 1917 in a belt about 150 mi long and 20 mi wide along the foot of the Blue Ridge in west-central North and South Carolina.

Bedrock Monazite

The western source belt stretches from east-central Virginia 600 mi southwestward into Alabama. The eastern belt has been traced from near Fredericksburg, Virginia, 200 mi south-southwestward into North Carolina and may continue further. The western or principal belt is underlain by injection gneiss discontinuously flanked on both sides by down-faulted, lower-grade (younger?) metamorphic rocks. The injection ortho- and paragneiss zone has been regionally metamorphosed to varying degrees, the core, 300×20 to 25 mi, characterized by accessory sillimanite, garnet, rutile, ilmenite, and monazite, and injected by concordant syntectonic bodies of quartz monzonite and related pegmatites and quartz veins.

The core rocks are the chief source of monazite, with a mean tenor of 0.006% monazite. Monazite from the eastern posttectonic plutons is markedly different in composition. Overstreet et al. (1956) state that high-grade tectonic and metamorphic conditions promoted monazite crystallization in the belt, whereas under lower-grade conditions rare earths and thorium were dispersed among other accessory minerals, and phosphorus formed only apatite. This inference that monazite is a mineral diagnostic of high-intensity conditions is not supported by its widespread distribution in a variety of deposits (pages 157–158).

Mertie (1953) conceives the belts as sites of premetamorphic valleys in which monazite collected. These sediments were converted to gneisses and partly remelted to form monazite-bearing intrusives. The ages of zircon and monazite from the metasediments and syntectonic quartz monzonite are both early Ordovician (about 400 m.y.). Zircon from posttectonic intrusives is probably Devonian in age (285 to 300 m.y.).

Colluvial Deposits

Colluvial deposits, poorly sorted and unconsolidated, consist of a clayey sand underlain by a thin quartz-pebble layer. Some are perhaps pre-Wisconsin, some are presently forming. They grade into, lap on, or are truncated by alluvial fill. A few colluvial deposits have 10 to 15 times the concentration of monazite in the crystalline sources, and such deposits, if reworked, give rise to alluvial deposits of tenor higher than those derived directly from saprolite.

Alluvial Deposits

Within the monazite belt valleys are small; larger valleys are common on both sides, but those on the west contain no monazite, and the eastern ones are poor in monazite. Richest monazite concentrations are in gravel and coarse sand near the base of the alluvial fill sequence, but some monazite also occurs in the progressively overlying clay, sand, and silt. An average concentrate contains, in order of abundance, ilmenite, garnet, monazite, sillimanite, zircon, and rutile. Some deposits also contain significant amounts of xenotime. The monazite ranges from about 1 to 42 lb/cu yd, with a mean of 8.4 (Mertie, 1953); values generally decrease downstream owing to dilution. Its mean ThO_2 content is 5.67%; its mean U_3O_8 content, 0.38%.

In Burke County, gold placers contain fergusonite pebbles with samarskite, monazite, and other heavies.

Coastal Plain Deposits

Fluviatile placers occur in streams that head within the Coastal Plain, deriving their monazite from Cretaceous rocks. Some are low grade; one with 1½ lb monazite/cu yd is on a branch of Sweetwater Creek, near Thomson, McDuffie County, Georgia. The source rock is the Tuscaloosa formation. Some are large and high grade: near Aiken, South Carolina, monazite and xenotime are recoverable from placers in the valleys of Horse and Holley Creeks (Fig. 13.1).

The heavy minerals in Coastal Plain sediments range from 0.001 to 0.1%, with monazite constituting less than 1 to 9% thereof.

Littoral Deposits

In general the Cretaceous and Tertiary sediments have served as intermediate hosts for monazite, between the crystalline sources (or vanished set of alluvial placers) and the littoral placers (Martens, 1935). The latter are Pleistocene to Recent, occurring generally 30 to 50 ft above sea level. However, some are on present beaches, and others are as high as 250 ft above sea level. In general, Pleistocene terraces are richer than Recent sites.

Fig. 13.1. Concentrate of detrital xenotime, Aiken, S.C. In medium with $n = 1.54$ ($\times 66$).

Fig. 13.2. Deposit of elevated beach sands enriched in heavy accessory minerals, Jacksonville Beach, Fla. Corner of battery of Humphreys Spirals for initial concentration, *right*. Cleaned sand, *foreground*.

FLORIDA

Distribution

Concentrations of heavy minerals occur in Florida along present-day beaches, in coastal Pleistocene beaches, and in inland Pleistocene beach deposits. Ilmenite, rutile, zircon, and other heavies are found in small amounts in the sand that covers most of Florida. Deposits at Mineral City were first exploited in 1916. Present major operations are at Jacksonville Beach, at Trail Ridge, near Lawtey, 17 mi north of Trail Ridge, and on Amelia Island. Numerous other occurrences are along the east coast, north of Fort Pierce, and on the west coast between Clearwater and Pensacola (Miller, 1945).

Mineral City

At Mineral City the deposits occur in long narrow strips near the back of the beach adjacent to the dune area. Some strips contain as much as 60% heavies, but the average is 20%. They range in thickness from 2 to 2½ ft and in width from 25 to 35 ft. The mineral content of the concentrate is:

Ilmenite	55%
Zircon	20
Rutile	6
Quartz	3
Monazite	2
Staurolite and epidote	14
Collophane	tr.

Jacksonville Beach

The Jacksonville Beach deposit (Fig. 13.2) lies about 40 ft above sea level and contains 2½ to 7% heavy minerals, 97.1% of which are between 0.21 and 0.074 mm in size. Concentrates (through Humphreys spirals, electrostatic and electromagnetic means) are prepared of (1) ilmenite, (2) rutile, (3) zircon, (4) monazite (Fig. 13.3), and (5) staurolite-kyanite-sillimanite. Also present

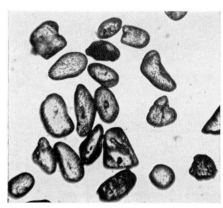

Fig. 13.3. Concentrate of detrital monazite, Jacksonville Beach, Fla. In medium with $n = 1.54$ ($\times 35$).

are garnet, epidote, hypersthene, hornblende, sphene, and tourmaline. The deposit is related to an abandoned channel of the St. John's River, probably lying at a former mouth.

Trail Ridge

At Trail Ridge the ore body averages about 1 mi wide, 35 ft deep, and is about 1½ mi wide at the north, tapering to a blunt point 3 mi to the south. Near the center the ore is 65 ft deep. Near the base below the water table is a zone of "hardpan," a few inches to 40 ft thick, consisting of sand cemented by black, tarry, partially carbonized organic material. The bottom of the ore zone is marked by a layer of dense woody remains consisting of unconsolidated carbonized branches, cones, peat, stumps, plant trash, and much argillaceous material. Values begin at the surface and average 4% heavy minerals, most between -48 and -150 mesh. The deposit contains ilmenite, leucoxene, zircon, staurolite, and kyanite-sillimanite, of which concentrates are made, and tourmaline, and a little garnet. Of the heavies 45% are titaniferous. Nearly absent are rutile, monazite, and epidote.

During the Sunderland stage of Pleistocene time, a small spit was extended from southern Georgia to the middle of present Florida, when sea level was 200 ft higher. Yoho (1956) also places the shaping of the spit in early to middle Yarmouth. The local concentration of heavy minerals took place on the west side during the formation of the spit which is now Trail Ridge (Carpenter et al., 1953).

Others

Vero Beach sands contain ilmenite—36%, rutile—27%, staurolite—20%, zircon—6%, and small amounts of corundum, hypersthene, epidote, garnet, kyanite, monazite, sphene, and tourmaline (Fig. 13.4). They are storm-line deposits, as are those at Ponte Vedra near Jacksonville.

IDAHO

"Radioactive Blacks"

The Bear Valley deposits, in western Valley County, 95 mi northwest of Boise, contain the following quantities of heavy minerals in pounds per cubic yard (Kline et al., 1953; Mackin and Schmidt, 1956): euxenite, 1.0, locally up to 3.0; monazite, 0.5; columbite, 0.2; zircon, 0.05; garnet, 5; ilmenite, 20; magnetite, 5. The deposits lie in the interior of the Idaho batholith, in whose rocks euxenite in trace amounts occurs at several widely scattered localities. The Bear Valley deposits are supplied by a 6-sq mi area of tonalite and associated pegmatites. In a single outcrop the weathered tonalite may range in euxenite from a trace to 0.05 lb/cu yd, with relatively rich concentrations segregated within a few square feet.

In addition to the minerals listed above, sphene, apatite, hornblende, biotite, epidote, rutile, anata·, allanite, xenotime, and spinel may be present. The ilmenite contains 0.80% Ta_2O_5 and 0.32% Nb_2O_5 (Shelton and Stickney, 1955). Alluvium deposited by streams entering from nonglaciated areas in early Wisconsin time contains an average of 30 lb heavy minerals/cu yd, whereas early Wisconsin outwash and morainal deposits average only 20 lb heavy concentrate/cu yd, and similar late Wisconsin deposits have but 10 lb heavy minerals/

FIG. 13.4. Heavy mineral recovery operation at Vero Beach, Fla., from elevated beach sand. Darker sand, *left and background,* is untreated; lighter, *right,* has had heavies removed.

FIG. 13.5. Concentrate of eluvial euxenite crystals, Bear Valley, Idaho ($\times 15$).

cu yd on the average. A deep pre-Wisconsin regolith was apparently available to nonglacial streams. The principal cause of accumulation of the valley fill in the Big Meadow part of the area is late Pleistocene glacial derangement of drainage.

In residual soil, euxenite appears as euhedra and angular crystal fragments 0.1 to 5.0 mm in size, with a tan alteration coating (Fig. 13.5). Within the first mile the average size of the larger grains decreases from 5.0 to 1.5 mm, and 5 mi from the source the average larger grain size is 0.8 mm, with few crystal faces. In another 5 mi the reduction of large grains is to about 0.5 mm. Because of this shattering the percentage of euxenite decreases very rapidly downstream.

Black sands from near Idaho City and Centerville, Boise County, are reported by Shannon (1922) to contain samarskite (euxenite?), columbite, polycrase, tapiolite(?), rutile, chalcopyrite, garnet, gold, monazite, ilmenite, zircon, and magnetite.

The heavy minerals in black sand from Dismal Swamp, Elmore County, are considerable columbite, less garnet and monazite, and small amounts of ilmenite, zircon (2.5% U and 5.5% Th), cassiterite, topaz, rutile, anatase, xenotime, samarskite, and fergusonite (Shelton and Stickney, 1955).

Brannerite occurs as crystals and grains in a gold placer near the head of Kelly Gulch, near Stanley, western Custer County.

Thorite Placers, Hailey

Thorite occurs as an accessory mineral in the quartz monzonite of a satellitic intrusion of the Idaho batholith, just southwest of Hailey in Blaine County (Robertson and Storch, 1955A,B). Segregations in the quartz monzonite contain as much as 1 lb thorite/cu yd, whereas adjacent rock averages but 0.005 lb/cu yd (Mackin and Schmidt, 1956). Common associated heavies are magnetite, sphene, hornblende, and apatite, and less common are garnet, ilmenite, zircon, allanite, rutile, and anatase. Small streams draining the richest source area contain gravel deposits with as much as 0.3 lb thorite/cu yd. The thorite in the residual soil and in the placers occurs as crystals and crystal fragments, several varieties, including uranothorite, thorite, and altered thorite, occurring together. Down valley the sharp decrease in grade is in part due to attrition, in part to dilution. The placers result from blocking of drainages by Pleistocene basalt flows. The mineral content in pounds per cubic yard is thorite, 0.5; zircon, 0.5; sphene, 1.0; garnet, 0.1; magnetite, 10.0.

Monazite Placers, Cascade

Monazite has been found in nearly every gold placer along the western margin of the Idaho batholith from Pierce at the north to the South Fork of the Boise River at the south (Storch and Robertson, 1954; Kline et al., 1955). The eastern margin of the batholith has apparently yielded little monazite, but gold placers with ilmenite and magnetite have been worked.

The monazite placers of the Cascade area, Valley County, which are in valley fill accumulated as the result of block faulting in Pleistocene time (Mackin and Schmidt, 1956), contain, in pounds per cubic yard, monazite,

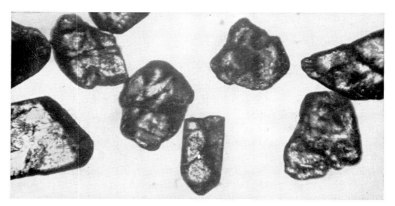

Fɪɢ. 13.6. Concentrate of euhedral and angular detrital monazite, Cascade, Idaho. Compare with Figs. 13.3, 13.8, 13.9. In medium with $n = 1.54$ ($\times 66$).

1.5; zircon, 0.2; garnet, 5.0; ilmenite, 40.0; magnetite, 1.0. Apatite also is usually present. Other minerals in placers on the western flank are corundum, gold, cinnabar, rutile, and columbite-tantalite. Monazite occurs as an accessory constituent of the Idaho batholith in porphyritic quartz monzonite-tonalite. The monazite is erratically distributed, ranging from nearly zero to as much as 0.3 lb/cu yd within a few tens of feet. The marginal migmatite is apparently poor in monazite, but local quartz-feldspar pods may contain up to 0.5 lb/cu yd.

Small streams heading in areas of rich granitic rocks have gravels containing as much as 10 lb monazite/cu yd. In Long Valley the deposits contain about 15½ lb of heavies/cu yd. Deposits of modern stable or slowly degrading streams have higher heavy mineral percentages than aggradational deposits in the same area formed by similar Pleistocene streams. In Pleistocene deposits, monazite decreases by 50% within 1 mi, whereas there is no significant change in modern deposits, owing to permanent withdrawal of some heavies in deposits not subject to reworking in aggrading streams (Mackin and Schmidt, 1956). Monazite, which can be traced from source areas for 25 mi, occurs upstream as euhedra and angular crystal fragments, 0.2 to 1.0 mm in size (Fig. 13.6). The ThO_2 content ranges from 1.6 to 3.2%. The zircon has a distinct yellow to red fluorescence.

In addition to the Cascade area, other important areas are in the Boise Basin, Boise County (Kline et al., 1950), and at Warren, southern Idaho County, which is estimated to contain 40,000,000 cu yd of gravels to a depth of 35 ft. Still other areas are listed by Schrader (1910) and by Kauffman and Baber (1956). The total of monazite sands in Idaho has been estimated at 200,000,000 cu yd.

CALIFORNIA

Beach Sands

Small amounts of uranothorite ($UO_2 = 6.95\%$) and monazite ($ThO_2 = 4.22\%$) occur in thin sheets and narrow lenses of black sand, many times repeated in depth in the back-shore zone of some California beaches between Princeton Beach, San Mateo County, and Pacific Grove, Monterey County (Hutton, 1951B, 1952) (Figs. 2.35, 2.36). Usual associates are hornblendes, pyroxenes, spinel, garnets, and zircon; rare are xenotime, allanite, euxenite, sphene, epidote minerals, cassiterite, apatite, rutile, brookite, chrysoberyl, diamond, tantalite, tourmaline, and other minerals. A beach sand at Crescent City yielded 56 lb of monazite per ton.

Gold Placers

Uranoan thorite occurs in black sands mined for gold in the Tuolumne River, near La Grange (George, 1951) and near Waterford and also in the Feather, Yuba, American, Mokelumne, and Merced Rivers between Oroville in Biggs County and Snelling in Merced County to the south, a distance of 200 mi. It occurs, too, in deposits from Scott River near Callahan in Siskiyou County to Atolia in San Bernardino County. Associates are garnet, chromite, hematite, zircon, rutile, monazite, ferromagnesian silicates, and local scheelite and cinnabar. Monazite has been recovered in a dragline gold-dredging operation near Lincoln, Placer County.

OTHER DEPOSITS

Stream placers in the San Luis Valley, Colorado, carry about 0.15% monazite. Heavy concentrates from Routt County have as much as 25% monazite.

In an Oregon sand from the Columbia River at Astoria 131 lb monazite/ton were found; others, however, had 1 lb or less. A beach at Gray's Harbor, Washington, yielded 71.5 lb monazite/ton (Bain, 1950). Other occurrences in Montana, Oregon, and Washington have been listed by Kauffman and Baber (1956).

OTHER NORTH AMERICAN DEPOSITS

ALASKA

Widespread Alaskan placer deposits that contain radioactive minerals are mainly small and low grade. Heavy concentrates from river placers very widely distributed range in radioactivity from 0.001 to 0.3% eU, but selected samples may be much higher. The radioactive minerals include zircon, monazite, sphene, allanite, xenotime, thorianite, thorite, uranothorite, and, less commonly, yttrocerite, thorogummite, gummite, eschynite, euxenite, pyrochlore, and radioactive hematite, malachite, and fluorite.

Beach placers occur around the point and south side of Seward Peninsula and contain zircon, monazite, allanite, sphene, xenotime, and locally a niobium mineral. The eU content of the heavy fraction ranges from 0.001 to 0.08%. Other beach and terrace placers occur along the coast of the Yakatago area, southern Alaska.

Detailed descriptions of individual placer deposits are presented by Moxham and Nelson (1952A,B), White (1952A,B), White et al. (1953), Bates and Wedow (1953), Gault et al. (1953), West (1953), Wedow et al. (1954A,B), Nelson et al. (1954), Robinson et al. (1955), and West and Benson (1953). Whether any Alaskan placers contain sufficient tonnages of radioactive minerals for economic exploitation remains to be determined (Matzko, 1955A).

CANADA

Black sands from the Fraser River near Lytton, British Columbia, contain (in decreasing abundance) magnetite (67%), garnet, ilmenite, zircon, rutile, olivine, platinum, gold, quartz, epidote, uranothorianite, chromite, feldspar, cinnabar, muscovite, calcite, scheelite, and sperrylite. The uranothorianite, both in cubes and rounded grains, is present in all sizes below 60 mesh (Thompson, 1954). Steacy (1953) has reported uraninite from a British Columbia placer at an unspecified locality, but from the accessory suite, the locality appears to be the Fraser River.

Black sands from Bugaboo Creek west of Brisco, British Columbia, contain "radioactive blacks," and according to Rowe (pers. com.) uraninite is present in minute euhedra, probably derived from a granitic intrusive in which it occurs finely disseminated. The primary occurrence thus may be similar to the source rocks for "radioactive blacks" in Idaho placers (pages 501–503).

On the southwest shore of Yamba Lake, 200 mi northeast of Yellowknife, Northwest Territories, heavy minerals have been concentrated where a large esker has been reworked by wave action. The nonmagnetic fraction contains 0.037% eU_3O_8, due chiefly to monazite (Lang, 1952).

SOUTH AMERICA

BRAZIL

Beach Placers

Distribution

Brazilian beach placers have been exploited for monazite since about 1895 and have been explored recently for ilmenite and rutile. During the first half of the twentieth century they supplied about half of the world's monazite. The deposits occur in a zone about 175 mi long from the northeast corner of the state of Rio de Janeiro north to the mouth of the Rio Dôce in Espirito Santo. Still further north is a group about 40 mi long in the southern part of Bahia, and some occur in Paraiba do Norte and Natal at the "hump" of Brazil. North of Macaé coastal sediments fringe the coast, lying thinly over Precambrian gneisses but becoming thicker northward, except where interrupted by river deltas. The beach deposits are associated closely with basal beds of these coastal plain sediments (Gillson, 1950).

General Geology

During Cretaceous peneplanation of the Precambrian rocks, a soil rich in heavy resistates was developed, and magnetite was eliminated. Following peneplanation, uplift caused rejuvenation and dumping of the regolith into shallow water of the continental shelf, where the sands were washed free of clay, to form Cretaceous or Tertiary sediments with a small percentage of resistates. Tremendous faulting along the coast dropped the seaward side, and where the shore line was made up of sediments, it was strongly eroded to form a sea cliff ("barreira"). Wave action against the "barreira" undercut it and concentrated resistates in a beach at its base. Offshore bars also were enriched. A recent uplift of about 5 m has elevated these deposits. Locally, however, the exposed strand has been completely destroyed and attack on the "barreira" has been renewed. Thus the deposits of heavy minerals are of the following types (Gillson, 1950): (1) elevated beaches, (2) elevated bars, (3) modern beaches, (4) rare dune deposits formed by wind modification of 1, 2, and 3.

Examples and Reserves

Deposits south of Vitoria in Espirito Santo and Rio de Janeiro are the most numerous and include the largest. Some, like several near Barra do Itabapoana, are nearly 2½ km long, with widths not over 20 to 50 m and depths to barren sand generally less than 4 m. The average grade here is 32% heavy minerals but some have more than 40% and locally up to 75%. The deposit near Guaratiba in Bahia is the longest bar of workable grade explored on the coast; it is 5,600 m long and 25 to 200 m wide. The deposits vary in size, shape, type, physiographic position, mineralogy, grade, and grain size. Some are covered with a veneer of as much as several feet of quartz sand.

In some deposits monazite is low; in others it is abundant, locally as thin golden streaks. The richest deposits are of the bar type, which are long, narrow, and shallow (Fig. 13.7). One of the richer large deposits is that of Comoxatiba in Bahia from which it is estimated 25,000 tons of monazite was produced. The mineral content of the sands is given in Table 13.2. The monazite contains 5

TABLE 13.2. *Heavy mineral content of Brazilian beach deposits* (*Gillson, 1950*)

Mineral	Per cent of heavies
Magnetite	tr.–3
Ilmenite	35–75
Monazite	1–20
Zircon	5–35
Rutile	0.5–5
Sillimanite	1.5–5
Kyanite	0.5–2
Corundum	tr.–0.5
Spinels	0.25–5
Staurolite	tr.–3
Rest *	tr.–3

* Rest includes garnet, tourmaline, andalusite, hornblende.

to 6% ThO_2 (Fig. 13.8). High-grade beach deposits are estimated to contain 50,000 to 100,000 tons of proved monazite reserves. The amount in low-grade deposits is great, but the recovery percentage probably would be low (Bain, 1950).

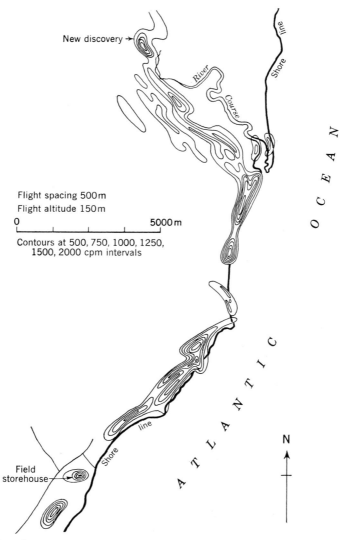

New discovery →

River

Course

Shore line

O C E A N

Flight spacing 500 m
Flight altitude 150 m

0   5000 m

Contours at 500, 750, 1000, 1250,
1500, 2000 cpm intervals

Shore line

A T L A N T I C

Field
storehouse →

Shore

N

Fig. 13.7. Airborne radiometric map of coastal monazite deposits, Brazil (MacFayden and Guedes, 1956).

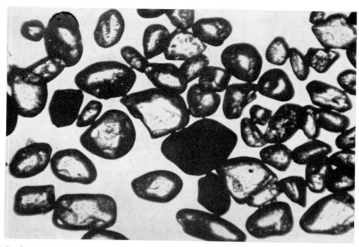

Fig. 13.8. Concentrate of detrital monazite with minor ilmenite (black), Bahia, Brazil. In Canada balsam ($\times$66).

River Placers

Monazite also occurs in gold placers in numerous localities in interior Brazil, as for example in the Santa Isabel do Rio Preto district; in the Pardo River near Maracao in diamond gravels; in the Contas River near Bom Jesus dos Meiras also in diamond gravels; and in gold gravels of Rio Paraiba do Sul. In gold gravels of the Rio Pomba and Rio Muriaba, monazite occurs with thorite, zircon, rutile, spinel, corundum, cassiterite, sphene, topaz, and garnet and other heavy silicates at 177 workable localities (Miller and Singewald, 1919). In some places as many as five layers have been found ranging from 4 to 48 in. thick. The deposits and others similar are estimated to have a total of 100,000 tons of monazite, of which 50% may be recoverable (Bain, 1950).

OTHER SOUTH AMERICAN OCCURRENCES

Coastal beach sands in several parts of Uruguay contain ilmenite and monazite, together with rutile, magnetite, hematite, garnet and fluorescent opal (Goñi, 1950). Monazite and xenotime occur in the Marudi Mountain gold placers of the Rupumini district of British Guiana. In Colombia, gold placers of Pato Consolidated Gold Dredging, Ltd., have 0.016% eU_3O_8 due to monazite and a mineral of the euxenite group that shows 1.4% eU_3O_8 (Davidson, 1953).

EUROPE

EAST PRUSSIA

Monazite-zircon placers occur on the south shore of the Baltic Sea in East Prussia, northeast of Sarkau in the Kurisch Haff. The deposits, which cover 955,000 sq m and extend to 0.4 m, contain 10% heavy minerals, of which garnet may be as much as 30%. Zircon forms 0.89%, and monazite 0.02% of the sand. Other constituents are rutile, magnetite, ilmenite, kyanite, staurolite, tourmaline, and hornblende. Reserves are estimated to be 4,000 tons zircon and 200 tons monazite (Wirtz, 1952).

SPAIN

A little monazite has been produced from beaches at the extreme northwest corner of Spain, in southern Galicia.

ITALY

Thorium, in hosts of monazite, uranothorite, and perrierite (Bonatti and Gottardi, 1950), occurs in Tyrrhenian beach placers derived from Quaternary potassic lavas and tuffs exposed in south-central Italy (Ippolito et al., 1956; Ippolito, 1956). Deposits of potential interest along the shore between Nettuno and just north of Torre Astura contain 440,000 tons of sand to a depth of 1 m, with an average of 60 g/ton of ThO_2. The pyroxene-rich sand also contains magnetite, ilmenite, garnet, zircon, and traces of cassiterite and gold.

Small amounts of thorite also occur in sands near Bracciano.

U.S.S.R.

Radioactive minerals are widely distributed in stream sands of the U.S.S.R. Monazite in some quantities is found in the Urymkau River in eastern Transbaikalia. Cassiterite is associated with monazite in parts of Transbaikalia. In gold placers of Aldan of the South Yenessei, monazite occurs. Monazite also is a constituent of alluvial deposits of the Selenga and Argun Rivers in eastern Siberia. In cassiterite placers of the near-polar Urals, thorite has been found, and monazite occurs in gold placers in the northern Urals. Monazite placers are found along the Yellow River in the Krivoi Rog region. The ilmenite sands along the Azov Sea are radioactive. In sands of the Tyzyl, Urdin, and Gizgit Rivers, northern Caucasus, monazite is found. Monazite-bearing gold placers occur in the foothills of the Pamirs, south of Tyuya Muyun. The Tchoruk River gold placers contain monazite, samarskite, and thorite. A conglomerate on the north side of the Timan Range is reported to be radioactive (Bain, 1950).

Davidson (1953) has reported that the radioactivity of Russian gold placer samples mainly from Siberia averages 0.005% eU_3O_8. The radioactive minerals are monazite, thorite, xenotime, samarskite, blomstrandine, and zircon. Bain (1950) estimates that 3,000 tons of monazite could be obtained annually by-product to recovery of 2,000,000 oz of placer gold.

AFRICA

During World War II, black sands with ilmenite, monazite, and zircon were worked near Rosetta and Damietta, near the mouth of the Nile, Egypt (Mertie, 1949). This represents one of the few deltaic deposits worked for heavy minerals.

On the Pampana River, Sierra Leone, gold placers have 0.7% $eThO_2$ or 0.23%

eU_3O_8, uranium being virtually absent. The radioactive minerals are monazite and a species akin to betafite (Davidson, 1953).

In the Ankobra River district of Ghana, radioactivity ($<0.1\%$ eU_3O_8) stems from monazite, xenotime, and zircon (Davidson, 1953).

Samples from gold placers in the Belgian Congo assay generally less than 0.02% eU_3O_8, with a few over 0.2%, one up to 0.6%. Radioactive minerals are monazite, thorite, euxenite, samarskite, and zircon (Davidson, 1953).

Monazite and somewhat more common thorite occur in tin placers of the Plateau tinfields in Nigeria; samarskite also is present.

In Nyasaland, monazite occurs in sands of the Shira River near Chiromo and in old beach sands on the southern shore of Lake Nyasa. The latter also contain as much as 59% ilmenite and magnetite. In the Tambani area alluvial sands contain assemblages of monazite, thorite, pyrochlore, betafite, and uranothorianite (Davidson, 1956B).

In Somaliland, monazite is a significant constituent of sands of the Suba River. In Northern Rhodesia near the Congo border, gold placers average about 0.4% $eThO_2$, which stems from large amounts of high-thoria (3 to 10%) monazite (Davidson, 1953).

Mozambique deposits at Marracuene have as much as 1% monazite; other deposits occur at the mouth of the Rovuma River.

Monazite occurs in stream deposits on Madagascar in long northwest-flowing rivers and in short east-flowing rivers. Some concentrates have 10% ThO_2. Some coastal sands contain monazite and thorianite. A few tons have been produced (Bain, 1950).

Other east and south African occurrences include Patta Island, Kenya; several localities in Tanganyika (including some Tertiary coastal sediments) and Uganda; with complex oxide minerals and cassiterite in Swaziland; and on Durban beaches, Union of South Africa.

ASIA

INDIA

Distribution

Monazite has been produced from ilmenitic deposits on the southwest coast of Travancore, India, which between 1911 and 1945 supplied about 40% of the world's monazite. The beach and dune deposits extend with interruptions from Cape Comorin, through Travancore-Cochin and Malabar, up to the Gujarat coast as far north as the Narmoda Estuary near Broach (Tipper, 1914; Wadia, 1956). The Travancore deposits are chiefly in four areas: near Chavara, between Muttum and Puddur, between Anjengo and Warkalli, and near Kovilam, south of Trivandrum (Nininger, 1954). The most important deposits are on an 11-mi beach near Chavara north of Quilan and on a mile-long beach at Manavalakurichi near Kovilam. The Travancore-Cochin sector of the coast is estimated to contain reserves of a little more than a million tons of monazite (Wadia, 1956). A rock ridge parallel with the coast has helped to form a rich deposit between the Neendakara and Kayankulam Bars. The deposit varies with the season, thick black sands up to several feet thick settling from the rough seas in monsoon months starting in June. The black sand contains ilmenite, about 80%; zircon, 4 to 6%; sillimanite, 3 to 5%; rutile, 4 to 6%; garnet, <0.5%; quartz, 4 to 5%; monazite, 0.5 to 1%.

On the east coast, deposits extend through Madras and Andhra up to Orissa.

Origin

The heavy minerals are derived from the crystalline basement rocks, chiefly granitic and migmatitic, on which they were initially concentrated in a deep, post-Pliocene laterite in which magnetite was destroyed. An important secondary source is the late Tertiary Varkalai formation which commonly crops out close to the beach deposits. At Manavalakurichi, heavies move from the Precambrian complex to the regolith and thence to the beaches. At Chavara, however, they are largely derived from the Tertiary sediments (Davidson, 1956D). Swept by rivers into the sea, the heavy minerals formed sand bars along the drowned coast. These were then concentrated into beach deposits, which were elevated and buried under dunes, later reworked by wave action. The localization of some deposits results from changes in land level and intricate stream diversions (Gillson, 1949). Deposits occur on present beaches, barrier beaches, and old, elevated inland beaches buried under dune sands.

On the east coast the currents flow from south to north with resulting northward movement of material, whereas on the west coast strong south-flowing currents transfer monazite southward.

Fig. 13.9. Concentrate of detrital monazite, Travancore, India. A few grains of ilmenite (black). In medium with $n = 1.54$ ($\times 66$).

Composition and Grade

Beach deposits contain up to 80% heavy minerals; dunes on elevated bars have 40 to 50% heavies. The minerals are ilmenite, rutile, zircon, monazite (Fig. 13.9), sillimanite, and kyanite. Rare are cheralite, baddeleyite, thorianite, sphene, cinnabar, and gold (Davidson, 1953). The average monazite content is 3%, rarely as high as 6%, with $ThO_2 = 8$ to 10%.

The total reserves for India are estimated to be 2 million tons of monazite (based on an average content of 2% monazite), containing 150,000 to 180,000 tons of ThO_2 (Wadia, 1956).

CEYLON

Beach Deposits

Monazite-bearing beach sands occur along the west coast of Ceylon from Colombo northward 130 mi to Mannar and south and east for 140 mi to Hambantota (Mertie, 1949). The chief deposits are at Kaikawala beach, Induruwa; Kelani-ganga; Kalu-ganga; Gin-ganga and Mahamodera; and Kudremalai. On the east coast, deposits are at Pulmoddai-Kokkilai, which is the largest black sand deposit on the island (at least 3 million tons with 0.3 to 0.4% monazite), and at Tirukkovil (Wadia and Fernando, 1945).

Black sand deposits are formed on beaches mainly at the mouths of rivers, but some occur in bays marking former mouths. Buried monazite deposits also occur in marshy land immediately inland from the beach. East coast deposits, although large, are low in monazite, containing as much as 75% ilmenite and less than 0.25% monazite. West coast deposits are smaller but richer in monazite, the monazite content ranging from 2 to 14%, locally reaching 20 to 22% (Kudremalai), and exceptionally up to 47% (Kaikawala).

The Kaikawala deposit has been formed by re-sorting of old alluvium between two headlands, about ½ mi apart. Rich concentrates are exposed only at two seasons between monsoons, the better harvest being secured in April to May before the southwest monsoon. Other minerals in the sands are ilmenite, rutile, zircon, garnet, spinel, kyanite, staurolite, hypersthene, hornblende, and a trace of gold. The zircon contains 0.3% ThO_2.

Alluvial Deposits

In alluvial deposits of the highland interior of Ceylon, thorianite in unabraded cubes is widely distributed and locally recovered in placer gem operations. In the Peak district, 9 tons were reportedly obtained between 1904 and 1910. The pockety deposits lie in narrow ravines near outcrops of thorianite-bearing pegmatites. The largest is in a small valley at Getahetta, the richest site being about half an acre of paddy fields, the alluvium of which contains up to 0.008% eU_3O_8 (Davidson, 1953).

KOREA AND JAPAN

Monazite-bearing gold placers in Korea have been worked for over 50 yr, but no monazite has been recovered. Shallow beach deposits also occur along the central part of the east Korean coast facing the Sea of Japan. Deposits at Pi-in on the west coast contain an estimated 6,250 metric tons of 80% monazite concentrates with 5,000 metric tons of recoverable monazite. Other localities are listed by Yun (1956). Samarskite occurs in a placer at Ryujomen and in at least two other deposits; fergusonite is recorded from three placers (Yun, 1956).

In Japan in Naegi-Machi and vicinity, in Gifu prefecture, stream placers derived from granite with vuggy pegmatites contain monazite, fergusonite, zircon, allanite, samarskite, and radioactive apatite, together with other minerals and cassiterite for which they were worked from the seventeenth to the twentieth century. The content of radioactive minerals ranges from 100 to 300 g/cu m.

CHINA

Taiwan

Monazite occurs on Taiwan (Formosa) in (1) coastal beach and dune deposits, (2) offshore bars off the southwestern coast, and (3) fluviatile placers (Shen, 1956). Most of the beach deposits occur along the high-tide line as narrow streaks averaging 1.2 m in depth and 4.5% heavy minerals, with as much as 40% locally. Those on the northern coast are low in monazite, but those of the northwestern coast contain monazite (3.4%) and zircon (8%).

Stream placers occur in central-western and southwestern Taiwan, in the latter several kilometers from the mouths of the rivers. They contain 5% monazite and 10.8% zircon.

Mainland

Monazite is said to occur in economic amounts in northeastern Kwangsi in the districts of Fuchuan, Hohsien, Kungchen, and Chungshan in cassiterite-bearing sands with ilmenite and magnetite. It is derived from the Kuposhan granite. It also occurs in Kianghwa in Hunan, along the coasts of Liaoning and Shantung Provinces, and in stream sands of Heilungkiang Province.

SOUTHEASTERN ASIA

Thailand

Monazite, euxenite, and an unidentified uranium-bearing Ti-Nb-Ta complex oxide mineral occur in cassiterite deposits associated with Cretaceous granites of Thailand. The minerals occur in weathered pegmatite and granite and in related eluvial and alluvial deposits, together with columbite-tantalite, zircon, ilmenite, rutile, garnet, tourmaline, topaz, some sulfides, and gold (Delegation of Thailand, 1956). Samarskite and brannerite are reported by Davidson (1956D).

Burma tin deposits also contain some monazite.

Malaya

Monazite commonly occurs widespread with cassiterite in eluvial and alluvial deposits in Malaya, particularly those in flat valleys. Concentrates from the Kemaman River also contain zircon and xenotime (Scrivenor, 1928). Monazite with 3.5% ThO_2 forms 41.3% of concentrates from Karangan and also is abundant at the Kambau mines. Euxenite has been reported in cassiterite concentrates from Titi, Jelebu field.

A few thousand tons of monazite reportedly were obtained as by-product to cassiterite mining between 1942 and 1944. A large number of samples from the chief states had an average ratio of monazite to 1 cassiterite unit as follows: Trenganu 15, Kedah 2, Dindings 0.3, and Pohang 0.2 (Bain, 1950). The monazite is reported to average 6% ThO_2 with significant uranium.

Indonesia

Some residual cassiterite deposits on granite in the Muntok district of Northwest Bangka contain large quantities of monazite and xenotime. The area is underlain by the Menumbing and Plangas granites, which have intruded and metamorphosed shales and sandstones of Permian or Triassic age (Bodenhausen, 1954). Ore concentrates from two mines in the Menumbing area contain 19 to 22% monazite, 1 to 5% xenotime, and 3% zircon.

The west coast of Sumatra has abundant monazite, which also has been identified at Dendang on Billiton, on Singkep, and on Borneo. Between 1936 and 1938, the Netherlands East Indies produced 1,570 tons of monazite.

AUSTRALIA

BEACH DEPOSITS

Distribution and Reserves

Large concentrations of zircon occur in beach sands chiefly

1. Along the eastern coast of Australia in northeastern New South Wales and extending north into southeastern Queensland, between Lennox Head on the south and Southport on the north (about 28 localities in 50 mi)

Other deposits are:

2. South of this main belt on the east coast at Swansea, just north of Sydney in New South Wales
3. In Victoria at Cape Everard
4. In southwestern Western Australia east of Albany at Doubtful Island Bay and Cheyne Bay and just south of Bunbury, at Bunker's Bay, Minninup, and Wonnerup
5. In the Northern Territory, north and northeast of Darwin, on Bathurst Island and at Port Essington

Australia has been the world's largest producer of zircon; between 1934 and 1950 nearly 180,000 tons of zircon was obtained. In the main eastern belt, ten deposits produced zircon in 1950; only Swansea outside this belt also produced in 1950 (Gardner, 1951, 1955). Small amounts of by-product monazite have been obtained.

From Stradbroke Island to Lennox Head the proved reserves in high-grade deposits is 2,500,000 tons of heavy minerals, with 970,000 tons of zircon and 12,500 tons of monazite.

Geology

The heavy minerals, which range from 20 to 80%, appear as flat seams formed between low and extremely high tide lines, generally on north-south beaches that have a headland or barrier at the north end. The deposits are thickest landward, feather out seaward and also gradually to the south. Deposits formed on former beaches are preserved behind the present beach beneath dune sands, in places as much as 20 ft thick. The prevailing wind is from the southeast and storm surf from the same direction concentrates the heavy minerals northward against barriers. Zircon varies from 10 to 40% decreasing northward and landward from deposit to deposit. Zircon and monazite tend to be a little more abundant in lower parts of single deposits. The range in composition of the concentrates is:

$$
\begin{array}{ll}
\text{Zircon} \dots\dots\dots\dots & 18\text{–}65\% \\
\text{Rutile} \dots\dots\dots\dots & 15\text{–}45 \\
\text{Ilmenite} \dots\dots\dots & 10\text{–}63 \\
\text{Monazite} \dots\dots\dots & 0.1\text{–}2.0 \\
\end{array}
$$

Other minerals are garnet and rare baddeleyite at Byron Bay.

The immediate source rocks are considered to be the Triassic-Jurassic Clarence series (Fisher, 1948), which obtained the minerals from Permian granite plutons of the New England area. Some of the minerals may have entered the placers directly. At the close of Pleistocene a 100- to 200-ft submergence allowed wave action to build bay bars and spits from promontories. A Recent emergence of about 10 ft has elevated the old coast line.

"RADIOACTIVE BLACKS" ALLUVIAL PLACERS

In several localities in Western Australia various complex oxide minerals occur in alluvial placers, derived from pegmatites (Table 13.3).

NEW ZEALAND

Radioactive minerals occur in beach sands on the west coast of South Island and of Stewart Island, in three main areas (Grange, 1955):

1. Recent beaches and elevated beaches from Bruce Bay to Hokitika contain uranothorite (Fig. 2.34).

2. Beach sands from the Grey River and coastal localities to the north (Greymouth to Westport) have monazite (4.93% ThO_2 and 1.15% U_3O_8) (Fig. 2.21).

3. Beach sands in the Port Pegasus area contain monazite (low U_3O_8).

In 10,000 cu yd of sand from Gillespie Beach (southwest of Greymouth) and Grey Valley, the content of radioactive minerals is: Gillespie Beach, 500 lb radioactives; Ngahere, Grey Valley, 200 lb monazite. The radioactivity is about 0.14% eU_3O_8.

TABLE 13.3. *"Radioactive blacks" placer deposits in Western Australia*

Minerals and per cent in concentrates	Locality
Samarskite................	Hillside
Fergusonite................	Copley
Gadolinite (30–32%), yttrotantalite (4–10%), allanite (16%), monazite (2%), euxenite	Cooglegong, 36 mi southwest of Marble Bar
Yttrotantalite (14%), monazite, cassiterite	Split Rock Station, 23 mi southwest of Marble Bar
"Calciosamarskite" (80%)..	4 mi northwest of Hillside Station, 43 mi south-southwest of Marble Bar
Yttrotantalite, cassiterite...	10 mi west of Hillside Station
Euxenite, cassiterite........	5 mi south of Francisco Well, 91 mi south of Port Hedland
Xenotime................	Nullagine, 55 mi southeast of Marble Bar
Euxenite (27%), monazite (69%), from cassiterite operation	Eleys Tin Field, 35 mi south-southwest of Marble Bar
Xenotime................	Donnybrook, 117 mi south of Perth
Xenotime, cassiterite.......	Greenbushes, 130 mi south of Perth

Other radioactive species found in New Zealand beach sands are (Hutton, 1950): gadolinite (Barrytown dredge), allanite(?), huttonite, thorite, phosphatian thorite, sphene, xenotime (Fig. 2.42), and zircon (Figs. 1.6, 2.45, 2.48). Some radioactive minerals may eventually be obtained as by-products to gold recovery.

CONSOLIDATED PLACERS

GOODRICH QUARTZITE, MICHIGAN

In the Palmer area, Marquette County, Michigan, the Goodrich quartzite (Upper Huronian) has a local basal cobble or boulder conglomerate and alternating beds of coarse quartzite and arkosic quartz-pebble conglomerate. Monazite, as rounded to subrounded detrital grains 0.10 to 0.20 mm in diameter, locally makes up more than 50% of the quartz-pebble conglomerate matrix, associated with hematite, magnetite, ilmenite, and rutile. It contains from 6 to 50 lb monazite/ton, and some glacial boulders contain 90 lb/ton. The monazite, which contains 8.3% ThO_2 and 0.22% UO_2 (Vickers, 1956A,B), is concentrated in 1-in. to 2-ft pebble conglomerate beds separated by quartzite layers 1 to 10 ft or more thick. Most of the monazite apparently occurs more than 300 ft above the base of the formation, which is 850 ft thick and overlies the Negaunee iron formation.

MONAZITE TYPE, WYOMING

Light gray to brown conglomerate in the basal part of the Deadwood (Cambrian) formation in Sheridan and Bighorn Counties, Wyoming, contains detrital monazite grains in the matrix. The monazite-bearing parts of the formation are as much as 8 ft thick and crop out for long distances along the Little Bighorn River valley. The grade ranges from 8 to 30 lb monazite/ton (Twenhofel and Buck, 1956).

ILMENITE-ZIRCON TYPE, ROCKY MOUNTAIN AREA

Radioactive, titaniferous, consolidated placer deposits occur in sandstones of Upper Cretaceous strata in Montana and Wyoming, subparallel with the Rocky Mountain front, and contain up to 0.056% eU and 0.02% U (Murphy and Houston, 1955; Houston, 1955; Murphy, 1955). In Montana, deposits are in the Virgelle sandstone, Horsethief sandstone, and St. Mary River formation between the Sweetgrass Arch and the eastern front of the Rockies from west of Cut Bank to northwest of Chouteau. In Wyoming, deposits occur around the peripheries of intermontane basins (1) on the southwest side of the Bighorn Basin on the flanks of Grass Creek and Waugh anticlines in basal Mesaverde formation; (2) on the extreme eastern margin of the Wind River Basin 25 mi west of Casper in the Lewis shale; (3) at the north end of Sheep Mountain near Laramie in the Pine Ridge member of the Mesaverde; (4) at the south end of the Rock Springs uplift in the lower part of the Ericson sandstone; (5) on the north flank of the Uinta Mountains; and (6) near Cumberland Gap, 17 mi south of Kemmerer in the lower part of the Frontier formation.

The deposits are beach concentrations transitional between marine and nonmarine facies, except those in the St. Mary River formation, which are fluviatile or estuary. Several cycles of advance and retreat may be represented by deposits at several horizons. They are lenticular, generally trending north, showing fine and cross lamination. The deposit at Grass Creek is at least 4 mi long and 800 ft wide. Some deposits are 3 to 6 ft thick.

The average content of heavy minerals is 70%, which consists of:

Ilmenite and anatase	78%
Zircon	17
Rutile	1
Garnet	3
Monazite	0.5
Tourmaline	0.3

Also present are magnetite, epidote, staurolite, spinel, and sphene, in a matrix of carbonate and hematite. Much of the hematite has been derived by destruction of ilmenite to anatase with release of ferric oxide. In Montana, magnetite is more abundant than ilmenite, whereas in Wyoming the ilmenite:magnetite ratio is 7:3. Some ilmenorutile with Nb may be present. The zircon is of two types: a euhedral colorless type that fluoresces bright orange, and a lavender, well-rounded, nonfluorescent type with 10 times more Sc and Y.

Numerous radioactive titaniferous deposits also have been found in several places in the San Juan Basin in Colorado and New Mexico in the upper parts of massive, well-sorted, regressive littoral sandstones of Upper Cretaceous age (Chenoweth, 1956). Another has been discovered on the flank of Grand Mesa, 20 mi east of Grand Junction. The resistant, ferruginous, lenticular zones contain up to 32% titanium in ilmenite, rutile, and anatase and 0.01% U and 0.051% eU in zircon (some fluorescent) and monazite. Other constituents are hematite, magnetite, garnet, tourmaline, and several rare-earth opaque minerals.

Five miles west of Gallup, New Mexico, a titaniferous, olive-green sandstone with irregular reddish streaks caps the massive cliff-forming middle member of the Gallup sandstone (Allen, 1956). The stratum is less than 4 ft thick, rarely more than 100 ft wide, and is traceable for 1,000 ft N. 25° W. As much as 40% of the rock consists of brookite, rutile, anatase, leucoxene, ilmenite, and radioactive zircon. Similar Cretaceous deposits also have been discovered in Utah and Arizona.

Radioactive zones that occur in the Stump sandstone (late Jurassic) along Gibbs Creek, Sublette County, Wyoming, contain as much as 0.003% eU in zircon (Houston and Love, 1956).

VIRGINIA

Zircon

A zirconiferous sandstone that crops out near Ashland, Hanover County, about 20 mi north of Richmond, Virginia, forms the western edge of the Calvert (Miocene) formation, which transgresses older Coastal Plain formations to rest unconformably upon Piedmont crystalline rocks (Watson and Hess, 1913). The bed is probably 2 to 3 ft thick, forming a narrow lens ⅝ mi long, trending N. 20° E. It contains quartz, limonite cement, 13 to 30% zircon, ilmenite, and an accessory heavy suite of staurolite, kyanite, garnet(?), and spinel(?).

Monazite

About 5 mi southwest of Martinsville, Henry County, an iron ore band in Wissahickon schist crops out along Highway 687. The banded ore, 12 to 20 in. thick, consists of 69% magnetite, 15% ilmenite, 9% monazite, 3% zircon, 2% corundum, and 2% quartz and other minerals. The well-rounded monazite and zircon have ages of 770 and 510 m.y. respectively, indicating that they were eroded from Lower Cambrian or Precambrian rocks (Mertie, 1955).

SPAIN

Medina (1956) notes radioactive beds in the Lower Silurian of the provinces of Jaén and Ciudad Real. They consist of quartzose sandstones of considerable extent, containing ilmenite, zircon, and a refractory mineral of the brannerite type.

> "Well," said the girl, "I can't marry you; dad has
> struck ile."
>
> Underground or Life Below the Surface
> Thomas W. Knox

• chapter fourteen

RADIOACTIVE HYDROCARBONS

URANIUM AND DAUGHTER ELEMENTS IN PETROLEUM FIELDS

Some crude oils are appreciably radioactive, and abnormal concentrations of radioactive elements and their decay products, including U, Th, and Rn, Ra, He, and A, have been found in some oil and gas fields of the United States and in some other countries. In addition the ashes of crude oils generally show enrichment in such metals as V, Ni, Co, Mo, Mn, Cr, Cu, Pb, Zn, As, and Sn. The presence of many others has been demonstrated, including Na, Mg, Ca, Ba, Al, Si, Ti, Ga, Pt, Ag, Au, Be, Ge, Li and P (Rankama and Sahama, 1950). Although some of these elements average only a few parts per million in petroleum, their concentration in the ash compared to those of the more common elements is unusual (Erickson et al., 1954; Pierce et al., 1956). Of the radioactive elements, radon and uranium tend to be concentrated in petroleum, whereas radium is concentrated in the associated brines.

The uranium and associated metals in petroleum may be present as colloidal particles or as dissolved metallo-organic complexes. If they are present in colloidal form, the uranium content of the source rock would have to be of the order 0.01 to 0.1% (Pierce et al., 1956). If they occur in solution, it is expectable that they are concentrated in a surface-active fraction coating the pore walls of the reservoir rock. Since the uranium content of ash derived from petroleum extracts or asphaltites of rocks is high compared to that of the ash of crude oil, and since uranium is usually enriched in seep oil compared to crude oil produced at the wellhead, it seems that the latter theory is the more likely (Pierce et al., 1956).

Tomkeieff (1946) estimates that the average uranium content in petroleum is 100 g/ton. According to Bell et al. (1940) the average content of radium in petroleum is 0.018×10^{-6} g/ton. The highly variable radioactivity of petroleum and the fact that crude oils from nonuraniferous provinces generally contain only negligible amounts of uranium (Erickson et al., 1954) suggest

520

that the uranium in petroleum is epigenetic. This is further indicated by the highly variable radon and radium contents of petroleum, in which the Rn/Ra ratio is over 4. Thus (1) the radon came from a source other than the radium, (2) radon was selectively collected by petroleum, (3) radium has been selectively removed from petroleum, or (4) radon and radium were present together in the same source but radium was selectively removed by another agency. The presence of abnormal amounts of radium in oil field brines without appropriate amounts of uranium indicate that the last is the likely hypothesis.

Breger and Deul (1956, pp. 420–444) state,

The association of uranium with petroleum is undoubtedly a result of the ability of petroleum constituents with certain functional groups to pick up and carry the element. Although porphyrins have long been considered important in the transport of metals by crude petroleum, it seems likely that asphaltenes, which are known to have carboxyl groups, and naphthenic acids may be more important as carriers. The association of uranium with petroleum is anomalous.

Banded precipitates of gypsum, barite, celestite, with minor limonite derived from brines in many oil fields in central and southwestern United States contain abnormal concentrations of radium, the radioactivity ranging from $0.0x$ to over 10% eU_3O_8, with concentration of radium in the brines themselves known to be even higher. The precipitates have been found in subsurface samples, in oil pipes, on the bottom of separator tanks, and in brine disposal ditches and ponds. Uranium in the precipitates is low (up to 0.006% U_3O_8), and in the brines there is no correlation between the radium and uranium contents.

The amount of uranium present is usually only a very small fraction of that required to support the level of radium. Autoradiographs show that celestite is the chief radium-bearing mineral. The sulfates have been precipitated because of solubility changes during pumping of brines and because of intermingling of Sr- and Ba-rich waters with sulfate waters (Gott and Hill, 1953; Pierce et al., 1956).

In a few wells in southeastern Kansas, some vuggy limestones and dolomites (Arbuckle and Kansas City groups) have an abnormal radium content, the highest radioactivity being equivalent to that of 0.26% U_3O_8 (Gott and Hill, 1953), but uranium is low in these rocks. The presence of minor amounts of some minerals (talc, fluorite, oligoclase, garnet, and magnetite) in the limestones and the concentration of radium in small areas suggest that the source rocks contain localized hydrothermal deposits of uranium. Knight and Landes (1932) have described igneous intrusives and hydrothermally altered rocks in southeastern Kansas. The cavities possibly represent molds from which mineral grains or hydrocarbons were removed, probably very recently, perhaps even upon contact with the drilling solutions.

Gas from wells in the vicinity of helium-bearing gas wells in Central and Southwestern United States also contains radon in abnormal concentrations, in some fields as much as 25 to 40 times the average radon content of soil gases, although no direct correlation between radon and helium contents has been found (Faul et al., 1954; Pierce et al., 1956). The highest radon concentrations in the helium-bearing gases of the Panhandle field coincide with the presence of uraniferous asphaltites. in the reservoir rocks. The association of gamma-ray anomalies, uraniferous asphaltites, radium-bearing brines, and in some cases also concentrations of radon with accumulations of helium in gas and oil fields, suggests that the major part of the helium is radiogenic, derived from petroleum source rocks and rocks through which petroleum moved. Further support for this theory lies in the fact that the helium content of natural gases increases with the age of the reservoir and in the fact that the measured ratios of He^3, He^4, and A^{40} in the gases are in close agreement with ratios calculated to result from radiogenic decay of the amounts of U, Th, and K^{40} present in crustal rocks.

Pierce et al. (1956, p. 498) conclude that

Uranium has been redistributed and concentrated within the interstices of rocks through which petroleum has migrated or in which it has accumulated. The concentration and redistribution of uranium has been associated in time with structural and diagenetic events including recrystallization, solution, cementation, and adsorption of metalliferous surface-active fractions of migrating petroleum. The result has been to make uranium and its daughter elements easily accessible to fluids and gases.

URANIFEROUS SOLID HYDROCARBONS

GENERAL

Radioactive hydrocarbons occur in a wide variety of geological environments:

1. Pegmatite dikes (thucolite, carburan)—Pied des Monts, Quebec; Wallingford pegmatite, Buckingham, Quebec; Conger and Henvey Townships, Parry Sound district, Ont.; De Kalb Junction, Lawrence County, N.Y.; Amaki village, Fukuoka prefecture, Japan; Osterby, Darlana, Sweden; Northern Karelia, U.S.S.R.

2. Skarn iron ores ("anthracite")—Norberg, Dannemora, Eriks mine, Lilla Kallmora mine, Sweden.

3. Polymetallic hydrothermal veins and lodes (thucolite, "anthracite," anthraxolite)—Moonta copper mine, Adelaide, South Australia (page 252); Laxey Pb-Zn mine, Isle of Man (Davidson and Bowie, 1951); Boliden Au-As mine, Sweden (Aminoff, 1943); Nicholson and Box mines (Co, Ni, U), Goldfields district, Sask.; Port Arthur area, Ont. (with Ag and Ni); Placerville district, Colo., Black King and White Spar mines; in one mine of the Idaho Springs district, Colo. (Sims and Tooker, 1956). In mineralized metaconglomerates—Blind River, Ont. (pages 261–263); Witwatersrand, Union of South Africa (page 322).

4. Veins of asphaltite—Mendoza and Neuquén, Argentina; ashes have up to 1% U (Angelelli, 1956); veinlets and nodules in slate along felsite dikes near Chaleur Bay, New Brunswick (Gross, 1957).

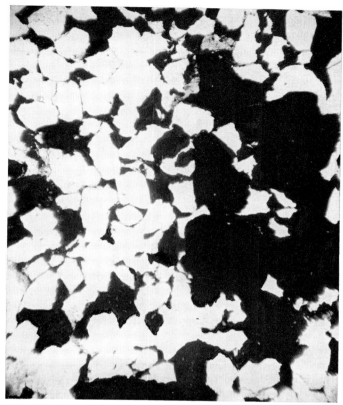

FIG. 14.1. Uraniferous asphaltite (black), interstitial to and corroding quartz grains, Moss Back sandstone, Chinle formation, Marsh Bank mine, Temple Mt., Utah ($\times 35$).

5. Impregnations in granite gneiss and mica schist (humite)—Nullaberg, Värmland Province, Sweden.

6. Seams, pellets, nodules, and pore and fracture fillings in quartzose and arkosic sandstones and conglomerates—west-central California; northeastern Utah; south-central Oklahoma (Hill, 1954); southwestern Missouri; scattered localities in Texas, New Mexico, Wyoming, and Montana (Hail et al., 1956); Temple Mountain, Utah (Fig. 14.1) (pages 408–410); Ambrosia Lake, N.Mex. (pages 413–416).

The hydrocarbon material varies widely in composition, physical and optical properties, and radioactivity (pages 121, 124). In many cases more than one organic substance may be distinguished microscopically. The radioactivity in most cases stems from minute, discrete particles of uraninite, coffinite, thorite, and less commonly thorian uraninite or possibly thorianite(?) (Davidson and Bowie, 1951; Pierce et al., 1956; Gross, 1957), although locally in some deposits the distribution of the radioactivity is so uniform and on such a scale as to indicate that a urano-organic compound may be present, e.g., at Temple Mountain, Utah (Kerr and Kelley, 1956), in the Rand (Ramdohr, 1955B), the oil and gas fields of the Panhandle and the Amarillo-Wichita uplift, Texas, and the flanks of the Wichita Mountains, Oklahoma (Pierce et al., 1956).

ASPHALTITES IN SEDIMENTARY ROCKS

Oklahoma, Texas, and Other Western States

Asphaltite deposits in Oklahoma occur in Ordovician, Pennsylvanian, and Permian bentonitic and arkosic red shale and sandstone. The uranium content of the ash ranges from 0.001 to 0.221% U (Hail et al., 1956). The largest deposits are in the Oil Creek sandstone (Ordovician) in the Sulphur area, Murray County, which crops out over a square mile and is 6 to 240 ft thick. All other asphaltites are also in quartzose sandstone, except in the Dougherty area where asphaltic limestone is exceptionally low in uranium (0.001% U).

Uraniferous asphaltic materials are widespread in oil and gas fields along the Amarillo-Wichita uplift in southwestern Oklahoma and the Texas Panhandle (Hill, 1954; Pierce et al., 1956). The asphaltite forms botryoidal pellets 1 mm or less to 5 cm across, as well as pore and fracture fillings. The pellets are largest and most abundant along permeable zones containing secondary anhydrite and celestite cement, and are surrounded by bleached halos. The metal content of the asphaltite includes about 3% As, 1% U, 0.1% each of Ni, Co, Cu, 0.1% yttrium group, Fe, a trace to 0.03% Ag, and 0.01% V. The uranium is evenly distributed. The mineral phases uraninite, coffinite, thorite, chloanthite-smaltite, pyrite, dolomite, celestite, and quartz have been identified by x-rays. They occur as micron-sized inclusions, in some samples grading into larger euhedral crystals that have been brecciated and healed by asphaltite. Patches of fine, mineral-filled pores also may be present.

In Utah, asphaltic sandstone in the Uinta and Green River formations of Eocene age and in the Navajo formation occur in the Uinta Basin. That of the Vernal area in the Uinta formation contains 0.001 to 0.150% U in the ash of the extracted oil. The unit ranges in thickness from a few feet to 190 ft. One of the largest asphaltic deposits in the United States occurs in the Sunnyside area, containing 0.003 to 0.048% U in the ash of extracted oil.

In California, asphaltite in sandstones of Miocene or Pliocene formations possibly originated in the Monterey shale (Miocene). The deposits of the Edna area, San Luis Obispo County, in arkosic sandstone of the Pismo formation (Miocene-Pliocene), contain the highest uranium concentrations of any sampled in the Western states—0.035 to 1.9% U of the ash of extracted oil. In the Los Alamos area, Santa Barbara County, Careaga quartzose sandstone beds (Pliocene), with an aggregate thickness of 225 ft, contain asphalt with 0.010 to 0.330% U in the ash of oil extracts. The beds underlie at least 5 sq mi.

Other occurrences and deposits have been sampled in Montana, Wyoming, New Mexico, and Missouri (Hail et al., 1956).

The uraniferous asphaltite deposits of the Colorado Plateau include those of Temple Mountain, San Rafael Swell, Utah (pages 408–410), and the extraordinarily large ones of the Ambrosia Lake area, Grants district, New Mexico (pages 413–416).

ASPHALTITE AND RELATED SUBSTANCES IN PEGMATITES AND HYDROTHERMAL DEPOSITS

United States

In the Black King and White Spar mines, Placerville, Colorado, veins follow faults that strike N. 45 to 50° W. and dip 60° NE. and cut the Dolores formation (Triassic) of sandstone, limestone, mudstone, and conglomerate. They contain pyrite, chalcopyrite, galena, sphalerite, tetrahedrite, chalcocite, molybdenite, gold, and silver in a calcite-barite gangue. Erythrite, molybdite, azurite, and malachite (Hess, 1917) also are present. The radioactive material is a hydrocarbon in rounded to irregular masses up to 6 in. across in both the veins and adjacent argillized wall rocks. Limestone on the hanging wall is impregnated with chromian muscovite. Everhart (1956B) also reports antimony sulfide in the veins. In the hydrocarbon, which has as much as 9.8% U in its ash, coffinite and pitchblende have been detected by x-ray methods (Stocking and Page, 1956). Some hydrocarbon is not radioactive. Minor autunite and uranophane are present. According to Wilmarth (1953A), in the first stage of mineralization calcite, pyrite, and barite were deposited, followed by the hydrocarbons and then by the rest of the sulfides.

Canada

Near Port Arthur, Ontario, fracture fillings as much as 6 in. across in Animikie metasediments and diabase contain radioactive anthraxolite along with various of the following: sulfides of Fe, Cu, Pb, Zn, Ni, and Ag, native Ag, quartz, fluorite, calcite, and barite (Ellsworth, 1934; Lang, 1952).

Robinson (1955B) reports a group of vein deposits in New Brunswick cutting Paleozoic rocks and containing pitchblende, hydrocarbon, pyrite, galena, and sphalerite. Other occurrences there have been recorded by Gross (1957). A uraniferous hydrocarbon (no thorium) occurs with hisingerite at the Nicholson mine, Goldfields area, Saskatchewan (page 309).

Europe

Laxey, Isle of Man

The radioactive hydrocarbon in the Laxey mine occurs as a 3-in. band on the hanging-wall side of the lode in the chalcopyrite zone of this old lead-zinc deposit. The hydrocarbon, which consists of two phases, contains subangular uraninite grains partly replaced by hydrocarbon and spheroids of pitchblende surrounded by a spherulitic rim of hydrocarbon. Some spheroids show syneresis fractures filled by chalcopyrite, pyrite, calcite, and rare galena specks (Davidson and Bowie, 1951). The ash also contains Al, As, Co, Cu, Fe, N, P, Pb, Si, and W.

FIG. 14.2. Nodules of titano-thucolite, Boliden mine, Sweden ($\times 1$) (Aminoff, 1943).

Boliden, Sweden

Titano-thucolite forms nodules (Fig. 14.2) up to a few centimeters across in sericite streaks in a metasomatic quartz-andalusite rock and in quartz veins cutting this rock (Aminoff, 1943; Grip and Ödman, 1944). The ash contains Ti, Fe, Pb, Th, Mn, Zn, Mo(?), and rare earths.

France

Boussac, Creuse. Uranium deposits in Creuse in the western part of the Massif Central are related to the granites of Marche, which flank the Boussac crushed zone on the south. In the Lavanfranche quarry, granites and mylonites along the trend of the Marche zone are cut by numerous fractures coated with autunite and gummite. One, which strikes N. 65° W., contains pitchblende, pyrite, and quartz (Geffroy and Sarcia, 1954).

The deposit at Pont-Auville, also on the Marche mylonitic zone, is a nearly vertical fracture that strikes west-northwest across mylonites. The mineralization consists of pitchblende, and later pyrite, marcasite, chalcopyrite, and covellite. Some transformation to secondary uranyl minerals has taken place, in association with the deposition of carbonaceous material of two types:

1. A soft, very abundant type, apparently replacing pitchblende and penetrating autunite cleavages. Contains C, P, Si, Fe^2, Cu, Zn

2. A hard, uncommon type in spherulites locally disseminated in the soft variety. C, P, Fe^2, Si (more abundant)

Both are isotropic.

Ronchamp, Haute-Saône. The deposit of Ronchamp consists of mineralized breccia of fragments of sandstone and carbonaceous shale, cemented by pitchblende, dolomite, barite, chalcopyrite, pyrite, galena, sphalerite, and hydrocarbon. Spherulites of pitchblende are veined and replaced by hydrocarbon, which also replaces schist fragments (Geffroy and Sarcia, 1954).

ORIGIN

The association of uranium with asphaltic material has been explained in three general ways:

1. The uranium was transported in petroleum, which was subsequently oxidized; the uranium may have been reconcentrated subsequently. But the organic material and the uranium are essentially contemporaneous.

2. The asphaltite represents material derived from petroleum present in the rocks prior to uranium mineralization and subsequently served as a precipitant for uranium. A variation of this idea states that hydrothermal solutions depositing uranium also converted petroleum to asphaltite.

3. The uranium as uraninite was deposited first and subsequently served to polymerize petroleum or natural gas to liquid phases that partly dissolve and replace preexisting uraninite. This is followed first by consolidation of the hydrocarbon gel, with flocculation of the colloidally dispersed pitchblende and then by aging of the colloid and minor redistribution of pitchblende and sulfides along syneresis cracks.

The polymerization theory or minor variations of it are advocated by Davidson and Bowie, 1951; Davidson and Ponsford, 1954; Joubin, 1955; Davidson, 1955, 1956E; Isachsen, 1956A. Hausen (1956) also favors a posturanium mineralization origin for the Temple Mountain asphaltite, which is regarded as a petroleum derivative, with some of its coaliferous characteristics acquired by absorption of lignitic material associated with uranium.

Breger (1955) regards the Colorado Plateau asphaltite as an extract from coalified wood. He considers it possible that the carbonaceous material and uranium were simultaneously precipitated from solution (Breger and Deul, 1955). Gruner (1955A, 1956B) has suggested that the asphaltite originated by the decay of plants and has served as an ion exchange collector of uranium from younger solutions. Gott and Erickson (1952) believe that the uranium and other metals of Temple Mountain deposits were transported by migrating petroleum from more distant uranium deposits, including the petroleum source bed. The asphaltite of Temple Mountain may have resulted from the polymerization and oxidation of oil by the hydrothermal solutions that deposited the uranium (Kerr, 1956A; Kerr and Kelley, 1956).

Ramdohr (1955B) agrees on the postpitchblende age of the Rand thucolite but dismisses the overlying Karoo beds as sources of gaseous or liquid hydrocarbon, largely because of his textural evidence that gold and pyrrhotite are younger than thucolite and because the presence of disseminated radiogenic galena in the thucolite indicates a very great age (pre-Karoo) for the time of replacement of pitchblende by hydrocarbon. He suggests the possibility of thucolite originating bacteriogenically or as the result of an exhalation from Ventersdorp vulcanism. Miholíc (1954) favors a biogenetic accumulation of uranium by microorganisms living under anaerobic conditions for the uranium in the Rand gold ores. The hydrocarbon thus formed later precipitated gold from hydrothermal solutions. He also rejects the pegmatitic thucolite pseudomorphs after uraninite, concluding instead that they represent skeletal metacrysts of uraninite that has been separating from the uraniferous hydrocarbon.

The bulk of the textural and geological evidence seems to favor a post-mineralization origin for most thucolite or asphaltite in such occurrences as pegmatites, hydrothermal veins, skarns, and deposits of the Rand type, with either natural gas or petroleum as the hydrocarbon source. That fluid hydrocarbons can be polymerized by the radioactive bombardment has been demonstrated experimentally. The literature on the effects of alpha radiation on simple and complex organic compounds is extensive (see, for example, Lind and Bardwell, 1926; Lind, Bardwell, and Perry, 1926; Heising, 1931, 1935; Sheppard and Burton, 1946; Sheppard and Whitehead, 1946, 1954; Rosenblum, 1948; Breger, 1948; and Dainton, 1949). Alpha radiation will break down fatty acids and other large organic molecules found in many marine sediments to form saturated and unsaturated hydrocarbons and other gases. These reactions have been used by some writers to explain in part the formation of petroleum. Alpha particles cause unsaturated hydrocarbons to polymerize and condense, whereas the saturated ones are often dehydrogenated to build up larger molecules, or to form unsaturated compounds, which in turn polymerize.

Irradiated hydrocarbons are apparently activated by fragmentation and ionization of molecular groups to react with pitchblende, forming urano-organic complexes. Asphaltite that is uraniferous differs from nonuraniferous asphaltite in having higher specific gravity, hardness, opacity, reflectivity, refractive index, anisotropism, and brittleness. It changes in luster from vitreous to submetallic and becomes much more insoluble and fuses at a higher temperature (Hausen, 1956). Similarly, however, induration of fluid hydrocarbons may result from oxidation at elevated temperatures, and such material also will abstract uranium from solution to form a urano-organic complex (Kerr and Kelley, 1956).

The asphaltites of Oklahoma and other Western states, which do not occur in direct association with uranium deposits (as does the asphaltite of Temple Mountain), probably are the result of oxidation of petroleum. Their uranium content may have been in part original and in part collected during migration of the petroleum (Hail et al., 1956).

Dietrich (1956) has investigated numerous anthraxolites that occur in veins and as disseminations, by a variety of methods, and concludes that usually it is not possible to distinguish between those derived from petroleum and those derived from coal, except possibly on the ash content, anthraxolite with less than 2 to 3% ash probably being derived from oil.

• chapter fifteen

DEPOSITS FORMED BY WEATHERING

AND GROUND-WATER ACTION

RADIOACTIVE GOSSANS AND LATERITES

GENERAL

Deposits of uranium and thorium and other ore deposits in many places in the Western United States and in several other countries are found to have associated deposits relatively rich in limonitic material which is radioactive. In some cases the limonite occurs as part of or near weathered vein, lode, or even pegmatite outcrops, forming a typical gossan. In other cases the radioactive limonitic material is rather widely distributed in a residual soil or laterite. Although in some cases radioactive gossans are directly relatable to underlying or nearby primary uranium or thorium deposits, and thus have been used as a field guide to ore, most of them have not been demonstrated to be genetically connected with such deposits (Lovering, 1955). Mineralogically the limonitic aggregates consist chiefly of hematite-goethite mixtures with minor jarosite or siderite, pyrite, rare lepidocrocite, and variable amounts of chalcedony, quartz, and manganese oxides. Other secondary species identified in radioactive gossans include copper carbonates, chrysocolla, hydrozincite, erythrite, and annabergite. Such elements as As, Zn, Co, Cu, Mo, and V may be enriched in the gossans but show no consistent correlation with uranium from district to district.

The uranium occurs in three different ways:

1. As very rare sooty pitchblende(?)
2. As veinlets and flakes of uranyl minerals, including uranophane, carnotite, tyuyamunite, and torbernite
3. As submicroscopic particles of unidentifiable uranyl minerals within

529

goethite; ferruginous chert, chrysocolla, mimetite, and hydrozincite; less commonly in hematite

The high-thorium gossans contain minute discrete grains of thorite and thorogummite. Thorium-rich gossans also contain a relatively consistent suite of accessory elements including Cr, Ni, and the rare earths Ce, La, Nd, and Sm (Lovering, 1955). Fergusonite has been identified in a deposit in the Goldfields district, Saskatchewan, described as a gossan capping (Robinson, 1955A) (on a pegmatite?). Lateritic clays resulting from the decomposition of the Jacupiranga, Brazil, alkalic rocks (pages 327–329) contain as much as 2.33% ThO_2 (De Moraes, 1956).

The radioactivity of gossan samples studied by Lovering (1955) ranges from 0.001 to 0.7% U, 0.003 to 5.3% eU, and 0.001 to 4.16% ThO_2. His investigations also strongly indicate that radioactive gossans usually contain abundant goethite, rather than hematite.

EXAMPLES

In the Goodsprings district, Clark County, Nevada, uranium is carried not only in limonite but also in hydrozincite, chrysocolla, and ferruginous chert (Barton, 1956):

$$U_3O_8,$$
per cent

Limonite...........	0.106
Hydrozincite.......	0.239
Chrysocolla........	0.116

In addition to numerous occurrences in the Western United States (Lovering, 1955; Barton, 1956), radioactive limonites (0.06% eU) have been reported in limestone in the Lost River area, Seward Peninsula, Alaska (White and West, 1953); in the Goldfields area, Saskatchewan (Robinson, 1955A); in the Rum Jungle area, Northern Territory, and Mt. Painter, South Australia (Fisher and Sullivan, 1954); and at the Cactus Poort mine in Southern Rhodesia (Davidson, 1956B).

The terra rossa overlying many carbonatites shows high radioactivity which stems largely from absorption of daughter elements of Th and U (Davidson, 1956D). Weakly radioactive soils also are reported from a volcanic area near the Kenya-Uganda border in eastern Africa (0.004% U_3O_8, 0.006 to 0.41% ThO_2) and in Rhodesia. Radioactive pistolitic laterite occurs in the Rum Jungle area of Australia (Fisher and Sullivan, 1954). As is the case with the gossans, the bulk of the radioactivity is associated with the iron oxide minerals in the laterite.

ORIGIN

Uranium in an oxidizing sulfide environment enters ground waters as uranyl sulfate in the presence of ferric sulfate. Where such acid waters are neutralized, colloid ferric oxide hydrate forms by hydrolysis of the sulfate. Its particles remove uranium from solution by absorption, and with aging of the colloid and crystallization to goethite, uranium is rejected as exceedingly minute particles of uranyl minerals (Lovering, 1955). Laboratory experiments show that uranyl carbonate, uranyl hydroxide, and uranyl ions are absorbed both by synthetic colloidal limonite and synthetic hydrozincite (Barton, 1956) and that with crystallization of the adsorbents the uranium either forms discrete uranium minerals or is returned to solution. Most thorium minerals, being relatively resistant to destruction by weathering, are retained unchanged in the gossans; thus thorium-rich gossans are more likely to have been formed from material locally available.

Uranium may be derived from weakly to strongly radioactive ore deposits near or underlying the limonitic aggregate or from adjacent igneous rock masses. In the Rum Jungle area of Australia the fluctuation of the water table is as much as 200 ft between the dry and wet seasons.

VEIN DEPOSITS OXIDIZED IN PLACE

GENERAL

In the weathering environment, veins or other hydrothermal deposits that contain pitchblende may be extensively altered to yield a variety of uranyl minerals. In many cases alteration and solution of pitchblende and redisposition of secondary species occur essentially in place, although there may be some local redistribution, generally within the framework of the vein structures themselves or in altered wall rocks within a few to 10 ft of the veins. Deposits rich in iron sulfides furnish abundant H_2SO_4 to meteoric waters which strongly attack uraninite. Phair and Levine (1953) have shown that sulfuric acid solutions preferentially leach U^{6+} with respect to U^{4+}, Ra, and Pb. UO_3 forms very soluble uranyl compounds in acid solutions:

$$UO_3 + H_2SO_4 \rightarrow UO_2^{2+} + SO_4^{2-} + H_2O$$

Thus low-temperature uraninites, especially sooty varieties, i.e., those with a high initial U^6/U^4 ratio, or those that have undergone considerable oxidation, are especially susceptible to leaching by acid solutions. Not uncommonly, a zone rich in sooty pitchblende lies between the zone of ordinary uraninite, below the uppermost zone of uranyl minerals.

Weathered uraninite commonly contains minute blebs or fracture fillings showing abnormally high radioactivity. They consist of secondary colloidal radium and lead salts, generally sulfates, precipitated in capillary openings. They may also appear in associated gangue minerals (Yagoda, 1949).

MINERALOGY

The common uranyl species found in oxidized vein deposits are chiefly combinations of UO_2^{2+} with the anions PO_4^{3-}, SO_4^{2-}, and SiO_4^{4-}, and the cations Ca^{2+} and Cu^{2+}. Autunite, torbernite, and uranophane are especially widespread. The phosphates parsonite, uranocircite, and saléeite, the silicate kasolite, the sulfates zippeite and uranopilite, and the carbonate schroeckingerite are of significance in some deposits. Vanadates such as carnotite are rare except where the primary ore minerals contain some vanadium, as, for example, in the davidite deposits of Radium Hill, Australia, where the associated ilmenite probably provides vanadium in small amounts. Arsenates, such as zeunerite, require the presence of arsenides in the primary ores, e.g., in some deposits of the Erzgebirge. Uranyl silicates may be preferentially deposited in siliceous wall rocks, as at Marysvale.

Uranyl oxides, e.g., schoepite and becquerelite, or $Pb-UO_2^{2+}$ oxides, e.g., curite and fourmarierite, normally form essentially in place as alteration shells about uraninite, the transformation involving oxidation of U^{4+}, addition of H_2O, and incorporation of radiogenic lead, which has been concentrated with respect to U^6 in outer parts of leached uraninite (Phair and Levine, 1953). Once formed, these oxides are susceptible to destruction, thus are uncommon where abundant ground waters are in motion. Many of these minerals have been synthesized at room temperature (Frondel et al., 1954; Bignand, 1955).

The phosphate ion usually is obtained locally from gangue apatite, but may also be derived by ground waters in transit through sedimentary phosphorites or fossil bone. Although carbonate ions are abundant in ground waters, uranyl carbonates, because of their solubility, rarely remain deposited in quantity except under conditions of considerable aridity. Calcium is supplied usually by ground water from external sources but may be locally derived from apatite or calcite.

In some districts, metaforms, i.e., the lower hydrates, predominate among the uranyl minerals. Emerson and Wright (1957) have found that meta-autunite and metatorbernite were deposited at ordinary temperatures by ground water in oxidized veins of the Boulder batholith (pages 331–333) and concluded the stability fields of the metaforms were lowered by the presence of minor amounts of other elements.

GEOLOGY

Deposition of uranyl phosphates can result where the acidity of ground waters is lowered upon entering calcitic environments, where solutions are neutralized by reactions with basic wall rocks, and where solutions enter vugs or breccia zones and evaporate.

In many oxidized vein deposits that were rich in pyrite, upper parts are leached of uranium, although radioactivity may still be high owing to radium concentrations. Most of the leached uranium is dispersed owing to lack of a suitable agency to neutralize the strongly acid transporting solutions or due to intensive surface leaching, in some cases under tropical conditions. In the Rum Jungle area of Australia, for example, surface radioactivity amounts to only 4 or 5 times background over deposits that average 1% U_3O_8 at 30 ft.

Oxidation may extend to considerable depths. In the Central City district of Colorado some veins are thoroughly oxidized to 100 ft; at Marysvale, Utah, partly oxidized veins occur at 400 ft; at Shinkolobwe unoxidized vein material begins to appear at about 150 ft. Exceptional depth of oxidation occurs at the Gunnar deposit, Goldfields district, Saskatchewan, where uranophane persists to 1,000 ft.

Although in some districts the zone of oxidation is definitely demarcated by the water table, in others it extends below the water table for considerable distances, owing to (1) a fluctuating water table related to pronounced seasonable rainfall variation, (2) marked localized variation in permeability related to fracture concentrations, or (3) previously lowered water tables later raised by a general climatic change.

In some regions, zones of oxidized uranium minerals may have been materially diminished owing to glacial stripping, e.g., deposits in the Canadian Shield. Conversely the occurrence of a near-surface deposit of uranyl minerals does not guarantee the presence of an underlying deposit of primary uranium ore, for uranyl species may migrate considerable distances for their source.

HYPOGENE URANYL MINERALS

Although the formation of uranyl minerals in near-surface parts of pitchblende veins has generally been ascribed to supergene solutions, some investigators have suggested that hypogene solutions may have deposited these species in some deposits. For the Marysvale district, Utah, Walker and Osterwald (1956A, page 286) suggest ". . . that some of these uranyl minerals and part, if not all, of the sooty pitchblende may have been deposited directly by warm solutions, either juvenile water or heated phreatic water." Their arguments include (1) equivalent uranium contents of oxidized and unoxidized veins, (2) less fluorite and pyrite in some oxidized veins, and (3) restriction of uranyl minerals to the veins and their wall rocks. Under near-surface conditions of low temperature and pressure ". . . a change in the redox potential of rising, uranium-bearing, thermal solutions could cause reaction of uranium with available phosphate, sulfate, carbonate, or silicate anions derived through alteration of the wall rocks or from other sources. From such reaction, direct precipitation of uranyl phosphate, silicate, carbonate or sulfate minerals might be expected."

Hydrothermal deposition of some uranyl minerals at Wölsendorf, Bavaria (pages 352–353), has also been suggested (Kohl and Haller, 1934). In the Weissenstadt district, Fichtelgebirge, Germany, torbernite occurs in concentrations at vein intersections, and has been found at depths of 600 ft; Kohl (1954) concludes that the torbernite is primary. Sims et al. (1955) suggest the possibility that torbernite may be a primary mineral in some deposits of the Central City district, Colorado (pages 298–302). In the veins of Lachaux, France, parsonite is regarded by Poughon and Moreau (1955) as a primary mineral (pages 536–538).

ECONOMIC SIGNIFICANCE

Many oxidized or partly oxidized vein deposits are or have been of commercial importance. Noteworthy are the Marysvale, Utah, and Spokane, Washington, veins in the United States; the Gunnar deposit, Goldfields district, Canada; the Urgeirica mine, Viseu district, Portugal; the veins near Lachaux, France; and the Shinkolobwe mine, Katanga, Belgian Congo.

EXAMPLES

United States

Table 15.1 summarizes the characteristics of some selected vein deposits of the United States, which are in part oxidized. Other examples are described in some detail.

Bald Mountain, Northern Black Hills, South Dakota

In the Bald Mountain gold district, Lawrence County, South Dakota, gold-silver replacement deposits occur mainly in the fractured Cambrian Deadwood formation. Some are radioactive, and pitchblende and secondary autunite, torbernite, uranocircite, and zeunerite also occur in the overlying Whitewood limestone (Ordovician) and in altered Tertiary intrusive rocks. Samples contain up to 0.19% eU, and some thorium and rare earths. Differential supergene leaching has disturbed the original Th/U ratio (Vickers, 1954). The rare-earth content appears to decrease outward from the gold-producing center, and uranium minerals occur on the fringes of the area.

Silver Cliff Mine, Lusk, Wyoming

The Silver Cliff deposit in south-central Niobrara County, Wyoming, has been described by Lind and Davis (1919), Larsen et al. (1926), Wilmarth (1952), and Wilmarth and Johnson (1954). It consists mainly of uranophane as fracture fillings and replacement pods in faulted and fractured Cambrian(?) sandstone that unconformably overlies Precambrian schist and pegmatite. The north-trending, high-angle reverse Silver Cliff fault and its hanging-wall sandstone have been mineralized by pitchblende, uranophane, metatorbernite, gummite, native silver, chalcocite, cuprite, native copper, copper carbonates, and chrysocolla in a gangue of calcite, limonite, and clinozoisite. The fault can be traced for 1,200 ft, but the mineralization is now discontinuous owing to erosion. The main ore body is in sandstone, contains chiefly uranophane, and ranges in grade from 0.001 to 0.23% U. The primary minerals, pitchblende, calcite, and chalcocite, were altered by supergene solutions in place and also were redeposited.

Yellow Canary Deposit, Utah

The Yellow Canary deposit on the west side of Red Creek Canyon in the northern Uinta Mountains, Daggett County, Utah, contains mineralization in highly fractured quartzite near the top of the Precambrian Red Creek formation. The chief radioactive mineral is tyuyamunite associated with carnotite, volborthite, hematite, azurite, malachite, brochanthite, and hyalite (Wilmarth, 1953C). The quartzite is cut by three northeast normal faults and by diorite dikes and their associated quartz ± carbonate veins which also contain chalcopyrite, chalcocite, and bornite (Wilson, 1955).

Mount Spokane Area, Washington

Economically significant discoveries of autunite and uranophane were made on lands of the Spokane Tribe Indians northwest of Spokane, Stevens County,

TABLE 15.1. *Selected examples of oxidized and partly oxidized vein deposits in the United States*

Deposit	Geology	Chief secondary uranium minerals	Reference
Surprise claims, Gibbonsville, Lemhi County, Idaho	Northwest fissures in Belt quartzite	Autunite, metatorbernite	Everhart, 1956B
Miracle mine, Kern County, Calif.	Fracture zones with fluorite in granodiorite	Autunite, sooty pitchblende	p. 349
Perry Jones group, Plumas County, Calif.	Quartz veins in granodiorite	Metazeunerite, torbernite(?)	Walker et al., 1956
Green Monster mine, Clark County, Nev.	Breccia zone in Mississippian dolomite	Kasolite, dumontite	Lovering, 1954
Majuba Hill mine, Pershing County, Nev.	Complex rhyolite plug (Tertiary) in Triassic sediments, both sericitized, silicified, and tourmalinized. Uranium in vein, breccia, and gouge. Copper and tin minerals associated	Zeunerite, torbernite, metatorbernite, autunite	Lovering, 1954
Red bluff mine, Gila County, Ariz.	Major vertical west-northwest fractures and minor north-northeast fractures in Precambrian Dripping Spring quartzite	Metatorbernite, carnotite, tyuyamunite, uranophane	Nininger, 1954; Everhart, 1956B
White Signal District, N.Mex.	Mineralization along fractures and as disseminations in mafic and intermediate dikes near quartz-pyrite veins in Precambrian granite	Autunite, torbernite	Granger and Bauer, 1951, 1952; Gillerman, 1952
San Acacia mine, Socorro County, N.Mex.	North-trending fault zone in Tertiary flows; copper sulfides	Autunite, torbernite, tyuyamunite	Everhart, 1956B
Marysvale, Utah	Fluorite-silica-rich veins in fault zones in quartz monzonite	Autunite, torbernite, metatorbernite, uranophane	pp. 350–351
Los Ochos mine, Saguache County, Colo.	East-west fault and lesser cross faults across Precambrian granite and Morrison sandstone	Autunite, uranophane	pp. 333–334
Central City district, Colo.	Pyritic fissure veins along faults in gneisses and granites	Torbernite, metatorbernite, autunite	pp. 298–302
Boulder Batholith, Mont.	Silica-rich veins along shear zones in quartz monzonite	Uranophane, beta-uranophane, meta-autunite, metatorbernite	pp. 331–333

535

TABLE 15.2. *Selected examples of oxidized and partly oxidized vein deposits in Canada and Alaska*

Deposit	Geology	Chief secondary uranium minerals	Reference
Gunnar mine, Gold-fields, Sask.	Breccia pipe in altered granite	Uranophane, per-sists to 1,000 ft	p. 314
Brooks Mt. area, York district, Seward Peninsula, Alaska	Quartz-tourmaline veins in granite; weathered gran-ite zone near limestone con-tact with fluorite, tourma-line, hematite	Metazeunerite	White et al., 1952
Ear Mt., Seward Peninsula, Alaska	Quartz-tourmaline vein along contact granite and mafic dike	Metazeunerite-metatorbernite	Killeen and Ordway, 1955

Washington (Thurlow, 1956A; Davis and Sharp, 1957; Norman, 1957). The mineralization occurs in shear zones along a contact between a granodioritic phase of the Loon Lake granite (coarse-grained and locally pegmatitic) and the Deer Trail argillites (part of the Paleozoic Stevens series), on the flank of a major anticline in argillite. Both rocks have been altered and contain autunite, uranophane, and gummite. The mineralized zone is 2,000 ft long and averages 8 ft wide. Assays of some parts range from 0.67 to 1.12% U_3O_8. Mineralization follows the arcuate contact rather closely. The main Dahl ore body is along a large east-west shear zone dipping 10 to 30° N. Especially rich shoots appear to lie along intersections with faults that strike northwest. Autunite is found in granite as much as 20 ft from the contact. Some of it occurs in crystals of exceptional size and quality, occurring as vug linings in individuals as much as 15 in. thick (Fig. 15.1). Pitchblende and pyrite have been identified from drill cores from a depth of 150 ft. Coffinite also has been reported at depth.

The five Daybreak properties are reported to contain reserves of 55,800 tons proved ore, 461,700 tons inferred ore, 1,158,900 tons potential ore. The grade ranges from 0.06 to >2.0% U_3O_8.

Similar autunite deposits also have been discovered in Pend Oreille County in the Lamb Creek district and at the Quartz Ridge claims, Lost Creek district.

Parsonite Veins, Lachaux, France

Unusual uraniferous veins are exploited in the vicinity of Lachaux in the northern part of the Forez and Madeleine Mountains in Auvergne, France, about 20 km southeast of Vichy, where radioactive minerals were found in 1927 (Poughon and Moreau, 1955; Roubault, 1956). Parsonite is here found in mineable quantities in several veins. The district, which is underlain chiefly by a coarse- to medium-grained, two-mica granite, is bounded geologically on the east by the Terrasson crushed zone and on the west by the Limage fault.

The principal deposits are Reliez, Bancherelle, Gagnol, and l'Etang de Reliez, of which the last is the largest. The granite, which is cut by dioritic lamprophyres and quartz veins, has been altered along fractures to sericite, chlorite, hematite, and various clay minerals. The uraniferous veins are in two groups, one set trending east-west to N. 70° E., the other trending N. 40 to 60° W. They are banded siliceous veins, over a meter thick, containing quartz, opal, and scattered grains of galena, pyrite, chalcopyrite, and rare sphalerite and fluorite. Parsonite is the chief radioactive mineral, but minor autunite, torbernite, and radioactive pyromorphite are widespread. Traces of kasolite and renardite are recorded. Also present are covellite, chalcocite, malachite, azurite, psilomelane, hematite, cerussite, anglesite, and clay minerals. Pitchblende is absent. In nonuraniferous veins the quartz is white or smoky; in uraniferous veins it is always smoky. The parsonite usually forms finely disseminated crystals.

The veins are cut at right angles by argillaceous fracture or fault zones, accompanied by intense brecciation, producing a breccia of smoky or colorless quartz cemented by resinous opal. Some vein sections are vuggy. Uranium concentrations occur (1) where smoky quartz includes sulfides, (2) in the vicinity of dikes, and (3) at intersections of veins and faults. Drilling has shown that the grade of the deposits, which locally reaches 1 to 2% uranium, decreases sharply with depth. The l'Etang de Reliez deposit extends to at least 140 m.

The sequence of mineral formation for the l'Etang de Reliez deposit, which is typical, has been (1) white quartz, (2) smoky quartz and sulfides, (3) opal, (4) hematite, parsonite, pyromorphite, and (5) hematite, clay minerals, autunite. In one of the segments of the Gagnol vein, parsonite occurs above 22 m, torbernite between 22 and 40 m, and autunite from 40 to 60 m. The

FIG. 15.1. Exceptionally large autunite crystals. Mount Spokane area, Washington (courtesy E. W. Martin).

parsonite is regarded as having been formed as a primary mineral, under near-surface conditions by ascending circulating solutions containing uranyl bicarbonate (Poughon and Moreau, 1955).

Goten, Bulgaria

The Goten deposit, which occurs 200 m below the summit of the Goten, 7 km from Bukhovo and 20 km north of Sofia, consists of a lens of uranyl minerals and limonite along a brecciated zone in sandstone. The radioactive minerals are torbernite and metatorbernite. The lens, 4 to 15 m wide and 50 to 70 m long, is estimated to have contained 6,000 cu m of low-grade ore to a depth of 10 ft, 4 cu m of which yielded a hand-picked concentrate assaying 2% U_3O_8 (Bain, 1950). The deposit apparently is of supergene origin, and Bain (1950) suggests that the uranium may have been derived from formerly overlying Jurassic oil shale.

Recent reports indicate the discovery of another new uranium deposit nearby, and of a relatively large deposit between Madan and Zilatograd in the Rhodope Mountains.

Mount Painter, South Australia

In the Mount Painter area, torbernite occurs in or near three masses of granitic breccia, the largest of which is about 800 ft wide and 2,000 ft long along a northeast axis. The breccias are in granite gneiss and are cut by shears that trend generally northwest and dip moderately to steeply mainly southwest but also northeast. The breccia bodies, which appear to be bottomed at relatively shallow depths, have been pyritized locally. Of approximately 24 torbernite occurrences, only 6 are outside of breccia, northeast of the main breccia mass (Betheras, 1955).

DEPOSITS FORMED BY GROUND-WATER REDISTRIBUTION

GENERAL

It is probable that uranium is transported in ground water as complex alkaline-uranyl or alkaline earth-uranyl carbonates, for (1) the uranyl ion complexes with these elements, (2) such compounds are soluble in ground water and are stable above pH 7.0, (3) these complexing ions are readily available in ground water, and (4) the more alkaline waters contain the most uranium. Uranyl minerals are slowly dissolved by H_2SO_4 at pH 2.5 (Gruner, 1956C), and the uranyl ion is stable in acid solution.

The uranium content of ground water varies greatly—$n \times 10^{-8}$ gm/l to $n \times 10^{-2}$ gm/l (Saukoff, 1956)—and usually is highest in mine waters from uranium deposits and in regions in which uranium deposits are numerous (Walton, 1956; Murphy, 1956).

Hydrological radioactive anomalies are detectable for distances up to several kilometers in ground water around uranium deposits, depending upon the size and grade of the deposit. In most uraniferous areas, ground waters ordinarily contain 1 to 120 ppb U (Fix, 1956). In some areas uraniferous ground

TABLE 15.3. *Selected examples of oxidized and partly oxidized vein deposits outside of North America*

Deposit	Geology	Chief secondary uranium minerals	Reference
Cornwall, England	Fissure veins in or near granite associated with Sn and Cu lodes	Autunite, torbernite, zippeite	pp. 280–282
Viseu region, north-central Portugal	Veins in brecciated fault zones in Hercynian granite	Autunite, meta-autunite, sabuga-lite, saléeite, phosphuranylite, torbernite, uranophane	pp. 335–336
Sierra Morena, Spain	Northeast fractures across post-Hercynian granite filled by quartz, chalcedony, calcite, pyrite, and chalcopyrite	Torbernite, autunite	Alia, 1956A
Black Forest area, Germany	Veins in granite with adjacent impregnations	Torbernite, autunite, zeunerite	pp. 288–289
Wölsendorf, Germany	Fluorite veins in Hercynian granite	Torbernite, autunite, parsonite, other uranyl phosphates, silicates, and hydrous oxides	pp. 352–353
Cuneo-Lurisia district, Maritime Alps, Italy	Premetamorphic(?) lenses in folded and fractured Permian schists (metaporphyries) associated with quartz-pyrite-chalcopyrite veinlets	Torbernite, autunite, uranophane, sooty pitchblende	Nininger, 1954; Ippolito, 1956
Erzgebirge, Germany, and Czechoslovakia	Fissure veins in metamorphic rocks	Autunite, torbernite, zippeite, uranopilite, metazeunerite, uranophane, beta-uranophane	pp. 282–288
Shinkolobwe, Katanga, Belgian Congo	Fissure veins in metamorphic rocks	Becquerelite, curite, schoepite, torbernite, parsonite, kasolite, uranophane	pp. 289–297
Rum Jungle, Northern Territory, Australia	Replacements in graphitic slate	Torbernite, saléeite	pp. 317–319
Edith River, Northern Territory, Australia	Siliceous brecciated veins along shears in greisenized granite	Meta-autunite, torbernite	p. 319

539

water also contains above-normal amounts of such elements as Mo, V, Cu, P, Zn, As, and others (Denson et al., 1956).

Possible precipitants of uranium from ground water include carbonaceous material, coal, petroleum(?), hydrogen sulfide, pyrite, bone collophane, clay minerals, calcite, and iron oxide minerals.

IN LIGNITE, COAL, AND ASSOCIATED BLACK SHALE

General

Although normally coal is one of the least radioactive of all sedimentary rocks, in many places in the United States and in other countries relatively high concentrations of uranium occur locally in it and also in closely associated paludal carbonaceous shales (Kehn, 1957). Uraniferous coal was discovered in the United States in the Laramie (Cretaceous) formation at the Old Leyden coal mine, northwest of Denver, Colorado (Berthoud, 1875). Although even the most radioactive coals are usually but submarginal ores, in the ash of coal is contained a potentially large low-grade uranium reserve. Unfortunately, uranium in coals occurs chiefly in impure and low-rank coals, including shaly, lignitic, and subbituminous types, and but rarely in the low-ash, high-rank coals most suitable as fuels. However, in 1954, thin, impure lignite beds in the Cave Hills area of northwestern South Dakota were found to contain 0.3 to 5% uranium, thus constituting ore where present in sufficient volume. Chief problems in obtaining uranium from such highly radioactive coals include development of extraction techniques, economic mining of beds only 12 to 18 in. thick, and the inability of lignites to sustain combustion to produce an ash of higher grade.

Although coals with more than 0.1% U may contain one or more uranyl minerals disseminated along bedding planes and fractures (carnotite, autunite, meta-autunite, torbernite, and zeunerite, among others), these minerals do not account for all of the uranium present. In coals of lower radioactivity such species usually are absent, and no discrete uranium minerals are recognizable, although coffinite has been reported by Gruner in highly uraniferous coal from La Ventana Mesa, New Mexico (Vine, 1956A). That most of the uranium is associated with the organic material rather than with mineralogical impurities has been shown for a lignite from the Mendenhall mine, Harding County, South Dakota (Breger et al., 1955). In this lignite, only about 1% of the uranium is held by ion exchange; continuous extraction with hot 6N HCl removes 98.6% of the uranium. Elutriation experiments indicate that the uranium exists as a urano-organic complex soluble at a pH of less than 2.18. Studies by Schopf and Gray (1954) on uraniferous lignites from Slim Buttes, nearby in Harding County, show that no quantitative correlation exists between uranium content and any of the coal petrographic constituents (anthraxylon, fusain, opaque or translucent attritus). However, samples richest in uranium also contain relatively large amounts of humic attrital material formed by decomposition and microbial decay, suggesting such material may have been most favorable for uranium introduction. Mineralogical constituents of uraniferous lignites include quartz, clay minerals, analcite, gypsum, jarosite, calcite, pyrite, and marcasite.

Various minor elements have been detected in the ash of uraniferous low-rank coals. In Western states these include Mo, Co, Ni, V, Cr, Sr, Ba, Ti, Mn, B, Zr, Sc, Ge, Sn, Pb, Cu, Ga, Be, Y, Yb (Deul and Annell, 1956). No correlation exists between the content of any of these elements and of uranium except in Dakota coal in which a uranium-molybdenum correlation exists. All coals analyzed were enriched in B, Ba, Sr, nearly all in Ga, some in Mo, with respect to average percentages in the earth's crust. High concentrations of Sn, Cu, Zr, B, Ba, Sr were found in coal from Milam County, Texas. Lignite from Harding County, South Dakota, also contains As and Zn as well as all the elements listed previously (Breger et al., 1955). Some of these trace elements are enriched within the top and bottom few inches of some coal seams and especially concentrated in black, brittle, lustrous vitrains that form thin isolated bands or lenses overlying thicker seams (Davidson and Ponsford, 1954).

Although the uranium in individual specimens of low-grade coal may be uniformly distributed, uranium may have a highly irregular distribution in individual beds.

Eastern United States

Although numerous coals have been investigated as uranium sources in Eastern and Central states, none of any significance has been found to carry as much as 0.005% U (McKelvey et al., 1955). In general these coals are at least of bituminous rank. Bituminous coals from southern West Virginia and southwestern Virginia assayed less than 0.001% eU; the semianthracite Merrimac coal (Mississippian) from Montgomery County, Virginia, may contain as much as 0.001% U (Snider, 1953). Coals from eastern Kentucky and Logan and Mingo Counties, West Virginia (90 samples), contain 0.000 to 0.001% eU (Welch, 1953). Coal in the Dunkard series (Permian) in northern West Virginia may contain 0.002 to 0.004% eU (Patterson, 1954). Of some 30 samples from commercial coal beds in the Pottsville, Allegheny, and Monongahela series (Pennsylvanian) in eastern Ohio, only 5 contained as much as 0.001 to 0.003% eU (Snider, 1954A).

Dakotas and Eastern Montana

Lignites underlie large areas in western North Dakota, in northwestern South Dakota, and in eastern Montana. In North Dakota alone original reserves are estimated at 350,910 million tons (Brant, 1953). In North Dakota, uraniferous lignites occur at Sentinel Butte in Golden Valley County, at Bullion Butte in Billings County, at Medicine Pole Hills, Bowman County, and at Chalky and H. T. Buttes in Slope County; in South Dakota in the Cave Hills and Slim Buttes area, Harding County, and at Lodgepole Buttes in Perkins County; and in Montana in the Long Pine Hills and Ekalaka Hills, Carter County (Schopf and Gray, 1954; Breger et al., 1955; Denson, 1955; Denson and Gill, 1956; King, 1956B,C; Bergstrom, 1956; Deul and Annell, 1956).

The radioactive lignites occur locally at many horizons in the Hell Creek formation (late Cretaceous), in the Ludlow, Tongue River, and Sentinel Butte

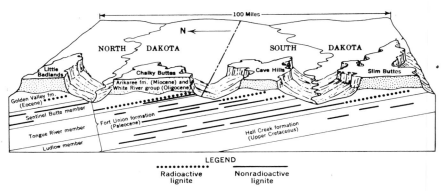

Fig. 15.2. Diagrammatic section across the Dakotas showing stratigraphic distribution of uraniferous lignite (Denson and Gill, 1956; *U.S. Geol. Survey*).

shale members of the Fort Union formation (Paleocene) and in the overlying Golden Valley formation (Eocene), involving a total thickness of 2,210 ft or more, chiefly of fluvatile, soft sandy shales and sandstone.

The lignitic formations, which lie on the southwestern flank of the Williston Basin, strike northwest and dip 10 to 40° NE. They are overlain unconformably by tuffaceous sandstones and bentonitic clays of the Oligocene White River group and Miocene Arikaree formation, 300 ft or more thick. These rocks show two to six times normal radioactivity, containing an average of 0.0015% U, about 12 times that of the average sedimentary rock. Most of the radioactive lignites are on flanks of high buttes capped by volcanic beds and all are within 40 to 140 ft of the unconformity at the base of these layers, without regard to the age of the host formation. In series of flat-lying beds, those lignites stratigraphically and topographically higher are most radioactive, with highest uranium values concentrated at the tops of beds, diminishing downward (Fig. 15.2). A lignite bed overlain by permeable sandstone is more uraniferous than where it is overlain by shale.

The uranium content ranges from less than 0.001% to over 10%, with an average of 0.008% (Vine, 1956A). The deposits contain 90 million tons of radioactive lignite in beds averaging 4 ft thick (Denson and Gill, 1956). Locally in lignite and associated sandstone occur zeunerite, autunite, torbernite, abernathyite, and carnotite (King, 1956B,C). The unusual amounts of As, V, Cu, and P in the coal are largely contained in these minerals. Molybdenum, also enriched, parallels uranium in values (Deul and Annell, 1956).

Red Desert, Wyoming

In the Red Desert area of south-central Wyoming, near the central part of the interior drainage Great Divide Basin, about 300 sq mi is underlain by uraniferous coal and carbonaceous shale of the Eocene Wasatch formation (Denson, 1955; Breger et al., 1955; Pipiringos, 1956; Masursky, 1956; Vine, 1956A; Wyant et al., 1956). The lenticular subbituminous coal beds are as much as 40 ft thick. Much coal averages a few thousandths of one per cent uranium; the major part of the reserves has 0.02 to 0.03% U in the ash; small amounts contain as much as 0.18% U in the ash. Toward the north and east from the center of the area, uranium increases as the enclosing rocks become coarser and more permeable. Uranium values in individual coal beds are high adjacent to underlying sandstone. At Creston Ridge, where the beds are unconformably overlain by the tuffaceous Browns Park formation (Miocene?), the uppermost coal bed contains an upper concentration of uranium of 0.05%, whereas a bed 40 ft lower contains but 0.001%. Showing parallel distribution with uranium are the trace elements Ga, Ge, Fe, Mo, Pb, V, and rare earths.

Idaho

Uraniferous coaly shale in a 2- to 6-ft bed occurs in the early Cretaceous Bear River formation in the Fall Creek area, Bonneville County, eastern Idaho (Vine and Moore, 1952; Denson, 1955). The sheared rock locally contains up to 0.1% U, but it and the overlying carbonaceous limestone average only 0.02% U. Remnants of Miocene and Pliocene volcanic rocks occur on hilltops overlooking the occurrence. Most of the uranium is in the top part of the coal bed, along with Ge and Mo.

In the Goose Creek intermontane basin of southern Cassia County, Idaho, and adjoining parts of Nevada and Utah, the Miocene-Pliocene Payette and Salt Lake formation contain lignite and carbonaceous shale with local concentrations of uranium up to 0.1%. The uraniferous beds are in a 2,300-ft section of shale, volcanic ash, and welded rhyolite tuff. In general only the top few inches of the beds, which are 2 to 8 ft thick, contain as much as 0.03 to 0.09% uranium. The main mineralized areas lie on the flanks and in the trough of a syncline in which ground waters may have been impounded (Denson, 1955; Vine, 1956A).

New Mexico

A uraniferous coal and black shale of the Allison and Gibson members of the Mesaverde formation (late Cretaceous) crops out in erosional remnants on La Ventana Mesa, Sandoval County, New Mexico. The buttes, which are capped by the fractured 65-ft La Ventana sandstone, lie along the axis of the La Ventana syncline. The mildly radioactive Bandelier rhyolite tuff (Pliocene?) crops out east of the Sierra Nacimiento which lies to the east of the mesa, and probably at one time extended unconformably across the La Ventana sandstone (Denson, 1955; Cannon and Starrett, 1956). The 1- to 3-ft beds average 0.05% uranium, with a high of 0.6% U. The uraniferous layer is the carbonaceous zone that is highest stratigraphically. It contains appreciable concentrations of Se, S, and Mo, with traces of Pb, Cr, Cu, Co, and Ni. Selenium- and sulfur-indicator plants grow on slopes below the outcrops, and branches of piñon and juniper growing in sandstone above the coal contain 0.1 to 2.3 ppm in the ash.

Paludal black shales, impure lignites, and associated sandstones containing uranium mineralization occur at the base of the Dakota formation (upper Cretaceous) in several places around the margins of the San Juan Basin in northwestern New Mexico. The lower Dakota unit represents a combined lagoonal-paludal environment traversed by anastomosing streams (Gabelman, 1956B). Uranium occurs either in carbonaceous shale or in carbonaceous sandstone, rarely in significant amounts in both rocks in the same deposit.

No discrete uranium species occur in the shale or impure lignite, but carnotite(?) and tyuyamunite are found in the sandstones. Associated minerals are limonite, jarosite, gypsum, and in the sandstones, calcite as well.

Nevada

Uraniferous lignites occur on the west side of the Desatoya Range in southeastern Churchill County in southwestern Nevada. On the Gamma property, five lignites, less than 1 ft to $3\frac{1}{2}$ ft thick, are interbedded with several hundred feet of gently dipping Tertiary clays and sandstones overlain by volcanic rocks (Lovering, 1954). The thickest bed, 3.5 ft, contains 0.006 to 0.059% U. The beds are exposed for 1,285 ft.

Other United States Occurrences

Minor occurrences of uraniferous coal and carbonaceous shale include Montana, Lewis and Clark County; California, Amador, Los Angeles, and San Benito Counties; Wyoming, Campbell and Johnson Counties; Colorado, Old Leyden coal mine, Jefferson County, San Miguel County, Paradox formation (Pennsylvanian).

Springs in at least two areas in Kern and Fresno Counties, California, at 5,000 to 8,000 ft in Sierra Nevada meadows are depositing ore-grade uranium. The uranium is precipitated by plant debris at the surfaces of bogs from spring water issuing from granitic rocks (Davis and Sharp, 1957). Samples contain as much as 0.7% U_3O_8, with chemical uranium three times the radiometric assay.

European Occurrences

Davidson and Ponsford (1954) have summarized data on occurrences of uraniferous coal from several European localities (Table 15.4).

Other radioactive coals in Europe include (1) Ryton coal, less than 1 ft thick, Warwickshire, England—0.008% U_3O_8; (2) Burke mine, Freital district, Dresden, Germany—0.003 to 0.12% eU_3O_8.

Liassic brown coal in the Mecsek Mountain area of Hungary has radiation intensities (rock radiation/background) of 0.9 to 8.3; associated carbonaceous shales have intensities of the range 2.95 to 12.78 (Földvari, 1952). The highest uranium content is about 0.01%, with thinner seams having highest values. Investigations by Szalay (1954) delineated other areas of radioactive coal in Hungary, which occur in the detritus zones of granitic mountain massifs or where interbedded with sills of phonolite and other alkalic rocks. Radioactive lignites, brown and hard coals, have been discovered in Yugoslavia, in Slovenia, Croatia, and Bosnia (Ristic, 1956). The Tertiary coals, 0.8 to 8 m thick, contain 20 to 450 ppm U. Only the lowermost coal beds are radioactive—those beds directly overlying an unconformity truncating Cretaceous limestones in which karst topography was developed in pre-Tertiary time.

TABLE 15.4. *Uranium content of European coal and peat (Davidson and Ponsford, 1954)*

Rock	Locality	Uranium content $\times 10^{-4}\%$
Five bituminous coals (avg.)........	France	0.63
Noncoking coal.................	Leicestershire, England	0.20
Noncoking coal.................	Derbyshire, England	0.16
Cannel coal.....................	Lancashire, England	0.20
Cannel coal.....................	Lancashire, England	0.003
Anthracite......................	South Wales, Great Britain	0.09
Compact peat..................	Upper Danube	1.0
Brown coal.....................	Wolfsegg, Austria	3.3
Hard coal......................	Upper Silesia	2.5
Coal dust......................	Beuthen, Upper Silesia	2.5
Coal...........................	Pilsen, Czechoslovakia	7.6

Madagascar

Near and south of Antsirabe at Vinaninkarena occur Quaternary lacustrine beds of gravel, sand, and peaty clay and silts about 20 m thick. Two beds, with an aggregate thickness of 1 m, contain uranocircite in disseminated flakes as fracture coatings and as wormhole fillings. The deposit underlies about 1 sq km. Hand-sorting can produce material with up to 8 to 10% U_3O_8 (Bain, 1950). Small amounts of uranium ore have been produced in the past, but presently operations are abandoned (Roubault, 1956). The uranium is believed to have been derived by weathering of the adjacent granitic complex, rich in pegmatites themselves locally rich in a variety of radioactive minerals (Table 5.5, page 207). The uranium apparently has been precipitated by the peaty organic material in certain of the beds.

Origin

Three general hypotheses may be listed to explain abnormal concentrations of uranium in some coals:

1. The uranium was concentrated in the vegetation from which coal was ultimately formed. The uranium thus is syngenetic. Hoffman (1943) has found that plant material from peat contains uranium in amounts similar to that in living plants and that with coalification the uranium content is increased.

2. Uranium was deposited essentially contemporaneously with the plant material but was not initially contained in it. The uranium thus is diagenetic.

3. The uranium was introduced by precipitation, chiefly from ground waters, following coalification. The uranium thus is epigenetic.

The last theory has been most widely accepted with some modifications by, among others, Szalay (1954), Davidson and Ponsford (1954), Miller and Gill

(1954), McKelvey et al. (1955), Denson (1955), Breger (1955), Breger et al. (1955), Vine (1956A), Masursky (1956), and Denson and Gill (1956). Factors supporting the epigenetic theory include:

1. The irregular distribution of the uranium, its concentration in uppermost parts of beds or in the highest coal bed of a sequence, and its decrease down dip in a given bed.

2. The increase in radioactivity in those coals that are in contact with more permeable beds, especially coarse, poorly consolidated sandstones.

3. The localization of deposits with respect to structural features capable of impounding ground water or permitting its access in quantity to the coaly beds, e.g., positions on flanks and troughs of synclines and beneath unconformities.

4. The presence in many areas of overlying or interbedded volcanic rocks, particularly acid pyroclastics which are abnormally radioactive and contain uranium and other elements in readily leachable form (pages 166–167). Waters from seeps and springs issuing from such rocks have 10 to 100 times more uranium than ordinary ground water (Denson, 1955; Denson et al., 1956) and in some areas such water also contains significant amounts of As, Cu, P, V, and Mo, e.g., water from the White River and Arikaree volcanics in the Dakotas (Denson, 1955).

The ability of carbonaceous and woody material to concentrate uranium has been demonstrated and emphasized by several investigators, by Tolmachev as early as 1943. Szalay (1954) performed laboratory experiments revealing that decomposed plant debris, peat, lignite, and brown coal have a very high adsorption power and capacity for uranium from carbonate-rich solutions containing uranium as the complex sodium-uranyl ion. He concluded the precipitation was effected chiefly by colloidal humic acid particles. Davidson and Ponsford (1954) have commented on the remarkable affinity of wood for uranium, noting absorption of the metal by mine timbers and wood vats at the Urgeirica mine, Portugal (pages 335–336). That living plants also selectively absorb uranium over ore bodies has been demonstrated and used as an aid to prospecting (Cannon, 1952; Cannon and Starrett, 1956), but the order of magnitude of such enrichment is insufficient to account for uranium concentrations in coal. Experiments by Moore (1954) demonstrated that peat, lignite, and subbituminous coal are exceedingly effective agents for removing uranium from solution. Plant material in bogs in the Sierra Nevada is precipitating uranium from spring water.

It is not concluded that the source of the uranium in all deposits has been overlying or formerly overlying volcanic rocks. Indeed four types of sources appear likely:

1. Acid volcanic rocks—Dakotas, Idaho

2. Granitic terranes ($\pm$ uraniferous pegmatites $\pm$ uraniferous veins)—Vina-ninkarena, Madagascar; some Hungarian coals; Freital, Germany

3. Alkalic sills and dikes intruding the coals, on higher sediments or in nearby terrains—some Hungarian coals

4. Uraniferous hydrothermal solutions—Old Leyden coal mine, Colorado, where the coal bed is cut by a shear zone and vein deposits of pitchblende are relatively close

Breger et al. (1955) have pointed out that alkali uranyl carbonates are sensitive to acids and where their solutions encounter zones of low pH in lignites sodium humate and uranyl humate may be expected as precipitates:

$$Na_4(UO_2)(CO_3)_3 + 6HA \rightarrow 4NaA + UO_2A_2 + 3CO_2 + 3H_2O$$

As McKelvey et al. (1955) have noted, the mechanisms outlined above do not explain all the relations of lignite, potential volcanic source rocks, and uranium. Some lignites near radioactive volcanic rocks are not uraniferous (Duncan, 1953). Nevertheless, the factors controlling the distribution of uranium in coal appear to be:

1. A uraniferous source, capable of supplying readily leachable uranium
2. Ground water and structures or rocks capable of permitting its access to coaly beds
3. Time for continued movement of uraniferous waters to coaly beds
4. Coaly material of the correct rank, ash content, and permeability, and containing acid organic material capable of precipitating uranium stabilized as urano-organic compounds

URANIFEROUS BONE

Fossil bones and teeth from widely distributed localities commonly have uranium contents distinctly higher than those of similar modern material (Jaffe and Sherwood, 1951; Davidson and Atkin, 1953). There is a wide range in the order of radioactivity with a tendency, at least for specimens from British strata (Table 15.5), for the material from sandy or gravelly deposits to be more radioactive (Davidson and Atkin, 1953).

Autoradiographic studies by Davidson and Atkin (1953) show, in the case of a shark's tooth from South Carolina (Tertiary), a marked concentration of radioactivity at the surface of the tooth, whereas in a fish plate (*Homostius*) from the Old Red Sandstone (Devonian) the density of the alpha track pattern was practically uniform throughout. In *Homostius* from Thurso, Scotland, Bowie and Atkin (1956) found 0.48% eU_3O_8 and by analysis 0.32% U_3O_8 and 0.51% ThO_2. The uranium is chiefly in the carbonate-fluorapatite of the bone, whereas the thorium is concentrated in a hydrocarbon that fills bone cavities. Normally, however, thorium appears to be low or absent in fossil bone.

Phosphatic bone and tooth material is of widespread distribution in many phosphorites of marine origin; both marine and terrestrial animals are commonly represented. Such material occurs with marine phosphatic nodules of Quaternary age on the present edge of the continental shelf (Dietz et al., 1942). Phosphatic bone pieces of terrestrial creatures also may be locally abundant in nonmarine beds, where they commonly show fragmentation and other results of fluvatile transportation, e.g., in the Morrison formation of the Western United States. Such bones also may be radioactive, even strongly so. Examples are discoveries of radioactive dinosaur bone fragments in the Morrison formation along

TABLE 15.5. *Radioactivity of fossil bone material* (*Davidson and Atkin,* 1953)

	Per cent of eU_3O_8
Middle Old Red Sandstone fish, *Coccosteus* sp., Thurso, Caithness (GSM53334)	0.027
Middle O.R.S. fish, *Thursius* sp., Stromness, Orkney (GSM53403)	0.005
Middle O.R.S. fish, *Glyptolepis* sp., Thurso, Caithness (GSM53498)	0.120
Middle O.R.S. fish, *Thursius* sp., Baligill, Sutherland (GSM58637)	0.550
Middle O.R.S. fish, *Glyptolepis* sp., Gamrie, Banff (GSM88899)	0.001
Middle O.R.S. fish, *Glyptolepis* sp., Thurso, Caithness (GSM88900)	0.025
Middle O.R.S. fish, *Coccosteus* sp., Thurso, Caithness (GSM88985)	0.110
Middle O.R.S. fish, *Homostius* sp., Thurso, Caithness (GSM89069)	0.160
Asteracanthus bone, Swanage. Purbeck	0.002
Lepidotus bone, *Weald.* Wealden	<0.001
Bone fragments. Near Bletchley, Bedfordshire. Cretaceous	0.005
Rib bones of whale. Felixstowe. Pliocene Red Crag	0.007
Phosphatized cetacean bones. Felixstowe. Pliocene Red Crag	0.015
Phosphatized saurian bones. Ely. Kimmeridge clay	0.003
Phosphatized saurian bones. Knapwell, Cambridgeshire. Kimmeridge clay	0.007
Phosphatized bone fragments. Lyme Regis. Rhaetic	0.002
Shark's tooth from phosphate deposit. South Carolina (GSM22865)	0.190
Phosphatized shark's teeth. Florida. Pliocene	0.025

TABLE 15.6. *Radioactive fossil bones from Wyoming* (*Smith and Bradley,* 1951; *Love,* 1953B)

Locality	Material	Analyses, per cent		
		eU	U	V_2O_5
Mink Creek........	Fossil bone from white tuff	0.005	0.006	0.10
Pilgrim Creek......	Fossil bone from gray tuff	0.005	0.005	0.06
Camp Davis........	Fossil bone from white tuff	0.020	0.021	0.06
Split Rock.........	Fossil bone from Miocene gray sandstone	0.020	0.020	0.11
Split Rock.........	Fossil bone fragment from Pliocene sandstone	0.17	0.015	0.27
Marshall area......	Fossil bison bone from Pleistocene	0.028	0.086	0.06
Gros Ventre Creek, Teton County......	Fossil dinosaur bones, Morrison fm.		0.04–0.135	

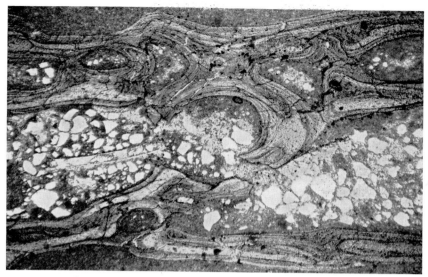

Fig. 15.3. Radioactive dinosaur bone fragment, Morrison formation, Gros Ventre Creek, Wyo. Fractures across bone structure have permitted stream waters to wash in sand and clay particles ($\times$35).

Gros Ventre Creek, Teton County, Wyoming (Fig. 15.3) (Smith and Bradley, 1951, Table 15.6), and three skeletons of Mesohippus(?) on a bluff 2 mi west of Hagerman, Idaho, reported containing 0.1% U_3O_8. At the northeast end of the Salt Valley anticline the writer secured numerous fragments of dinosaur bones from the Morrison, ranging from 0.07 to 0.09% eU_3O_8. About 200 lb of radioactive dinosaur bones have been unearthed from the Morrison(?) formation on Turkey Creek Ranch, 17 mi southwest of Colorado Springs, Colorado. The presence of fossil bones and teeth along with fossil plant material in association with uranium deposits on the Colorado Plateau was noted early by Hess (1913), and Stokes (1952B, p. 44) states for the Thompsons area, Grand County, Utah, "Dinosaur bones are common in the ore deposits and are frequently observed replaced by high-grade minerals." The presence of abundant bone material in some areas on the Plateau may also have been a significant source for PO_4 in producing secondary uranium phosphates. Hill (1950) has shown that Tertiary and Quaternary bones from the Uruguayan Pampas usually are relatively highly radioactive.

Thus, although it appears that for marine formations at least some of the uranium in bones may have been derived by adsorption from sea water, it is probable that much of the radioactivity of bones and teeth in both marine and nonmarine rocks is due to uranium introduced epigenetically, probably by the reaction of uraniferous ground water with collophane. The precipitating action of rat and rabbit bones on uranium has been demonstrated; in favorable circumstances uranium may be adsorbed on such bone surfaces in amounts up to 4% U_3O_8 in the bone ash (Neuman et al., 1948). Thus, as Davidson and Atkin

(1953) have concluded, the radioactivity of fossil bone can be a function of (1) the geological age of the fossil, (2) the permeability of the rock in which it is buried, and (3) the availability and uranium content of ground water. Therefore younger fossils may be either more or less radioactive than older ones, and the radioactivity may be uniformly or nonuniformly distributed.

IN SEDIMENTARY AND PYROCLASTIC ROCKS

Since the genetic status of many "Colorado Plateau-type" deposits remains in considerable doubt, they have been described as a unit, based upon structural and mineralogical features (pages 397–401). Nevertheless evidence strongly indicates that some deposits possessing many of the geological characteristics of the Plateau type have originated as the result of deposition of uranium minerals from ground water, which may have secured the uranium and other elements from (1) granitic rocks, (2) uranium veins, (3) arkoses derived from granitic terranes, or (4) abnormally radioactive acid pyroclastic rocks (pages 180–182). Some examples of this type of deposit are described in this section. Deposition has resulted from contact with carbonaceous material or in some cases from evaporation. Clayey seams have served to prevent downward percolation and dissipation.

In the Cameron area in northeastern Arizona, uraniferous deposits occur in the Shinarump, Chinle, and Kayenta formations, with most production from the Petrified Forest member of the Chinle. The primary deposits, consisting of uraninite and Fe and Cd, Pb, and Cu sulfides, have undergone recent uranium redistribution (Austin, 1957). Evidence for redistribution includes: specimens commonly are out of radioactive equilibrium; secondary uranium minerals cement otherwise unconsolidated Pleistocene gravel; and radioactive diffusion halos of secondary iron and manganese oxides surround a mineralized log. The halos also are out of equilibrium. Austin (1957) concludes that acid and sulfate solutions derived from oxidizing sulfides have recently redistributed U, Mn, Co, Mo, and Cu, but have not removed the uranium from the area of the deposits. The solutions may also have bleached the host rocks, transforming montmorillonite to illite.

On both sides of Virgin Valley, 40 mi west of Denio, Humboldt County, Nev., near the Oregon line, uraniferous opal occurs as discontinuous layers, as much as 6 ft thick and ½ mi long in Tertiary vitric tuff and ash beds (Staatz and Bauer, 1951B; Lovering, 1954). On the east side of the valley 4 of 7 opal layers are abnormally radioactive and on the west side 4 of 15 layers are abnormally radioactive. Powdery carnotite coats fractures in opal, which contains 0.002 to 0.12% U.

Carnotite deposits in carbonaceous Dakota sandstone in the San Juan Basin of New Mexico are associated with uraniferous black shales of paludal origin (pages 543–544). The agent of deposition apparently has been ground water.

The Copper Mountain area in northeastern Fremont County is about 20 mi northeast of Shoshoni, along the foothills of the Owl Creek Mountains. Uranium mineralization, a 14-sq mi area north of the Cedar Ridge fault, is found in Precambrian granite, in weathered Precambrian granite debris; in the early Eocene

Wind River formation, in middle and upper Eocene tuffaceous rocks, and in Recent conglomerates (Tourtelot, 1952; Loomis, 1956). A substantial ore body occurs at the junction of two belts of mineralization. At the Little Mo deposit the ore is in granite, whereas at the Kermac deposit meta-autunite follows fracture networks along bedding planes in Eocene mudstone (Grutt, 1956).

In the basal limestone of the Sundance formation of late Jurassic age, near Mayoworth, Johnson County, on the east flank of the Bighorn Mountains, meta-tyuyamunite coats fractures and replaces calcite oolites and cement (Love, 1954B; Guilinger and Theobald, 1957). The uranium content ranges from 0.017 to 0.32%. The beds, which dip 10 to 15° NE., have been mineralized at intervals over a distance of at least a mile. The most radioactive material occurs along ferruginous clayey partings. Some uranium (as a black, unidentified mineral) may be syngenetic; some metatyuyamunite has been concentrated along ground-water channels. Radioactive dinosaur bones occur abundantly in Morrison sandstone, 2 mi to the south.

A channel sandstone of the Chadron formation (Oligocene) in the White River Badlands, Pennington County, South Dakota, locally contains uranocircite, associated with barite and apatite. The mineral is localized in the lower 2 ft of the 7-ft bed and especially in the basal few inches overlying an impermeable bentonitic claystone (Moore and Levish, 1955). Metatyuyamunite(?) is found at one locality in fresh-water limestone at the top of the Chadron, and carnotite coats chalcedony veinlets at several places in the overlying Brule formation also of Oligocene age. The upper part of the Brule is almost entirely volcanic ash which contains an average of 0.001% U. Moore and Levish (1955) believe the uranium occurrences in the Badlands were formed by leaching of uranium from the Brule pyroclastics and precipitation of uranyl minerals from ground water over a long period of time.

In the southern part of the Slim Butte area, Harding County, South Dakota, carnotite occurs as disseminated flakes and fracture coatings in fine-grained tuffaceous sandstone and sandy claystone of the Chadron formation of Oligocene age. The uraniferous unit, 9 ft thick, contains most of the carnotite in the upper 4 ft and over a distance of 300 ft. Locally assays of as much as 0.23% U have been obtained. The overlying tuffaceous Arikaree formation (Miocene) contains on the average about 0.0015% U. Gill and Moore (1955) postulate that meteoric waters percolating through the Arikaree dissolved uranium, vanadium, and other elements and redeposited them as carnotite in sandstone along the base of the perched water table. Water from springs issuing from this water table perched on bentonite contains 42 to 170 ppb uranium and 290 ppb vanadium, in contrast to waters in the underlying formations, which are uranium-poor. A similar origin has been suggested for the uranium in lignite in this area (pages 541–542).

The Middle Lake deposits, near Stony Rapids east of Lake Athabasca, Saskatchewan, Canada, consist of autunite and phosphuranylite disseminated through sandstones and conglomerates of the Athabasca series (Blake, 1956). The discontinuous mineralization is concentrated in basal layers along the unconformity with underlying Tazin-type rocks, extending into the subjacent regolith.

IN PLUTONIC IGNEOUS AND METAMORPHIC ROCKS

General

Some occurrences of plutonic igneous rocks that are locally abnormally radio-active owe their radioactivity to various uranyl minerals including autunite, tor-bernite, uranophane, and others. Commonly these minerals are disseminated in altered rocks, especially granites, but minor concentrations also occur along joints in relatively fresh rocks. The minerals have been formed under supergene conditions, but sources of the uranium and distances that it has migrated vary considerably. In some cases the plutonic rock appears to have been mineralized hydrothermally along shear zones with pitchblende, and subsequent oxidation and relatively local redistribution have produced the uranyl minerals. In some instances nearby weathered, radioactive pegmatites have been the uranium source. In other cases the uranyl species have been deposited in a more ex-tensive manner from ground water that obtained its uranium from distant pri-mary veins or lodes, from formerly overlying or nearby slightly uraniferous tuffaceous rocks, or even from the accessory radioactive minerals and the leach-able uranium fraction of the plutonic rock itself.

Examples

Two long-known examples occur in the Eastern United States. One is in the Philadelphia area where autunite (and torbernite?) formerly was found abun-dantly as scales along fractures in a gneissic to pegmatitic granite containing numerous xenoliths of biotite schist.

In the Stone Mountain area of Georgia, flakelets of uranophane occur with coatings of hyalite in light gray, biotite-bearing muscovite granite (Watson, 1910; Furcron, 1955).

In the Copper Mountain area of Fremont County, Wyoming, meta-autun-ite(?) is disseminated in amounts of potential economic significance in granite.

Several deposits in California contain uranyl minerals localized in or near shear zones in plutonic rocks. Primary uranium minerals usually have not been found, but the distribution of the mineralization together with the presence of oxidized copper minerals and quartz-fluorite gangue indicate that the original mineralization was of hydrothermal origin, and the uranyl species, formed under oxidizing conditions, have not wandered far. Examples include the Miracle mine in the Kern River Canyon, 35 mi northeast of Bakersfield, Kern County, where autunite forms erratic disseminations in a 2-ft zone of limonitic clayey gouge and in altered Isabella granodiorite (late Jurassic–early Creta-ceous) along a shear. Fluorite is in the gangue. About 3,000 ft south of the Miracle mine is the Kergon deposit where similar mineralization along frac-ture zones in weathered biotite granite contains as much as 1.08% U_3O_8 together with 1.84% Mo and 1.1% fluorite (Walker et al., 1956). In San Luis Obispo County, the Wakefield deposit near La Panza Summit contains torbernite dis-tributed irregularly along a shear zone 6 in. wide in granite.

Zeunerite is disseminated in hematite that fills vugs in a highly oxidized lens of pegmatitic granite and in fractures in the surrounding weathered granite on the southwest flank of Brooks Mountain, Seward Peninsula, Alaska. Lesser amounts of zeunerite form surface coatings in a few quartz-tourmaline veins (West and White, 1952).

Disseminated torbernite intergrown with autunite is known in a muscovite-rich, tourmaline-bearing granite near Trasquilan, 9 km south of Cáceres, central Estremadura, Spain (Webel, 1955).

Torbernite and autunite are present in various metamorphic and plutonic igneous rocks in Baden, in many instances derived from the alteration of pitchblende veins and lodes, but in some localities relatively widely redistributed. Autunite, for example, occurs in clefts of the Blau granite near Badenweiler, Germany.

In the iron districts of northern Michigan, pitchblende and uranyl minerals have been found in association with various sulfides in small deposits along tension fractures in middle Precambrian (upper Huronian) slates and quartzites. Three of the four deposits are associated with soft iron ores, localized at or near contact between oxidized rock and unaltered rock. The uranyl minerals are metatyuyamunite, meta-autunite, metatorbernite, and bassetite, and the sulfides are pyrite, chalcopyrite, sphalerite, galena, bornite, and greenockite; there is no appreciable gangue. Vickers (1956D) suggests that the uranium and associated metals were leached from carbonaceous slates during weathering and deposited in unaltered rock under reducing conditions. Evidence to support this hypothesis includes (1) the slates contain as much as 0.004% U and appreciable amounts of the other metals; (2) weathering of the pyritic slates can provide acid waters capable of leaching the metals; and (3) unweathered slates provide an environment sufficiently reducing to cause precipitation of pitchblende and sulfides below the weathering zone.

RADIOACTIVE SPRINGS AND SPRING DEPOSITS

The radioactivity of ground waters varies very greatly; some springs contain but 10^{-8} gm U/l, whereas waters that have traversed uranium deposits have between 10^{-5} to 10^{-3} gm U/l (with radium and radon as well) and exceptionally as much as 10^{-2} gm U/l (Saukoff, 1956). The radioactivity of most so-called "radioactive" hot springs depends chiefly on their content of radon. Radon is obtained by underground waters (1) by dissolution of radon gas escaping from certain minerals of open-lattice-type structures,[1] and (2) by decay of previously dissolved radium by the waters. Acid waters, such as those traversing heavy pyrite ores, tend to dissolve uranium preferentially with respect to radium, and the uranyl ion is stable in acid solution.

The uranyl ion can complex with carbonates to form the complex ions $UO_2(CO_3)_2^{2-}$ and $UO_2(CO_3)_3^{4-}$ (Blake et al., 1955), which as alkaline or alkaline earth uranyl carbonates are stable above pH 7.0. As the uranyl ion, therefore, uranium may be transported in either acid or alkaline media. The ability of the uranous ion to form similar complexes is unknown. Waters circu-

[1] The degree to which a radioactive mineral loses the radon generated within it is called its emanating power, expressed in per cent loss. Carnotites may have an emanating power of about 70%; zircon with a closed-lattice-type structure loses very little of its radon and thus has a low emanating power.

lating under reducing conditions do not become enriched in uranium but attain high concentrations of radium and radon. The solubility of radon in water is a steep inverse function of temperature; at near-freezing temperature water will dissolve approximately twice as much radon as at room temperature (Faul, 1954). Yet in some areas, e.g., Tiberias, Israel, cold springs contain lower concentrations of radon than do hot springs (Rosenblatt and Lindeman, 1952). The waters of these hot springs also contain an element with a relatively long half-life, probably Radium F. The Grant View hot spring in the East Walker River area, Lyon County, Nevada, gives counter readings of 2.5 times normal, but contains only 0.02 ppm U after standing several weeks (Staatz and Bauer, 1953). Since radon has a very short half-life,[1] radioactivity of springs varies widely, depending upon (1) the nature and degree of radioactivity of the source rocks and minerals, (2) the speed of underground circulation, and (3) the yield of the spring. Other factors equal, radioactivity is greater in wet than in dry years (Miholíc, 1956).

In Yugoslavia waters issuing from Carboniferous and Cretaceous strata show distinctly higher radioactivities than those from sediments of other periods, pointing to the influence of the source material (Miholíc, 1952). In Nebraska and adjacent states, waters derived from Tertiary strata contain 4 to 110 ppb U, contents higher than those in waters from other terranes in which uranium deposits are likewise absent. The uranium contents are believed to be derived from radioactive tuffaceous Tertiary rocks (Tourtelot, 1955). Some spring deposits also contain uranium (Table 15.7).

Spring deposits of travertine or less usually siliceous sinter may also display unusual radioactivity. In general most of their radioactivity stems from their radium content, which is usually concentrated in barite. Sulfate ions will coprecipitate radium and barium sulfate in the presence of a considerable excess of Ba over Ra, even though the solubility product of radium is not exceeded (Doerner and Hoskins, 1925). Radiobarites in hot springs deposits are known, for example, from Hokuto, on Taiwan Island; at Shibukuro, Japan; at Teplitz and Karlsbad, Czechoslovakia; and in the Limestone Hills area, Kiowa County, Oklahoma (pages 127–128). A radioactive thermal spring deposit near Jemez Springs, Sandoval County, New Mexico, consists of calcareous tufa containing 0.002 to 0.006% eU. Some black sooty bands as much as 15 ft long and 2 ft thick contain up to 0.20% eU. The major radioactive element is Ra, with uranium ranging from 0.000 to 0.002. Barium ranges from 0.01 to 0.1% in the tufa and from 0.1 to 1.0% in the black layers (Lovering, 1956). Radiobarite deposited from ground water is abundant in upper parts of the Tyuya Muyun deposits, U.S.S.R., together with reported radiocarbonate (pages 438–440).

The radioactivity of very recent spring deposits of calcareous and siliceous material is commonly higher than that of the waters issuing from them. Older deposits in a particular area are usually appreciably less radioactive than younger layers.[2] In the deposits of some districts radioactivity is markedly concentrated in darker layers, which are usually richer in hydrous oxides of man-

[1] The longest-lived isotope, Rn^{222}, has a half-life of 3.825 days.

[2] Of the four natural isotopes of radium, Ra^{226} has the longest half-life, 1,590 years.

TABLE 15.7. *Selected examples of radioactive spring deposits*

Location	Occurrence	Radioactivity	Reference
Stokes and Stowell properties, Plumas County, Calif.	"Spring deposits"	Due to radium	Walker et al., 1956
Allen property, Erskine Creek, Kern County, Calif.	Calcareous spring deposit filling fractures in and forming a cap on weathered granite. Cold spring present	Mainly due to radium(?). Maximum radioactivity of 1.30% eU_3O_8 in black sooty material underlying limy cap rock. Cap rock has 0.88% eU_3O_8 and 0.01% U_3O_8	Walker et al., 1956
Seth-La-Kai diatreme, Hopi Buttes, Ariz.	Radioactive travertine over 15 ft thick; associated epigenetic deposits in sandstone. In Bidahochi (Tertiary) formation	Travertine averages 0.03% U_3O_8. Tuffaceous sandstone averages 0.20% U_3O_8 for a 2-ft thickness and is traced 150 ft. It contains limonite, gypsum, psilomelane, montmormillonite, celadonite, laumontite, and an unidentified nonfluorescent secondary uranyl mineral	Lowell, 1956
Badgastein, Austria	Warty and calcareous sinter hot springs deposits; blue algae aid in deposition	Radioactivity of spring water due to Rn and Ra. Sinters contain $1–50 \times 10^{-6}$ g U/gm. Fledermaus spring deposit contains 10^{-3} g U/gm	Scheminzky and Grabherr, 1951
Teplitz and Karlsbad, Czechoslovakia	Sulfatic hot spring deposits	Radiobarite, $1.4–7 \times 10^{-6}$% U; more radioactive on surfaces and along fractures	Haberlandt, 1938
Hokuto-tei, Taiwan	Spring-deposited barite cements alluvial boulders and gravel	Radioactive plumbian barite (hokutolite). Surface is 10 $\times$ more radioactive than interior	Kimura, 1940
Shibukuro, Japan	Spring deposits	Radioactive plumbian barite	
Kasempa district, Northern Rhodesia	Very recent calcareous sinter around hot springs	Uranium absent. High-grade radioactivity due to radium and its daughter elements	Davidson, 1956B

ganese and to a lesser extent iron. The affinity of hydrous iron oxide colloids for uranium has been discussed (pages 529–531); analogously manganese-rich lake and bog iron ores as well as manganese oxide nodules of marine origin contain abnormal radium concentrations, particularly in their outer layers, as much as 135×10^{-6} g/ton Ra. Thus it appears that much of the radioactivity of spring deposits can be ascribed to either (1) the presence of radium in barite, $(Ba,Ra)SO_4$, or (2) to its presence absorbed in subcrystalline manganese oxide mixtures (wad).

The relationship of radioactivity and manganese content is illustrated by the radioactive hot springs deposits in Ouray Township, northwestern San Juan Mountains, Colorado, where several radioactive hot springs deposits occur near a major fault separating Precambrian from Paleozoic rocks (Burbank and Pierson, 1953). Some of the calcareous tufa deposits are pre-Pleistocene and contain iron oxides and manganese oxides. One has been mined for manganese.

In some areas there is a marked increase in radioactivity of spring waters after they have percolated through their previously deposited sinters.

Jetzt haben wir gegessen
Und sind noch nicht satt.
Wir hätten mehr gegessen
Hätten wir mehr gehabt.

BIBLIOGRAPHY

Abbott, A. T. (1954) Monazite deposits in calcareous rocks, northern Lemhi County, Idaho. *Idaho Bur. Mines Geol. Pam.* 99.

Abraham, E. M. (1953) Preliminary report on the geology of parts of Long and Spragge Townships, Blind River uranium area, district of Algoma. *Ontario Dept. Mines, Prelim. Rept.* 1953–52.

Adams, J. A. S. (1954) Uranium and thorium contents of volcanic rocks. In Nuclear geology. John Wiley & Sons, Inc., New York, 89–98.

——— (1955) The uranium geochemistry of Lassen Volcanic National Park, California. *Geochim. et Cosmochim. Acta* 8:74–85.

——— and Pliler, R. (1956) Geochemistry of the actinides as a possible clue in interpreting the development of the earth's atmosphere (abs.). *Geol. Soc. Am., Bull.* 67:1663.

——— and Saunders, D. F. (1953) Uranium content of the lavas of Lassen Volcanic National Park, California (abs.). *Geol. Soc. Am., Bull.* 64:1389.

Adams, J. W. (1953) Beryllium deposits of the Mount Antero region, Chaffee County, Colorado. *U.S. Geol. Survey Bull.* 982-D.

———, Gude, A. J. III, and Beroni, E. P. (1953) Uranium occurrences in the Golden Gate Canyon and Ralston Creek areas, Jefferson County, Colorado. *U.S. Geol. Survey Circ.* 320.

——— and Stugard, F. Jr. (1956A) Wall-rock control of certain pitchblende deposits in Golden Gate Canyon, Jefferson County, Colorado. *Intern. Conf. Peaceful Uses Atomic Energy, Proc.* 6:279–282 (also *U.S. Geol. Survey Profess. Paper* 300:113–116, 1956).

——— and ——— (1956B) Wall-rock control of certain pitchblende deposits in Golden Gate Canyon, Jefferson County, Colorado. *U.S. Geol. Survey Bull.* 1030-G.

Agar, W. M. (1933) The pegmatites of Bedford, New York. *16th Intern. Geol. Congr., Guidebook* 9:123–128.

Agard, J. (1956) Les gites minéraux associés aux roches alcalines et aux carbonatites (abs.). *20th Congr. géol. intern. Resúmenes Trabajos Presentados* 393.

Alia, M. (1956A) Radioactive deposits and possibilities in Spain. *Intern. Conf. Peaceful Uses Atomic Energy, Proc.* 6:196–197.

——— (1956B) Yacimientos de radioactivos en el Silurico español (abs.). *20th Congr. géol. intern. Resúmenes Trabajos Presentados* 82.

Allan, J. A. (1914)   Geology of Field map-area, British Columbia and Alberta. *Can. Geol. Survey Mem.* 55.

Allen, J. E. (1956)   Titaniferous Cretaceous beach placer in McKinley County, New Mexico (abs.). *Geol. Soc. Am., Bull.* 67:1789.

Allen, R. B., MacDonald, B. C., and Smith, E. E. N. (1954)   Pitchblende deposits of the St. Louis fault, Beaverlodge area, Saskatchewan. *Can. Mining Met. Bull.* 47:67–70.

Alsdorf, P. R. (1916)   Occurrence, geology and economic value of the pitchblende deposits of Gilpin County, Colorado. *Econ. Geol.* 11:266–275.

Althausen, M. N. (1956)   Reasons for the accumulation of rare metals and phosphorus in marine sediments during the lower Paleozoic (abs.). *20th Congr. géol. intern. Resúmenes Trabajos Presentados* 82–83.

Altschuler, Z. S., Clarke, R. S. Jr., and Young, E. J. (1954)   Uranium in apatite (abs.). *Geol. Soc. Am., Bull.* 65:1225–1226.

———, Jaffe, E. B., and Cuttitta, F. (1956)   The aluminum phosphate zone of the Bone Valley formation and its uranium deposits. *Intern. Conf. Peaceful Uses Atomic Energy, Proc.* 6:507–513 (also *U.S. Geol. Survey Profess. Paper* 300: 495–504, 1956).

Aminoff, G. (1943)   A titano-thucolite from the Boliden mine. *Geol. Fören. Förh.* 65:31–36.

Anderson, C. (1910)   Mineralogical notes: No. IX—Topaz, quartz, monazite, and other Australian minerals. *Records Australian Museum* 8(2):120–129.

Anderson, E. C. (1957)   The metal resources of New Mexico and their economic features through 1954. *New Mexico Bur. Mines Mineral Resources Bull.* 39.

Anderson, R. Y., and Kurtz, E. B. Jr. (1955)   Biogeochemical reconnaissance of the Annie Laurie uranium prospect, Santa Cruz County, Arizona. *Econ. Geol.* 50: 227–232.

Anderson, T. P., and Waddell, G. G. (1952)   Examination of the Stalin's Present mine, Pershing County, Nevada. *U.S. Atomic Energy Comm.* RMO-927.

Angelelli, V. (1956)   Distribution and characteristics of the uranium deposits and occurrences in the Argentine republic. *Intern. Conf. Peaceful Uses Atomic Energy, Proc.* 6:63–90.

Appleman, D. E. (1956)   Crystal structure of liebigite (abs.). *Geol. Soc. Am., Bull.* 67:1666.

——— (1957)   Crystal-chemical study of Johannite (abs.). *Geol. Soc. Am., Bull.* 68:1696.

Arambourg, C., and Orcel, J. (1951)   Observations préliminaires sur la présence d'un vanadate d'urane dans les gisements de phosphates du Maroc. *Acad. sci. Paris, Compt. rend.* 233:1635.

Archbold, N. L. (1955)   Relationships of calcium carbonate to lithology and vanadium-uranium deposits in the Salt Wash sandstone member of the Morrison formation (abs.). *Geol. Soc. Am., Bull.* 66:1526.

Argentiere, R. (1957)   Algumas ocorrencias de minerais do grupo da allanita no Rio Grande do Norte. *Eng., .nineração e met.* 24(147):129–132.

Armstrong, E. J. (1935)   Schroeckingerite from Bedford, New York. *Am. Mineralogist* 20:62–63.

Armstrong, F. C. (1952)   Pitchblende deposits on Quartz Hill, Central City district, Gilpin County, Colorado (abs.). *Geol. Soc. Am., Bull.* 63:1232.

——— (1954)   Radioactivity in the northwest (abs.). *Geol. Soc. Am., Bull.* 65:1331.

Asayama, T. (1953)   On the radioactivity of rocks in Japan and vicinity, I. Radium of volcanic rocks. *Kyoto Univ., Sci. Tech. Mem.* 2-B:53–67.

Austin, S. R. (1957)   Recent uranium redistribution in the Cameron, Arizona deposits. *2d Nuclear Eng. Sci. Conf. Paper* 57-NESC-43.

Australia, Commonwealth of, Dept. Natl. Develop. (1956)   The natural occurrence of uranium and thorium in Australia. *Intern. Conf. Peaceful Uses Atomic Energy Proc.* 6:91–92.

Axelrod, J. M., Grimaldi, F. S., Milton, C., and Murata, K. J. (1951)   The uranium minerals from the Hillside mine, Yavapai County, Arizona. *Am. Mineralogist* 36:1–22.

Bailey, S. W., Cameron, E. N., Spedden, H. R., and Weege, R. J. (1956)   The alteration of ilmenite in beach sands. *Econ. Geol.* 51:263–279.

Bain, G. W. (1950)   Geology of the fissionable materials. *Econ. Geol.* 45:273–323.

—— (1952)   The age of the "Lower Cretaceous" from Bisbee, Arizona uraninite. *Econ. Geol.* 47:305–315.

—— (1957)   Discussion of urano-organic ores. *Econ. Geol.* 52:192–195.

Baker, B. H. (1953)   The alkaline igneous complex of Jombo. *Geol. Survey Kenya, Rept.* 24:32–48.

Baker, K. E., Smith, L. E., and Rapaport, I. (1952)   Carnotite deposits near Edgemont, South Dakota. *U.S. Atomic Energy Comm.* RMO-881.

Bakken, R., Gleditsch, E., and Pappas, A. C. (1948)   The uraninites. *Bull. soc. chim. France* 515–517.

Ball, S. H., and Shaler, M. K. (1914)   Economic geology of the Belgian Congo, Central Africa. *Econ. Geol.* 9:605–663.

Bandy, M. C. (1951)   The Ribaue-Alto Ligonha pegmatite district, Portuguese East Africa. *Rocks and Minerals* 26:512–521.

Bannister, F. A., and Horne, J. E. (1950)   A radioactive mineral from Mozambique related to davidite. *Mineral. Mag.* 29:101–112.

Barnes, V. E. (1954)   Phosphorite in eastern Llano uplift of central Texas. *Texas Univ. Bur. Econ. Geol., Rept. Invest.* 23.

Barth, T. (1927)   Die Pegmatitgänge der kaledonischen Intrusivgesteine im Seiland-Gebiete. *Norske Videnskaps-Akad. Oslo Skrifter. I. Mat.-Naturv. Kl.* 8.

Barthauer, G. L., Rulfs, C. L., and Pearce, D. W. (1953)   Investigation of thucolite. *Am. Mineralogist* 38:802–814.

Barton, P. B. Jr. (1956)   Fixation of uranium in the oxidized base metal ores of the Goodsprings district, Clark County, Nevada. *Econ. Geol.* 51:178–191.

Bastin, E. S. (1939)   The nickel-cobalt-native silver ore type. *Econ. Geol.* 34:1–40.

Bateman, A. M. (1950)   Economic mineral deposits. John Wiley & Sons, Inc., New York, 2d ed., 916 pp.

—— and Jensen, M. L. (1956)   Notes on the origin of the Rhodesian copper deposits: Isotope composition of the sulfides. *Econ. Geol.* 51:555–564.

Bateman, J. D. (1955)   Recent uranium developments in Ontario. *Econ. Geol.* 50:361–372.

Bates, R. G., and Wedow, H. Jr. (1953)   Preliminary summary review of thorium-bearing mineral occurrences in Alaska. *U.S. Geol. Survey Circ.* 202.

Bates, T. F., and Strahl, E. O. (1956)   Regional study of the mineralogy and petrology of the Chattanooga shale (abs.). *Geol. Soc. Am., Bull.* 67:1669.

—— and —— (1957)   Mineralogy, petrography, and radioactivity of representative samples of Chattanooga shale. *Geol. Soc. Am., Bull.* 68:1305–1314.

——, ——, Short, N. M., Silverman, E. N., and Camilli, E. (1954)   Mineralogy and petrography of the Chattanooga shale (abs.). *Geol. Soc. Am., Bull.* 65:1230.

Beard, E. H. (1950) Thorotungstite, a misnomer. *Colonial Geol. and Mineral Resources* 1:50–51.

Beck, G. (1954) Über Funde von Monazit, Xenotim, Autunit und Bazzit an der Grimsel. *Schweiz. mineral. petro. Mitt.* 34:188–189.

Becraft, G. E. (1953) Preliminary report on the Comet area, Jefferson County, Montana. *U.S. Geol. Survey Circ.* 277.

―――― (1956A) Uranium deposits of the Boulder batholith, Montana. *Intern. Conf. Peaceful Uses Atomic Energy, Proc.* 6:270–274 (also *U.S. Geol. Survey Profess. Paper* 300:117–121, 1956).

―――― (1956B) Uranium deposits of the northern part of the Boulder batholith, Montana. *Econ. Geol.* 51:362–374.

―――― and Pinckney, D. M. (1954) Uranium deposits of the Boulder batholith, Montana (abs.). *Geol. Soc. Am., Bull.* 65:1230.

Beer, K. E. (1951) The petrology of some of the riebeckite-granites of Nigeria. *Geol. Survey Gt. Brit., Rept.* 116.

Behrend, F. (1933) Uranerzführende Pegmatitgänge in Südafrika und ihre Geochemie. *Arch. Lagerstättenforsch.* 54.

Beintema, J. (1938) On the composition and the crystallography of autunite and the meta-autunites. *Rec. trav. chim., Pay-Bas,* 57:155–175.

Bell, H., and Bales, W. E. (1955) Uranium deposits in Fall River County, South Dakota. *U.S. Geol. Survey Bull.* 1009-G.

――――, Gott, G. B., Post, E. V., and Schnabel, R. W. (1956) Lithologic, structural, and geochemical controls of uranium deposition in the southern Black Hills, South Dakota. *Intern. Conf. Peaceful Uses Atomic Energy, Proc.* 6:407–411 (also *U.S. Geol. Survey Profess. Paper* 300:345–349, 1956).

Bell, K. G. (1954) Uranium and thorium in sedimentary rocks. In Nuclear geology. John Wiley & Sons, Inc., New York, 98–114.

―――― (1956) Uranium in precipitates and evaporites. *Intern. Conf. Peaceful Uses Atomic Energy, Proc.* 6:520–524 (also *U.S. Geol. Survey Profess. Paper* 300:381–386, 1956).

――――, Goodman, C., and Whitehead, W. L. (1940) Radioactivity of sedimentary rocks and associated petroleum. *Bull. Am. Assoc. Petrol. Geologists* 24:1529–1547.

Belluco, A. (1956) Uranium-bearing quartz veins of the "President Perón" deposit, Mendoza. *Intern. Conf. Peaceful Uses Atomic Energy, Proc.* 6:82–90.

Benson, W. E., Trites, A. F. Jr., Beroni, E. P., and Feeger, J. A. (1952) Preliminary report on the White Canyon area, San Juan County, Utah. *U.S. Geol. Survey Circ.* 217.

Bentor, Y. K. (1953) Relations entre la tectonique et les dépôts de phosphates dans le Neguev Israelien. *19th Congr. géol. intern., Compt. rend.,* sec. XI, fasc. XI, 93–101.

Bergendahl, M. H. (1955) Wavellite spherulites in the Bone Valley formation of central Florida. *Am. Mineralogist* 40:497–504.

Bergstrom, J. R. (1956) The general geology of uranium in southwestern North Dakota. *N. Dakota Geol. Survey, Rept. Invest.* 23.

Berman, E. R. (1955) Unit cell dimensions of uraninite. *Am. Mineralogist* 40:925–927.

Berman, J. (1952) Studies of metamict minerals (II): Reexamination of fergusonite (abs.). *Geol. Soc. Am., Bull.* 63:1235.

―――― (1953) Nature of crystallization of metamict minerals (abs.). *Geol. Soc. Am., Bull.* 64:1395.

―――― (1955) Identification of metamict minerals by x-ray diffraction. *Am. Mineralogist* 40:805–827.

Berman, R. (1957A)   Some physical properties of naturally irradiated fluorite. *Am. Mineralogist* 42:191–203.

———— (1957B)   Studies of uranium minerals (XXIII): Torbernite, zeunerite and uranospherite. *Am. Mineralogist* 42:905–908.

Beroni, E. P., and Derzay, R. C. (1955)   The uranium deposits of the Fish Creek district, Colorado. *Rocky Mtn. Assoc. Geol., Guidebook Geol. Northwest Colo.* 123.

———— and King, R. U. (1952)   The Mike Doyle carnotite deposit, El Paso County, Colorado. *U.S. Geol. Survey* TEM-133-A.

Berthoud, E. L. (1875)   On the occurrence of uranium, silver, iron, etc., in the Tertiary formation of Colorado Territory. *Acad. Nat. Sci. Phila. Proc.* 27:363–365.

Betheras, F. N. (1955)   Exploration of Mount Painter uranium field 1946–1950. *South Australia Dept. Mines, Mining Rev.* 98:162–180.

Bethke, P. M. (1956)   Sulfo-selenides of mercury (abs.). *Geol. Soc. Am., Bull.* 67:1671.

Bieler, B. H., and Wright, H. D. (1956)   Relationship of vein color to minor-element content of some uranium-bearing "siliceous reef" veins in the Boulder batholith, Montana (abs.). *Geol. Soc. Am., Bull.* 67:1672.

Bignand, C. (1955)   Sur les propriétés et les synthèses de quelques minéraux uranifères. *Bull. soc. franç. minéral. et crist.* 78:1–26.

————, Goñi, J., and Guillemin, C. (1954)   La phosphuranylite ses rélations avec la dewindtite et la renardite. *Bull. soc. franç. minéral. et crist.* 77:1299–1306.

Billings, M. P., and Keevil, N. B. (1946)   Petrography and radioactivity of four Paleozoic magma series in New Hampshire. *Geol. Soc. Am., Bull.* 57:797–828.

Birch, F. (1954)   Heat from radioactivity. In Nuclear geology. John Wiley & Sons, Inc., New York, 148–174.

Bird, A. G. (1956)   Primary pitchblende deposits at the Ralston Creek mine. *Uranium and Modern Mining* 3(8):8, 44.

Björlykke, H. (1935)   The mineral paragenesis and classification of granite pegmatites of Iveland, Setesdal, southern Norway. *Norsk Geol. Tidsskr.* 14:211–311.

———— (1937A)   Mineral paragenesis of some granite pegmatites near Kragerö, southern Norway. *Norsk Geol. Tidsskr.* 17:1–16.

———— (1937B)   The granite pegmatites of southern Norway. *Am. Mineralogist* 22:241–255.

———— (1955)   The niobium deposits at Sove, southern Norway. *Mining J., London* 244(6243):412–413.

Blake, C. A., Brown, K. B., Hill, D. G., Lowrie, R. S., and Schmitt, J. M. (1955)   Studies in the carbonate-uranium system. *Nuclear Eng. Sci. Congr.,* preprint 221.

Blake, D. A. W. (1956)   Geological notes on the region south of Lake Athabasca and Black Lake, Saskatchewan and Alberta. *Can. Geol. Survey Paper* 55-33.

Boardman, R. L., Ekren, E. B., and Bowers, H. E. (1956)   Sedimentary features of upper sandstone lenses of the Salt Wash sandstone member and their relation to uranium-vanadium deposits in the Uravan district, Montrose County, Colorado. *Intern. Conf. Peaceful Uses Atomic Energy, Proc.* 6:331–334 (also *U.S. Geol. Survey Profess. Paper* 300:221–226, 1956).

Bodenhausen, J. W. A. (1954)   The mineral assemblage of some residual monazite- and xenotime-rich cassiterite deposits of Banka (Indonesia). *Koninkl. Ned. Akad. Wetenschap., Proc.,* ser. B 57(3):322–328.

Bodine, M. W. Jr., and Kerr, P. F. (1956)   Hydrothermal dolomitization of sandstone, Temple Mountain, Utah (abs.). *Geol. Soc. Am., Bull.* 67:1673–1674.

Bøggild, O. B. (1953)   The mineralogy of Greenland. *Univ. Copenhagen, Mineral. Geol. Museum, Contrib. Mineral.* 41.

Bohnstedt, E. and others (1937)   Minerals of the Khibina and Lovozero tundras. Description of the minerals. *Lomonosov Inst. Acad. Sci. U.S.S.R.* 37–152.

Bonatti, S., and Gottardi, G. (1950)   Perrierite, nuovo mineral ritrovato nella sabbia di Nettuno (Roma). *Atti (Rend.) accad. naz. Lincei, classe sci. fis. mat. e nat.,* ser. 8, 9 (sem. 2) 361–368.

Bond, G. (1948)   Outgrowths on zircon from Southern Rhodesia. *Geol. Mag.* 85:35–40.

Borisov, P. A. (1937)   Pegmatites of the Chupa Fjord district. *17th Intern. Geol. Congr. U.S.S.R. The Northern Excursion—The Karelian Autonomous Sov. Socialist Rep.* 117–128.

Botinelly, T., and Weeks, A. D. (1957)   Mineralogic classification of uranium-vanadium deposits of the Colorado Plateau. *U.S. Geol. Survey Bull.* 1074-A.

Bowen, N. L. (1919)   Abnormal birefringence of torbernite. *Am. J. Sci.* 48:195–198.

Bowie, S. H. U. (1951)   Autoradiographic techniques in geological research. *Geol. Survey Gt. Brit., Bull.* 3:58–70.

——— (1955)   Thucolite and hisingerite-pitchblende complexes from Nicholson mine, Saskatchewan, Canada. *Geol. Survey Gt. Brit., Bull.* 10:45–57.

——— and Atkin, D. (1956)   An unusually radioactive fossil fish from Thurso, Scotland. *Nature* 177:487–488.

——— and Horne, J. E. T. (1953)   Cheralite, a new mineral of the monazite group. *Mineral. Mag.* 30:93–99.

Boyle, R. W. (1953)   On the colour of black and grey quartz from Yellowknife, Northwest Territories, Canada. *Am. Mineralogist* 38:528–535.

Bradbury, J. C., Ostrom, M. E., and McVicker, L. D. (1955)   Preliminary report on uranium in Hardin County, Illinois. *Illinois State Geol. Survey Circ.* 200.

Braddock, W. A. (1957)   Stratigraphic and structural controls of uranium deposits on Long Mountain, South Dakota. *U.S. Geol. Survey Bull.* 1063-A.

Branche, G., Chervet, J., and Guillemin, C. (1951)   Nouvelles espèces uranifères francaises. *Bull. soc. franç. minéral. et crist.* 74:457–487.

———, Ropert, M., Chautret, F., Morignat, B., and Pouget, R. (1957)   La francevillite, nouveau minéral uranifère. *Compt. rend.* 245(1):89–91.

Brant, R. A. (1953)   Lignite resources of North Dakota. *U.S. Geol. Survey Circ.* 226.

Brasseur, H. (1948)   Properties and chemical formula of fourmarierite. *Am. Mineralogist* 33:619–621.

——— (1949)   Étude de la billietite. *Acad. roy. Belg., Bull. classe sci.* 35:793–804.

Breger, I. A. (1948)   Transformation of organic substances by alpha particles and neutrons. *J. Phys. & Colloid Chem.* 52:551–563.

——— (1955)   The association of uranium with a naturally occurring coal extract (abs.). *Geol. Soc. Am., Bull.* 66:1534.

——— and Deul, M. (1955)   Association of carbonaceous material with uranium in the Temple Mountain area (abs.). Atomic Energy Comm.—U.S. Geol. Survey symposium program. *U.S. Geol. Survey Papers* 2–3.

——— and ——— (1956)   The organic geochemistry of uranium. *Intern. Conf. Peaceful Uses Atomic Energy, Proc.* 6:418–421 (also *U.S. Geol. Survey Profess. Paper* 300:505–510, 1956).

———, ———, and Meyrowitz, R. (1955)   Geochemistry and mineralogy of a uraniferous subbituminous coal. *Econ. Geol.* 50:610–624.

———, ———, and Rubinstein, S. (1955)   Geochemistry and mineralogy of a uraniferous lignite. *Econ. Geol.* 50:206–226.

Bright, J. H. (1955)   Gould uranium mine of the southern Black Hills, South Dakota (abs.). *Geol. Soc. Am., Bull.* 66:1672–1673.

Brögger, W. C. (1890) Die Mineralien der Syenitpegmatitgänge der südnorwegischen Augit- und Nephelinsyenite. *Z. Kryst.* 16, 663 pp.

—— (1906) Die Mineralien der südnorwegischen Granitpegmatitgänge I. Niobate, Tantalate, Titanate, und Titaniobate. *Norske Videnskaps-Akad. Oslo Skrifter. I. Mat.-Naturv. Kl.* 6, 162 pp.

—— (1921) Die Eruptivgesteine des Kristianiagebietes. IV. Das Fengebiet in Telemark, Norwegen. *Norske Videnskaps-Akad. Oslo Skrifter I. Mat.-Naturv. Kl.* 9.

——, Vogt, T., and Schetelig, J. (1922) Die Mineralien der südnorwegischen Granitpegmatitgänge. II. Silikateder seltenen Erden (Y-Reihe und Ce-Reihe). *Norske Videnskaps-Akad. Oslo Skrifter I. Mat.-Naturv. Kl.* 1.

Brooker, E. J., and Nuffield, E. W. (1952) Studies of radioactive compounds: IV. Pitchblende from Lake Athabasca, Canada. *Am. Mineralogist* 37:363–385.

Brophy, G. P., and Kerr, P. F. (1951) Preliminary Memorandum, Papsy's Hope Prospect, Marysvale, Utah. *U.S. Atomic Energy Comm.* RMO-833

—— and —— (1953) Hydrous uranium molybdate in Marysvale ore. *U.S. Atomic Energy Comm.* RME-3046, 45–51.

Brotzen, O. (1952) Die zonaren Zirkone des Ramberggranites. *Geol. Fören. Förh.* 74:173–184.

Broughton, H. J., Chadwick, L. D., and Deans, T. (1950) Iron and titanium ores from the Bukusu Hill alkaline complex, Uganda. *Colonial Geol. and Mineral Resources* (*Gt. Brit.*) 3:262–266.

Brown, A. (1956) Uranium in the Chattanooga shale of eastern Tennessee. *Intern. Conf. Peaceful Uses Atomic Energy, Proc.* 6:439–444 (also *U.S. Geol. Survey Profess. Paper* 300:457–462, 1956).

Brown, H., and Silver, L. T. (1955) The possibilities of securing long range supplies of uranium, thorium and other substances from igneous rocks. *Intern. Conf. Peaceful Uses Atomic Energy* 8/P/850 (also *U.S. Geol. Survey Profess. Paper* 300:91–95, 1956).

Brown, J. H. Jr., and Keller, W. D. (1952) Uranium in the clay of a black radioactive shale. *Science* 116:632–633.

Brown, J. S., Emery, J. A., and Meyer, P. A. Jr. (1954) Explosion pipe in test well on Hicks Dome, Hardin County, Illinois. *Econ. Geol.* 49:891–902.

Bruÿn, K. (1955) Uranium country. University of Colorado Press, Boulder, Colo., 165 pp.

Bucher, W. H., and Gilkey, A. K. (1953) Fracture pattern and uranium ore of the Zuni uplift, New Mexico (abs.). *Geol. Soc. Am., Bull.* 64:1402.

Buck, K. L. (1957) Selected annotated bibliography of thorium and rare-earth deposits in the United States including Alaska. *U.S. Geol. Survey Bull.* 1019-F.

Bueno, O., and Jesus, A. (1955) Yacimientos de uranio y otros metales en la region de la Baja, Municipio de California, Departamento de Santander. *Colombia, Inst. geol. nacl., Bol. geol.* 3(3).

Buffam, B. S. W. (1951) Uranium deposits, Beaverlodge area, Saskatchewan, Canada (abs.). *Geol. Soc. Am., Bull.* 62:1427.

Bültemann, H. W. (1954) Fluoreszenzanalytische Untersuchungen an sekundären Uranmineralien. *Neues Jahrb. Mineral., Abhandl.* 86(2):155–162.

Burbank, W. S., and Pierson, C. T. (1953) Preliminary results of radiometric reconnaissance of parts of the northwestern San Juan Mountains, Colorado. *U.S. Geol. Survey Circ.* 236.

Burton, V. L., and Sullivan, G. R. (1951) Carbon content and radioactivity of marine rocks. *Trans. Am. Geophys. Union* 32:881–884.

Busch, W. (1956) Oklahoma zircon locality. *Rocks and Minerals* 31(2–3):118–119.

Bush, A. L. (1956)   Vanadium-uranium deposits in the Entrada sandstone, western San Juan Mountains, Colorado (abs.). *Geol. Soc. Am., Bull.* 67:1678.

Butler, A. P. Jr., and Schnabel, R. W. (1956)   Distribution of uranium occurrences in the United States. *Intern. Conf. Peaceful Uses Atomic Energy, Proc.* 6: 224–230 (also *U.S. Geol. Survey Profess. Paper* 300:27–40, 1956).

Butler, B. S., Loughlin, G. F., Heikes, V. C., and others (1920) The ore deposits of Utah. *U.S. Geol. Survey Profess. Paper* 111:115.

Butler, J. R. (1957)   Rare earths and thorium in lyndochite. *Am. Mineralogist* 42:671–675.

Butterfield, J. A. (1936)   Outgrowths on zircon. *Geol. Mag.* 73:511–516.

Buttgenbach, H. (1925A)   La droogmansite, nouvelle espèce minérale. *Ann. soc. géol. Belg.* 48:1–3.

——— (1925B)   Minéralogie du Congo Belge. *Mém. soc. roy. sci. Liège,* ser. 3, 13.

——— (1947)   Les minéraux de Belgique et du Congo Belge. H. Vaillant-Carmanne, S.A., Liège, Belgium.

Cadigan, R. A. (1954)   Correlative units in the San Rafael group on the Colorado Plateau (abs.). *Geol. Soc. Am., Bull.* 65:1237–1238.

——— (1955)   Possible relationship between uranium ore deposits and the presence of kaolin in Triassic sandstone (abs.). Atomic Energy Comm.–U.S. Geol. Survey symposium program, *U.S. Geol. Survey Papers,* 5–6.

Cameron, E. N., and others (1954)   Pegmatite investigations, 1942–45, New England. *U.S. Geol. Survey Profess. Paper* 255.

———, Jahns, R. H., McNair, A. H., and Page, L. R. (1949)   Internal structure of granitic pegmatites. *Econ. Geol. Monograph* 2.

Campana, B., Wilson, R. B., and Whittle, A. W. G. (1953)   The geology of the Jervis and Yankalilla military sheets. *South Australia Geol. Survey Rept. Invest.* 3.

Canada Geological Survey (1953)   Information on the economics of radioactive pegmatites in Canada. *Can. Geol. Survey, Radioactive Div.* 5 pp.

Canadian Inst. Mining Met., Beaverlodge branch (1957)   The Beaverlodge uranium district. 56 pp.

Cannon, H. L. (1952)   The effect of uranium-vanadium deposits on the vegetation of the Colorado Plateau. *Am. J. Sci.* 250:735–770.

——— and Starrett, W. H. (1956)   Botanical prospecting for uranium on La Ventana mesa, Sandoval County, New Mexico. *U.S. Geol. Survey Bull.* 1009-M.

Capdecomme, Laurent (1953)   Étude minéralogique des gîtes de phosphates alumineux de la région de Thiès (Sénégal). *19th Congr. géol. intern., Compt. rend.,* sec. XI, fasc. XI, 103–117.

Capdecomme, Léon (1952)   Sur les phosphates alumineux de la région de Thiès (Sénégal). *Acad. sci. Paris, Compt. rend.* 235:187–189.

Carithers, L. W., and Clinton, N. J. (1956)   Uranium in shoreline sandstones of terrestrial and marine origin, Colorado Plateau. *Intern. Conf. Peaceful Uses Atomic Energy, Proc.* 6:383–386.

Carlson, W. A. (1955)   Spatial and stratigraphic distribution of uranium deposits as related to structure in Grants, New Mexico area (abs.). Atomic Energy Comm.–U.S. Geol. Survey symposium program, *Atomic Energy Comm. Papers* 4–5.

Carpenter, J. H., Detweiler, J. C., Gillson, J. L., Weichel, E. C. Jr., and Wood, J. P. (1953)   Mining and concentration of ilmenite and associated minerals at Trail Ridge, Florida. *Am. Inst. Mining Engrs., Trans.* 789–795.

Carter, G. E. L. (1931)   An occurrence of vanadiferous nodules in the Permian beds of South Devon. *Mineral. Mag.* 22:609–613.

Cater, F. W. Jr. (1954) Geology of the Bull Canyon Quadrangle. *U.S. Geol. Survey,* geol. quad. map GQ 33.

Cathcart, J. B. (1956) Distribution and occurrence of uranium in the calcium phosphate zone of the land-pebble phosphate district of Florida. *Intern. Conf. Peaceful Uses Atomic Energy, Proc.* 6:514–519 (also *U.S. Geol. Survey Profess. Paper* 300:489–494, 1956).

———, Blade, L. V., Davidson, D. F., and Ketner, K. B. (1953) The geology of the Florida land-pebble phosphate deposits. *19th Congr. géol. intern., Compt. rend.,* sec. XI, fasc. XI, 77–91.

Cavaca, R. (1956) Uranium prospecting in Portugal. *Intern. Conf. Peaceful Uses Atomic Energy, Proc.* 6:183–188.

Chapman, R. W., Gottfried, D., and Waring, C. L. (1955) Age determinations of some rocks from the Boulder batholith and other batholiths of western Montana. *Geol. Soc. Am., Bull.* 66:607–610.

Chen, P. Y. (1953) Heavy mineral deposits of western Taiwan. *Geol. Survey Taiwan (Formosa), Bull.* 4:13–22.

Chenoweth, W. L. (1955) The geology and uranium deposits of the northwest Carrizo area, Apache County, Arizona. *Four Corners Geol. Soc. Guidebook, Field Conf. 1955,* 177–185.

——— (1956) Radioactive titaniferous heavy-mineral deposits in the San Juan Basin, New Mexico and Colorado (abs.). *Geol. Soc. Am., Bull.* 67:1792.

Chernikov, A. A., Krutetskaya, O. V., and Organov, N. I. (1957) Sodium-autunite. *Atomnaya Energ.* 3:135–140.

Chervet, J., and Branche, G. (1955) Contribution a l'étude des minéraux secondaires d'uranium francais. *Ann. école natl. supérieure géol. appl. prospection minière univ. Nancy* 3(1–2):1–186.

Chirvinsky, N. (1925) Tyuyamunite from the Tyuya-Muyun radium mine in Fergana. *Mineral. Mag.* 20:287–295.

Christ, C. L., and Clark, J. R. (1955) Crystal chemical studies of uranium oxide hydrates (abs.). *Geol. Soc. Am., Bull.* 66:1542.

———, Dwornik, E. J., and Tischler, M. S. (1954) Application of electron diffraction to the study of metamict minerals (abs.). *Geol. Soc. Am., Bull.* 65:1240.

Christie, A. M. (1953) Goldfields-Martin Lake map-area, Saskatchewan. *Can. Geol. Survey, Mem.* 269.

Christman, R. A., Heyman, A. M., Dellwig, L. F., and Gott, G. B. (1953) Thorium investigations 1950–52, Wet Mountains, Colorado. *U.S. Geol. Survey Circ.* 290.

Cissarz, A. (1930) Quantitativ-spektralanalytische Untersuchung eines Mansfelder Kupferschieferprofils. *Chem. Erde* 5:48–75.

Clark, J. R., and Christ, C. L. (1956) Observations on rutherfordine. *Am. Mineralogist* 41:844–850.

Clemente, A., and Reyes, E. (1956) Uranium deposits in the Philippines. *Intern. Conf. Peaceful Uses Atomic Energy, Proc.* 6:182.

Clinton, N. J., and Carithers, L. W. (1956) Uranium deposits in sandstones of marginal marine origin. *U.S. Geol. Survey Profess. Paper* 300:445–449.

Coats, R. R. (1956) Distribution of uranium and certain other trace elements in felsic volcanic rocks of Cenozoic age of the western United States. *Intern. Conf. Peaceful Uses Atomic Energy, Proc.* 6:248–251 (also *U.S. Geol. Survey Profess. Paper* 300:75–78, 1956).

Codazzi, R. L. (1927) Sur quelques minéraux de Colombie. *Bull. soc. franç. minéral.* 50:481–485.

Coelho, A. V. P. (1954) O minerio de urânio de Mavudzi–Tete (Moçambique). *Garcia orta* 2(2):209–219.

Coffin, R. C. (1921)   Radium, uranium, and vanadium deposits of southwestern Colorado. *Colo. Geol. Survey, Bull.* 16.

—— (1954)   History of radium-uranium mining in the Plateau province. *Utah Geol. Soc. Guidebook Geol. Utah* 9:1–7.

Cohen, W. J. (1951)   Silver Bell Shaft, Free Enterprise Property, Boulder, Montana. *Ann. Rept. for July 1, 1950 to June 30, 1951. U.S. Atomic Energy Comm.* RMO-797, 59–61.

—— (1953)   A note on pitchblende and uraninite. *Ann. Rept. for June 30, 1952 to April 1, 1953. U.S. Atomic Energy Comm.* RME-3046, 58–63.

Coleman, R. G. (1956)   The occurrence of selenium in sulfides from sedimentary rocks of the western United States (abs.). *Am. Inst. Mining Engrs., Min. Branch, Abs. 1956 Ann. Meeting* 16–17.

—— (1957)   Mineralogical evidence on the temperature of formation of the Colorado Plateau uranium deposits. *Econ. Geol.* 52:1–4.

—— and Appleman, D. E. (1957)   Umohoite from the Lucky Mc mine, Wyoming. *Am. Mineralogist* 42:657–660.

—— and Delevaux, M. (1957)   Occurrence of selenium in sulfides from some sedimentary rocks of the western United States. *Econ. Geol.* 52:499–527.

Collins, C. B., Farquhar, R. M., and Russell, R. D. (1954)   Isotopic constitution of radiogenic leads and the measurement of geological time. *Geol. Soc. Am., Bull.* 65:1–22.

——, Lang, A. H., Robinson, S. C., and Farquhar, R. M. (1952)   Age determinations for some uranium deposits in the Canadian shield. *Geol. Assoc. Can., Proc.* 63:15–41.

Collins, W. H. (1925)   North shore of Lake Huron. *Can. Geol. Survey, Mem.* 143.

Conant, L. C. (1956)   Environment of accumulation of the Chattanooga shale. *Intern. Conf. Peaceful Uses Atomic Energy, Proc.* 6:435–438 (also *U.S. Geol. Survey Profess. Paper* 300:463–467, 1956).

Connah, T. H. (1954)   Uranium discoveries, Mount Isa. *Queensland Govt. Mining J.* 55(633):581–582.

Conrad, S. G., Elmore, R. T. Jr., and Maher, S. W. (1954)   Stratigraphy of the Chattanooga black shale in the Flynn Creek structure, Jackson County, Tennessee (abs.). *Geol. Soc. Am., Bull.* 65:1358.

Conybeare, C. E. B., and Campbell, C. D. (1951)   Petrology of the red radioactive zones north of Goldfields, Saskatchewan. *Am. Mineralogist* 36:70–79.

—— and Ferguson, R. B. (1950)   Metamict pitchblende from Goldfields, Saskatchewan, and observations on some ignited pitchblendes. *Am. Mineralogist* 35:401–406.

Cook, F. S., and Wylie, E. T. (1956)   The geology of the Woodrow mine (abs.). *Am. Inst. Mining Engrs., Program, Ann. Meeting, Min. Branch* 33.

Cooper, R. A. (1923)   Mineral constituents of Rand concentrates. *J. Chem. Met. Mining Soc. South Africa* 24:90–95.

Coppens, R. (1950)   Étude de la radioactivité de quelques roches par l'emulsion photographique. *Bull. soc. franç. minéral. et crist.* 73:216–325.

Cornet, J. (1912)   Sur un cas d'enrichissement primitif de la craie phophatée de Ciply autour d'un tronc d'arbre lignitifié. *Ann. soc. géol. Belg.* 40:123.

Councill, R. J. (1955)   An introduction to radioactive minerals in North Carolina. *N. Carolina Dept. Conserv. and Develop. Inform. Circ.* 14.

Craig, L. C. (1955)   The application of stratigraphy to the search for uranium deposits on the Colorado Plateau. *Nuclear Eng. Sci. Congr.*, preprint 251.

—— and others (1955)   Stratigraphy of the Morrison and related formations, Colorado Plateau region. A preliminary report. *U.S. Geol. Survey Bull.* 1009-E.

Crawford, J. E., and Paone, J. (1956) Facts concerning uranium exploration and production. *U.S. Bur. Mines Handbook,* 130 pp.

Croft, W. J. (1954) An x-ray line study of uraninite. *Ann. Rept. for June 30, 1953 to April 1, 1954. U.S. Atomic Energy Comm.* RME-3096 (pt. 2), 7–72.

Cross, C. W., and Hillebrand, W. F. (1885) Contributions to the mineralogy of the Rocky Mountains. *U.S. Geol. Survey Bull.* 20.

Curtis, D. (1957) Selected annotated bibliography of the geology of uranium-bearing phosphorites in the United States. *U.S. Geol. Survey Bull.* 1059-B.

Dainton, F. S. (1949) Chemical reactions induced by ionising radiation. *Ann. Rept. on Progr. Chem. 1948, Chem. Soc. London* 5–33.

Daniels, F. (1954) Radioactivity, energy storage, and volcanism. In Nuclear geology. John Wiley & Sons, Inc., New York, 188–194.

Daugherty, L. H. (1941) The Upper Triassic flora of Arizona. *Carnegie Inst. Wash. Publ.* 526.

Davidson, C. F. (1949) A prospector's handbook to radioactive mineral deposits.

——— (1951) Distribution of radioactivity. *Mineral. Mag.* 85:329–340. *Gr. Brit. Geol. Survey and Mus.*

——— (1953) The gold-uranium ores of the Witwatersrand. *Mineral. Mag.* 88:73–85.

——— (1955) Concentration of uranium by carbon compounds. *Econ. Geol.* 50:879–880.

——— (1956A) The radioactive mineral resources of Great Britain. *Intern. Conf. Peaceful Uses Atomic Energy, Proc.* 6:204–206.

——— (1956B) Radioactive minerals in the Central African Federation. *Intern. Conf. Peaceful Uses Atomic Energy, Proc.* 6:207–209.

——— (1956C) Radioactive minerals in the British colonies. *Intern. Conf. Peaceful Uses Atomic Energy, Proc.* 6:210.

——— (1956D) The economic geology of thorium. *Mineral. Mag.* 94:197–208.

——— (1956E) Concentration of uranium by carbon compounds. *Econ. Geol.* 51:724–725.

——— (1957) On the occurrence of uranium in ancient conglomerates. *Econ. Geol.* 52:668–693.

——— and Atkin, D. (1953) On the occurrence of uranium in phosphate rock. *19th Congr. géol. intern. 1952,* sec. XI, fasc. XI, 13–31.

——— and Bennett, J. A. E. (1950) The uranium deposits of the Tete district, Mozambique. *Mineral. Mag.* 29:291–303.

——— and Bowie, S. H. U. (1951) On thucolite and related hydrocarbon-uraninite complexes with a note on the origin of the Witwatersrand gold ores. *Geol. Survey Gt. Brit., Bull.* 3:1–19.

——— and Cosgrove, M. E. (1955) On the impersistence of uraninite as a detrital mineral. *Geol. Survey Gt. Brit., Bull.* 10:74–80.

——— and Ponsford, D. R. A. (1954) On the occurrence of uranium in coals. *Mineral. Mag.* 91:265–273.

Davidson, D. F., and Gulbrandsen, R. A. (1957) Selenium in the Phosphoria formation in Idaho, Wyoming, Utah, and Montana (abs.). *Geol. Soc. Am., Bull.* 68:1714.

Davidson, E. S. (1956) Rainy Day uranium deposit, Garfield County, Utah (abs.). *Geol. Soc. Am., Bull.* 67:1685.

Davies, K. A. (1947) The phosphate deposits of the Eastern Province, Uganda. *Econ. Geol.* 42:137–146.

——— (1954) Cement manufacture in Uganda. *Colonial Geol. and Mineral Resources* 4:366–372.

Davis, D. L., and Hetland, D. L. (1956)   Uranium in clastic rocks of the Basin and Range province. *Intern. Conf. Peaceful Uses Atomic Energy, Proc.* 6:387–391 (also *U.S. Geol. Survey Profess. Paper* 300:351–359, 1956).

———— and Sharp, B. J. (1957)   Uranium west of the Colorado Plateau. *2d Nuclear Eng. Sci. Conf. Paper* 57-NESC-28.

Davis, G. L. (1947)   Radium content of ultramafic igneous rocks: I. Laboratory investigations. *Am. J. Sci.* 245:677–693.

———— and Hess, H. H. (1949)   Radium content of ultramafic igneous rocks, II: Geological and chemical implications. *Am. J. Sci.* 247:856–882.

Davis, G. R. (1954)   The origin of the Roan Antelope copper deposit of Northern Rhodesia. *Econ. Geol.* 49:575–615.

Davison, E. H. (1927)   Recent evidence confirming the zonal arrangement of minerals in the Cornish lodes. *Econ. Geol.* 22:475–479.

Dawson, K. R. (1951)   A petrographic description of the wall-rocks and alteration products associated with pitchblende-bearing veins in the Goldfields region, Saskatchewan. *Can. Geol. Survey, Paper* 51-24.

———— (1956)   Petrology and red coloration of wall-rocks, radioactive deposits, Goldfields region, Saskatchewan. *Can. Geol. Survey, Bull.* 33.

De Almeida, S. C., Johnston, W. D. Jr., Leonardos, O. H., and Scorza, E. P. (1944)   The beryl-tantalite-cassiterite pegmatites of Paraiba and Rio Grande Do Norte, northeastern Brazil. *Econ. Geol.* 39:206–223.

Deans, T. (1948)   The Kupferschiefer and the associated lead-zinc mineralization in the Permian of Silesia, Germany, and England. *18th Intern. Geol. Congr.,* pt. 7, sec. F, 340–352.

———— and McConnell, J. D. C. (1955)   Isokite, $CaMgPO_4F$, a new mineral from Northern Rhodesia. *Mineral. Mag.* 30:681–690.

De Freitas, R. O. (1956)   Considerações sôbre a tectônica e a geologia do vale do Paraíba. *Eng., mineração e met.* 24(143):276–283.

Delaney, C. F. G., Matthews, C. M. E., and Poole, J. H. J. (1953)   The uranium content of some specimens of phosphate rock. *Roy. Dublin Soc., Sci. Proc.* 26:165–172.

De Moraes, L. J. (1956)   Known occurrences of uranium and thorium in Brazil. *Intern. Conf. Peaceful Uses Atomic Energy, Proc.* 6:134–139.

Dennen, W. H., and Shields, R. (1956)   Yttria in zircon. *Am. Mineralogist* 41:655–657.

Denson, N. M. (1955)   Uranium-bearing coal in the western United States. *Nuclear Eng. Sci. Congr.,* preprint 255.

————, Bachman, G. O., and Zeller, H. D. (1950)   Summary of new information on uraniferous lignites in the Dakotas. *U.S. Geol. Survey* TEM 175.

———— and Gill, J. R. (1956)   Uranium-bearing lignite and its relation to volcanic tuffs in eastern Montana and the Dakotas. *Intern. Conf. Peaceful Uses Atomic Energy, Proc.* 6:464–467 (also *U.S. Geol. Survey Profess. Paper* 300:413–431, 1956).

————, Zeller, H. D., and Stephens, J. G. (1956)   Water sampling as a guide in the search for uranium deposits and its use in evaluating widespread volcanic units as potential source beds for uranium. *Intern. Conf. Peaceful Uses Atomic Energy, Proc.* 6:794–800 (also *U.S. Geol. Survey Profess. Paper* 300:673–680, 1956).

De Oliveira, A. I. (1956)   Ocorrencias Brasileiras de uranio. *Eng. Min. Metal.* 24(142):209–211.

Derby, O. A. (1891)   On the magnetite ore districts of Jacupiranga and Ipanema, São Paulo, Brazil. *Am. J. Sci.* 41:311–321.

———— (1900)   Notes on monazite. *Am. J. Sci.* 10:217–221.

Derriks, J. J., and Vaes, J. F. (1956) The Shinkolobwe uranium deposit: current status of our geological and metallogenic knowledge. *Intern. Conf. Peaceful Uses Atomic Energy, Proc.* 6:94–128.

Derzay, R. C. (1956) The Los Ochos uranium deposit. *Intern. Conf. Peaceful Uses Atomic Energy, Proc.* 6:468–472 (also *U.S. Geol. Survey Profess. Paper* 300:137–141, 1956).

Deul, M. (1955) Mode of occurrence of uranium in the Chattanooga shale (abs.). *Geol. Soc. Am., Bull.* 66:1549.

——— and Annell, C. S. (1956) The occurrence of minor elements in ash of low-rank coal from Texas, Colorado, North Dakota and South Dakota. *U.S. Geol. Survey, Bull.* 1036-H.

Dietrich, R. V. (1956) Is anthraxolite related genetically to coal or oil? *Econ. Geol.* 51:649–664.

Dietz, R. S., Emery, K. O., and Shepard, F. P. (1942) Phosphorite deposits on the sea floor off southern California. *Geol. Soc. Am., Bull.* 53:815–848.

Dines, H. G. (1930) Uranium in Cornwall. *Mineral. Mag.* 42:213–217.

Dix, G. P. Jr. (1954) The uranium deposits of Big Indian Wash, San Juan County, Utah. *U.S. Atomic Energy Comm.* RME-4022 (rev.).

Dixey, F., Smith, W. C., and Bisset, C. B. (1937) The Chilwa Series of Southern Nyasaland; a group of alkaline and other intrusive and extrusive rocks and associated limestones. *Nyasaland Geol. Survey, Bull.* 5.

Dixon, P., and Wylie, A. W. (1951) An unusual distribution of the lanthanons. *Nature* 167:526.

Dodd, P. H. (1950) Happy Jack mine, White Canyon, Utah. *U.S. Atomic Energy Comm.* RMO-660.

——— (1956) Some examples of uranium deposits in the upper Jurassic Morrison formation on the Colorado Plateau. *Intern. Conf. Peaceful Uses Atomic Energy, Proc.* 6:615–633 (also *U.S. Geol. Survey Profess. Paper* 300:243–262, 1956).

Doerner, H. A., and Hoskins, W. N. (1925) Coprecipitation of radium and barium sulphate. *Am. Chem. Soc. J.* 47(3): 662–675.

Donnay, G., and Donnay, J. D. H. (1953) Tyuyamunite, carnotite, and sengierite (abs.). *Geol. Soc. Am., Bull.* 64:1412–1413.

Douglas, G. V. (1955) Origin of the Roan Antelope copper deposit of Northern Rhodesia. *Econ. Geol.* 50:82–83.

——— (1956) Origin of the Rhodesian copper deposits. *Econ. Geol.* 51:391–392.

Drake, A. A. Jr. (1955) Occurrence of pitchblende at the Wood mine, Central City district, Gilpin County, Colorado (abs.). *Geol. Soc. Am., Bull.* 66:1673.

——— (1957) Geology of the Wood and East Calhoun mines, Central City district, Gilpin County, Colorado. *U.S. Geol. Survey Bull.* 1032-C.

Dresser, J. A., and Denis, T. C. (1944) Geology of Quebec. Vol. II, Descriptive Geology. *Quebec Dept. Mines, Geol. Rept.* 20.

Dryden, L., and Dryden, C. (1946) Comparative rates of weathering of some common heavy minerals. *J. Sediment. Petrol.* 16:91–96.

Duncan, D. C. (1953) A uranium-bearing rhyolitic tuff deposit near Coaldale, Esmeralda County, Nevada. *U.S. Geol. Survey Circ.* 291.

Dyson, J. L. (1955) Relation of stratigraphy and structure to uranium occurrences near Mauch Chunk, Pennsylvania. *Penn. Topo. Geol. Survey, Inform. Circ.* 5.

Eardley, A. J. (1951) Structural geology of North America. Harper & Brothers, New York, 624 pp.

———, Stokes, W. L., Christiansen, F. W., Williams, N. C., and Ashton, C. L. (1955) Uranium, the world's expanding frontier. Uran. Res. Center, 111 pp.

Eargle, D. H. (1956)   Some uranium occurrences in west Texas. *Texas Univ. Bur. Econ. Geol., Rept. Invest.* 27.

———— and Snider, J. L. (1957)   A preliminary report on the stratigraphy of the uranium-bearing rocks of the Karnes County area, south-central Texas. *Texas Univ. Bur. Econ. Geol., Rept. Invest.* 30.

Eckelmann, W. R., and Kulp, J. L. (1956)   Uranium-lead method of age determination. Pt. I: Lake Athabasca problem. *Geol. Soc. Am., Bull.* 67:35–54.

Ellsworth, H. V. (1928A)   Thucolite, a remarkable primary carbon mineral from the vicinity of Parry Sound, Ontario. *Am. Mineralogist* 13:419–441.

———— (1928B)   Thucolite and uraninite from the Wallingford mine near Buckingham, Quebec. *Am. Mineralogist* 13:442–448.

———— (1930)   Four stages in the alteration of the Villeneuve uraninite. *Am. Mineralogist* 15:455–460.

———— (1931)   Uraninite from Henvey Township, Parry Sound district, Ontario. *Am. Mineralogist* 16:576–579.

———— (1932)   Rare-element minerals of Canada. *Can. Geol. Survey, Econ. Geol. Ser.* 11.

———— (1934)   Nickeliferous and uraniferous anthraxolite from Port Arthur, Ontario. *Am. Mineralogist* 19:426.

Emerson, D. O., and Wright, H. D. (1957)   Secondary uranium minerals at the W. Wilson mine in the Boulder batholith, Montana. *Am. Mineralogist* 42:222–239.

Emmons, R. C., Reynolds, C. D., and Saunders, D. F. (1953)   Genetic and radioactivity features of selected lamprophyres. *Geol. Soc. Am., Mem.* 52:89–99.

Erickson, R. L., Myers, A. T., and Horr, C. A. (1954)   Association of uranium and other metals with crude oil, asphalt, and petroliferous rock. *Bull. Am. Assoc. Petrol. Geologists* 38:2200–2218.

Eskola, P. (1921)   On the igneous rocks of Sviatoy Noss in Transbaikalia. *Oversikt av Finska Velenskaps-Soc. Förh.* 63 A(1).

Evans, H. T. Jr. (1950)   Studies of uranium minerals (VI): walpurgite. *Am. Mineralogist* 35:1021–1027.

———— and Frondel, C. (1950)   Studies of uranium minerals (II): Liebigite and uranothallite. *Am. Mineralogist* 35:251–254.

———— and Mrose, M. E. (1955)   A crystal chemical study of montroesite and paramontroesite. *Am. Mineralogist* 40:861–875.

———— and ———— (1956)   Crystal chemistry of duttonite (abs.). *Geol. Soc. Am., Bull.* 67:1693–1694.

Evans, R. D., and Goodman, C. (1941)   Radioactivity of rocks. *Geol. Soc. Am., Bull.* 52:459–490.

Evensen, C. G. (1955)   Criteria studies on Holiday Mesa, Utah (abs.). Atomic Energy Comm.–U.S. Geol. Survey symposium abs. *Atomic Energy Comm. Papers,* 6–7.

Everett, F. D., and Bauerle, L. C. (1957)   Investigation of tuffs near Lysite, Wyoming, for selenium. *U.S. Bur. Mines, Rept. Invest.* 5296.

Everhart, D. L. (1951)   Geology of uranium deposits. *U.S. Atomic Energy Comm.* RMO-732.

———— (1954)   Origin of uranium deposits, a progress report. *Am. Inst. Mining Engrs., Trans.,* 904–907.

———— (1955)   Genetic relationships in uranium deposits. *Nuclear Eng. Sci. Congr.,* preprint 252.

———— (1956A)   Uranium geology—How much do we know: A forum report, uranium and the atomic industry. Atomic Ind. Forum, Inc., No. 11, 3–10.

Everhart, D. L. (1956B) Uranium-bearing vein deposits in the United States. *Intern. Conf. Peaceful Uses Atomic Energy, Proc.* 6:257–264 (also *U.S. Geol. Survey Profess. Paper* 300:97–103, 1956).

—— and Mathez, M. (1951) Geology of uranium deposits—a condensed version. *U.S. Atomic Energy Comm.* RMO-732.

—— and Wright, R. J. (1951) The paragenesis of pitchblende-bearing veins. *Denison Univ. Bull., J. Sci. Lab.* 42, Art. 6–10, 66–74.

—— and —— (1953) The geologic character of typical pitchblende veins. *Econ. Geol.* 48:77–96.

Evoy, E. F. (1956) Open pit development at Gunnar. *Mining Eng.* 8(5):501–505.

Fairchild, J. G. (1929) Base exchange in artificial autunites. *Am. Mineralogist* 14:265–276.

Faul, H. (1954) Rare gases and fission in nature. Helium, argon, and radon. In Nuclear geology. John Wiley & Sons, Inc., New York, 133–143.

——, Gott, G. B., Manger, G. E., Mytton, J. W., and Sakakura, A. Y. (1954) Radon and helium in natural gas. *19th Congr. géol. intern., Compt. rend.*, sec. 9, fasc. 9, 339–349.

Fawley, A. P., and James, T. C. (1955) A pyrochlore (columbium) carbonatite, southern Tanganyika. *Econ. Geol.* 50:571–585.

Ferguson, R. B. (1955) Crystallography of synthetic $YTaO_4$ and fused fergusonite (abs.). *Geol. Soc. Am., Bull.* 66:1557.

Fersman, A. E. (1937) Mineralogy and geochemistry of the Khibine and Lovozero Tundras. *17th Intern. Geol. Congr. U.S.S.R.* The Northern Excursion Kola Peninsula, 91–103.

—— (1940) Pegmatites, Russ. Acad. Sci., Moscow, 3d ed., vols. I–III. (Translated into French by R. du Trieu de Terdonck and J. Thoreau.)

Finch, J. W. (1933) Sedimentary copper deposits of the western states. *Am. Inst. Mining Engrs. Ore Deposits of the Western States* 481–487.

Finch, W. I. (1953) Distribution of uranium deposits in the Shinarump conglomerate of the Colorado Plateau (abs.). *Geol. Soc. Am., Bull.* 64:1422.

—— (1954) Geology of the Shinarump No. 1 uranium mine, Seven Mile Canyon area, Grand County, Utah. *U.S. Geol. Survey Circ.* 336.

—— (1955) Preliminary geologic map showing the distribution of uranium deposits and principal ore-bearing formations of the Colorado Plateau region. *U.S. Geol. Survey, Min. Invest. Field Studies Map* MF 16.

—— (1956) Uranium in terrestrial sedimentary rocks in the United States exclusive of the Colorado Plateau. *Intern. Conf. Peaceful Uses Atomic Energy, Proc.* 6: 600–604 (also *U.S. Geol. Survey Profess. Paper* 300:321–327, 1956).

Fine, M. M., and Frommer, D. W. (1954) Beneficiation of a Brazilian phosphate rock. *U.S. Bur. Mines, Rept. Invest.* 5078.

Finnell, T. L. (1957) Structural control of uranium ore at the Monument No. 2 mine, Apache County, Arizona. *Econ. Geol.* 52:25–35.

Fischer, R. P. (1936) Peculiar hydrothermal copper-bearing veins of the northeastern Colorado Plateau. *Econ. Geol.* 31:571–599.

—— (1937) Sedimentary deposits of copper, vanadium, uranium and silver in southwestern United States. *Econ. Geol.* 37:906–951.

—— (1942) Vanadium deposits of Colorado and Utah. *U.S. Geol. Survey Bull.* 936-P.

—— (1950) Uranium-bearing sandstone deposits of the Colorado Plateau. *Econ. Geol.* 45:1–11.

Fischer, R. P. (1955)   Vanadium and uranium in rocks and ore deposits (abs.). *Geol. Soc. Am., Bull.* 66:1558.

―― (1956)   Uranium-vanadium-copper deposits of the Colorado Plateau region. *Intern. Conf. Peaceful Uses Atomic Energy, Proc.* 6:605–614 (also *U.S. Geol. Survey Profess. Paper* 300:143–154, 1956).

―― and Hilpert, L. S. (1952)   Geology of the Uravan mineral belt. *U.S. Geol. Survey Bull.* 988-A.

Fisher, N. H. (1948)   Heavy mineral deposits of the east coast of Australia. *Mining Technol. Am. Inst. Mining Engrs., Tech. Publ.* 2455.

―― and Sullivan, C. J. (1954)   Uranium exploration by the Bureau of Mineral Resources, Geology and Geophysics, in the Rum Jungle province, Northern Territory, Australia. *Econ. Geol.* 49:826–836.

Fix, P. F. (1956)   Geochemical prospecting for uranium by sampling ground and surface waters. *Intern. Conf. Peaceful Uses Atomic Energy, Proc.* 6:788–791 (also *U.S. Geol. Survey Profess. Paper* 300:667–671, 1956).

Fleischer, M. (1955)   Hafnium content and hafnium-zirconium ratio in minerals and rocks. *U.S. Geol. Survey Bull.* 1021-A.

―― (1956)   New mineral names. *Am. Mineralogist* 41:537–538.

―― (1957)   New mineral names. *Am. Mineralogist* 42:440–444.

―― (1958)   New mineral names. *Am. Mineralogist* 43:378–384.

Florêncio, W. (1952)   Minerais de uranio e thorio. *Minas Gerais Inst. Tech. Ind. Bol.* 11.

Flores, R. (1942)   Geología de los yacimientos de cobre y oro de Chile. *Anales 1st congr. Panam. ing. minas y geol.* 3(2).

Flores, T. (1953)   Los yacimientos de fosfatos de calcio de México. *19th Congr. géol. intern., Compt. rend.,* sec. XI, fasc. XI, 66–75.

Foldvari, A. (1952)   The geochemistry of radioactive substances in the Mecsek Mountains. *Acta Geol. Acad. Sci. Hungary I,* fasc. 1–4.

Ford, R. B. (1955)   Mineralogy of a uraninite-bearing pegmatite, Lac La Ronge, Saskatchewan. *Econ. Geol.* 50:196–205.

Foster, W. R. (1948)   Useful aspects of the fluorescence of accessory-mineral-zircon. *Am. Mineralogist* 33:724–735.

Franco, R. R., and Loewenstein, W. (1948)   Zirconium from the region of Poços de Caldas. *Am. Mineralogist* 33:142–151.

Fraser, J. A. (1954)   Crackingstone, Saskatchewan. *Can. Geol. Survey Paper* 54-8.

Friedel, C., and Cumenge, E. (1899)   Sur un nouveau minéral d'urane. *Bull. soc. franç. minéral.* 22:26–29.

Friedensburg, F. (1956)   Die Bergwirtschaft der Erde. Ferd. Enke Verlag, Stuttgart, 562 pp.

Frohberg, M. H. (1950)   Uranium in Russian occupied Saxony. *Geol. Assoc. Can., Proc.* 2:43–49.

Frondel, C. (1950A)   Studies of uranium minerals (I): Parsonite and randite. *Am. Mineralogist* 35:245–250.

―― (1950B) Studies of uranium minerals (V): Phosphuranylite. *Am. Mineralogist* 35:756–763.

―― (1951A)   Studies of uranium minerals (VIII): Sabugalite, an aluminum-autunite. *Am. Mineralogist* 36:671–679.

―― (1951B)   Studies of uranium minerals (IX): Saléeite and novacekite. *Am. Mineralogist* 36:680–686.

―― (1952A)   Studies of uranium minerals (X): Uranopilite. *Am. Mineralogist* 37:950–959.

―― (1952B)   Studies of uranium minerals (XI): Gummite (abs.). *Geol. Soc. Am., Bull.* 63:1252–1253.

Frondel, C. (1953) Hydroxyl substitution in thorite and zircon. *Am. Mineralogist* 38: 1007–1018.

—— (1954) Bassetite and uranospathite. *Mineral. Mag.* 30:343–353.

—— (1956A) The mineralogy of thorium. *Intern. Conf. Peaceful Uses Atomic Energy, Proc.* 6:568–577 (also *U.S. Geol. Survey Profess. Paper* 300:567–579, 1956).

—— (1956B) The mineral composition of gummite. *Am. Mineralogist* 41:539– 568.

—— (1957A) Zirconium: mineralogy and geochemistry. *2d Nuclear Eng. Sci. Conf., Paper* 57-NESC-32.

—— (1957B) Mineralogy of uranium. *Am. Mineralogist* 42:125–132.

——, Collette, R. L., Ross, V., and Berman, E. (1954) Synthesis of uranium minerals. *U.S. Atomic Energy Comm.* RME-3101.

—— and Ito, J. (1956) Boltwoodite, a new uranium silicate. *Science* 124:93.

—— and Meyrowitz, R. (1956) Studies of uranium minerals (XIX): Rutherfordine, diderichite, and clarkeite. *Am. Mineralogist* 41:127–133.

——, Newhouse, W. H., and Jarrell, R. F. (1942) Spatial distribution of minor elements in single crystals. *Am. Mineralogist* 27:726–745.

——, Riska, D., and Frondel, J. W. (1956) X-ray powder data for uranium and thorium minerals. *U.S. Geol. Survey Bull.* 1036-G.

Frondel, J. W. (1951) Studies of uranium minerals (VII): Zeunerite. *Am. Mineralogist* 36:249–255.

—— and Cuttitta, F. (1953) Studies of uranium minerals (XII): The status of billietite and becquerelite. *Am. Mineralogist* 38:1019–1024.

—— and —— (1954) Studies of uranium minerals (XVI): An alteration product of ianthinite. *Am. Mineralogist* 39:1018–1020.

—— and Fleischer, M. (1950) A glossary of uranium- and thorium-bearing minerals. *U.S. Geol. Survey Circ.* 74.

—— and —— (1952) A glossary of uranium- and thorium-bearing minerals. 2d ed. *U.S. Geol. Survey Circ.* 194.

—— and —— (1955) Glossary of uranium- and thorium-bearing minerals. *U.S. Geol. Survey Bull.* 1009-F.

Fryklund, V. C., Harner, R. S., and Kaiser, E. P. (1954) Niobium (columbium) and titanium at Magnet Cove and Potash Sulphur Springs, Arkansas. *U.S. Geol. Survey Bull.* 1015-B.

Furcron, A. S. (1955) Prospecting for uranium in Georgia, Part I. *Georgia Mineral Newsletter* 8(2):38–46.

Furnival, G. M. (1939) A silver-pitchblende deposit at Contact Lake, Great Bear Lake area, Canada. *Econ. Geol.* 34:739–776.

Gabelman, J. W. (1955) Geographic relation of uranium and fluorite in the regional tectonic pattern (abs.). Atomic Energy Comm.—U.S. Geol. Survey symposium, *U.S. Atomic Energy Comm. Papers,* 6.

—— (1956A) Uranium deposits in limestone. *Intern. Conf. Peaceful Uses Atomic Energy, Proc.* 6:338–345 (also *U.S. Geol. Survey Profess. Paper* 300:387–404, 1956.)

—— (1956B) Uranium deposits in paludal black shales of the Dakota formation, San Juan basin, New Mexico. *Intern. Conf. Peaceful Uses Atomic Energy, Proc.* 6:422–429 (also *U.S. Geol. Survey Profess. Paper* 300:303–319, 1956).

——, Young, R. G., and Ealy, G. K. (1956) This is the Ambrosia Lake district. *Uran. Inform. Digest* 3(5):10–11, 37–40.

Gardner, D. E. (1951) Mineral resources of Australia, zirconium. *Australia Bur. Mineral Resources, Geol. and Geophys., Summary Rept.* 1.

Gardner, D. E. (1955) Beach-sand heavy-mineral deposits of eastern Australia. *Australia Bur. Mineral Resources, Geol. and Geophys., Bull.* 28.

Garlick, W. G. (1955) Origin of the Roan Antelope copper deposit of Northern Rhodesia. *Econ. Geol.* 50:880–884.

Garrels, R. M. (1953) Some thermodynamic relations among the vanadium oxides, and their relation to the oxidation state of the uranium ores of the Colorado Plateau. *Am. Mineralogist* 38:1251–1265.

—— (1955A) Some thermodynamic relations among the uranium oxides and their relation to the oxidation states of the uranium ores of the Colorado Plateau. *Am. Mineralogist* 40:1004–1021.

—— (1955B) Geochemistry of oxidation of the uranium deposits of the Colorado Plateau. *Nuclear Eng. Sci. Congr.*, preprint 250.

—— (1957) Geochemistry of "sandstone type" uranium deposits. *2d Nuclear Eng. Sci. Conf., Paper* 57-NESC-121.

——, Hostetler, P. B., Christ, C. L., and Weeks, A. D. (1957) Stability of uranium, vanadium, copper, and molybdenum minerals in natural waters at low temperatures and pressures (abs.). *Geol. Soc. Am., Bull.* 68:1732.

—— and Pommer, A. (1955) Detailed chemical study of a profile across an ore boundary (abs.). Atomic Energy Comm.–U.S. Geol. Survey symposium, *U.S. Geol. Survey Papers* 8.

—— and Richter, D. H. (1955) Is carbon dioxide an ore-forming fluid under shallow-earth conditions? *Econ. Geol.* 50:447–458.

Garson, M. S. (1955) Flow phenomena in carbonatites in Southern Nyasaland. *Colonial Geol. and Mineral Resources* 5:311–318.

Gault, H. R., Killeen, P. L., West, W. S., and others (1953) Reconnaissance for radioactive deposits in the northeastern part of the Seward Peninsula, Alaska, 1945–47 and 1951. *U.S. Geol. Survey Circ.* 250.

Gay, P. (1957) An x-ray investigation of some rare-earth silicates: cerite, lessingite, beckelite, britholite, and stillwellite. *Mineral. Mag.* 31:455–468.

Geffroy, J., and Sarcia, J. A. (1954) Contribution a l'étude des pechblendes francaises: *Sciences de la Terre. Ann. école natl. supérieure géol. appl. prospection minière univ.* Nancy, tome II, No. 1–2.

Geijer, P. (1921) The cerium minerals of Bastnäs at Riddarhyttan. *Sveriges Geol. Undersökn. Ser. C, No. 304, Årsbok* 14(1920), No. 6.

—— (1927) Some mineral associations from the Norberg district. *Sveriges Geol. Undersökn. Årsbok* 20(1926), No. 4.

George, D. R. (1949) Mineralogy of uranium and thorium bearing minerals. *U.S. Atomic Energy Comm.* RMO-563 rev.

—— (1951) Thorite from California, a new occurrence and variety. *Am. Mineralogist* 36:129–132.

Getseva, R. V., and Savel'eva, K. T. (1956) Rukovatsvo po opredeleniiu uranovykh mineralov, Moscow.

Gevers, T., Partridge, F., and Joubert, G. (1937) The pegmatite area south of Orange River, Namaqualand. *S. Africa Geol. Survey, Mem.* 31:172.

Gill, J. E., and Owens, O. E. (1956) Niobium-uranium deposits near North Bay, Ontario (abs.). *20th Congr. géol. intern., Resúmenes Trabajos Presentados* 90.

Gill, J. R., and Moore, G. W. (1955) Carnotite-bearing sandstone, in Cedar Canyon, Slim Buttes, Harding County, South Dakota. *U.S. Geol. Survey Bull.* 1009–I.

Gillerman, E. (1952) Uranium deposits of the White Signal district, New Mexico (abs.). *Geol. Soc. Am., Bull.* 63:1329.

—— and Whitebread, D. H. (1956) Uranium-bearing nickel-cobalt-native silver deposits, Black Hawk district, Grant County, New Mexico. *U.S. Geol. Survey Bull.* 1009-K.

Gillson, J. L. (1949)   Titanium: Industrial Minerals and Rocks. *Am. Inst. Mining Engrs.* 1042–1073.

——— (1950)   Deposits of heavy minerals on the Brazilian coast. *Am. Inst. Mining Engrs., Trans.* 187:685–693.

Gilluly, J. (1927)   Analcite diabase and related alkaline syenite from Utah. *Am. J. Sci.* ser. 5, 14, 199–211.

Gimmelfarb, B. M. (1956)   Fundamental geological laws governing phosphorite deposits and their genetic classification (abs.). *20th Congr. géol. intern., Resúmenes Trabajos Presentados* 90.

Goddard, E. N. (1946)   Fluorspar deposits of the Jamestown district, Boulder County, Colo. *Colo. Sci. Soc. Proc.* 15(1).

——— and Glass, J. J. (1940)   Deposits of radioactive cerite near Jamestown, Colorado. *Am. Mineralogist* 25:381–404.

Goldsztaub, S., and Wey, R. (1955)   Absorption des ions uranyles par les argiles. *Bull. soc. franç. minéral. et crist.* 78:242–248.

Golubkova, Y. M. (1930)   Novye dannye dlya izucheniya radioaktivnykh mineralov Srednei Azii. *Osved. Byull. Sredne-Aziatskoe raionne, Geol.-Razved. Upravl.* 1: 21.

Goñi, J. C. (1950)   Arenas negras ilmenítico-monacites del Uruguay. *Bol. fac. ing. Montevideo* 4(1):103–110.

Gordon, S. G. (1939)   Thorium-free monazite from Llallagua, Bolivia. *Acad. Nat. Sci. Phila., Not. Nat.* 2:1–7.

Gorman, D. H. (1952)   Studies of radioactive compounds: V—Soddyite. *Am. Mineralogist* 37:386–393.

——— (1957)   Studies of radioactive compounds, IX—sklodowskite *Can. Mineralogist* 6(1):52–60.

——— and Nuffield, E. W. (1955)   Studies of radioactive compounds: VIII—Uranophane and beta-uranophane. *Am. Mineralogist* 40:634–645.

Gott, G. B. (1956)   Inferred relationship of some uranium deposits and calcium carbonate cement in southern Black Hills, South Dakota. *U.S. Geol. Survey Bull.* 1046-A.

——— and Erickson, R. L. (1952)   Reconnaissance of uranium and copper deposits in parts of New Mexico, Colorado, Utah, Idaho, and Wyoming. *U.S. Geol. Survey Circ.* 219.

——— and Hill, J. W. (1953)   Radioactivity in some oil fields of southeastern Kansas. *U.S. Geol. Survey Bull.* 988-E.

Gottfried, D., Senftle, F. E., and Waring, C. L. (1956)   Age determination of zircon crystals from Ceylon. *Am. Mineralogist* 41:157–161.

———, Waring, C. L., and Worthing, H. W. (1956)   Hafnium content, hafnium to zirconium ratio, and radioactivity of zircon from igneous rocks (abs.). *Geol. Soc. Am., Bull.* 67:1700.

Graham, A. R. (1955)   Cerianite, CeO_2: a new rare-earth oxide mineral. *Am. Mineralogist* 40:560–564.

Grange, L. I. (1955)   Prospecting for radioactive minerals in New Zealand. *New Zealand Geol. Survey,* 28 pp.

Granger, H. C., and Bauer, H. L. Jr. (1951)   Results of diamond drilling, Merry Widow claim, White Signal, Grant County, New Mexico. *U.S. Geol. Survey* TEM-146A.

——— and ——— (1952)   Uranium occurrences on Merry Widow claim, White Signal district, Grant County, New Mexico. *U.S. Geol. Survey Circ.* 189.

Grant, S. C. (1955) Channel deposits of the Wind River formation in Fremont County, Wyoming, as a guide to uranium ore (abs.). *Geol. Soc. Am., Bull.* 66:1674–1675.

Graton, L. C. (1930) Hydrothermal origin of the Rand gold deposits. *Econ. Geol.* 25:S1–S185.

Gray, A. N. (1943) Phosphates and Superphosphate. Interscience Publishers, Inc., New York, 2d ed., 416 pp.

Green, J., and Kerr, P. F. (1951) Preliminary memorandum, East Slope area, Marysvale, Utah. *U.S. Atomic Energy Comm.* RMO-832.

——— and ——— (1953) Pseudomorphous illite after biotite (abs.). *Geol. Soc. Am., Bull.* 64:1429.

Gregory, M. (1946) Production of radium in Cornwall. *Trans. Roy. Geol. Soc. Cornwall*, 17, pt. 6, 306–312.

Griffiths, J. C., Groff, D. W., Cochran, J. A., and Kahn, J. S. (1954) Petrographical investigations of Salt Wash sediments. *U.S. Atomic Energy Comm.* RME-3097.

Griggs, R. L. (1954) A reconnaissance for uranium in New Mexico. *U.S. Geol. Survey Circ.* 354.

Grigoriev, I. F., and Dolomonova, E. I. (1957) Smirnovskite—a new mineral of the growth of hydrous fluoro-silicophosphates of thorium. *Zapiski Vses. Mineralog. Obschch.* 86:607–621.

Grigoriev, P. K. (1935) Pegmatites of north Karelia. *Trans. Cent. Geol. Prosp. Inst.*, fasc. 37.

Grip, E., and Odman, O. H. (1944) On thucolite and natural gas from Boliden. *Sveriges Geol. Undersökn. Årsbok* 38(6).

Gross, E. B. (1956) Mineralogy and paragenesis of the uranium ore, Mi Vida mine, San Juan County, Utah. *Econ. Geol.* 51:632–648.

Gross, G. A. (1957) Uranium deposits in Gaspé, New Brunswick, and Nova Scotia. *Can. Geol. Survey Paper* 57-2.

Gross, W. H. (1952) Radioactivity as a guide to ore. *Econ. Geol.* 47:722–742.

Groth, F. A. (1955) Stratigraphy of the Triassic Chinle formation of the San Rafael Swell, Utah (abs.). *Geol. Soc. Am., Bull.* 66:1675.

Gruner, J. W. (1951) Annual report for July 1, 1950 to June 30, 1951. *U.S. Atomic Energy Comm.* RMO-837.

——— (1952) Syntheses of uranium minerals at room and elevated temperatures (abs.). *Geol. Soc. Am., Bull.* 63:1257.

——— (1953) Interim report: uranium-bearing carbonaceous and asphaltic materials of the Colorado Plateau. *U.S. Atomic Energy Comm.* RME-3022.

——— (1954A) The origin of the uranium deposits of the Colorado Plateau and adjacent regions. *Mines Mag.* 44(3):53–56.

——— (1954B) The chemical formula of clarkeite. *Am. Mineralogist* 39:836–838.

——— (1955A) Concentration of uranium by carbon compounds. *Econ. Geol.* 50:542–543.

——— (1955B) Comments on uranium controls of the Happy Jack deposit, White Canyon, San Juan County, Utah. *Econ. Geol.* 50:751.

——— (1956A) A comparison of black uranium ores in Utah, New Mexico, and Wyoming. *Intern. Conf. Peaceful Uses Atomic Energy, Proc.* 6:530–532 (also *U.S. Geol. Survey Profess. Paper* 600:203–205, 1956).

——— (1956B) Concentration of uranium by carbon compounds. *Econ. Geol.* 51:284–285.

——— (1956C) Concentration of uranium in sediments by multiple migration-accretion. *Econ. Geol.* 51:495–520.

Gruner, J. W., Fetzer, W. G., and Rapaport, I. (1951) The uranium deposits near Marysvale, Piute County, Utah. *Econ. Geol.* 46:243–251.

—— and Gardiner, L. (1950) Tables of uranium and vanadium minerals which are largely of secondary origin. Univ. Minn.

—— and —— (1952) Mineral associations in the uranium deposits of the Colorado Plateau and adjacent regions with special emphasis on those in the Shinarump formation, Part III. *U.S. Atomic Energy Comm.* RMO-566.

——, Towle, C. C., and Gardiner, L. (1951) Uranium mineralization in Todilto limestone near Grants, McKinley County, New Mexico (abs.). *Geol. Soc. Am., Bull.* 62:1445.

Grutt, E. W. Jr. (1956) Uranium deposits in Tertiary clastics in Wyoming and northern Colorado. *Intern. Conf. Peaceful Uses Atomic Energy, Proc.* 6:392–402 (also *U.S. Geol. Survey Profess. Paper* 300:361–370, 1956).

—— (1957) Environment of some Wyoming uranium deposits. *2d Nuclear Eng. Sci. Conf., Paper* 57-NESC-69.

—— and Whalen, J. F. (1955) Uranium in northern Colorado and southern Wyoming. *Rocky Mtn. Assoc. Geol., Guidebook Geol. Northwest Colo.* 126–129.

Guilinger, R. R., and Theobald, P. K. (1957) Uranium deposits in oolithic limestone near Mayoworth, Johnson County, Wyoming. *U.S. Geol. Survey Bull.* 1030-K.

Guillemin, C. (1956) Contribution a la minéralogie des arséniates, phosphates et vanadates de cuivre. *Bull. soc. franç. minéral. et crist.* 79:7–95.

—— and Pierrot, R. (1956A) Nouvelle méthode de synthèse de la johannite $Cu(UO_2)_2(SO_4)_2(OH)_2 \cdot 6H_2O$. *Bull. soc. franç. minéral. et crist.* 79:170–172.

—— and —— (1956B) La sabugalite du gîte de Margnac II. Haute-Vienne. *Bull. soc. franç. minéral. et crist.* 79:179–182.

—— and —— (1956C) La schoepite du gîte de Margnac II. Haute-Vienne. *Bull. soc. franç. minéral. et crist.* 79:182–183.

Guimarães, D. (1947) Origem das rochas alcalinas. *Minas Gerais Inst. Tecno. Ind., Bol.* 5.

—— (1948) The zirconium ore deposits of the Poços de Caldas plateau, Brazil, and zirconium geochemistry. *Minas Gerais Inst. Tecno. Ind., Bol.* 6.

—— (1956) Areas geologically favorable to occurrence of thorium and uranium in Brazil. *Intern. Conf. Peaceful Uses Atomic Energy, Proc.* 6:129–133.

—— and Belezkij, W. (1956) The stano-tantalo-uraniferous deposits and occurrences in the region of São João del Rei, Minas Gerais, Brazil. *Intern. Conf. Peaceful Uses Atomic Energy, Proc.* 6:143–146.

——, Campos, M., and Figueiredo, D. G. (1953) Algumas rochas alcalinas de Poços de Caldas relacionadas com as jazidas de caldasito uranifero. *Univ. Minas Gerais, Esc. Eng., Publ.* 2.

Guntz, A. A. (1952) Sur la présence d'uranium dans les phosphates nord-africains. *Acad. Sci. Paris, Compt rend.* 234:868–870.

—— and Arene, M. (1953) Sur la présence de l'uranium dans les phosphates africains (abs.). *19th Congr. géol. intern.* 1952, sec. XI, fasc. XI, 11.

Haberlandt, H. (1938) Über die sogenannten Radiobaryte von Teplitz und Karlsbad. *Sitzber. Akad. Wiss. Vienna, Math.-naturw. Kl. Abt. IIa* 147:415–420.

—— and Hernegger, F. (1947) Uranbestimmungen an Glasopalen und anderen Mineralien mit Hilfe Fluoreszenzanalyse. *Sitzber. Akad. Wiss. Vienna, Math.-naturw. Kl. Abt. IIa* 155:359–370.

—— and Köhler, A. (1934) Fluoreszenzanalyse von Skapolithen. *Chem. Erde* 9:139–144.

Haberlandt, H., and Schiener, A. (1951)   Die Mineral- und Elementvergesellschaftung des Zentralgneisgebietes von Badgastein (Hohe Tauern). *Min. Petro. Mitt.* 3d ser. 2(3):292–354.

Hail, W. J. Jr., Myers, A. T., and Horr, C. A. (1956)   Uranium in asphalt-bearing rocks. *Intern. Conf. Peaceful Uses Atomic Energy, Proc.* 6:489–493 (also *U.S. Geol. Survey Profess. Paper* 300:521–526, 1956).

Hale, W. E. (1954)   Black Bay map-area, Saskatchewan. *Can. Geol. Survey Paper* 53-15.

Hamilton, P. K., and Kerr, P. F. (1954A)   Uranophane and beta-uranotile, Marysvale, Utah. *U.S. Atomic Energy Comm.* RME-3096 (pt. I), 38–48.

——— and ——— (1954B)   Phosphuranylite at Marysvale, Utah. *U.S. Atomic Energy Comm.* RME-3096 (pt. I), 49–51.

Hanley, J. B., Heinrich, E. W., and Page, L. R. (1950)   Pegmatite investigations in Colorado, Wyoming, and Utah. *U.S. Geol. Survey Profess. Paper* 227.

Hanson, R. A., and Pearce, D. W. (1941)   Colorado cerite. *Am. Mineralogist* 26:110–120.

Harada, Z. (1948)   Chemical analyses of Japanese minerals II. *J. Fac. Sci., Hokkaido Univ. Ser. IV, Geol. Mineral.* 7(2).

Harris, R. A., Davidson, D. F., and Arnold, B. P. (1954)   Bibliography of the geology of the western phosphate field. *U.S. Geol. Survey Bull.* 1018.

Harrison, J. E., and Leonard, B. F. (1952)   Preliminary report on the Jo Reynolds area, Lawson-Dumont district, Clear Creek County, Colorado. *U.S. Geol. Survey Circ.* 213.

Harshbarger, J. W., Repenning, C. A., and Irwin, J. H. (1957)   Stratigraphy of the uppermost Triassic and the Jurassic rocks of the Navajo Country. *U.S. Geol. Survey Profess. Paper* 291.

Hart, O. M. (1956)   Preliminary report on uranium deposits in the Pryor Mountains, Carbon County, Montana (abs.). *Grand Junction Geol. Soc., Geol. Uranium Program* 3.

Hass, W. H. (1956)   Age and correlation of the Chattanooga shale and the Maury formation. *U.S. Geol. Survey Profess. Paper* 286.

Hathaway, J. C. (1956)   Mixed layer structures in vanadium clays. Clays and Clay Minerals. *Natl. Acad. Sci., Natl. Research Council, Publ.* 456:387–388.

Hauptman, C. M. (1956)   Uranium in the Pryor Mountain area of southern Montana and northern Wyoming. *Uranium and Modern Mining* 3(11):14–15, 18–21.

Hausen, D. M. (1956)   Paragenesis of the Temple Mountain uraniferous asphaltites (abs.). *Geol. Soc. Am., Bull.* 67:1795.

Hawley, C. C., and Moore, F. B. (1955)   Control of uranium deposition by garnet-quartz rock in the Fall River area, Clear Creek County, Colorado (abs.). *Geol. Soc. Am., Bull.* 66:1675.

Hawley, J. E., and Rimsaite, Y. (1953)   Platinum metals in some Canadian uranium and sulphide ores. *Am. Mineralogist* 38:463–475.

Hayase, I. (1953)   The radioactivity of rocks and minerals studied with nuclear emulsions. 1. The minute radioactive minerals of the Tanakamiyama and Mikumo granites, Siga prefecture, Japan. *Mem. Coll. Sci., Univ. Kyoto, Ser. B* 20(4):247–260.

Hébert, C. (1947)   Contribution à l'étude de la chimie des phosphates de calcium. *Ann. mines* 136, Mem. 4.

Heinrich, E. W. (1948A)   Fluorite–rare earth mineral pegmatites of Chaffee and Fremont Counties, Colorado. *Am. Mineralogist* 33:64–75.

——— (1948B)   Pegmatites of Eight Mile Park, Fremont County, Colorado. *Am. Mineralogist* 33:420–448, 550–588.

Heinrich, E. W. (1949) Pegmatite mineral deposits in Montana. *Montana Bur. Mines Geol., Mem.* 28.

—— (1950) Accessory sulfides in North Carolina pegmatites. *Am. J. Sci.* 248:112–123.

—— (1953A) Characteristics of uranium and thorium minerals. *57th Ann. Meeting, Mich. Acad. Sci., Address.*

—— (1953B) Chemical differentiation of multi-generation pegmatite minerals (abs.). *Am. Mineralogist* 38:343.

—— (1956A) Classification of uranium and thorium deposits. *60th Ann. Meeting, Mich. Acad. Sci., Address.*

—— (1956B) Radioactive pegmatite deposits. *Can. Mining J.* 77(4):69–72, 100.

—— (1957) Geochemistry of the rare-earth elements. *61st Ann. Meeting, Mich. Acad. Sci., Address.*

—— and Bever, J. E. (1957) Radioactive mineral occurrences in the Guffey area, Park and Fremont Counties, Colorado. *Colo. School Mines Quart.* 52(4):23–36.

—— and Giardini, A. A. (1956) Radioactive columbite-tantalite (abs.). *Geol. Soc. Am., Bull.* 67:1704–1705.

—— and Levinson, A. A. (1955) Studies in the mica group; x-ray data on roscoelite and barium-muscovite. *Am. J. Sci.* 253:39–43.

——, ——, Levandowski, D. W., and Hewitt, C. H. (1953) Studies in the natural history of micas. *Univ. Mich. Eng. Research Inst. Final Rept., Project* M978.

Heising, G. B. (1931) The action of radon on some unsaturated hydrocarbons. *J. Am. Chem. Soc.* 53:3245–3263.

—— (1935) Action of radon on polymethylenes: cyclopentane and cyclopentene. *J. Phys. Chem.* 39:1067–1073.

Hernández-Pacheco, E. (1945) El mineral de uranio de Albalá (Cáceres). *Acad. cienc. exact., fís.-quím. y nat., Madrid, Rev.* 39(4):539–540.

Hess, F. L. (1908) Minerals of the rare-earth metals at Baringer Hill, Llano County, Texas. *U.S. Geol. Survey Bull.* 340:286–294.

—— (1913) Carnotite near Green River, Utah. *U.S. Geol. Survey Bull.* 530:161–164.

—— (1914) A hypothesis for the origin of the carnotites of Colorado and Utah. *Econ. Geol.* 9:675–688.

—— (1917) Vanadium in Colorado and New Mexico. Carnotite in Utah. *U.S. Geol. Survey Bull.* 530-K.

—— (1925A) Ilsemannite at Ouray, Utah. *U.S. Geol. Survey Bull.* 750, pt. I, 1–16.

—— (1925B) New and known minerals from the Utah-Colorado carnotite region. *U.S. Geol. Survey Bull.* 750, pt. I, 63–78.

—— (1931) Radioactive fluorspar from Wilberforce, Ontario. *Am. J. Sci.* ser. 5, 22, 215–221.

—— (1933A) Uranium, vanadium, radium, gold, silver, and molybdenum sedimentary deposits. *Am. Inst. Mining Engrs., Ore deposits of the Western States* 450–481.

—— (1933B) The pegmatites of the western states. *Am. Inst. Mining Engrs., Ore deposits of the Western States* 526–536.

—— and Schaller, W. T. (1914) Pintadoite and uvanite, two new vanadium minerals from Utah. *J. Wash. Acad. Sci.* 4:576–579.

—— and Wells, R. C. (1930) Samarskite from Petaca, New Mexico. *Am. J. Sci.* 19(109):17–26.

Hevesy, G., and Jantzen, V. T. (1924) Der Hafniumgehalt von Zirkonmineralien. *Z. anorg. u. allgem. Chem.* 133:113–118.

Hewett, D. F., and Glass, J. J. (1953) Two uranium-bearing pegmatite bodies in San Bernardino County, California. *Am. Mineralogist* 38:1040–1050.

Hewett, D. F., and Stone, J. (1957)   Uranothorite near Forest Home, San Bernardino County, California. *Am. Mineralogist* 42:104–107.

———, ———, and Levine, H. (1957)   Brannerite from San Bernardino County, California. *Am. Mineralogist* 42:30–38.

Hewitt, D. F. (1955)   Geology of Monteagle and Carlow Townships. *Ontario Dept. Mines, 63d Ann. Rept.*, pt. 6.

Heyl, A. V. (1957)   Zoning of the Bitter Creek vanadium-uranium deposit near Uravan, Colorado. *U.S. Geol. Survey Bull.* 1042–F.

Hidden, W. E. (1881)   Notes on mineral localities in North Carolina. *Am. J. Sci.* 22:23–26.

Hiemstra, S. A. (1955)   Baddeleyite from Phalaborwa, eastern Transvaal. *Am. Mineralogist* 40:275–282.

Hill, J. W. (1954)   Uraniferous asphaltic materials of southwestern Oklahoma (abs.). *Geol. Soc. Am., Bull.* 65:1377.

——— and Beroni, E. P. (1953)   Geological investigations of radioactive deposits. South-central district. *U.S. Geol. Survey* TEI-390, 199–201.

Hill, W. S. (1950)   Elementos radiactivos en los huesos fosiles del Terciario y del Cuaternario. *Ciencia e invest., Buenos Aires* 2:1.

Hilpert, L. S., and Freeman, V. L. (1956)   Guides to uranium deposits in the Gallup-Laguna area, New Mexico. *Intern. Conf. Peaceful Uses Atomic Energy, Proc.* 6:346–349 (also *U.S. Geol. Survey Profess. Paper* 300:299–302, 1956).

Hitchcock, E. (1833)   Report on the geology, mineralogy, botany, and zoology of Massachusetts. *Mass. Geol. Survey.*

Hobbs, W. H. (1889)   On the paragenesis of allanite and epidote as rock-forming minerals. *Am. J. Sci.* 38:223–228.

Hoehne, K. (1936)   Über einige Arsen-, Nickel-, Silber-, Wismut-, und Uranerzführende Kalkspatgänge der Grube Bergfreiheit zu Oberschmiedeberg im Riesengebirge. *Chem. Erde* 10:432–474.

Hoekstra, H. R., and Fuchs, L. H. (1956)   Synthesis of coffinite—$USiO_4$. *Science* 123:105.

——— and Katz, J. J. (1956)   The isotope geology of some uranium minerals. *Intern. Conf. Peaceful Uses Atomic Energy, Proc.* 6:547–550 (also *U.S. Geol. Survey Profess. Paper* 300:543–547, 1956).

Hoffman, J. (1940)   Uran im nördlichen Teil des Erzgebirgsbruches. *Akad. Wiss. Vienna, Math.-naturw. Kl. Anz.* 77, Jrg. 87–89.

——— (1943)   Uran in Kohlen und Torf. *Chem. Erde* 15(3):277–282.

Hogarth, D. D. (1951)   Studies of radioactive compounds: II. Metazeunerite, uranophane, kasolite and cuprosklodowskite in Canada. *Am. Mineralogist* 36:411–414.

——— and Nuffield, E. W. (1954)   Studies of radioactive compounds: VII—Phosphuranylite and dewindtite. *Am. Mineralogist* 39:444–447.

Hogg, N. (1948)   Mosher discovery of radioactive mineral, Pitt Township, District of Cochrane. *Ontario Dept. Mines, Prelim. Rept.* 1948-7.

Holland, H. D. (1954)   Radiation damage and its use in age determination. In *Nuclear geology.* John Wiley & Sons, Inc., New York, 175–180.

Holmes, A. (1931)   Radioactivity and geological time. *Natl. Research Council U.S., Bull.* 80.

———, Leland, W. T., and Nier, A. O. (1950)   Age of uraninite from a pegmatite near Singar, Gaya District, India. *Am. Mineralogist* 35:19–28.

Holmes, S. W. (1956)   Geology and mineralogy of the Pronto uranium deposit, district of Algoma, Ontario (abs.). *Am. Inst. Mining Engrs., Mining Branch Ann. Meeting, Program* 34–35.

Holmquist, P. J. (1910) The Archean geology of the coast regions of Stockholm. *Geol. Fören. Förh.* 32:789–911.

Honea, R. M. (1957) Identity of pilbarite with thorogummite and kasolite. *Am. Mineralogist* 42:908–910.

Horne, J. E. T. (1951) Notes on the photoluminescence of minerals. *Geol. Survey Gt. Brit., Bull.* 3:20–42.

——— and Davidson, C. F. (1955) The age of the mineralization of the Witwatersrand. *Geol. Survey Gr. Brit., Bull.* 10:58–73.

Houston, R. S. (1955) Petrography of Wyoming titaniferous sandstones (abs.). *Geol. Soc. Am., Bull.* 66:1676.

——— and Love, J. D. (1956) Titaniferous sandstone in marine rocks of late Jurassic age, northwestern Wyoming. *Wyoming Geol. Assoc. 11th Ann. Field Conf. Guidebook,* 72–74.

Hsieh, C. Y., and Chao, C. H. (1948) Note on the phosphate deposits in China. *Geol. Soc. China, Bull.* 28:71–74.

Huang, W. T. (1956) Novacekite from the Wichita Mountains, Oklahoma. *Am. Mineralogist* 41:152–153.

Huff, L. C. (1955) Preliminary geochemical studies in the Capitol Reef area, Wayne County, Utah. *U.S. Geol. Survey Bull.* 1015-H.

Hunt, C. B. (1956) Cenozoic geology of the Colorado Plateau. *U.S. Geol. Survey Profess. Paper* 279.

———, Averitt, P., and Miller, R. L. (1953) Geology and geography of the Henry Mountains region, Utah. *U.S. Geol. Survey Profess. Paper* 228.

Hurlbut, C. S. Jr. (1938) Mineralogical observations on the northern excursion of the XVII International Geological Congress. *Am. Mineralogist* 23:134–144.

——— (1950) Studies of uranium minerals (IV): Johannite. *Am. Mineralogist* 35:531–535.

——— (1954) Studies of uranium minerals (XV): Schroeckingerite from Argentina and Utah. *Am. Mineralogist* 39:901–907.

Hurley, P. M. (1950) Distribution of radioactivity in granites and possible relation to helium age measurements. *Geol. Soc. Am., Bull.* 61:1–8.

——— (1952) Alpha ionization damage as a cause of low helium ratios. *Am. Geophys. Union, Trans.* 33:174–183.

——— and Fairbairn, H. W. (1953) Radiation damage in zircon: a possible age method. *Geol. Soc. Am., Bull.* 64:659–674.

——— and ——— (1955) Ratio of thorium to uranium in zircon, sphene, and apatite (abs.). *Geol. Soc. Am., Bull.* 66:1578.

Hussak, E. (1894) Über ein neues Perowskitvorkommen in Verbindung mit Magneteisenstein von Catalão, Staat Goyaz, Brasilien. *Neues Jahrb. Mineral., Geol. II,* 297–300.

——— (1895) Mineralogische Notizen aus Brasilien (II Theil). *Mineral. u. petro, Mitt.* 14:395–414.

Hutchinson, R. W., and Claus, R. J. (1956) Pegmatite deposits, Alto Ligonha, Portuguese East Africa. *Econ. Geol.* 51:757–780.

Hutton, C. O. (1950) Studies of heavy detrital minerals. *Geol. Soc. Am., Bull.* 61:635–716.

——— (1951A) Occurrence, optical properties and chemical composition of huttonite. *Am. Mineralogist* 36:66–69.

——— (1951B) Uranoan thorite and thorian monazite from blacksand paystreaks, San Mateo County, California (abs.). *Geol. Soc. Am., Bull.* 62:1518–1519.

——— (1951C) Allanite from Yosemite National Park, Tuolumne County, California. *Am. Mineralogist* 36:233–248.

Hutton, C. O. (1952)   Accessory mineral studies of some California beach sands. *U.S. Atomic Energy Comm.* RMO-981.
——— (1954)   Wisaksonite is metamict uranoan thorite. *Am. Mineralogist* 39:825–829.
——— (1957)   Sengierite from Bisbee, Arizona. *Am. Mineralogist* 42:408–411.
Hyden, H. J. (1956)   Uranium and other trace metals in crude oils of the western United States. *U.S. Geol. Survey Profess. Paper* 300:511–519.

Iimori, T. (1941)   The microgranular uraninite from Iisaka and its absolute age. *Am. J. Sci.* 239:819–821.
Ilchenko, V., and Guimarães, D. (1954)   Apatita de Barreiro, Araxá, Minas Gerais. *Bol. Secretar. agr., ind., com. e trabalho, Minas Gerais,* Nos. 7–12, 1–49.
Ingerson, E. (1938)   Uraninite and associated minerals from Haddam Neck, Connecticut. *Am. Mineralogist* 23:269–276.
Ingram, W. N., and Keevil, N. B. (1951)   Radioactivity of the Bourlagaque, Elzevir, and Cheddar batholiths, Canada. *Geol. Soc. Am., Bull.* 62:131–148.
Ippolito, F. (1956)   Present state of uranium surveys in Italy. *Intern. Conf. Peaceful Uses Atomic Energy, Proc.* 6:167–173.
———, Baggio, P., Lorenzoni, S., Marinelli, G., Mittempergher, M., and Silvestro, F. (1956)   Studies of the mineralization of U and Th in Italy (abs.). *20th Congr. géol. intern., Resúmenes Trabajos Presentados* 92.
Isachsen, Y. W. (1954)   Ore deposits of the Big Indian Wash–Lisbon Valley area. *Utah Geol. Soc., Guidebook Geol. Utah* 9:95–105.
——— (1955)   Uranium deposits of the Big Indian Wash–Lisbon Valley mining district, San Juan County, Utah. *Nuclear Eng. Sci. Congr.,* preprint 281.
——— (1956A)   Geology of uranium deposits of the Shinarump and Chinle formations on the Colorado Plateau. *Intern. Conf. Peaceful Uses Atomic Energy, Proc.* 6:350–367 (also with C. G. Evensen in *U.S. Geol. Survey Profess. Paper* 300:263–280, 1956).
——— (1956B)   Influence of local, areal, and regional tectonics on the distribution of uranium in the Colorado Plateau area (abs.). *20th Congr. géol. intern., Resúmenes Trabajos Presentados* 218.
———, Mitcham, T. W., and Wood, H. B. (1955)   Age and sedimentary environments of uranium host rocks, Colorado Plateau. *Econ. Geol.* 50:127–134.

Jacob, K. D. (1953)   Fertilizer technology and resources in the United States. In *Agronomy,* vol. 3. Academic Press, Inc., New York, 454 pp.
Jaffe, E. B., and Sherwood, A. M. (1951)   Physical and chemical comparison of modern and fossil tooth and bone material. *U.S. Geol. Survey* TEM 149.
Jaffe, H. W. (1955)   Precambrian monazite and zircon from the Mountain Pass rare-earth district, San Bernardino County, California. *Geol. Soc. Am., Bull.* 66:1247–1256.
———, Evans, H. T. Jr., and Chapman, R. W. (1956)   Occurrence and age of chevkinite from the Devil's Slide fayalite-quartz syenite near Stark, New Hampshire. *Am. Mineralogist* 41:474–487.
———, Meyrowitz, R., and Evans, H. T. Jr. (1953)   Sahamalite, a new rare earth carbonate mineral. *Am. Mineralogist* 38:741–754.
———, Sherwood, A. M., and Peterson, M. J. (1948)   New data on schroeckingerite. *Am. Mineralogist* 33:152–157.
Jaffe, R. (1912)   Die Uranpecherzlagerstaetten des saechsischen Edelleutstollens bei St. Joachimsthal. *Z. prakt. Geol.* 20:425–452.
Jahns, R. H. (1946)   Mica deposits of the Petaca district, Rio Arriba County, New Mexico. *New Mexico Bur. Mines, Bull.* 25.

Jahns, R. H. (1951) Geology, mining, and uses of strategic pegmatites. *Am. Inst. Mining Engrs., Trans.* 190:45–59.

—— (1953) The genesis of pegmatites (II): Quantitative analysis of lithium-bearing pegmatite, Mora County, New Mexico. *Am. Mineralogist* 38:1078–1112.

—— (1954) Pegmatites of southern California. *Calif. Div. Mines, Bull.* 170, chap. VII, 37–50.

—— (1955) The study of pegmatites. *Econ. Geol.,* 50th ann. vol., pt. II, 1025–1130.

—— and Wright, L. A. (1944) The Harding beryl-tantalum-lithium pegmatites, Taos County, New Mexico (abs.). *Econ. Geol.* 39:96–97.

James, C. C. (1945) Uranium ores in Cornish mines. *Trans. Roy. Geol. Soc. Cornwall,* 17, pt. 5, 256–268.

James, T. C. (1956) Carbonatites and rift valleys in east Africa (abs.). *20th Congr. géol. intern., Resúmenes Trabajos Presentados* 402.

James, W. F., Lang, A. H., Murphy, R., and Kesten, S. N. (1950) Canadian deposits of uranium and thorium. *Am. Inst. Mining Engrs., Trans.* 187:239–255.

Janisch, E. P. (1926) The occurrence of phosphates in the Zoutpansberg District of the Northern Transvaal. *Trans. Geol. Soc. S. Africa* 29:109–135.

Japan Geological Survey (1956) Natural occurrence of uranium and thorium in Japan. *Intern. Conf. Peaceful Uses Atomic Energy, Proc.* 6:174–175.

Jarrard, L. D. (1957) Some occurrences of uranium and thorium in Montana. *Montana Bur. Mines Geol., Misc. Contrib.* 15.

—— and Moen, W. S. (1955) Uranium in the northwest. Published by The Authors, P. O. Box 136, Butte, Montana.

Jensen, M. L. (1957) Significance of S^{32}/S^{34} ratios on the origin of sulfides in uranium deposits of the Colorado Plateau (abs.). *Geol. Soc. Am., Bull.* 68:1752–1753.

Jobin, D. A. (1956) Regional transmissivity of the exposed sediments of the Colorado Plateau as related to distribution of uranium deposits. *Intern. Conf. Peaceful Uses Atomic Energy, Proc.* 6:317–320 (also *U.S. Geol. Survey Profess. Paper* 300:207–211, 1956).

John, T. U., and Paulo, K. L. (1954) A note on the occurrence of columbite in the Younger granites of the Jos Plateau, Nigeria. *Geol. Mag.* 91:245–248.

Johnson, H. S. Jr. (1957) Uranium resources of the San Rafael district, Emery County, Utah—a regional synthesis. *U.S. Geol. Survey Bull.* 1046-D.

Jolliffe, A. W. (1952) The north-western part of the Canadian Shield. *18th Intern. Geol. Congr. Rept.,* pt. XIII, 141–149.

—— (1955) The Gunnar uranium deposit. *Nuclear Eng. Sci. Congr.,* preprint 285.

—— (1956) The Gunnar "A" orebody. *Can. Mining Met. Bull.* 59:181–185.

—— and Bateman, J. D. (1944) Map of the Eldorado mine area. *Can. Geol. Survey Spec. Map.*

Joly, J. (1915) Pleochroic haloes. *Smithsonian Rept. for 1914,* 313–327.

Jones, D. J. (1954) Sedimentary features and mineralization of the Salt Wash sandstone at Cove Mesa, Carrizo Mountains, Apache County, Arizona. *U.S. Atomic Energy Comm.* RME-3093, pt. 2.

Jones, R. J. (1957) Columbium (niobium) and tantalum. *Can. Dept. Mines and Tech. Surveys, Mines Branch Mem. Ser.* No. 135.

Jones, R. S., Frost, I. C., and Rader, L. F. Jr. (1956) A comparison of chemical analyses of plants and soils as aids to prospecting for uranium in the southern Black Hills, South Dakota (abs.). *20th Congr. géol. intern., Resúmenes Trabajos Presentados* 366.

Jost, K. (1932) Über den Vanadiumgehalt der Sedimentgesteine und sedimentären Lagerstatten. *Chem. Erde* 7:177–290.

Joubin, F. R. (1954)   Uranium deposits of the Algoma district, Ontario. *Can. Mining Met. Bull.* 47(510):673–679.

—— (1955A)   Some economical uranium deposits in Canada. *The Precambrian* 28:6–8.

—— (1955B)   Uranium deposits of the Algoma (Blind River) district, Ontario. *Nuclear Eng. Sci. Congr.,* preprint 286.

—— (1955C)   Widespread occurrence and character of uraninite in the Triassic and Jurassic sediments of the Colorado Plateau. *Econ. Geol.* 50:233–234.

—— and James, D. H. (1956A)   Uranium deposits of the Blind River district, Ontario. *Mining Eng.* 8(6):611–613.

—— and ——— (1956B)   Rexspar uranium deposits. *Can. Mining J.* 77(7):59–60.

Jouravski, G. (1952)   Découverte de molybdenite à Bou Azzer, Sud-Marocain. *Acad. Sci. Paris, Compt. rend.* 234:124.

Jung, H. (1937)   Vanadiumhaltiger Muskovit von Schmiedefeld (Kreis Saalfeld, Thür.). *Chem. Erde* 11:38–44.

Kaiser, E. P. (1952)   The Papsy's Hope autunite prospect, Marysvale district, Piute County, Utah. *U.S. Geol. Survey* TEM-145A.

—— (1956)   Recent discoveries of niobium minerals in alkalic rocks of the United States (abs.). *Am. Inst. Mining Engrs. Ann. Meeting, Min. Branch Abs.* 20.

Kaitaro, S. (1953)   Geologic structure of the late pre-Cambrian intrusives in the Åva area, Åland Islands. *Bull. comm. géol. Finlande* 162.

Kauffman, A. J. Jr., and Baber, K. D. (1956)   Potential of heavy mineral bearing alluvial deposits in the Pacific Northwest. *U.S. Bur. Mines, Circ.* 7767.

—— and Jaffe, H. W. (1946)   Chevkinite (tscheffkinite) from Arizona. *Am. Mineralogist* 31:582–588.

Kautzsch, E. (1956)   Moderne Auffassung über die Entstehung des Kupferschiefers (abs.). *20th Congr. géol. intern., Resúmenes Trabajos Presentados* 93.

Kazakov, A. V. (1937)   The phosphorite facies and the genesis of phosphorites. *Geol. Invest. Agricultural Ores, Trans. Sci. Inst. Fertilizers Insecto-fungicides,* No. 142.

Keevil, N. B. (1938)   Thorium-uranium ratios of rocks and their relation to lead ore genesis. *Econ. Geol.* 33:685–696.

—— (1943)   The distribution of helium and radioactivity in rocks, V: Rocks and associated minerals from Quebec, Ontario, Manitoba, New Jersey, New England, New Brunswick, Newfoundland, Tanganyika, Finland, and Russia. *Am. J. Sci.* 241:277–306.

—— (1944)   Thorium-uranium ratios in rocks and minerals. *Am. J. Sci.* 242:309–321.

——, Larsen, E. S., and Wank, F. J. (1944)   The distribution of helium and radioactivity in rocks. VI. The Ayer granite-migmatite at Chelmsford, Mass. *Am. J. Sci.* 242:345–353.

Kehn, T. M. (1957)   Selected annotated bibliography of the geology of uranium-bearing coal and carbonaceous shale in the United States. *U.S. Geol. Survey Bull.* 1059-A.

Keller, W. D. (1952)   Torbernite in Missouri fire clay. *Am. Mineralogist* 37:125–128.

—— (1955)   Red and green clay problem and clay mineralogy of productive vs. barren rocks (abs.). Atomic Energy Comm.–U.S. Geol. Survey symposium, *U.S. Geol. Survey Papers* 9–10.

Kelley, D. R., and Kerr, P. F. (1957)   Clay alteration and ore, Temple Mountain, Utah. *Geol. Soc. Am., Bull.* 68:1101–1116.

Kelley, V. C. (1955A)   Regional tectonics of the Colorado Plateau and relationship to the origin and distribution of uranium. *Univ. New Mex. Publ. Geol. Ser.* 5.

Kelley, V. C. (1955B) Tectonic history of the Colorado Plateau (abs.). *Geol. Soc. Am., Bull.* 66:1583–1584.

—— (1955C) Monoclines of the Colorado Plateau. *Geol. Soc. Am., Bull.* 66:789–804.

—— (1955D) Regional structure and uranium distribution on the Colorado Plateau. *Nuclear Eng. Sci. Congr.*, preprint 254.

—— (1956) Influence of regional structure upon the origin and distribution of uranium in the Colorado Plateau. *Intern. Conf. Peaceful Uses Atomic Energy, Proc.* 6:299–306 (also *U.S. Geol. Survey Profess. Paper* 300:171–178, 1956).

Kerr, P. F. (1945) Cattierite and vaesite: new Co-Ni minerals from the Belgian Congo. *Am. Mineralogist* 30:483–497.

—— (1956A) The significance of collapse structures on the San Rafael Swell (abs.). *Grand Junction Geol. Soc., Geol. of Uranium Program* 5.

—— (1956B) The natural occurrence of uranium and thorium. *Intern. Conf. Peaceful Uses Atomic Energy, Proc.* 6:5–59.

—— (1956C) Rock alteration criteria in the search for uranium. *Intern. Conf. Peaceful Uses Atomic Energy, Proc.* 6:679–684 (also *U.S. Geol. Survey Profess. Paper* 300:633–639, 1956).

——, Anderson, T. P., Hamilton, P. K., and Pill, R. J. (1951) Preliminary memorandum Marysvale, Utah. *U.S. Atomic Energy Comm.* RMO-797, 1–7.

——, Bodine, M. W. Jr., Kelley, D. R., and Keys, W. S. (1957) Collapse features, Temple Mountain uranium area, Utah. *Geol. Soc. Am., Bull.* 68:933–982.

——, Brophy, G., Dahl, H. M., Green, J., and Woolard, L. E. (1952A) Annual Report for July 1, 1951 to June 30, 1952. Pt. 1. A geologic guide to the Marysvale area. *U.S. Atomic Energy Comm.* RMO-924.

——, ——, ——, ——, —— (1952B) Alteration and uranium mineralization, Marysvale, Utah (abs.). *Geol. Soc. Am., Bull.* 63:1270–1271.

—— and Cohen, W. J. (1951) Note on alteration along uranium-bearing vein Alhambra, Montana. *Ann. Rept. for July 1, 1950 to June 30, 1951. U.S. Atomic Energy Comm.* RMO-797, 62–68.

—— and Dahl, H. (1953) Uranium-fluorite association in the Todilto limestone, Grants, New Mexico. *U.S. Atomic Energy Comm.* RME-3051.

——, Hamilton, P. K., Brophy, G. P., Simpson, W. L., Cohen, W., Dahl, H., and Green, J. (1953) Annual report for June 30, 1952 to April 1, 1953. *U.S. Atomic Energy Comm.* RME-3046.

—— and Holland, H. D. (1951) Differential thermal analyses of davidite. *Am. Mineralogist* 36:563–572.

—— and Kelley, D. R. (1956) Urano-organic ores of the San Rafael Swell, Utah. *Econ. Geol.* 51:386–391.

——, ——, Keys, W. S., and Bodine, M. W. Jr. (1955) Collapse features at Temple Mountain, Utah (abs.). *Am. Inst. Mining Engrs. Ann. Meeting Abs. Mineral., Geol., Geophys. Div.* 41–42.

—— and Kulp, J. L. (1952) Pre-Cambrian uraninite, Sunshine mine, Idaho. *Science* 115:86–87.

—— and Robinson, R. F. (1953) Uranium mineralization in the Sunshine mine, Idaho. *Mining Eng.* 5(5):495–511.

Keys, W. S. (1956) Deep drilling in the Temple Mountain collapse, San Rafael Swell, Utah. *Intern. Conf. Peaceful Uses Atomic Energy, Proc.* 6:371–378 (also with R. L. White, *U.S. Geol. Survey Profess. Paper* 300:285–298, 1956).

Kidd, D. F. (1932A) A pitchblende-silver deposit, Great Bear Lake, Canada. *Econ. Geol.* 27:145–159.

Kidd, D. F. (1932B) Great Bear Lake-Coppermine River area, Mackenzie District, N.W.T. *Can. Geol. Survey Summary Rept.* 1931, pt. C, 47c–69c.

—— (1936) Rae to Great Bear Lake, Mackenzie District, N.W.T. *Can. Geol. Survey Mem.* 187.

—— and Haycock, M. H. (1935) Mineragraphy of the ores of Great Bear Lake. *Geol. Soc. Am., Bull.* 46:879–960.

Killeen, P. L., and Ordway, R. J. (1955) Radioactive investigations at Ear Mountain, Seward Peninsula, Alaska, 1945. *U.S. Geol. Survey Bull.* 1024-C.

Kilpady, S., and Deshpande, G. G. (1954) Outgrowths on detrital zircon from the Kamthi sandstones. *J. Univ. Geol. Soc. Nagpur* 1(2):16–18.

Kimball, G. (1904) Discovery of carnotite. *Eng. Mining J.* 77:956.

Kimura, K. (1940) Study on radioactivity of hokutolite in Taiwan by means of a counter with linear amplifier. *Mem. Coll. Sci. Kyoto Imp. Univ., Ser. A,* 23:7–17.

King, A. G. (1957) Pyrite-uraninite polycrystal. *Am. Mineralogist* 42:648–656.

King, J. W. (1956A) Uranium deposits in the Black Hills. *Am. Inst. Mining Engrs., Trans.* 8(1):41–46.

—— (1956B) High-grade uraniferous lignites in Harding County, South Dakota. *Intern. Conf. Peaceful Uses Atomic Energy, Proc.* 6:473–483 (also with H. B. Young, *U.S. Geol. Survey Profess. Paper* 300:419–431, 1956).

—— (1956C) Uraniferous lignites in the western Dakotas. *Uran. Inform. Digest* 3(6):16–18, 24.

King, R. U. (1951A) Radioactivity in the Jo Reynolds mine, Clear Creek County, Colorado. *U.S. Geol. Survey* TEM-5.

—— (1951B) Investigations in the Wood mine, Colorado. *U.S. Geol. Survey* TEM-102A.

—— (1952) Vein deposits of uranium at the Caribou mine, Boulder County, Colorado. *U.S. Geol. Survey* TEM-13A.

—— and Granger, H. C. (1952) Torbernite occurrence at the Robineau claims, Clear Creek County, Colorado. *U.S. Geol. Survey* TEM-24A.

——, Leonard, B. F., Moore, F. B., and Pierson, C. T. (1953) Uranium in the metal-mining districts of Colorado. *U.S. Geol. Survey Circ.* 215.

——, Moore, F. B., and Hinrichs, E. N. (1952) Pitchblende deposits in the United States. *U.S. Geol. Survey Circ.* 220:8–12.

Kithil, K. L., and Davis, J. A. (1917) Mining and concentration of carnotite ores. *U.S. Bur. Mines, Bull.* 103.

Klemic, H., and Baker, R. C. (1954) Occurrences of uranium in Carbon County, Pennsylvania. *U.S. Geol. Survey Circ.* 350.

Klepper, M. R. (1950) Forty-Niner, King Solomon Ridge, and West End claims near Clancy, Jefferson County, Montana. *U.S. Geol. Survey* TEM-31.

—— and Wyant, D. G. (1955) Geology of uranium (abs.). *Geol. Soc. Am., Bull.* 66:1585–1586.

—— and —— (1956) Uranium provinces. *Intern. Conf. Peaceful Uses Atomic Energy, Proc.* 6:217–223 (also *U.S. Geol. Survey Profess. Paper* 300:17–25, 1956).

Kline, M. H., Carlson, E. J., and Griffith, R. H. (1950) Boise Basin monazite placers, Boise County, Idaho. *U.S. Atomic Energy Comm.* RME-3129.

——, ——, and Horst, H. W. (1955) Corral Creek monazite placer area, Valley County, Idaho. *U.S. Atomic Energy Comm.* RME-3135.

——, ——, Storch, R. H., and Robertson, A. F. (1953) Beaver Valley radioactive mineral placers, Valley County, Idaho. *U.S. Atomic Energy Comm.* RME-3130.

Knight, G. L., and Landes, K. K. (1932) Kansas laccoliths. *J. Geol.* 40:1–15.

Knopf, A. (1956) Argon-potassium determination of the age of the Boulder bathylith, Montana. *Am. J. Sci.* 254:744–745.

——— (1957) The Boulder bathylith of Montana. *Am. J. Sci.* 255:81–103.

Koeberlin, F. R. (1938) Sedimentary copper, vanadium-uranium, and silver in southwestern United States. *Econ. Geol.* 33:458–461.

Kohl, E. (1941) Über das Uranpecherz nebst Abkömmlingen im Bereich des Mansfelder Kupferschiefers und seine Herkunft. *Z. prakt. Geol.* 49(9):99–110.

——— (1954) Uran. Die metallischen Rohstoffe, 10 heft. Ferd. Enke Verlag, Stuttgart, 234 pp.

——— and Haller, H. (1934) Die Mineralführung der Wölsendorfer Flussspatgänge. *Z. prakt. Geol.* 42:69–79.

Kokscharow, N. v. (1855) Materialien zur Mineralogie Russlands. St. Petersburg, vol. II, 60–66.

Konigsmark, T. A. (1955) Color changes and uranium deposits of the Morrison formation, McKinley County, New Mexico (abs.). Atomic Energy Comm.–U.S. Geol. Survey symposium, *Atomic Energy Comm. Papers* 2–3.

Kopchenova, E. V., and Skvortsova, K. V. (1957) Sodium uranospinite. *Doklady Akad. Nauk S.S.S.R.* 114:634–636.

Kostov, I. (1940) Über den Orthit aus den Migmatit-Pegmatiten von Michalkowo (Zentralrhodopen). *Ann. Univ. Sofia II Fac. Phys.-Math. Livre 3 Sci. Nat.* 36, pt. 3, 187–194.

Kraus, M. (1916) Das staatliche Uranpecherz-Bergbaurevier bei St. Joachimsthal in Böhmen. *Bergbau und Hütte*, vols. 1–10, 3–30, 45–63, 93–112, 128–148, 168–183.

Krauskopf, K. B. (1955) Sedimentary deposits of rare metals. *Econ. Geol.* 50th ann. vol., pt. I, 411–463.

——— (1956) Uraniferous magnetite-hematite deposit at the Prince mine, New Mexico. *Econ. Geol.* 51:725–727.

Krieger, P. (1932) An association of gold and uraninite from Chihuahua, Mexico. *Econ. Geol.* 27:651–660.

Krumbein, W. C., and Slack, H. A. (1956) Statistical analysis of low-level radioactivity of Pennsylvanian black fissile shale in Illinois. *Geol. Soc. Am., Bull.* 67:739–762.

Kulp, J. L., Volchok, H. L., and Holland, H. D. (1952) Age from metamict minerals. *Am. Mineralogist* 37:709–718.

Kuno, H. (1946) Modes of occurrence of some rare element minerals in pegmatites of Hai-cheng District, South Manchuria. *Proc. Japan. Acad.* 22(10):310–313.

——— (1950) Pegmatites of Sui-chung District, South Manchuria. A further contribution to the study of pegmatites containing rare element minerals. *J. Geol. Soc. Japan* 56:79–83.

Lacroix, A. (1922) Minéralogie de Madagascar. Paris, vol. I-III.

Landes, K. K. (1932) The Baringer Hill, Texas, pegmatite. *Am. Mineralogist* 17:381–390.

——— (1933) Origin and classification of pegmatites. *Am. Mineralogist* 18:33–56, 95–103.

——— (1935) Colorado pegmatites. *Am. Mineralogist* 20:319–333.

——— (1942) Effect of structure on intrusion of pegmatites. In Ore deposits as related to structural features. Princeton University Press, Princeton, N.J., 140–143.

Lang, A. H. (1952) Canadian deposits of uranium and thorium. *Can. Geol. Survey, Econ. Geol. Ser.* 16.

Larsen, E. S. Jr. (1942) Alkalic rocks of Iron Hill, Gunnison County, Colorado. *U.S. Geol. Survey Profess. Paper* 197.

Larsen, E. S. Jr. (1948)   Batholith and associated rocks of Corona, Elsinore, and San Luis Rey Quadrangles, southern California. *Geol. Soc. Am., Mem.* 29.

—— and Berman, H. (1934)   The microscopic determination of the nonopaque minerals. *U.S. Geol. Survey Bull.* 848.

—— and Cross, W. (1956)   Geology and petrology of the San Juan region, southwestern Colorado. *U.S. Geol. Survey Profess. Paper* 258.

—— and Gonyer, F. A. (1937)   Dakeite, a new uranium mineral from Wyoming. *Am. Mineralogist* 22:561–563.

——, Hess, F. L., and Schaller, W. T. (1926)   Uranium minerals from Lusk, Wyoming. *Am. Mineralogist* 11:155–164.

—— and Keevil, N. B. (1942)   The distribution of radioactivity and helium in rocks. *Am. J. Sci.* 240:204–215.

—— and —— (1947)   Radioactivity of the rocks of southern California. *Geol. Soc. Am., Bull.* 58:483–494.

——, ——, and Harrison, H. C. (1952)   Method for determining the age of igneous rocks using the accessory minerals. *Geol. Soc. Am., Bull.* 63:1045–1052.

—— and Phair, G. (1954)   The distribution of uranium and thorium in igneous rocks. In nuclear geology. John Wiley & Sons, Inc., New York, 75–89.

——, ——, Gottfried, D., and Smith, W. L. (1956)   Uranium in magmatic differentiation. *Intern. Conf. Peaceful Uses Atomic Energy, Proc.* 6:240–247 (also *U.S. Geol. Survey Profess. Paper* 300:65–74, 1956).

——, Waring, C. L., and Berman, J. (1953)   Zoned zircon from Oklahoma. *Am. Mineralogist* 38:1118–1125.

Laverty, R. A., and Gross, E. B. (1956)   Paragenetic studies of uranium deposits of the Colorado Plateau. *Intern. Conf. Peaceful Uses Atomic Energy, Proc.* 6:533–539 (also *U.S. Geol. Survey Profess. Paper* 300:195–201, 1956).

Lawrence, L. J., See, G. T., McBride, F., and Hofer, H. (1957)   Davidites from the Mt. Isa-Cloncurry district, Queensland. *Econ. Geol.* 52:140–148.

Le Conte, J. L. (1847)   On coracite, a new ore of uranium. *Am. J. Sci.* 3(2d ser.):173–175.

Lenoble, A., Salvan, H., and Ziegler, V. (1952)   Découverte de l'uranium dans les niveaux phosphatés du Maroc. *Acad. sci. Paris, Compt. rend.* 234:976–977.

——, ——, and —— (1954)   Sur la découverte de l'uranium dans les niveaux phosphatés du Maroc (Regions de Chichaoua, Imi n'Tanout, Louis Gentil et Khouribga). *Acad. sci. Paris, Compt. rend.* 238(17):1720–1721.

Leonard, B. F. (1952)   Relation of pitchblende deposits to hypogene zoning in the Front Range mineral belt, Colorado (abs.). *Geol. Soc. Am., Bull.* 63:1274–1275.

Leonardos, O. H. (1936)   Tantalo, niobio, uranio e radio no Brasil. *Brazil, Dept. nac. prod. mineral, Bol.* 11.

—— (1955)   A industrialização dos fosfatos de Pernambuco. *Eng., mineração e met.* 22(128):85–87.

—— (1956)   Carbonatitos com apatita e pirocloro no estrangeiro e no Brasil. *Eng., mineração e met.* 23(136):157–163.

Lepierre, C. (1937)   Yttrocolumbite de Mocambique. *Mem. Acad. Cienc. Lisboa, Class Ciencias* 1:369–375.

Leutwein, F. (1941)   Geochemie und Vorkommen des Vanadiums. *Ber. freiberger geol. Ges.* 18:73 (in *Neues Jahrb. Mineral.*, Ref. II, 92–95, 1942).

Levy, S. I. (1915)   The rare earths. Longmans, Green & Co., Inc., New York, 345 pp.

Lewis, R. Q. (1955)   Fluorescent silica as a guide to prospecting and exploration in the Shinarump conglomerate, Monument Valley area, Utah (abs.). Atomic Energy Comm.–U.S. Geol. Survey symposium, *Atomic Energy Comm. Papers* 11.

Liebenberg, W. R. (1957) The occurrence and origin of gold and radioactive minerals in the Witwatersrand System, the Dominion Reef, the Ventersdorp Contact Reef, and the Black Reef. *Uranium in South Africa: 1946–1956*, vol. 1: 20–218.

Linares, E. (1956) The "Eva Perón" deposit, Malargue, Mendoza. *Intern. Conf. Peaceful Uses Atomic Energy, Proc.* 6:75–81.

Lind, S. C., and Bardwell, D. C. (1926) The chemical action of gaseous ions produced by alpha particles. IX. Saturated hydrocarbons. *J. Am. Chem. Soc.* 48:2335–2351.

———, ———, and Perry, J. H. (1926) The chemical action of gaseous ions produced by alpha particles. VII. Unsaturated hydrocarbons. *J. Am. Chem. Soc.* 48:1556–1575.

——— and Davis, C. W. (1919) A new deposit of uranium ore. *Science,* 49(n.s.):441–443.

Lindgren, W. (1933) Mineral deposits. McGraw-Hill Book Company, Inc., New York, 4th ed., 930 pp.

Lokka, L. (1935) Über den Chemismus der Minerale (Orthit, Biotit u.a.) eines Feldspatbruches in Kangasala, SW-Finnland. *Bull. comm. géol. Finlande* 111.

——— (1950) Contributions to the knowledge of the chemistry of the radioactive minerals of Finland. *Bull. comm. géol. Finlande* 149.

Loomis, T. H. W. (1956) Uranium occurrences in the Copper Mountain area, Fremont County, Wyoming (abs.). *Grand Junction Geol. Soc., Abs. Geol. Uranium* 3.

López de Azcona, J. M., and Abbad, M. (1941) A pseudomorph of pitchblende after beryl, from the Sierra de la Albarrana (Cordoba). *Rept. Comm. Meas. Geol. Time, 1940–1941,* 115.

Love, J. D. (1952) Preliminary report on uranium deposits in the Pumpkin Buttes area, Powder River basin, Wyoming. *U.S. Geol. Survey Circ.* 176.

——— (1953A) Preliminary report on uranium deposits in the Miller Hill area, Carbon County, Wyoming. *U.S. Geol. Survey Circ.* 278.

——— (1953B) Geologic investigations of radioactive deposits. Wyoming. Reconnaissance. *U.S. Geol. Survey* TEI-390, 63–67.

——— (1954A) Preliminary report on uranium in the Gas Hills area, Fremont and Natrona Counties, Wyoming. *U.S. Geol. Survey Circ.* 352.

——— (1954B) Uranium in the Mayoworth area, Johnson County, Wyoming—a preliminary report. *U.S. Geol. Survey Circ.* 358.

Lovering, T. G. (1954) Radioactive mineral deposits of Nevada. *U.S. Geol. Survey Bull.* 1009-C.

——— (1955) Progress in radioactive iron oxides investigations. *Econ. Geol.* 50:186–195.

——— (1956) Radioactive deposits in New Mexico. *U.S. Geol. Survey Bull.* 1009-L.

Lovering, T. S., and Goddard, E. N. (1950) Geology and ore deposits of the Front Range, Colorado. *U.S. Geol. Survey Profess. Paper* 223.

Lowell, J. D. (1955) Applications of cross-stratification studies to problems of uranium exploration, Chuska Mountains, Arizona. *Econ. Geol.* 50:177–185.

——— (1956) Occurrences of uranium in Seth-La-Kai diatreme, Hopi Buttes, Arizona. *Am. J. Sci.* 254:404–412.

Lowell, W. R. (1952) Phosphatic rocks in the Deer Creek-Wells Canyon area, Idaho. *U.S. Geol. Survey Bull.* 982-A.

Lukashev, V. P. (1937) On the search for rare element deposits of the region adjoining the Azov Sea. *Problems Soviet Geol.* 7(2):176–182.

Lundegårdh, P. H. (1944) A new occurrence of allanite-bearing pegmatite in central Roslagen, Sweden. *Arkiv. Kemi., Mineral. Geol.* 18B(7).

Lynd, L. E., Sigurdson, H., North, C. H., and Anderson, W. W. (1954) Characteristics of titaniferous concentrates. *Mining Eng.* 6(8):817–824.

Lyon, R. J. P. (1956) Anomalous fluorescence in torbernite from Rum Jungle, Northern Territory, Australia. *Am. Mineralogist* 41:789–792.

McAndrew, J., and Scott, T. R. (1955) Stillwellite, a new rare-earth mineral from Queensland. *Nature* 176:509–510.

McCall, G. J. H. (1956) Alkaline and carbonatite ring complexes in the Kavirondo rift valley, Kenya (abs.). *20th Congr. géol. intern., Resúmenes Trabajos Presentados* 405.

McConnell, D. (1953) Radioactivity of phosphatic sediments. *Econ. Geol.* 48:147–148.

McConnell, R. B. (1945) Ufipa orthite. *Tanganyika Territ. Dept. Geol. Survey, Mineral Res. Pam.* 38.

McDougall, D. J. (1954) The marginal luminescence of certain intrusive rocks and hydrothermal ore deposits. *Econ. Geol.* 49:717–726.

McDowell, J. P. (1957) Sedimentary petrology of the Mississagi quartzite in the Blind River area, Ontario (abs.). *Geol. Soc. Am., Bull.* 68:1764.

MacFadyen, D. A., and Guedes, S. V. (1956) Air survey applied to the search for radioactive minerals in Brazil. *Intern. Conf. Peaceful Uses Atomic Energy, Proc.* 6:726–739.

McKay, E. J. (1955) Criteria for outlining areas favorable for uranium deposits in parts of Colorado and Utah. *U.S. Geol. Survey Bull.* 1009-J.

Mackay, R. A., and Schnellmann, G. A. (1956) An occurrence of apatite and pyrochlore in association with a carbonatitic plug in Uganda (abs.). *20th Congr. géol. intern., Resúmenes Trabajos Presentados* 405.

McKee, E. D. (1954) Stratigraphy and history of the Moenkopi formation of Triassic age. *Geol. Soc. Am., Mem.* 61.

McKelvey, V. E. (1955) Search for uranium in the United States. *U.S. Geol. Survey Bull.* 1030-A.

—— (1956) Uranium in phosphate rock. *Intern. Conf. Peaceful Uses Atomic Energy, Proc.* 6:499–502 (also *U.S. Geol. Survey Profess. Paper* 300:477–481, 1956).

—— and Carswell, L. D. (1956) Uranium in the Phosphoria formation. *Intern. Conf. Peaceful Uses Atomic Energy, Proc.* 6:503–506 (also *U.S. Geol. Survey Profess. Paper* 300:483–487, 1956).

——, Everhart, D. L., and Garrels, R. M. (1955) Origin of uranium deposits. *Econ. Geol.*, 50th Ann. Vol., pt. I, 464–533 (also *Intern. Conf. Peaceful Uses Atomic Energy, Proc.* 6:551–561, 1956; also *U.S. Geol. Survey Profess. Paper* 300:41–53, 1956).

—— and Nelson, J. M. (1950) Characteristics of marine uranium-bearing sedimentary rocks. *Econ. Geol.* 45:35–53.

——, Swanson, R. W., and Sheldon, R. P. (1953) The Permian phosphorite deposits of Western United States. *19th Congr. géol. intern., Compt. rend.*, sec. XI, fasc. XI, 45–64.

McKeown, F. A., and Klemic, H. (1953) Reconnaissance for uranium in the United States. Northeast district. *U.S. Geol. Survey* TEI-390, 195–198.

—— and —— (1956) Rare-earth-bearing apatite at Mineville, Essex County, New York. *U.S. Geol. Survey Bull.* 1046-B.

Mackin, J. H., and Schmidt, D. L. (1956) Uranium- and thorium-bearing minerals in placer deposits in Idaho. *Intern. Conf. Peaceful Uses Atomic Energy, Proc.* 6:587–592 (also *U.S. Geol. Survey Profess. Paper* 300:375–380, 1956).

McWhirter, D. J. L. (1956) Witwatersrand gold and uranium. *Mining Mag.* (*London*) 94:84–86.

Magakyan, I. G. (1955) Geneticheskie tipi zarubezhnikh miestorozhdienii urana. *Notes All-Soviet Mineral. Soc.* 74(3):276–288.

Mansfield, G. R. (1940) The role of fluorine in phosphate deposition. *Am. J. Sci.* 238:833–879.

Mapel, W. J. (1956) Uranium in black shale deposits, northern Rocky Mountains and Great Plains. *U.S. Geol. Survey Bull.* 1030-H.

Marble, J. P. (1939) The analysis of two samples of pitchblende ore from Great Bear Lake, Canada. *Am. Mineralogist* 24:272–273.

——— (1950) Lead-uranium ratio and possible geologic age of allanite from Greenwich, Massachusetts. *Am. Mineralogist* 35:845–852.

Marckwald, W. (1906) Über Uranerze aus Deutsch-Ostafrika. *Centr. Mineral., Geol.* 761.

Markewicz, F. J., Chao, E. C. T., and Milton, C. (1957) Radioactive minerals of New Jersey (abs.). *Geol. Soc. Am., Bull.* 68:1763.

Marshall, R. R. (1955) Absorption spectra of smoky quartz from an Arkansas vein deposit and from a Sierran miarolitic granite. *Am. Mineralogist* 40:535–537.

Martens, J. H. C. (1935) Beach sands between Charleston, South Carolina, and Miami, Florida. *Geol. Soc. Am., Bull.* 46:1563–1596.

Mason, B., and Roberts, C. N. (1949) Minerals of the Osterby pegmatite, Dalarna, Sweden. *Geol. Fören. Förh.* 71:537–544.

Masters. J. A. (1955) Geology of the uranium deposits of the Lukachukai Mountains area, northeastern Arizona. *Econ. Geol.* 50:111–126.

Masursky, H. (1956) Trace elements in coal in the Red Desert, Wyoming. *Intern. Conf. Peaceful Uses Atomic Energy, Proc.* 6:458–463 (also *U.S. Geol. Survey Profess. Paper* 300:439–444, 1956).

Matheson, R. S., and Searl, R. A. (1956) Mary Kathleen uranium deposit, Mount Isa-Cloncurry district, Queensland, Australia. *Econ. Geol.* 51:529–540.

Matzko, J. J. (1955A) Reconnaissance for uranium and thorium in Alaska. *Geol. Soc. Am., Bull.* 66:1704–1705.

——— (1955B) Phosphate rock from the Brooks Range, northern Alaska: a preliminary mineralogic report (abs.). *Geol. Soc. Am., Bull.* 66:1705.

Maurice, O. D. (1957) Preliminary report on Oka area, Electoral District of Deux-Montagnes. *Quebec Dept. Mines, Prelim. Rept.* 351.

Mawdsley, J. B. (1954) Radioactive, pronouncedly differentiated pegmatite sill, Lac La Ronge district, northern Saskatchewan. *Econ. Geol.* 49:616–624.

——— (1955) Radioactive pegmatites of northern Saskatchewan. *Can. Prosp. Develop. Assoc. Address.*

Mawson, D. (1944) The nature and occurrence of uraniferous mineral deposits in South Australia. *Trans. Roy. Soc. S. Australia* 68:334–357.

Medina, M. A. (1956) Yacimientos de radioactivos en el Silurico Español (abs.). *20th Congr. géol. intern., Resúmenes Trabajos Presentados* 82.

Meen, V. B. (1948) A uraninite crystal of unusual size. *Univ. Toronto Studies, Geol. Ser.* 52:90–91.

Meister, E. (1926) Ueber ein neues Vorkommen von Uranpechblende auf der Bergfreiheitsgrube in Schmiedeberg i. R. *Z. prakt. Geol.* 34:44–45.

Meixner, H. (1938) Monazit, Xenotim, und Zirkon aus apatitführenden Pegmatiten des steirischkärntnischen Altkristallins. *Z. Krist.* 99A:50–55.

Meixner, H. (1940A)   Notizen über neue Vorkommen einige Uranminerale. *Zentr. Mineral. Geol.* A(7):145–148.

——— (1940B)   Fluoreszenzanalytische, optische und chemische Beobachtungen an Uranmineralen. *Chem. Erde* 12(3):433–450.

——— (1940C)   Fluoreszenz von Uranmineralien. *Mineral. u. petrog. Mitt.* 52:275–277.

——— (1953)   Kahlerit, ein neues Mineral der Uranglimmergruppe, aus der Hüttenberger Erzlagerstätte. *Der Karinthin* 23:277–280.

Melkov, V. G. (1956)   Record of Proceedings of Session 7B, *Intern. Conf. Peaceful Uses Atomic Energy, Proc.* 6:824–825.

Mélon, J. (1938)   La sharpite, nouveau carbonate d'uranyl du Congo Belge. *Inst. roy. colonial belge, Bull.* 9:333–336.

Mencher, A. H. (1956)   Central Wyoming uranium. *Uranium Mag.* 3(6):12–14, 16.

Mennell, F. P. (1946)   Ring structures with carbonate cores in Southern Rhodesia. *Geol. Mag.* 83:137–140.

Mertie, J. B. Jr. (1949)   Monazite. *Industrial Rocks and Minerals, Am. Inst. Mining Engrs.* 629–636.

——— (1953)   Monazite deposits of the southeastern Atlantic states. *U.S. Geol. Survey Circ.* 237.

——— (1955)   Ancient monazite placer (abs.). *Geol. Soc. Am., Bull.* 66:1692–1693.

Merwin, S. S. (1956)   Uranium. Occurrences, control, and potential of Colorado's Front Range. *Uranium Mag.* 3(3):10–12, 86; 3(5):30–31, 34–36; 3(6):20–24.

Messer, E. (1955)   Kupferschiefer, Sanderz und Kobaltrücken im Richelsdorfer Gebirge (Hessen). *Hess. Lagerstättenarch.* No. 3.

Michailov, A. (1937)   The Tagashet thorium-rare earth deposit. *Problems Soviet Geol.* 7, 84.

Miesch, A. T. (1955) Regional variation of accessory extrinsic elements in sandstone type uranium deposits in the central part of the Colorado Plateau (abs.). Atomic Energy Comm.–U.S. Geol. Survey symposium, *U.S. Geol. Survey Papers* 11–12.

Miholić, S. (1952)   Radioactivity of waters issuing from sedimentary rocks. *Econ. Geol.* 47:543–547.

——— (1954)   Genesis of the Witwatersrand gold-uranium deposits. *Econ. Geol.* 49:537–540.

——— (1956)   Genesis of radioactive waters (abs.). *20th Congr. géol. intern., Resúmenes Trabajos Presentados* 219.

Miller, B. J., and Singewald, J. T. (1919)   The mineral deposits of South America. McGraw-Hill Book Company, Inc., New York.

Miller, L. J. (1952)   Uranium ore controls in the Happy Jack mine and vicinity, White Canyon, Utah (abs.). *Geol. Soc. Am., Bull.* 63:1280.

——— (1955)   Uranium ore controls of the Happy Jack deposit, White Canyon, San Juan County, Utah. *Econ. Geol.* 50:156–169.

——— and Kerr, P. F. (1954)   Progress report on the chemical environment of pitchblende. *U.S. Atomic Energy Comm.* RME-3096 (pt. 2), 72–99.

Miller, R. III (1945)   The heavy minerals of Florida beach and dune sands. *Am. Mineralogist* 30:65–75.

Miller, R. L., and Gill, J. R. (1954)   Uranium from coal. *Sci. American* 191(4):36–39.

Milne, I. H., and Nuffield, E. W. (1951)   Studies of radioactive compounds I—Vandenbrandeite. *Am. Mineralogist* 36:394–410.

Minto, W. L. (1956)   Fluorescent thorium mineral. *Science* 123:419.

Mitcham, T. W. (1955)   Uranium-bearing horizons. *Nuclear Eng. Sci. Congr.,* preprint 256.

Mitcham, T. W., and Evensen, C. G. (1955) Uranium ore guides, Monument Valley district, Arizona. *Econ. Geol.* 50:170–176.

Moen, W. S. (1954) Uranium mineralization at the Mooney claim, Silver Bow County, Montana. *U.S. Atomic Energy Comm.* RME-2006.

Montgomery, A. (1954) Uranium minerals of the Mauch Chunk area, Pennsylvania. *Penn. Acad. Sci. Proc.* 28.

——— (1957) Three occurrences of high-thorium near Easton, Pennsylvania. *Am. Mineralogist* 42:804–820.

Moore, F. B., and Butler, C. R. (1952) Pitchblende deposits at the Wood and Calhoun mines, Central City mining district, Gilpin County, Colorado. *U.S. Geol. Survey Circ.* 186.

——— and Cavender, W. S. (1952) Pitchblende deposit at the Caribou mine, Boulder County, Colorado (abs.). *Geol. Soc. Am., Bull.* 63:1281.

Moore, G. W. (1954) Extraction of uranium from aqueous solution by coal and some other materials. *Econ. Geol.* 49:652–658.

——— and Levish, M. (1955) Uranium-bearing sandstone in the White River Badlands, Pennington County, South Dakota. *U.S. Geol. Survey Circ.* 359.

Mountain, E. D. (1931) Pegmatites of the Cape Province. *Rec. Albany Museum (Grahamtown)* 4(1):122–144.

Moxham, R. M., and Nelson, A. E. (1952A) Reconnaissance for radioactive deposits in south-central Alaska, 1947–49. *U.S. Geol. Survey Circ.* 184.

——— and ——— (1952B) Reconnaissance for radioactive deposits in the southern Cook Inlet region, Alaska. *U.S. Geol. Survey Circ.* 207.

———, Walker, G. W., and Baumgardner, L. H. (1955) Geologic and airborne radioactivity studies in the Rock Corral area, San Bernardino County, California. *U.S. Geol. Survey Bull.* 1021-C.

——— and West, W. S. (1953) Radioactive investigations in the Serpentine-Kougarok area, Seward Peninsula, Alaska, 1946. *U.S. Geol. Survey Circ.* 265.

Mrose, M. E. (1950) Studies of uranium minerals (III): Saléeite from Schneeberg, Saxony. *Am. Mineralogist* 35:525–530.

——— (1953) Studies of uranium minerals (XIII): Synthetic uranospinites. *Am. Mineralogist* 38:1159–1168.

Muilenberg, G. A., and Keller, W. D. (1950) Carnotite and radioactive shale in Missouri. *Am. Mineralogist* 35:323–324.

Mullens, T. E., and Freeman, V. L. (1957) Lithofacies of the Salt Wash member of the Morrison formation, Colorado Plateau. *Geol. Soc. Am., Bull.* 68(4):505–526.

Murata, K. J., Rose, H. J. Jr., and Carron, M. K. (1953) Systematic variation of rare earths in monazite. *Geochim. et Cosmochim. Acta* 4:292–300.

———, ———, ———, and Glass, J. J. (1957) Systematic variation of rare-earth elements in cerium-earth minerals. *Geochim. et Cosmochim. Acta* 11:141–161.

Murdoch, J., and Webb, R. W. (1954) Minerals in southern California. *Calif. Div. Mines, Bull.* 170, chap. VII, 5–12.

Murphy, J. F. (1955) Titaniferous sandstone of Wyoming and adjacent areas (abs.). *Geol. Soc. Am., Bull.* 66:1678.

——— (1956) Uranium-bearing water in the Crow Creek and Muskrat Creek areas, Fremont County, Wyoming. *Geol. Survey Wyoming, Rept. Invest.* 5.

——— and Houston, R. S. (1955) Titanium-bearing black sand deposits of Wyoming. *Wyoming Geol. Assoc. 10th Ann. Field Conf., Guidebook* 190–196.

Murphy, R. (1948) Eldorado mine: Structural geology of Canadian ore deposits. *Can. Inst. Mining Met.* 259–268.

Mutch, A. D. (1956)   A critical evaluation of the classification of ore deposits of magmatic affiliations. *Econ. Geol.* 51:665–685.

Narten, P. F., and McKeown, F. A. (1952)   Reconnaissance of radioactive rocks of the Hudson Valley and Adirondacks Mountains, New York. *U.S. Geol. Survey* TEI-70.

Nelson, A. E., West, W. S., and Matzko, J. J. (1954)   Reconnaissance for radioactive deposits in eastern Alaska, 1952. *U.S. Geol. Survey Circ.* 348.

Neuerburg, G. J. (1954)   Allanite pegmatite, San Gabriel Mountains, Los Angeles County, California. *Am. Mineralogist* 39:831–834.

——— (1956)   Uranium in igneous rocks of the United States of America. *Intern. Conf. Peaceful Uses Atomic Energy, Proc.* 6:231–239 (also *U.S. Geol. Survey Profess. Paper* 300:55–64, 1956).

———, Antweiler, J. C., and Bieler, B. H. (1956)   Uranium content and leachability of some igneous rocks and their geochemical significance (abs.). *20th Congr. géol. intern., Resúmenes Trabajos Presentados* 221.

Neuhaus, A. (1954)   Über Uraninit im Granit von Weissenstadt, Fichtelgebirge. *Fortschr. Mineral.* 32:80–81.

Neuman, W. F., and others (1948)   The deposition of uranium in bone. *J. Biol. Chem.* 175:705–715.

Neumann, H. (1954)   Kobberforekomstene på Straumsheia. *Norg. Geol. Unders., Årsbok* 18–29.

Nickel, E. H. (1956)   Niocalite—a new calcium niobium silicate mineral. *Am. Mineralogist* 41:785–786.

Nininger, R. D. (1954)   Minerals for Atomic Energy. D. Van Nostrand Company, Inc., Princeton, N.J., 367 pp.

Norman, H. W. (1957)   Uranium deposits of northeastern Washington. *Mining Eng.*, June 1957, 662–666.

Norton, D. A. (1957)   X-ray fluorescence as applied to cyrtolite. *Am. Mineralogist* 42:492–505.

Novacek, R. (1935)   Study on some secondary uranium minerals. *Věstník králov. Ceské společnosti nauk., Třida II,* 1–36.

Noyes, F. C. (1944)   Phosphate rock industry of foreign countries. *Mining and Met.*, Oct. 1944, 495–506.

Nuffield, E. W. (1950)   Preliminary report on the geology of part of Township 29, Range XIV, District of Algoma. *Ontario Dept. Mines,* P.R. 1950-5.

——— (1956)   Geology of the Montreal River area. *Ontario Dept. Mines, Ann. Rept.* 1955, 64(3).

——— and Milne, I. H. (1953)   Studies of radioactive compounds: VI—Meta-uranocircite. *Am. Mineralogist* 38:476–488.

O'Brien, M. W. (1953)   Phosphatic horizons in the Upper Carboniferous of Ireland. *19th Congr. géol. intern., Compt. rend.,* sec. XI, fasc. XI, 135–143.

Ohashi, R. (1920)   Note on the plumbiferous barytes from Shibukuro, Prefecture of Akita, Japan. *Mineral. Mag.* 19:73–76.

Olson, J. C. (1956)   Association of rare-earth metals with alkalic rocks at Mountain Pass, California, and at other localities (abs.). *Am. Inst. Mining Engrs., Min. Branch 1956 Ann. Meeting, Program* 18.

——— and Pray, L. C. (1954)   The Mountain Pass rare-earth deposits. *Calif. Div. Mines, Bull.* 170, chap. VIII, 23–29.

———, Shawe, D. R., Pray, L. C., and Sharp, W. N. (1954)   Rare-earth mineral deposits of the Mountain Pass district, San Bernardino County, California. *U.S. Geol. Survey Profess. Paper* 261.

Olson, J. C., and Wallace, S. R. (1956) Thorium and rare-earth minerals in Powderhorn district, Gunnison County, Colorado. *U.S. Geol. Survey Bull.* 1027-O.

Osterwald, F. W. (1956) Relation of tectonic elements in Precambrian rocks to uranium deposits in the Cordilleran foreland of the western United States. *Intern. Conf. Peaceful Uses Atomic Energy, Proc.* 6:293–298.

Ostrom, M. E., Hopkins, M. E., White, W. A., and McVicker, L. D. (1955) Uranium in Illinois black shales. *Illinois State Geol. Survey Circ.* 203.

Overstreet, W. C., Cuppels, N. P., and White, A. M. (1956) Monazite in southeastern United States. *Intern. Conf. Peaceful Uses Atomic Energy, Proc.* 6:593–596 (also *U.S. Geol. Survey Profess. Paper* 300:597–601, 1956).

Pabst, A. (1951A) Huttonite, a new monoclinic thorium silicate. *Am. Mineralogist* 36:60–65.

—— (1951B) X-ray examination of uranothorite. *Am. Mineralogist* 36:557–562.

—— (1952) The metamict state. *Am. Mineralogist* 37:137–157.

—— (1954) Brannerite from California. *Am. Mineralogist* 39:109–117.

Page, L. R. (1950A) Uranium in pegmatites. *Econ. Geol.* 45:12–34.

—— (1950B) Interim report of geologic investigations. Lost Creek schroekingerite (sic) deposits, Sweetwater County, Wyoming. *U.S. Geol. Survey* TEM-183-A.

—— and Redden, J. A. (1952) The carnotite prospects of the Craven Canyon area, Fall River County, South Dakota. *U.S. Geol. Survey Circ.* 175.

Palache, C., and Berman, H. (1933) Oxidation products of pitchblende from Bear Lake. *Am. Mineralogist* 18:20–24.

——, ——, and Frondel, C. (1944) Dana's system of mineralogy. John Wiley & Sons, Inc., New York, 7th ed., vol. 1.

——, ——, —— (1951) Dana's system of mineralogy. John Wiley & Sons, Inc., New York, 7th ed., vol. 2.

—— and Ellsworth, H. V. (1928) Zircon from North Burgess, Ontario. *Am. Mineralogist* 13:384–391.

Panteleyev, P. G. (1938) On titanium, niobium and tantalum in the alkaline complex of the Ilmensky Mountains in the Urals. *Acad. Sci. U.S.S.R., Bull., Classe Sci. Math. Nat., Ser. Geol.* 827–836.

Parkin, L. W., and Glasson, K. R. (1954) The geology of the Radium Hill uranium mine, South Australia. *Econ. Geol.* 49:815–825.

Parks, J. M. Jr., and Saunders, D. F. (1951) Age of mineralization: thermoluminescence and radioactivity of fluorite (abs.). *Geol. Soc. Am., Bull.* 62:1468.

Patchick, P. F. (1955) A remarkable occurrence of allanite and zircon crystals from a southern California pegmatite. *Rocks and Minerals* 246:237–246.

Patterson, E. D. (1954) Radioactive coal and shale of Pennsylvanian and Permian age in northern West Virginia. *U.S. Geol. Survey* TEI-494.

Patton, W. W. Jr. (1955) Phosphate deposits in northern Alaska (abs.). *Geol. Soc. Am., Bull.* 66:1707.

Peacock, M. A. (1935) On johannite from Joachimsthal and Colorado. *Z. Krist.* 90:112–119.

Pearce, R. (1875) Memorandum on pitchblende in Colorado. *Trans. Roy. Geol. Soc. Cornwall* 9, pt. 1, 102.

Pecora, W. T. (1942) Nepheline syenite pegmatites, Rocky Boy Stock, Bearpaw Mountains, Montana. *Am. Mineralogist* 27:397–424.

—— (1948) Telescoped, xenothermal mineral association in alkalic pegmatites and related veins, Vermiculite prospect, Bearpaw Mountains, Montana (abs.). *Am. Mineralogist* 33:205–206.

Pecora, W. T. (1956) Carbonatites: a review. *Geol. Soc. Am., Bull.* 67:1537–1556.

—— and Kerr, J. H. (1953) Burbankite and calkinsite, two new carbonate minerals from Montana. *Am. Mineralogist* 38:1169–1183.

———, Klepper, M. R., Larrabee, D. M., Barbosa, A. L. M., and Frayha, R. (1950) Mica deposits in Minas Gerais, Brazil. *U.S. Geol. Survey Bull.* 964-C.

Pellas, P. (1954) Sur une fergusonite anisotrope de Naegi (Japon). *Bull. soc. franç. minéral. et crist.* 77:461–473.

Penrose, R. A. F. Jr. (1915) The pitchblende of Cornwall, England. *Econ. Geol.* 10:161–171.

Permingeat, F. (1952A) Présence de l'uranium et du tungstène dans la mineralisation d'Azegour (Haut-Atlas des Guedmioua, Maroc). *Acad. sci. Paris, Compt. rend.* 234:123–124.

—— (1952B) Présence de la pechblende dans la mineralisation du gîte d'Azegour (Haut-Atlas), Maroc. *Acad. sci. Paris, Compt. rend.* 234:232.

Perutz, M. (1939) Radioactive nodules from Devonshire, England. *Mineral. u. petrog. Mitt.* 51:141–161.

Peters, W. C. (1956) Uranium-fluorite deposits. *Uran. Inform. Diges*t 3(8):7–8, 25.

Petersen, R. G. (1955) Origin of the land-pebble phosphate deposits of Florida determined from their clay-mineral content (abs.). *Geol. Soc. Am., Bull.* 66:1696.

———, Hamilton, J. C., and Myers, A. T. (1957) Occurrence of rhenium, associated with uraninite, in Coconino County, Arizona (abs.). *Geol. Soc. Am., Bull.* 68: 1778.

Phair, G. (1952) Radioactive Tertiary porphyries in the Central City district, Colorado and their bearing upon pitchblende deposition. *U.S. Geol. Survey* TEI-247.

—— and Levine, H. (1953) Notes on the differential leaching of uranium, radium, and lead from pitchblende in H_2SO_4 solutions. *Econ. Geol.* 48:358–369.

—— and Shimamoto, K. O. (1952) Hydrothermal uranothorite in fluorite breccias from the Blue Jay mine, Jamestown, Boulder County, Colorado. *Am. Mineralogist* 37:659–666.

—— and Sims, P. K. (1954) Paragenesis and age of the uranium minerals in the Copper King mine, Larimer County, Colorado (abs.). *Geol. Soc. Am., Bull.* 65:1385.

Phillips, W. (1816) On the oxyd of uranium, the production of Cornwall, together with a description and series of its crystalline forms. *Trans. Geol. Soc. London* 3:112–120.

Phoenix, D. A. (1956) Relation of carnotite deposits to permeable rocks in the Morrison formation, Mesa County, Colorado. *Intern. Conf. Peaceful Uses Atomic Energy, Proc.* 6:321–325 (also *U.S. Geol. Survey Profess. Paper* 300:213–219, 1956).

Picard, M. D. (1954) Generalized stratigraphic section of southeastern Utah. *Utah Geol. Soc. Guidebook Geol. Utah* 9:12–15.

Picciotto, E. (1950) Distribution de la radioactivité dans un granite. *Acad. sci. Paris, Compt. rend.* 230:2282–2284.

Pierce, A. P., Mytton, J. W., and Gott, G. B. (1956) Radioactive elements and their daughter products in the Texas Panhandle and other oil and gas fields in the United States. *Intern. Conf. Peaceful Uses Atomic Energy, Proc.* 6:494–498 (also *U.S. Geol. Survey Profess. Paper* 300:527–532, 1956).

Pierson, C. T., Burbank, W. S., and Singewald, Q. D. (1952) Some uranium occurrences in the central and southwestern parts of the Colorado mineral belt (abs.). *Geol. Soc. Am., Bull.* 63:1368.

Pinckney, D. M. (1955) Preliminary studies of some of the ore deposits in the northern part of the Boulder batholith, Montana (abs.). *Geol. Soc. Am., Bull.* 66:1659.

Pipiringos, G. N. (1956) Uranium-bearing coal in the central part of the Great Divide Basin, Sweetwater County, Wyoming. *Intern. Conf. Peaceful Uses Atomic Energy, Proc.* 6:484–488 (also *U.S. Geol. Survey Profess. Paper* 300:433–438, 1956).

Poldervaart, A. (1955) Zircons in rocks. I. Sedimentary rocks. *Am. J. Sci.* 253:433–461.

––– and Eckelmann, F. D. (1955) Growth phenomena in zircon of autochthonous granites. *Geol. Soc. Am., Bull.* 66:947–948.

Pommer, A. M. (1957) Laboratory investigations on the origin of uranium and vanadium in the ores of the Colorado Plateau (abs.). *2d Nuclear Eng. Sci. Conf., Program* 44.

Ponsford, D. R. A. (1955) Radioactivity studies of some British sedimentary rocks. *Geol. Survey Gt. Brit., Bull.* 10:24–44.

Poole, F. G., and Williams, G. A. (1956) Direction of transportation of the sediment constituting the Triassic and associated formations of the Colorado Plateau. *Intern. Conf. Peaceful Uses Atomic Energy, Proc.* 6:326–330 (also *U.S. Geol. Survey Profess. Paper* 300:227–231, 1956).

Pough, F. H. (1945) Simpsonite and the northern Brazilian pegmatite region. *Geol. Soc. Am., Bull.* 56:505–514.

Poughon, A., and Moreau, M. (1955) Les gisements à parsonite de Lachaux. *Ann. école natl. supérieure géol. appl. prospection minière univ. Nancy, Sci. Terre* III(1–2):192–235.

Pray, L. C., and Sharp, W. N. (1951) Bastnaesite discoveries near Mountain Pass, California (abs.). *Geol. Soc. Am., Bull.* 62:1519.

Proctor, P. D. (1953) Geology of the Silver Reef (Harrisburg) mining district, Washington County, Utah. *Utah Geol. Mineral. Survey, Bull.* 44.

Protas, J. (1956) Synthèse de la billiétite. *Bull. soc. franç. minéral. et crist.* 79:350–351.

––– (1957A) Propriétés et synthèse d'un oxyde hydraté d'uranium et de calcium de Shinkolobwe, Katanga. *Compt. rend.* 244:91–93.

––– (1957B) La wölsendorfite, nouvelle espèce uranifère. *Compt. rend.* 244:2942–2944.

Przibram, K., and Caffyn, J. E. (1956) Irradiation colours and luminescence. Pergamon Press, Ltd., London. 332 pp.

Pulfrey, W. (1944) Note on the Homa Bay area, Kavirondo, Kenya. *Geol. Soc. London, Quart. J.* 100:101–102.

––– (1950) Ijolitic rocks near Homa Bay, western Kenya. *Geol. Soc. London, Quart. J.* 105:425–459.

Pulou, R. (1957) Méta-uranocircite d'Entraygues (Aveyron). *Bull. soc. franç. minéral. et crist.,* 80(1–3):32–38.

Quennell, A. M. (1951) The geology and mineral resources of (former) Trans-Jordan. *Colonial Geol. and Mineral Resources* 2:85–115.

Quensel, P. (1940) Minerals of the Varuträsk pegmatite. XIX. The uraninite minerals (ulrichite and pitchblende). *Geol. Fören. Förh.* 62:391–396.

Radcliff, S. (1906) Radium at Moonta mines, South Australia. *Trans. Roy. Soc. S. Australia* 30:199–204.

Rade, J. (1956) Notes on the geotectonics and uranium mineralization in the northern part of the Northern Territory, Australia. *Econ. Geol.* 51:354–361.

—— (1957) Shearing along anticlines as an important structural feature in uranium mineralization in the northern part of the Northern Territory of Australia. *Econ. Geol.* 52:282–288.

Ramdohr, P. (1955A) Die Erzmineralien und ihre Verwachsungen. Akademie-Verlag G.m.b.H., Berlin, 875 pp.

—— (1955B) Neue Beobachtungen an Erzen des Witwatersrands in Südafrika und ihre genetische Bedeutung. *Abhandl. deut. Akad. Wiss. Berlin, Kl. Math. u. allgem. Naturw.* 1954, No. 5.

Rankama, K. (1954) Isotope Geology. McGraw-Hill Book Company, Inc., New York, 535 pp.

—— and Sahama, T. G. (1950) Geochemistry. University of Chicago Press, Chicago, 912 pp.

Rasor, C. A. (1956) Ore genesis of the black uranium ores of the Colorado Plateau. *Uran. Inform. Digest* 3(7):12–13, 22–24.

Reeve, W. H., and Deans, T. (1954) An occurrence of carbonatite in the Isoka district of Northern Rhodesia. *Colonial Geol. and Mineral Resources* 4:271–281.

Reinhardt, E. V. (1954) Structural controls of uranium deposits. *Mining Congr. J.,* Oct. 1954, 49–52, 56.

Reuning, E. (1933) Mikrolithvarietäten von Donkerhuk, Südwestafrika. *Chem. Erde* 8:186–218.

Reyna, J. G. (1956) Riqueza minera y yacimientos minerales de Mexico, 3d ed. *Banco Mex., Dept. Invest. Ind.* 304–310.

Reyner, M. L. (1950) Reconnaissance of Basin-Boulder-Clancey area, Jefferson County, Montana. *U.S. Atomic Energy Comm.* RMO-674.

—— and Ashwill, W. R. (1956) Preliminary report on uranium deposits in Tertiary lake sediments in Yavapai County, Arizona (abs.). *Grand Junction Geol. Soc., Geol. Uranium Program* 2.

Richmond, W. E. Jr. (1937) Paragenesis of the minerals from Blueberry Mountain, Woburn, Massachusetts. *Am. Mineralogist* 22:290–300.

Ridland, G. C. (1950) Radioactivity at the Caribou silver mine, Boulder County, Colorado. *Am. Inst. Mining Engrs. Trans.* 187:98–101.

Riedel, H. (1954) Untersuchungen im Flussspatlagerstättenbereich westlich der Naab in der Oberpfalz. *Neues Jahrb. Mineral. Abhandl.* 87(2):240–320.

Ries, H. (1897) Allanite crystals from Mineville, Essex County, New York. *Trans. N.Y. Acad. Sci.* 16:327–329.

Ristic, M. (1956) Uranium and thorium deposits in Yugoslavia. *Intern. Conf. Peaceful Uses Atomic Energy, Proc.* 6:634–640.

Roberts, W. A., and Gude, A. J. III (1953A) Uranium-bearing deposits west of Clancey, Jefferson County, Montana, *U.S. Geol. Survey Bull.* 988-F.

—— and —— (1953B) Geology of the area adjacent to the Free Enterprise mine, Jefferson County, Montana. *U.S. Geol. Survey Bull.* 988-G.

Robertson, A. F., and Storch, R. H. (1955A) Camp Creek radioactive mineral placer area, Blaine and Camas Counties, Idaho. *U.S. Atomic Energy Comm.* RME-3136.

—— and —— (1955B) Rock Creek radioactive mineral placer area, Blaine County, Idaho. *U.S. Atomic Energy Comm.* RME-3139.

Robertson, D. S. (1955) Uranium ores and associations in the Blind River Basin, Ontario. *Uranium Mag.* 2(12):38–44.

—— and Steenland, N. C. (1957) A proposed placer origin for Blind River uranium ores (abs.). *Am. Inst. Mining Engrs. Ann. Meeting, Min. Branch Abs.* 4–5.

Robertson, T., and Dines, H. G. (1929) The South Terras radium deposit, Cornwall. *Mineral. Mag.* 41:147–153.

Robinson, G. D., Wedow, H. Jr., and Lyons, J. B. (1955) Radioactivity investigations in the Cache Creek area, Yenta district, Alaska, 1945. *U.S. Geol. Survey Bull.* 1024-A.

Robinson, R. F. (1950) Uraninite in the Coeur d'Alene district, Idaho. *Econ. Geol.* 45:818–819.

Robinson, S. C. (1955A) Mineralogy of uranium deposits, Goldfields, Saskatchewan. *Can. Geol. Survey Bull.* 31.

—— (1955B) Mineralogy and geochemistry of uranium in Canada. *Nuclear Eng. Sci. Congr.*, preprint 284.

——, Evans, H. T. Jr., Schaller, W. T., and Fahey, J. J. (1957) Nolanite, a new iron-vanadium mineral from Beaverlodge, Saskatchewan. *Am. Mineralogist* 42:619–628.

—— and Sabina, A. P. (1955) Uraninite and thorianite from Ontario and Quebec. *Am. Mineralogist* 40:624–633.

Rogers, A. F. (1947) Uraninite and pitchblende. *Am. Mineralogist* 32:90–91.

Rogers, C. L., De Cserna, Z., Tavera, E., and Ulloa, S. (1956) General geology and phosphate deposits of Concepción del Oro district, Zacatecas, Mexico. *U.S. Geol. Survey Bull.* 1037-A.

——, Tavera, E., and Ulloa, S. (1953) Los depositos fosforiticos de la region de Concepción del Oro y Mazapil, Zacatecas, Mexico. *19th Congr. géol. intern.*, *Compt. rend.*, sec. XI, fasc. XI, 33–43.

Rogers, G. S. (1915) The phosphate deposits of South Carolina. *U.S. Geol. Survey Bull.* 580:183–220.

Rogers, J. J. W., and Adams, J. A. S. (1956) Distribution of alpha-emitting elements in the volcanic rocks of Mount Lassen, California (abs.). *Geol. Soc. Am., Bull.* 67:1728.

Roscoe, S. M. (1957) Geology and uranium deposits, Quirke Lake-Elliot Lake, Blind River area, Ontario. *Can. Geol. Survey, Paper* 56–7.

Rosenblatt, D. B., and Lindeman, H. (1952) The radioactivity of the hot springs at Tiberias. *Science* 116:689–690.

Rosenblum, C. (1948) Benzene formation in the radiochemical polymerization of acetylene. *J. Phys. Colloid Chem.* 52:474–478.

Rosenqvist, I. T. (1949) Samarskit-Yttrotantalit ved Bjortjenn i Mykland herred. *Norsk Geol. Tidsskr.* 28:40–43.

Rosenzweig, A., and Gross, E. B. (1955) Goldichite, a new hydrous potassium ferric sulfate from the San Rafael Swell, Utah. *Am. Mineralogist* 40:469–480.

——, Gruner, J. W., and Gardiner, L. (1954) Widespread occurrence and character of uraninite in the Triassic and Jurassic sediments of the Colorado Plateau. *Econ. Geol.* 49:351–361.

Ross, C. S. (1937) Sphalerite from a pegmatite near Spruce Pine, North Carolina. *Am. Mineralogist* 22:643–650.

——, Henderson, E. P., and Posnjak, E. (1931) Clarkeite, a new uranium mineral. *Am. Mineralogist* 16:213–220.

Ross, V. F. (1952) Autoradiographic study of marine shales. *Econ. Geol.* 47:783–793.

—— (1955) Studies of uranium minerals (XXI): Synthetic hydrogen-autunite. *Am. Mineralogist* 40:917–919.

—— (1956) Studies of uranium minerals (XXII): Synthetic calcium and lead uranyl phosphate minerals. *Am. Mineralogist* 41:915–926.

Roubault, M. (1955) Essai de classification des gisements d'uranium et de thorium. *Acad. sci. Paris, Compt. rend.* 240:214–216.

Roubault, M. (1956)   The uranium deposits of France and French overseas territories. *Intern. Conf. Peaceful Uses Atomic Energy, Proc.* 6:152–161.

Rowe, R. B. (1952)   Petrology of the Richardson radioactive deposit, Wilberforce, Ontario. *Can. Geol. Survey, Bull.* 23.

——— (1954)   Notes on geology and mineralogy of the Newman columbiun-uranium deposit, Lake Nipissing, Ontario. *Can. Geol. Survey, Paper* 54-5.

——— (1955A)   Notes on columbium mineralization, Oka district, Two Mountains County, Quebec. *Can. Geol. Survey, Paper* 54-22.

——— (1955B)   Columbium deposits. *Can. Prosp. Develop. Assoc. Address.*

Roy, S. K., Sharma, N. L., and Chattopadhyay, G. C. (1939)   The mica-pegmatites of Kodarma, India. *Geol. Mag.* 76:145–164.

Rubey, W. W. (1943)   Vanadiferous shale in the Phosphoria formation, Wyoming and Idaho (abs.). *Econ. Geol.* 38:87.

Rumbold, R. (1954)   Radioactive minerals in Cornwall and Devon. *Mineral. Mag.* 91:16–27.

Runnels, R. T. (1949)   Preliminary report on phosphate-bearing shales in eastern Kansas. *Kansas Geol. Survey Bull.* 82:37–48.

———, Schleicher, J. A., and Van Nortwick, H. S. (1953)   Composition of some uranium-bearing phosphate nodules from Kansas shales. *Kansas Geol. Survey Bull.* 102:93–104.

Rusakov, V. (1933)   De la teneur en radium et en thorium des phosphorites. *Acad. Sci. U.S.S.R., Compt. rend., Ser. A,* No. 3, 26–33.

Russ, W., and Andrews, C. W. (1924)   The phosphate deposits of Abeokuta Province. *Geol. Survey Nigeria, Bull.* 7.

Russell, R. T. (1956)   Spectrographic analyses of selected uranium deposits in the western United States (abs.). *20th Congr. géol. intern., Resúmenes Trabajos Presentados* 224.

Ryan, J. P. (1956)   Reconnaissance of phosphate-rock deposits in Arkansas, Kansas, Oklahoma, and Texas. *U.S. Bur. Mines, Rept. Invest.* 5222.

Saggerson, E. P. (1953)   The carbonatites of Homa Mountain (Kenya). *6th Interterritorial Conf., Paper.*

Sahinen, U. M. (1956)   Prospecting for uranium in Montana. *Montana Bur. Mines Geol., Inform. Circ.* 6.

Salo, N. E., and Lekas, M. A. (1956)   Results of geologic mapping of the Mi Vida mine, San Juan County, Utah (abs.). *Grand Junction Geol. Soc., Geol. Uranium Program* 1.

Salvan, H. (1952)   Géologie des gîtes minéraux marocains. Phosphates. *Notes et mem. serv. géol. Maroc* 87:283–320.

Samoilov, J. V. (1917)   Palaeophysiology: the organic origin of some minerals occurring in sedimentary rocks. *Mineral. Mag.* 18:87–98.

Satterly, J. (1943)   Mineral occurrences in the Haliburton area. *Ontario Dept. Mines, 52d Ann. Rept.,* pt. II.

——— (1955)   Radioactive mineral occurrences in the vicinity of Hawk and Richard Lakes. *Ontario Dept. Mines, Geol. Circ.* 1.

——— and Hewitt, D. F. (1955)   Some radioactive mineral occurrences in the Bancroft area. *Ontario Dept. Mines, Geol. Circ.* 2.

Saukoff, A. A. (1956)   Radiohydrogeological method in prospecting for uranium deposits. *Intern. Conf. Peaceful Uses Atomic Energy, Proc.* 6:756–759.

Savage, W. S. (1954)   The search for uranium. *Ontario Dept. Mines, Bull.* 148.

Schatsky, N. S. (1956)   Types de gisements des phosphorites (abs.). *20th Congr. géol. intern., Resúmenes Trabajos Presentados* 101.

Scheminzky, F., and Grabherr, W. (1951) Über Uran anreichernde Warzen- und Knopfchensinter an osterreichischen Thermen, inbesondere in Gastein. *Mineral. u. petro, Mitt.* 3d ser., 2(3):257–282.

Schlee, J. (1957) Petrology of the Jackpile sandstone, New Mexico (abs.). *Geol. Soc. Am., Bull.* 68:1793.

Schlottman, J. D., and Smith, L. E. (1954) Preliminary report on uranium mineralization in the Troublesome formation, Middle Park, Grand County, Colorado. *U.S. Atomic Energy Comm.* RME-1042.

Schneiderhöhn, H. (1955) Erzlagerstätten. Gustav Fischer Verlag, Stuttgart, 3d ed., 375 pp.

Schoep, A. (1922) Sur la becquerelite, nouveau minéral radioactif. *Acad. sci. Paris, Compt. rend.* 174:1240.

——— (1923) Sur la parsonite, nouveau minéral radioactif. *Acad. sci. Paris, Compt. rend.* 176:171.

——— (1926A) Sur l'ianthinite nouveau minéral uranifère. *Ann. soc. géol. Belg.* 49:B188–B192.

——— (1926B) Nouvelles observations sur l'ianthinite. *Ann. soc. géol. Belg.* 49:B310–B312.

——— (1927A) Over de vormen van Curiet en van Janthinietkristallen. *Natuurwet. Tijdschr.* 9(1):1–3.

——— (1927B) Kristallografische mededeelingen, kristallen van kasoliet, soddyiet en brochantiet. *Natuurwet. Tijdschr.* 9(2):25–30.

——— (1927C) Isomorfie van sklodowskiet met uranofaan. *Natuurwet. Tijdschr.* 9(2):30–33.

——— (1932) La vandenbrandeite, un nouveau minéral uranifère. *Ann. Musée roy. Congo Belge A* ser. 1, 1, fasc. 3, 22–31.

——— and Scholz, A. (1931) Sur les minéraux uranifères (pechblende, ianthinite, kasolite, etc.) découverts à Wölsendorf (Baviere), et sur un nouveau mineral d'uranium. *Soc. Belg. géol., Bull.* 41:71–75.

——— and Stradiot, S. (1947) Paraschoepite and epiianthinite, two new minerals from Shinkolobwe (Belgian Congo). *Am. Mineralogist* 32:344–350.

——— and ——— (1948) Additional data on the properties of becquerelite and billietite. *Am. Mineralogist* 33:503–507.

Schopf, J. M., and Gray, R. J. (1954) Microscopic studies of uraniferous coal deposits. *U.S. Geol. Survey Circ.* 343.

Schrader, F. C. (1910) An occurrence of monazite in northern Idaho. *U.S. Geol. Survey Bull.* 430:184–191.

Schreiter, R. (1925A) Über vanadiumhaltige Bleichungsringe und Bleichungszonen in den Schieferletten des Rotliegende aus Heinrichschacht bei Ölsnitz i. Erzg. *Zentr. Mineral.* A, 214–222, 242–250.

——— (1925B) Über Bleichungszonen im Schieferletten aus dem Heinrichschacht der Gewerkschaft Gottes Segen in Lugau. *Zentr. Mineral.* A, 143–145.

Schurmann, H. M. E. (1956)' Age determination of radio-active minerals from igneous rocks (abs.). *20th Congr. géol. intern., Resúmenes Trabajos Presentados* 224.

Scrivenor, J. B. (1928) The geology of Malayan ore-deposits. Macmillan & Co., Ltd., London, 216 pp.

Senftle, F. E., and Keevil, N. B. (1947) Thorium-uranium ratios in the theory of genesis of lead ores. *Trans. Am. Geophys. Union* 28:732–738.

Shand, S. J. (1921) The nepheline rocks of Sekukuniland. *Trans. Geol. Soc. S. Africa* 24:111–149.

Shand, S. J. (1931) The granite-syenite-limestone complex of Palabora, eastern Transvaal, and the associated apatite deposits. *Trans. Geol. Soc. S. Africa* 34:81–105.

Shannon, E. V. (1922) Mineralogy of some black sands from Idaho, with a description of the methods used for their study. *U.S. Natl. Museum, Proc.* 60, Art. 3, 1–33.

Sharp, B. J. (1956) Uranium deposits in volcanic rocks of the Basin and Range Province. *Intern. Conf. Peaceful Uses Atomic Energy, Proc.* 6:252–256 (also *U.S. Geol. Survey Profess. Paper* 300:79–83, 1956).

Sharp, W. N., McKeown, F. A., McKay, E. J., and White, A. M. (1956) Geology and uranium deposits of the Pumpkin Buttes area, Powder River Basin, Wyoming. *Intern. Conf. Peaceful Uses Atomic Energy, Proc.* 6:403–406 (also *U.S. Geol. Survey Profess. Paper* 300:371–374, 1956).

Shaub, B. M. (1938) The occurrence, crystal habit and composition of the uraninite from the Ruggles mine, near Grafton Center, New Hampshire. *Am. Mineralogist* 23:334–341.

Shawe, D. R. (1956A) Significance of roll ore bodies in genesis of uranium-vanadium deposits on the Colorado Plateau. *Intern. Conf. Peaceful Uses Atomic Energy, Proc.* 6:335–337.

—— (1956B) Alteration related to Colorado Plateau ore deposits (abs.). *Geol. Soc. Am., Bull.* 67:1732–1733.

Sheldon, R. P. (1957) Physical stratigraphy of the Phosphoria formation in northwestern Wyoming. *U.S. Geol. Survey Bull.* 1042-E.

Shelton, J. E., and Stickney, W. A. (1955) Beneficiation studies of columbium-tantalum-bearing minerals in alluvial black-sand deposits. *U.S. Bur. Mines, Rept. Invest.* 5105.

Shen, J. T. (1956) Exploration of monazite and associated minerals in the province of Taiwan, China. *Intern. Conf. Peaceful Uses Atomic Energy, Proc.* 6:147–151.

Sheppard, C. W., and Burton, V. L. (1946) The effects of radioactivity on fatty acids. *J. Am. Chem. Soc.* 68:1636–1639.

—— and Whitehead, W. L. (1946) Formation of hydrocarbons from fatty acids by alpha-particle bombardment. *Am. Assoc. Petrol. Geologists, Bull.* 30:32–51.

Shimkin, D. B. (1949) Uranium deposits in the USSR. *Science* 109:58–60.

Shoemaker, E. M. (1954) Structural features of southeastern Utah and adjacent parts of Colorado, New Mexico and Arizona. *Utah Geol. Soc. Guidebook Geol. Utah* 9:48–69.

—— (1955) Variation of vanadium, copper, lead, nickel, and cobalt in the differentiation of calc-alkaline igneous rocks of the Colorado Plateau (abs.). Atomic Energy Comm.–U.S. Geol. Survey symposium, *U.S. Geol. Survey Papers* 13.

—— (1956A) Occurrence of uranium in diatremes on the Navajo and Hopi reservations, Arizona, New Mexico, and Utah. *Intern. Conf. Peaceful Uses Atomic Energy, Proc.* 6:412–417 (also *U.S. Geol. Survey Profess. Paper* 300:179–185, 1956).

—— (1956B) Structural features of the central Colorado Plateau and their relation to uranium deposits. *U.S. Geol. Survey Profess. Paper* 300:155–170.

——, Newman, W. L., and Miesch, A. T. (1956) Sources of the elements in the sandstone-type uranium deposits of the Colorado Plateau (abs.). *20th Congr. géol. intern., Resúmenes Trabajos Presentados* 102–103.

Siggerud, T. (1956) The occurrence of uranium and thorium in Norway. *Intern. Conf. Peaceful Uses Atomic Energy, Proc.* 6:178–181.

Silberminz, V. (1929) Sur le gisement de cérite, bastnaésite et d'un minéral nouveau, la lessingite, dans le district minier de Kychtym (Oural). *Acad. sci. U.R.S.S., Compt. rend., Ser. A,* 55–60.

Silman, J. F. B. (1954) Native tin associated with pitchblende at Nesbitt LaBine uranium mines, Beaverlodge, Saskatchewan. *Am. Mineralogist* 39:529–531.

Silver, L. T., and Grunenfelder, M. (1957) Alteration of accessory allanite in granites of the Elberton area, Georgia (abs.). *Geol. Soc. Am., Bull.* 68:1796.

Simon, M. R. (1956) Uranium deposits of central and south-central Colorado. *Rocky Mountain Assoc. Geol., Guidebook to the Geology of the Raton Basin, Colo.* 84–85.

Simpson, E. S. (1912) Radium-uranium ores from Wodgina. *Geol. Survey W. Australia, Rept.* 9, *Bull.* 48.

——— (1928) Famous mineral localities: Wodgina, North West Australia. *Am. Mineralogist* 13:457–468.

Sims, P. K. (1955) Paragenesis and structure of pitchblende-bearing veins, Central City district, Gilpin County, Colorado (abs.). *Geol. Soc. Am., Bull.* 66:1617.

——— (1956) Paragenesis and structure of pitchblende-bearing veins, Central City district, Gilpin County, Colorado. *Econ. Geol.* 51:739–756.

———, Osterwald, F. W., and Tooker, E. W. (1955) Uranium deposits in the Eureka Gulch area, Central City district, Gilpin County, Colorado. *U.S. Geol. Survey Bull.* 1032-A.

——— and Tooker, E. W. (1955) Localization of metatorbernite in altered wall rocks, Central City district, Gilpin County, Colorado (abs.). *Geol. Soc. Am., Bull.* 66:1680.

——— and ——— (1956) Pitchblende deposits in the Central City district and adjoining areas, Gilpin and Clear Creek Counties, Colorado. *Intern. Conf. Peaceful Uses Atomic Energy, Proc.* 6:265–269 (also *U.S. Geol. Survey Profess. Paper* 300:105–111, 1956).

Singewald, Q. D., and Brock, M. R. (1956) Thorium deposits in the Wet Mountains, Colorado. *Intern. Conf. Peaceful Uses Atomic Energy, Proc.* 6:578–581 (also *U.S. Geol. Survey Profess. Paper* 300:581–585, 1956).

Slack, H. A. (1949) Radioactivity measurements in the Kirkland Lake area, northern Ontario. *Trans. Am. Geophys. Union* 30:867–874.

——— and Whitham, K. (1951) A further investigation of the radioactivity of the Round Lake and Elzevir batholiths. *Trans. Am. Geophys. Union* 32:44–48.

Smith, C. T. (1951) Problems of Jurassic stratigraphy of the Colorado Plateau and adjoining regions. *N.Mex. Geol. Soc. Guidebook S. and W. Sides San Juan Basin, N.Mex. and Ariz.* 99–102.

Smith, D. K. Jr., Gruner, J. W., and Lipscomb, W. N. (1957) The crystal structure of uranophane $Ca(H_3O)_2(UO_2)(SiO_4)_2 \cdot 3H_2O$. *Am. Mineralogist* 42:594–618.

Smith, J. L. (1848) Two new minerals—medjidite (sulphate of uranium and lime)—liebigite (carbonate of uranium and lime). *Am. J. Sci.* 5(2d ser.):336–338.

Smith, K. G., and Bradley, D. A. (1951) Radioactive dinosaur bones from the Camp Davis region, western Wyoming. *Mich. Acad. Sci., Papers* 37:257–263.

Smith, L. E., and Baker, K. E. (1951) Uranium in Fall River area, Clear Creek County, Colorado. *U.S. Atomic Energy Comm.* RMO-913.

Smith, W. C. (1953) Carbonatites of the Chilwa Series of southern Nyasaland. *Brit. Museum (Nat. History) Mineral., Bull.* 1(4).

Smith, W. L., and Cisney, E. A. (1956) Bastnaesite, an accessory mineral in the Redstone granite from Westerly, Rhode Island. *Am. Mineralogist* 41:76–81.

———, Stone, J., Riska, D. D., and Levine, H. (1955) Doverite, a new yttrium mineral. *Science* 122:31.

Smithson, F. (1937) Outgrowths on zircon in the middle Jurassic of Yorkshire. *Geol. Mag.* 74:281–283.

Snider, J. L. (1953)　Reconnaissance for uranium in coal and shale in southern West Virginia and southwestern Virginia. *U.S. Geol. Survey* TEI-409.

—— (1954A)　Radioactivity of some coal and shale of Pennsylvanian age in Ohio. *U.S. Geol. Survey* TEI-404.

—— (1954B)　Reconnaissance for uranium in the Indiana coal field. *U.S. Geol. Survey* TEM-784.

Soboleva, M. V., and Pudovkina, I. A. (1957)　Mineraly Urana, Spravochnik, Moscow.

Soloviev, S. P. (1936)　The granodiorite laccolith of the Malka River (North Caucasus) and its content of radium. *Am. J. Sci.* 232:380–391.

Soulé, J. H. (1956)　Reconnaissance of the "red bed" copper deposits in southeastern Colorado and New Mexico. *U.S. Bur. Mines, Inform. Circ.* 7740.

Spence, H. S. (1932A)　The pitchblende and silver discoveries at Great Bear Lake, Northwest Territories. *Can. Dept. Mines, Invest. Mineral Res. 1931, Publ.* 727:55–92.

—— (1932B)　Character of the pitchblende ore from Great Bear Lake, Northwest Territories. *Can. Mining J.* 53:483–487.

—— and Carnochan, R. K. (1930)　The Wilberforce radium occurrence. *Can. Inst. Mining Met., Trans.* 33:34–73.

Staatz, M. H., and Bauer, H. L. Jr. (1950)　Preliminary examination of the uranium prospect at the Spider No. 1 claim, Honeycomb Hills, Juab County, Utah. *U.S. Geol. Survey* TEM-165.

—— and —— (1951A)　A preliminary report on radioactive fluorite deposits, Thomas Range, Juab County, Utah. *U.S. Geol. Survey* TEM-167A.

—— and —— (1951B)　Virgin Valley Opal district, Humboldt County, Nevada. *U.S. Geol. Survey Circ.* 142.

—— and —— (1952)　Uraniferous fluorspar pipes and veins in the Thomas Range, Juab County, Utah (abs.). *Geol. Soc. Am., Bull.* 63:1371.

—— and —— (1953)　Uranium in the East Walker River area, Lyon County, Nevada. *U.S. Geol. Survey Bull.* 988-C.

—— and Osterwald, F. W. (1956)　Uranium in the fluorspar deposits of the Thomas Range, Utah. *Intern. Conf. Peaceful Uses Atomic Energy, Proc.* 6:275–278 (also *U.S. Geol. Survey Profess. Paper* 300:131–136, 1956).

—— and Trites, A. F. (1950)　Relation of type of country rock to the shape of granitic pegmatite intrusions (abs.). *Geol. Soc. Am., Bull.* 61:1505–1506.

—— and —— (1955)　Geology of the Quartz Creek pegmatite district, Gunnison County, Colorado. *U.S. Geol. Survey Profess. Paper* 265.

Staley, W. W., and Browning, J. S. (1949)　Preliminary investigation of concentrating certain minerals in Idaho placer sand. *Idaho Bur. Mines, Geol. Pam.* 87.

Starik, I. E., Kravchenko, L. L., and Melikova, O. S. (1941)　A finding of ferrithorite in North Kirghizia. *Acad. sci. U.R.S.S., Compt. rend.* 32:254–255.

Steacy, H. R. (1953)　An occurrence of uraninite in a black sand. *Am. Mineralogist* 38:549–550.

Steen, C. A., Dix, G. P. Jr., Hazen, S. W. Jr., and McLellan, R. R. (1953)　Uranium-mining operations of the Utex Exploration Company, in the Big Indian district, San Juan County, Utah. *U.S. Bur. Mines, Inform. Circ.* 7669.

Steinocher, V., and Nováček, R. (1939)　On β-uranotile. *Am. Mineralogist* 24:324–338.

Step, J., and Becke, F. (1904)　Das Vorkommen des Uranpecherzes zu St. Joachimsthal. *Akad. Wiss. Vienna Sitzber. Math.-naturw. Kl.* 113 (Abt. I), 1–34.

Stern, T. W., and Annell, C. S. (1954)　A second locality of novacekite. *Am. Mineralogist* 39:675–676.

Stern, T. W., Stieff, L. R., Evans, H. T. Jr., and Sherwood, A. M. (1957) Doloresite, a new vanadium oxide mineral from the Colorado Plateau. *Am. Mineralogist* 42:587–593.

———, ———, Girhard, M. N., and Meyrowitz, R. (1956) The occurrence and properties of meta-tyuyamunite, $Ca(UO_2)_2(VO_4)_2 \cdot 3\text{–}5H_2O$. *Am. Mineralogist* 41:187–201.

———, ———, and Sherwood, A. M. (1955) Coffinite, $U(SiO_4)_{1-x}(OH)_{4x}$; its widespread occurrence in unoxidized uranium ores and its properties (abs.). *Geol. Soc. Am., Bull.* 66:1621.

——— and Weeks, A. D. (1952) Second occurrence of bayleyite in the United States. *Am. Mineralogist* 37:1058–1060.

Stevenson, J. S. (1951) Uranium mineralization in British Columbia. *Econ. Geol.* 46:353–366.

Stewart, J. H., and Williams, G. A. (1954) Stratigraphic relations of the Triassic Shinarump conglomerate and a prominent sandstone unit of the Chinle formation in southeastern Utah (abs.). *Geol. Soc. Am., Bull.* 65:1387.

Stieff, L. R., and Stern, T. W. (1952) Lead-uranium ages of some uraninites from Triassic and Jurassic sedimentary rocks of the Colorado Plateau (abs.). *Geol. Soc. Am., Bull.* 63:1299–1300.

——— and ——— (1953) Isotopic composition of lead in lead minerals from the Colorado Plateaus (abs.). *Geol. Soc. Am., Bull.* 64:1478–1479.

——— and ——— (1955) The relation of lead isotope age data to theories of origin of the Colorado Plateau uranium deposits (abs.). Atomic Energy Comm.–U.S. Geol. Survey symposium, *U.S. Geol. Survey Papers* 14–15.

———, ———, Cialella, C. M., and Warr, J. J. (1956) Preliminary age determinations of some uranium ores from the Blind River area, Algoma district, Ontario, Canada (abs.). *Geol. Soc. Am., Bull.* 67:1736–1737.

———, ———, and Milkey, R. G. (1953) A preliminary determination of the age of some uranium ores of the Colorado Plateaus by the lead-uranium method. *U.S. Geol. Survey Circ.* 271.

———, ———, and Sherwood, A. M. (1955) Preliminary description of coffinite—a new uranium mineral. *Science* 121:608–609.

———, ———, and ——— (1956) Coffinite, a uranous silicate with hydroxyl substitution: a new mineral. *Am. Mineralogist* 41:675–688.

Stillwell, F. L. (1952) Uraninite from Rum Jungle and Fergusson River, Northern Territory. *Univ. Adelaide, Sir Douglas Mawson Ann. Vol.* 161–166.

Stocking, H. E., and Page, L. R. (1956) Natural occurrence of uranium in the United States—a summary. *U.S. Geol. Survey Profess. Paper* 300:5–12.

Stokes, W. L. (1952A) Lower Cretaceous in the Colorado Plateau. *Am. Assoc. Petrol. Geologists, Bull.* 36:1766–1776.

——— (1952B) Uranium-vanadium deposits of the Thompsons area, Grand County, Utah. *Utah Geol. Mineral. Survey, Bull.* 46.

——— (1954A) Stratigraphy of the southeastern Utah uranium region. *Utah Geol. Soc. Guidebook Geol. Utah* 9:16–47.

——— (1954B) Relation of sedimentary trends, tectonic features, and ore deposits in the Blanding district, San Juan County, Utah. *U.S. Atomic Energy Comm.* RME-3093 (Pt. 1).

——— (1955) Mapping channels in the Salt Wash and Shinarump of the Colorado Plateau (abs.). *Geol. Soc. Am., Bull.* 66:1622–1623.

Storch, R. H., and Robertson, A. F. (1954) Beaver Creek monazite placer area, Valley County, Idaho. *U.S. Atomic Energy Comm.* RME-3132.

Stow, M. H. (1955) Uranium in Virginia. *Virginia Minerals* 1(4):1–5.

Strauss, C. A., and Truter, F. C. (1951A)   The alkali complex at Spitzkop, Sekukuni-land, eastern Transvaal. *Trans. Geol. Soc. S. Africa* 53:81–130.

——— and ——— (1951B)   Post-Bushveld ultrabasic, alkali, and carbonatitic eruptives at Magnet Heights, Sekukuniland, eastern Transvaal. *Trans. Geol. Soc. S. Africa* 53:169–191.

Strøm, K. M. (1948)   A concentration of uranium in black muds. *Nature* 162:922.

Strouth, H. S. (1955)   Canada's new uranium camp at Blind River. *Mining Eng.* 7(5):462–465.

Strunz, H. (1952)   Die Flussspatgänge bei Donaustauf und Wölsendorf. *Acta Albert. Ratisb. Regensburger Naturw., Sonderheft* 20:118–126.

Strutt, R. J. (1908)   The accumulation of helium in geological time. *Proc. Roy. Soc. London, Ser. A,* 81:272.

Strydom, H. C. (1950)   The geology and chemistry of the Laingsburg phosphorites. *Ann. Univ. Stellenbosch* 26, *Sec. A*(3–11), 267–285.

Stugard, F. Jr. (1952)   Two uranium deposits in sandstone, Washington and Kane Counties, Utah (abs.). *Geol. Soc. Am., Bull.* 63:1373.

Stutzer, O., and Wetzel, W. (1932)   Die wichtigsten Lagerstätten der "Nicht-Erze." Phosphat-Nitrat. Gebrüder Borntraeger, Berlin, 390 pp.

Sullivan, C. J. (1954)   Metallic melting point and ore deposition. *Econ. Geol.* 49:555–574.

——— (1955)   Australian uranium deposits. *Nuclear Eng. Sci. Cong.,* preprint 257.

——— and Matheson, R. S. (1952)   Uranium-copper deposits, Rum Jungle, Australia. *Econ. Geol.* 47:751–758.

Sun, M. S., and Weber, R. H. (1955)   Ardennite from the Grants uranium district, New Mexico (abs.). *Am. Mineralogist* 40:338.

——— and ——— (1957)   Santafeite, a new hydrated vanadate from New Mexico (abs.). *Geol. Soc. Am., Bull.* 68:1802.

Svenke, E. (1956)   The occurrence of uranium and thorium in Sweden. *Intern. Conf. Peaceful Uses Atomic Energy, Proc.* 6:198–199.

Swanson, V. E. (1953)   Uranium in the Chattanooga shale (abs.). *Geol. Soc. Am., Bull.* 64:1481.

——— (1956)   Uranium in marine black shales of the United States. *Intern. Conf. Peaceful Uses Atomic Energy, Proc.* 6:430–434 (also *U.S. Geol. Survey Profess. Paper* 300:451–456, 1956).

Swift, W. H. (1952)   The geology of Chishanya, Buhera district, Southern Rhodesia. *Edinburgh Geol. Soc., Trans.* 15:346–359.

Szalay, S. (1954)   The enrichment of uranium in some brown coals in Hungary. *Acta Geol. Acad. Sci. Hung.,* II, fasc. 3–4, 299–310.

Szilard, B. (1949)   Le radium, 6,233,1909. (Cited in Yagoda, 1949.)

Tanton, T. L. (1948)   Radioactive nodules in sediments of the Sibley series, Nipigon, Ontario. *Trans. Roy. Soc. Can.* 42:69–75.

Taylor, A. O., Anderson, T. P., O'Toole, W. L., Waddell, G. G., Gray, A. W., Douglas, H., Cherry, C. L., and Caywood, R. M. (1951)   Geology and uranium deposits of Marysvale, Utah. *U.S. Atomic Energy Comm.* RMO-896.

Thailand, The Delegation of (1956)   Natural occurrence of uranium and thorium in Thailand. *Intern. Conf. Peaceful Uses Atomic Energy, Proc.* 6:201–203.

Thompson, G. A., and Krauskopf, K. B. (1956)   Uranium deposits in Tertiary sediments of Wyoming (abs.). *20th Congr. géol. intern., Resúmenes Trabajos Presentados* 229.

Thompson, M. E. (1954)   Further studies of the distribution of uranium in rich phosphate beds of the Phosphoria formation. *U.S. Geol. Survey Bull.* 1009-D.

Thompson, M. E., Ingram, B., and Gross, E. B. (1956) Abernathyite, a new uranium mineral of the metatorbernite group. *Am. Mineralogist* 41:82–90.

—— and Roach, C. H. (1955) Mineralogy of the Peanut mine, Montrose County, Colorado (abs.). *Geol. Soc. Am., Bull.* 66:1625–1626.

——, ——, and Braddock, W. (1956) New occurrences of native selenium. *Am. Mineralogist* 41:156–157.

——, ——, and Meyrowitz, R. (1956) Simplotite, new calcium tetravanadite from the Colorado Plateau. *Science* 123:1078.

——, ——, and —— (1957) Duttonite, a new quadrivalent vanadium oxide from the Peanut mine, Montrose County, Colorado. *Am. Mineralogist* 42:455–460.

——, Weeks, A. D., and Sherwood, A. M. (1955) Rabbittite, a new uranyl carbonate from Utah. *Am. Mineralogist* 40:201–206.

Thompson, R. M. (1951) Mineral occurrences in western Canada. *Am. Mineralogist* 36:504–509.

—— (1954) Mineral occurrences in western Canada. *Am. Mineralogist* 39:525–528.

Thomson, E. (1932) Mineralogy of the Eldorado mine, Great Bear Lake, N.W.T. *Univ. Toronto Studies, Geol. Ser. 32, Contr. Can. Mineral.* 43–50.

—— (1934) The mineralogy of the silver-uraninite deposits of Great Bear Lake, N.W.T. *Univ. Toronto Studies, Geol. Ser. 36, Contr. Can. Mineral.* 25–31.

Thoreau, J. (1933) L'uranolépidite, nouveau minéral uranifère de Shinkolobwe (Katanga). *Ann. soc. géol. Belg., Publ. relat. Congo Belge,* 1931–1932, C3–C5.

—— and Du Trieu de Terdonck, R. (1933) Le gîte d'uranium de Shinkolobwe-Kasolo (Katanga). *Inst. col. Belge, Sec. sci. nat. méd. mem.* 1, fasc. 8.

—— and Vaes, J. F. (1932) La saléeite, nouveau minéral uranifère. *Soc. géol. Belg., Bull.* 42:96–100.

Thurlow, E. E. (1956A) Uranium deposits at the contacts of metasediments and granitic intrusives in the western United States. *Intern. Conf. Peaceful Uses Atomic Energy, Proc.* 6:288–292 (also *U.S. Geol. Survey Profess. Paper* 300:85–89, 1956).

—— (1956B) Uranium deposits in the Basin and Range province of the Western United States (abs.). *20th Congr. géol. intern., Resúmenes Trabajos Presentados* 106.

—— and Jarrad, L. D. (1954) Boulder batholith—potential Montana uranium province. *Mining Eng.* 6(7):697–698.

—— and Reyner, M. L. (1950) Free Enterprise uranium prospect, Jefferson County, Montana. *U.S. Atomic Energy Comm.* RMO-678.

—— and Wright, R. J. (1950) Uraninite in the Coeur d'Alene district, Idaho. *Econ. Geol.* 45:395–404.

Thurston, W. R. (1955) Pegmatites of the Crystal Mountain district, Larimer County, Colorado. *U.S. Geol. Survey Bull.* 1011.

——, Staatz, M. H., Cox, D. C., and others (1954) Fluorspar deposits of Utah. *U.S. Geol. Survey Bull.* 1005.

Tilton, G. R., and Nicolaysen, L. O. (1955) Heterogeneous distribution of uranium, thorium, and lead in monazite crystals (abs.). *Geol. Soc. Am., Bull.* 66:1627.

——, Patterson, C., Brown, H., Inghram, M., Hayden, R., Hess, D., and Larsen, E. Jr. (1954) The isotopic composition and distribution of lead, uranium, and thorium in a pre-Cambrian granite. *U.S. Atomic Energy Comm.* AECU-2840.

——, ——, ——, ——, ——, ——, and —— (1955) Isotopic composition and distribution of lead, uranium, and thorium in a Precambrian granite. *Geol. Soc. Am., Bull.* 66:1131–1148.

Tipper, G. H. (1914) The monazite sands of Travancore. *Geol. Survey India, Records* 44.

Tolmachev, I. M. (1943) Adsorption of uranyl salts on solid adsorbents. *Acad. Sci. U.S.S.R., Bull.* 1:28–34.

Tomkeieff, S. I. (1946) The geochemistry of uranium. *Sci. Prog.* 34:696.

Tooker, E. W. (1955A) Altered wall rocks in the Central City-Idaho Springs mining district, Colorado (abs.). *4th Natl. Clay Conf., Penn. State Univ., Program and Abstracts.*

—— (1955B) Investigation of wall-rock alteration, Central City and Idaho Springs districts, Gilpin and Clear Creek Counties, Colorado (abs.). *Geol. Soc. Am., Bull.* 66:1682.

—— (1956) Altered wall rocks along vein deposits in the Central City-Idaho Springs region, Colorado. Clays and clay minerals. *Natl. Acad. Sci., Natl. Research Council Publ.* 456:348–361.

Tourtelot, H. A. (1952) Reconnaissance for uraniferous rocks in northeastern Wind River Basin, Wyoming. *U.S. Geol. Survey* TEM-445.

—— (1955) Uranium content of water in the Great Plains region of Nebraska and in adjacent states (abs.). *Geol. Soc. Am., Bull.* 66:1627–1628.

Traill, R. J. (1952) Synthesis and x-ray study of uranium sulphate minerals. *Am. Mineralogist* 37:394–406.

—— (1954) A preliminary account of the mineralogy of radioactive conglomerates in the Blind River region, Ontario. *Can. Mining J.* 75(4):61–68.

Trask, P. D. (1925) The origin of the ore of the Mansfeld Kupferschiefer, Germany. A review of the current literature. *Econ. Geol.* 20:746–761.

Tremblay, L. P. (1954) Uranium City, Saskatchewan. *Can. Geol. Survey, Paper* 54-15.

—— (1957) Uranium City, Saskatchewan. *Can. Geol. Survey, Paper* 55-28.

Trites, A. F. Jr. (1955) Mineralogy and geochemistry of the uranium deposits in the White Canyon area, San Juan County, Utah (abs.). *Geol. Soc. Am., Bull.* 66:1628.

—— and Chew, R. T. III (1955) Geology of the Happy Jack mine, White Canyon area, San Juan County, Utah. *U.S. Geol. Survey Bull.* 1009-H.

——, Finnell, T. L., and Thaden, R. E. (1956) Uranium deposits in the White Canyon area, San Juan County, Utah. *Intern. Conf. Peaceful Uses Atomic Energy, Proc.* 6:379–382 (also *U.S. Geol. Survey Profess. Paper* 300:281–284, 1956).

—— and Tooker, E. W. (1953) Uranium and thorium deposits in east-central Idaho, southwestern Montana. *U.S. Geol. Survey Bull.* 988-H.

Troyer, M. L., McKay, E. J., Soister, P. E., and Wallace, S. R. (1954) Summary of investigations of uranium deposits in the Pumpkin Buttes area, Johnson and Campbell Counties, Wyoming. *U.S. Geol. Survey Circ.* 338.

Tschirwinsky, W. (1911) Zur Frage über die mineralogische Natur der russischen Phosphorite. *Neues Jahrb. Mineral.* 2:51–74.

Turneaure, F. S. (1955) Metallogenetic provinces and epochs. *Econ. Geol.* 50th ann. vol., pt. I, 38–98.

Turner, F. J., and Verhoogen, J. (1951) Igneous and metamorphic petrology. McGraw-Hill Book Company, Inc., New York, 602 pp.

Turner, H. W. (1928) Review of the radioactive minerals of Madagascar. *Econ. Geol.* 23:62–84.

Twenhofel, W. S., and Buck, K. L. (1956) The geology of thorium deposits in the United States. *Intern. Conf. Peaceful Uses Atomic Energy, Proc.* 6:562–567 (also *U.S. Geol. Survey Profess. Paper* 300:559–566, 1956).

Vaes, J. F. (1947) Six nouveaux minéraux d'urane provenant de Shinkolobwe (Katanga). *Ann. soc. géol. Belg.* 70:B212–B226.

Vaes, J. F. (1949) Becquerelite ou billietite (À propos d'un article de MM. Schoep et Stradiot). *Soc. géol. Belg., Bull.* 72:237–248.

—— and Kerr, P. F. (1949) Sengierite: a preliminary description. *Am. Mineralogist* 34:109–120.

Vaes, J. P. (1933) Sur un minéral de Kalongwe (Katanga). *Ann. soc. géol. Belg.* 56:B331–B332.

Van Aubel, R. (1935) Sur quelques minéraux tantalo-columbifères du Kivu. *Ann. soc. géol. Belg.* 58. *Annexe Publ. relat. Congo Belge,* fasc. 1, C38–C41.

Van Autenboer, T., and Skjerlie, F. J. (1957) Brannerite, a new mineral in Norway. *Norges Geol. Unders., Årbok* 1956, 200:5–7.

Van Vloten, R. (1956) On the origin of the phosphate deposits of northern Mexico (abs.). *20th Congr. géol. intern., Resúmenes Trabajos Presentados* 107.

Vickers, R. C. (1953) Reconnaissance for uranium in the United States. North-central district. *U.S. Geol. Survey* TEI-390, 202–205.

—— (1954) Occurrences of radioactive minerals in the Bald Mountain gold-mining area, northern Black Hills, South Dakota. *U.S. Geol. Survey Circ.* 351.

—— (1955) Wallrock alteration as a guide to carnotite deposits and their origin, northern Black Hills, South Dakota (abs.). *Geol. Soc. Am., Bull.* 66:1630.

—— (1956A) Geology and monazite content of the Goodrich quartzite, Palmer area, Marquette County, Michigan. *Intern. Conf. Peaceful Uses Atomic Energy, Proc.* 6:597–599 (also *U.S. Geol. Survey Profess. Paper* 300:593–596, 1956).

—— (1956B) Geology and monazite content of the Goodrich quartzite, Palmer area, Marquette County, Michigan. *U.S. Geol. Survey Bull.* 1030-F.

—— (1956C) Airborne and ground reconnaissance of part of the syenite complex near Wausau, Wisconsin. *U.S. Geol. Survey Bull.* 1042-B.

—— (1956D) Origin and occurrence of uranium in northern Michigan (abs.). *Geol. Soc. Am., Bull.* 67:1741.

—— (1957) Alteration of sandstone as a guide to uranium deposits and their origin, Northern Black Hills, South Dakota. *Econ. Geol.* 52:599–611.

Viebig, W. (1905) Die Silber-Wismutgänge von Johanngeorgenstadt in Erzgebirge. *Z. prakt. Geol.* 13:89–115.

Vine, J. D. (1956A) Uranium-bearing coal in the United States. *Intern. Conf. Peaceful Uses Atomic Energy, Proc.* 6:452–457 (also *U.S. Geol. Survey Profess. Paper* 300:405–411, 1956).

—— (1956B) Geology of uranium in the basins of Tertiary age in Wyoming and the northern Great Plains. *U.S. Geol. Survey Profess. Paper* 300:337–344.

—— and Moore, G. W. (1952) Uranium-bearing coal and carbonaceous rocks in the Fall Creek area, Bonneville County, Idaho. *U.S. Geol. Survey Circ.* 212.

—— and Prichard, G. E. (1953) Uranium in limestone. Miller Hill area, Carbon County, Wyoming. *U.S. Geol. Survey* TEI-390, 91–94.

—— and —— (1954) Uranium in the Poison Basin area, Carbon County, Wyoming. *U.S. Geol. Survey Circ.* 344.

Visse, L. (1954) Constatations la radioactivité des phosphates africains. *Acad. sci. Paris, Compt. rend.* 239(7):545–547.

Vogt, T. (1911) Vorläufige Mitteilung über Yttrofluorit, eine neue mineralspezies aus dem nördlichen Norwegen. *Centr. Mineral., Geol.* 373.

Von Buttlar, H., and Houtermans, F. G. (1951) Photographische Messung des U- and Th-Gehaltes nach der Auflagemethode. *Geochim. et Cosmochim. Acta* 2:43–61.

Von der Weid, F. (1941) Le gisement de molybdénite d'Azegour et la region des Guedmioua. Thesis, Univ. Geneva, Fac. Sci., No. 1034.

Von Eckermann, H. (1948)   The alkaline district of Alnö Island. *Sveriges Geol. Undersökn. Årsbok Avhandl.* 36.

—— and Wickman, F. E. (1956)   A preliminary determination of the maximum age of the Alnö rocks. *Geol. Fören. Förh.* 78:122–124.

Wadia, D. N. (1943)   Rare earth minerals of Ceylon. *Ceylon Records Dept. Mineral., Profess. Paper* 1.

—— (1956)   Natural occurrences of uranium and thorium in India. *Intern. Conf. Peaceful Uses Atomic Energy, Proc.* 6:163–166.

—— and Fernando, L. J. D. (1945)   Ilmenite, monazite and zircon, gems and semi-precious stones of Ceylon. *Ceylon Records Dept. Mineral., Profess. Paper* 2.

Waggaman, W. H. (1952)   Phosphoric acid, phosphates and phosphatic fertilizers. Reinhold Publishing Corporation, New York, 2d ed., 683 pp.

Walker, G. W. (1953)   Rosamond uranium prospect. *Calif. Div. Mines, Spec. Rept.* 37.

——, Lovering, T. G., and Stephens, H. G. (1956)   Radioactive deposits in California. *Calif. Div. Mines, Spec. Rept.* 49.

—— and Osterwald, F. W. (1956A)   Relation of secondary uranium minerals to pitchblende-bearing veins at Marysvale, Piute County, Utah. *Intern. Conf. Peaceful Uses Atomic Energy, Proc.* 6:283–287 (also *U.S. Geol. Survey Profess. Paper* 300:123–129, 1956).

—— and —— (1956B)   Uraniferous magnetite-hematite deposit at the Prince mine, Lincoln County, New Mexico. *Econ. Geol.* 51:213–222.

Walker, T. L., and Parsons, A. L. (1923)   Shattering of minerals and rocks about inclusions. *Univ. Toronto Studies, Geol. Ser.* 16:25–28.

Wallace, S. R., and Olson, J. C. (1956)   Thorium in the Powderhorn district, Gunnison County, Colorado. *Intern. Conf. Peaceful Uses Atomic Energy, Proc.* 6:582–586 (also *U.S. Geol. Survey Profess. Paper* 300:587–592, 1956).

Walthier, T. N. (1955)   Uranium occurrences of the eastern United States. *Mining Eng.* 7(6):545–547.

Walton, H. F. (1956)   The transport of uranium by ground water (abs.). *20th Congr. géol. intern., Resúmenes Trabajos Presentados* 107.

Ward, H. J. (1954)   The search for Australia's uranium. *Mining Eng.* 6(12):1169–1173.

Wasserstein, B. (1954)   Ages of uraninite by a new method. *Nature* 174:1004–1005.

Waters, A. C., and Granger, H. C. (1953)   Volcanic debris in uraniferous sandstones, and its possible bearing on the origin and precipitation of uranium. *U.S. Geol. Survey Circ.* 224.

Watson, T. L. (1910)   Granites of the southeastern Atlantic states. *U.S. Geol. Survey Bull.* 426.

—— and Hess, F. L. (1913)   Zirconiferous sandstone near Ashland, Virginia. *U.S. Geol. Survey Bull.* 530, pt. I, 165–171.

Webb, R. W. (1939)   Large sphene crystals from San Jacinto Mountains, California. *Am. Mineralogist* 24:344–346.

Webel, M. (1955)   Zur Lagerstättenkunde Westspaniens. Überblick über die Petrographie und mineralogische Beschreibung der Lagerstätten Zentral-Estremaduras. *Heidelberger Beitr. Mineral. u. Petrog.* 4:379–411.

Wedow, H. Jr., and others (1953)   Preliminary summary of reconnaissance for uranium and thorium in Alaska, 1952. *U.S. Geol. Survey Circ.* 248.

——, Killeen, P. L., and others (1954A)   Reconnaissance for radioactive deposits in eastern interior Alaska, 1946. *U.S. Geol. Survey Circ.* 331.

Wedow, H. Jr., White, M. G., and others (1954B) Reconnaissance for radioactive deposits in east-central Alaska, 1949. *U.S. Geol. Survey Circ.* 335.

Weeks, A. D. (1951) Red and gray clay underlying ore-bearing sandstone of the Morrison formation in western Colorado. *U.S. Geol. Survey* TEM-251.

—— (1952) Mineralogical studies on the Colorado Plateau (abs.). *Geol. Soc. Am., Bull.* 63:1309–1310.

—— (1955) Mineralogy of the Colorado Plateau uranium ores. *Nuclear Eng. Sci. Congr.,* preprint 283.

—— (1956) Mineralogy and oxidation of the Colorado Plateau uranium ores. *Intern. Conf. Peaceful Uses Atomic Energy, Proc.* 6:525–529 (also *U.S. Geol. Survey Profess. Paper* 300:187–193, 1956).

——, Cisney, E. A., and Sherwood, A. M. (1953) Montroesite, a new vanadium oxide from the Colorado Plateau. *Am. Mineralogist* 38:1235–1241.

—— and Thompson, M. E. (1954) Identification and occurrence of uranium and vanadium minerals from the Colorado Plateaus. *U.S. Geol. Survey Bull.* 1009-B.

——, ——, and Sherwood, A. M. (1955) Navajoite, a new vanadium oxide from Arizona. *Am. Mineralogist* 40:207–212.

——, Truesdell, A. H., and Haffty, J. (1957) Nature of the ore boundary and its relation to diagenesis and mineralization, Uravan district, Colorado (abs.). *Geol. Soc. Am., Bull.* 68:1810–1811.

Weir, D. B. (1952) Geologic guides to prospecting for carnotite deposits on Colorado Plateau. *U.S. Geol. Survey Bull.* 988-B.

Welch, S. W. (1953) Radioactivity of coal and associated rock in the coal fields of eastern Kentucky and southern West Virginia. *U.S. Geol. Survey* TEI-347A.

Wells, J. D., and Harrison, J. E. (1954) Radioactivity reconnaissance of part of north-central Clear Creek County, Colorado. *U.S. Geol. Survey Circ.* 345.

Wells, R. C. (1930) Uraninite from Placer de Guadalupe, Chihuahua. *Am. Mineralogist* 15:470–473.

—— (1934) Allanite from Wyoming. *Am. Mineralogist* 19:81–82.

West, W. S. (1953) Reconnaissance for radioactive deposits in the Darby Mountains, Seward Peninsula, Alaska, 1948. *U.S. Geol. Survey Circ.* 300.

—— and Benson, P. D. (1955) Investigations for radioactive deposits in southeastern Alaska. *U.S. Geol. Survey Bull.* 1024-B.

—— and White, M. G. (1952) The occurrence of zeunerite at Brooks Mountain, Seward Peninsula, Alaska. *U.S. Geol. Survey Circ.* 214.

Wherry, E. T. (1912) A new occurrence of carnotite. *Am. J. Sci.* 33:574–580.

—— (1915) Carnotite near Mauch Chunk, Pennsylvania. *U.S. Geol. Survey Bull.* 580:147–151.

White, M. G. (1952A) Reconnaissance for radioactive deposits along the Upper Porcupine and Lower Coleen Rivers, northeastern Alaska. *U.S. Geol. Survey Circ.* 185.

—— (1952B) Radioactivity of selected rocks and placer concentrates from northeastern Alaska. *U.S. Geol. Survey Circ.* 195.

—— (1956) Uranium in the Serra de Jacobina, State of Bahia, Brazil. *Intern. Conf. Peaceful Uses Atomic Energy, Proc.* 6:140-142.

—— and Killeen, P. L. (1953) Reconnaissance for radioactive deposits in the lower Yukon-Kuskokwim highlands region, Alaska, 1947. *U.S. Geol. Survey Circ.* 255.

—— and others (1953) Reconnaissance for radioactive deposits in the vicinity of Teller and Cape Nome, Seward Peninsula, Alaska, 1946–47. *U.S. Geol. Survey Circ.* 244.

—— and Stevens, J. M. (1953) Reconnaissance for radioactive deposits in the

Ruby-Poorman and Nixon Forks districts, west-central Alaska, 1949. *U.S. Geol. Survey Circ.* 279.

White, M. G., and West, W. S. (1953) Reconnaissance for uranium in the Lost River area, Seward Peninsula, Alaska. *U.S. Geol. Survey Circ.* 319.

———, ———, Tolbert, G. E., Nelson, A. E., and Houston, J. R. (1952) Preliminary summary of reconnaissance for uranium in Alaska, 1951. *U.S. Geol. Survey Circ.* 196.

White, W. S. (1953) Copper shales of Germany and Michigan (abs.). *Geol. Soc. Am., Bull.* 64:1491.

Whitehead, W. L. (1954) Hydrocarbons formed by the effects of radioactivity and their role in the origin of petroleum. In Nuclear geology. John Wiley & Sons, Inc., 195–218.

Whittie, A. W. G. (1954) Absite—a new mineral related to brannerite. *S. Australia Dept. Mines, Mining Rev. No. 97 for 1952,* 99–106.

Wilcox, R. (1936) An occurrence of large zircon needles in a basic pegmatite. *Am. Mineralogist* 21:459.

Williams, C. E. (1952) Carbonatite structure: Tororo Hills, eastern Uganda. *Geol. Mag.* 89:286–292.

Williams, F. A., Meehan, J. A., Paulo, K. L., John, T. U., and Rushton, H. G. (1956) Economic geology of the decomposed columbite-bearing granites, Jos Plateau, Nigeria. *Econ. Geol.* 51:303–332.

Wilmarth, V. R. (1952) Uranophane deposit at the Silver Cliff mine near Lusk, Niobrara County, Wyoming (abs.). *Geol. Soc. Am., Bull.* 63:1376.

——— (1953A) Placerville hydrocarbons, Colorado. *U.S. Geol. Survey* TEI-330: 107–108.

——— (1953B) Garo, Colorado. *U.S. Geol. Survey* TEI-330:109–110.

——— (1953C) Yellow Canary uranium deposits, Daggett County, Utah. *U.S. Geol. Survey Circ.* 312.

———, Bauer, H. L., Staatz, M. H., and Wyant, D. G. (1952) Uranium in fluorite deposits. *U.S. Geol. Survey Circ.* 220:13–18.

——— and Johnson, D. H. (1954) Uranophane at Silver Cliff mine, Lusk, Wyoming. *U.S. Geol. Survey Bull.* 1009-A.

Wilson, A. F. (1947) The charnockitic and associated rocks of north-western South Australia. Pt. I. The Musgrave Ranges—an introductory account. *Trans. Roy. Soc. S. Australia* 71:195–210.

Wilson, M. E. (1929) Fluorspar deposits of Canada. *Can. Geol. Survey Econ. Geol. Ser.* 6.

Wilson, W. H. (1955) Uranium deposits in southwestern Wyoming and north-eastern Utah. *Wyoming Geol. Assoc. Guidebook, 10th Ann. Field Conf.* 186–189.

Winterhalder, E. C. (1954) Preliminary reconnaissance for uranium in the Green River Basin and the Rock Springs uplift, Sweetwater and Fremont Counties, Wyoming. *U.S. Atomic Energy Comm.* RME-1045.

Wirtz, D. (1952) Über eine Zirkon- und Monazitseife im Kurischen Haff (Ostpreussen). *Neues Jahrb. Geol. u. Paläontol., Monatsh.* 1952, No. 6, 241–252.

Witkind, I. J. (1954) Localization of uranium minerals in channel sediments at the base of the Shinarump conglomerate, Monument Valley, Arizona (abs.). *Geol. Soc. Am., Bull.* 65:1327.

——— (1956A) Channels and related swales at the base of the Shinarump conglomerate, Monument Valley, Arizona. *Intern. Conf. Peaceful Uses Atomic Energy, Proc.* 6:368–370 (also *U.S. Geol. Survey Profess. Paper* 300:233–237, 1956).

——— (1956B) Uranium deposits at base of the Shinarump conglomerate, Monument Valley, Arizona. *U.S. Geol. Survey Bull.* 1030-C.

Wollard, L. E., and Kerr, P. F. (1951) Preliminary memorandum on the Dark Horse and Saturday areas, Marysvale, Utah. *U.S. Atomic Energy Comm.* RMO-860.

—— and —— (1952) Preliminary memorandum on the Beaver Creek area, Marysvale, Utah. *U.S. Atomic Energy Comm.* RMO-995.

Wood, H. B. (1956A) Age, environment and production of uranium host rocks on the Colorado Plateau. *Intern. Conf. Peaceful Uses Atomic Energy, Proc.* 6:307-316 (also *U.S. Geol. Survey Profess. Paper* 300:533-541, 1956).

—— (1956B) Uranium controls and guides in the San Rafael Swell, Utah (abs.). *20th Congr. géol. intern., Resúmenes Trabajos Presentados* 257.

—— and Grundy, W. D. (1956) Techniques and guides for exploration of Shinarump channels on the Colorado Plateau. *Intern. Conf. Peaceful Uses Atomic Energy, Proc.* 6:701-703 (also *U.S. Geol. Survey Profess. Paper* 300:651-657, 1956).

Wright, H. D. (1954) Mineralogy of a uraninite deposit at Caribou, Colorado. *Econ. Geol.* 49:129-174.

—— (1956) Relationships of uranium-bearing vein deposits in the Boulder batholith, Montana (abs.). *20th Congr. géol. intern., Resúmenes Trabajos Presentados* 107-108.

—— and Bieler, B. H. (1953) An investigation of the mineralogy of the uranium-bearing deposits in the Boulder batholith, Montana. *U.S. Atomic Energy Comm.* RME-3041.

——, ——, Shulhof, W. P., and Emerson, D. O. (1954) Mineralogy of the uranium-bearing deposits in the Boulder batholith, Montana. *U.S. Atomic Energy Comm.* RME-3095.

—— and Emerson, D. O. (1957) Distribution of secondary uranium minerals in the W. Wilson deposit, Boulder batholith, Montana. *Econ. Geol.* 52:36-59.

—— and Shulhof, W. P. (1956) Uranium content of base-metal sulfide minerals as an indication of the uranium concentration in ore-forming solutions (abs.). *Geol. Soc. Am., Bull.* 67:1745-1746.

—— and —— (1957) Mineralogy of the Lone Eagle uranium-bearing mine in the Boulder batholith, Montana. *Econ. Geol.* 52:115-131.

Wright, R. J. (1950) Reconnaissance of certain uranium deposits in Arizona. *U.S. Atomic Energy Comm.* RMO-679.

—— (1951) Annie Laurie prospect, Santa Cruz County, Arizona. *U.S. Atomic Energy Comm.* RMO-677.

—— (1955A) Ore controls in sandstone uranium deposits of the Colorado Plateau. *Econ. Geol.* 50:135-155.

—— (1955B) Colorado Plateau uranium deposits. *Econ. Geol.* 50:884-885.

Wyant, D. G. (1952) Lost Creek (Wamsutter) schroeckingerite deposit, Sweetwater County, Wyoming. *U.S. Geol. Survey* TEM-10B.

——, Sharp, W. N., and Sheridan, D. M. (1956) Reconnaissance study of uranium deposits in the Red Desert, Sweetwater County, Wyoming. *U.S. Geol. Survey Bull.* 1030-I.

Wylie, A. W. (1954) Lanthanon and scandium distribution in Western Australian fergusonite. *Am. Mineralogist* 39:667-668.

Wyman, R. V. (1954) Comments on metallic melting point and ore deposition. *Econ. Geol.* 49:904-905.

Yagoda, H. (1946A) The localization of uranium and thorium minerals in polished section. Pt. 1. The alpha ray emission pattern. *Am. Mineralogist* 31:87-124.

—— (1946B) Spatial orientation of uranium in samarskite (abs.). *Geol. Soc. Am., Bull.* 57:1246.

Yagoda, H. (1949) Radioactive measurements with nuclear emulsions. John Wiley & Sons, Inc., New York, 356 pp.

Yoho, W. H. (1956) Notes on the origin of the heavy mineral deposits at Trail Ridge in northeastern Florida (abs.). *20th Congr. géol. intern., Resúmenes Trabajos Presentados* 204.

Young, P. E., and others (1955) The Algoma district ore occurrences and developments. *Can. Prosp. Develop. Assoc., Address.*

Young, R. G., and Ealy, G. K. (1956) Uranium occurrences in the Ambrosia Lake area, McKinley County, New Mexico. *U.S. Atomic Energy Comm.* RME-86.

Yun, T. S. (1956) Occurrence of uranium and thorium in South Korea. *Intern. Conf. Peaceful Uses Atomic Energy, Proc.* 6:176–177.

Zeller, E. J. (1954) Thermoluminescence of carbonate sediments. In Nuclear geology. John Wiley & Sons, Inc., New York, 180–188.

Zeller, H. D., and Baltz, E. H. Jr. (1954) Uranium-bearing copper deposits in the Coyote district, Mora County, New Mexico. *U.S. Geol. Survey Circ.* 334.

Zeschke, G. (1956) Prospektion von Uran- und Thoriumerze. E. Schweizerbart'sche Verlag, Stuttgart, 76 pp.

INDEX OF MINERAL SPECIES

Only radioactive and rare-earth minerals are listed. Main species appear in **boldface** type; varieties and synonyms are shown in *italic* type; other species (doubtful, poorly defined, and minor) appear in regular type. Page references in **boldface** type denote main discussions of main species only.

Abernathyite, 15, 16, 19, 25, **97, 99,** 400, 405, 542
Absite, 49, 258
Abukumalite, 128
Adamite (radioactive), 149
Adelpholite, 38
Aeschynite, 45
Allanite, 9, 13, 21–23, 37–39, 42, 43, 75, 108, 110, 120, **140–142,** 143–146, 162, 167, 169, 171, 175, 177–181, 189–193, 195–197, 202, 203, 205–209, 211–218, 221, 223, 226, 227, 241, 242, 244–249, 256, 266, 325, 501, 505, 514, 517
  beryllian, 140, 142, 209
  magnesian, 247
  phosphatian, 142
Allophane, uraniferous, 400, 440, 445
Alpha-uraninite (α-uraninite), 26
Alpha-uranotile (α-uranotile), 116
Alvite, 39, 135, 139
Ammonium-uranospinite, 96
Ampangabeite, **50–52,** 198, 207
Ancylite, **127,** 241
Andersonite, 17, 19, 64–66, **68,** 400
Annerödite, 41
"*Anthracite,*" 121, 522
Anthraxolite, 121, 522, 525, 528
  nickeliferous, 124
Apatite, 9, 18, 21, 32, **128–129,** 169, 171, 175, 179, 180, 187, 216, 217, 221, 431, 495, 501, 504, 505, 514, 532
  rare-earth, 128, 240–241, 250
  thorian, 221
  yttrian, 209
Asphaltite, 97, 112, 121, 124, 128, 390, 397, 398, 409, 413, 415, 416, 430, 435, 438, 451, 484, 522–525, 527, 528
Auerlite, 108

Autunite, 9, 11, 13, 15–17, 19, 20, 53, **78, 80–81,** 82–85, **86,** 90, 91, 93–97, 116, 163, 182, 189, 190, 244, 252, 268, 280, 284, 288, 294, 301, 302, 316, 317, 319, 334, 336, 337, 340–342, 344, 347, 348, 351–353, 400, 412, 427, 429–437, 455, 525, 526, 531, 534–537, 539, 540, 542, 551–553
  meta-I, 13, 15, 80, 81, 84
  meta-II, 13, 80, 84

Baddeleyite, 9, 48, **125,** 126, 139, 161, 208, 227, 231, 235, 236, 327–329, 513, 516
Barite, plumbian, 127, 555
Barium (Ba)-uranyl-arsenate, 435
Bassetite, 19, 25, 81, **85, 89,** 97, 280, 400, 553
Bastnaesite, 78, 110, **127,** 131, 132, 140, 162, 163, 169, 226, 227, 241, 242, 246, 247, 250, 328
Bayleyite, 19, 64, **65–66, 69,** 400
Beckelite, **148**
Becquerelite, 16, 18, 19, 53, **55–56,** 57, **59,** 67, 119, 120, 278, 294–296, 311, 353, 400, 429, 532, 539
Betafite, 9, 13, 22, 32, 39, **43–44,** 45, **47,** 108, 110, 126, 180, 182, 198, 200, 203, 207–209, 226, 227, 238, 245, 496, 511
  plumbian, 43
  tantalian, 43
  titanian, 43
Beta-uraninite (β-uraninite), 26
Beta-uranophane, 9, 19, 53, 116, **117–118,** 121, **122,** 248, 284, 332, 351, 353, 410, 535
Beta-uranopilite, 71, **74**
Beta-uranotile, 117

INDEX OF LOCALITIES

621

SUBJECT INDEX

643